Processes for Air Pollution Control

Processes for Air Pollution Control

By specialist contributors

Edited by
G. NONHEBEL
M.A., D.Sc., F.R.I.C., F.Inst.F., M.I.Chem.E

A DIVISION OF
THE **CHEMICAL RUBBER** CO.
CLEVELAND, OHIO

INTERNATIONAL SCIENTIFIC SERIES

First English edition published in 1964 as
'Gas Purification Processes' by George Newnes Ltd
Second edition published by
Newnes-Butterworths, an imprint of the Butterworth Group, 1972

Library of Congress Catalog Card Number 75-175142

Filmset by Keyspools Ltd, Golborne, Lancashire, England.
Printed in England by C. Tinling & Co. Ltd, London and Prescot

Preface

The purpose of this volume is to supply design engineers and the managers in works with practical information on the purification of gases before discharge to atmosphere or before they are used in certain chemical reactors. (It is perhaps not generally known that by far the greatest tonnage of chemicals made today include some steps whereby the chemicals are reacted in gaseous form by passage over catalysts.)

All the authors of the various chapters have practical works experience with the processes they describe. It is assumed that users of this book are acquainted with the background theory of the processes or have access to the numerous appropriate textbooks. An exception has been made on the important unit process of absorption of gaseous impurities in liquids because there have been considerable advances in theoretical knowledge during the past decade.

The subject of smoke (soot) emission from combustion processes has not been treated because methods of achieving smokeless combustion are well documented.

The chapter on air pollution legislation deals almost entirely with British Legislation. This has been strengthened at intervals since the first Alkali etc. Works Act passed in 1863. The British system of 'best practicable means' has served as a model for many countries. Federal and State legislation in the U.S.A. is still in a state of flux.

The general plan for the chapters dealing with individual processes is to give:

  (i) A brief qualitative description of the equipment available for the particular process of purification.

 (ii) The formulae used in design equations for the basic plant with references only to their derivation, and the limitations of such equations.

(iii) The information which must be made available to the engineer designing a plant, including flowsheets for ancillary equipment, descriptions of laboratory or small pilot plant investigations required to provide this information and the limitations of knowledge on scaling-up.

 (iv) Advice on the choice of processes and on the preparation of enquiries for the purchase of plant and on the subsequent technical assessment of tenders.

  (v) Advice to works engineers on any specialized supervision necessary during the construction of the plant and on difficulties likely to be experienced in commissioning new plant, their diagnosis and cure.

(vi) Advice on instruments for manual and automatic control; also for monitoring of the performance of the plant, including reference to special methods of analysis developed for the control of particular processes.

(vii) Safety considerations.

(viii) Methods of operating the plant with high technical efficiency and low maintenance costs.

(ix) Detailed descriptions of one or two gas purification plants for the type of duty described.

The present volume is a substantially revised edition of *Gas Purification Processes* first published in England in 1964 by George Newnes Limited, London.

The preparation of a book of this nature has involved numerous discussions with contributors and my sincere thanks are due to them for bearing with me. Thanks are also due to the numerous organizations who have given permission for reproduction of data and illustrations.

GORDON NONHEBEL
Romsey, SO5 8JR,
England. 1971.

Contents

Contributors

H. ACTON, B.SC.(TECH), C.ENG., M.I.CHEM.E.
Simon-Carves Chemical Engineering Ltd

A. AIKENS, D.C.M., A.M.I.MECH.E., A.M.I.INST.F.
Oxy-Catalyst Company Ltd

L. BARBOUTEAU
Societe National des Petroles d'Aquitaine, France

D. M. BISHOP, M.A., M.INST.M.C.
Imperial Chemical Industries Ltd

J. A. BRINK, JR., B.S., M.S., PH.D., M.A.I.CH.E., A.C.S., A.P.C.A., F.A.I.C.
Monsanto Enviro-Chem Systems, Inc, St Louis, Missouri, U.S.A.

D. O. BRISCOE, B.SC., A.C.G.I., A.M.I.CHEM.E.
The British Oxygen Company Ltd

E. L. BROWN
Central Electricity Generating Board

J. DALMAN, C.ENG., M.I.E.E.
Central Electric Research Laboratories

F. DRANSFIELD, B.SC.(ENG.), C.ENG., F.I.MECH.E., F.I.E.E., F.INST.F.
Central Electricity Generating Board

G. LOWRIE FAIRS, M.A.
Consultant, formerly Imperial Chemical Industries Ltd

J. H. FLUX, B.SC.(ENG.), C. ENG., F.I.GAS.E., F.INST.F.
British Steel Corporation

R. D. FULKER
British Carbo Norit Union Ltd

R. GALAUD
Societe Nationale des Petroles d'Aquitaine, France

K. D. GREEN, A.M.I.H.V.E.
Prat-Daniels (Stroud) Ltd

P. J. HOFTYZER, A.M.I.CHEM.E.
Central Laboratory, DSM, Holland

J. HUISKAMP
Central Laboratory, DSM, Holland

A. JACKSON, M.SC.TECH., A.M.C.T., F.R.I.C., M.I.CHEM.E., A.M.INST.GAS E.
Simon-Carves Chemical Engineering Ltd

F. J. G. KWANTEN
Central Laboratory, DSM, Holland

A. LITTLE, B.SC.
Imperial Chemical Industries Ltd

P. E. LOVERING, B.SC., A.R.I.C.
Siebe Gorman & Co. Ltd

H. J. LOWE, B.SC., C.ENG., F.I.E.E., F.I.MECH.E., F.INST.P.
Central Electricity Research Laboratories

D. H. LUCAS, B.A., C.ENG., F.INST.P., F.I.E.E.
Central Electricity Research Laboratories

R. A. MOTT, D.SC., F.R.I.C., F.INST.F.
Formerly British Coke Research Association

J. J. L. MURRAY, B.SC., M.I.E.E., A.M.I.MECH.E.

G. NONHEBEL, M.A., D.SC., C.ENG., F.R.I.C., F.INST.F., M.I.CHEM.E.
Consultant, formerly Imperial Chemical Industries Ltd

F. F. RIXON, M.SC., A.R.C.S., D.I.C.
The Power-Gas Corporation Ltd

C. J. STAIRMAND, C.ENG., D.SC., M.I.CHEM.E., A.INST.P.
Imperial Chemical Industries Ltd

F. STEARMAN
Imperial Chemical Industries Ltd

D. E. WARD, PH.D., A.M.I.CHEM.E.
The British Oxygen Company Ltd

E. R. WARD, M.INST.GAS E., M.INST.F.
South Eastern Gas Board

N. R. WAY
Vokes Ltd

G. J. WILLIAMSON, B.A., M.I.MECH.E., M.I.CHEM.E.
Imperial Chemical Industries Ltd

CONVERSION FACTORS TO STRICT S.I. UNITS

The following table was prepared by F. P. Lees, M.A., B.Sc., A.M.I.Chem.E., of the Department of Chemical Engineering, University of Technology, Loughborough and is reproduced by permission from *The Chemical Engineer*, page CE 341–344 (October 1968).

Acceleration	1 cm/s^2	: 1.0000×10^{-2} m/s^2
	1 m/h^2	: 7.7160×10^{-8} m/s^2
	1 ft/s^2	: 3.0480×10^{-1} m/s^2
	1 ft/h^2	: 2.3519×10^{-8} m/s^2
Area	1 cm^2	: 1.0000×10^{-4} m^2
	1 ft^2	: 9.2903×10^{-2} m^2
	1 in^2	: 6.4516×10^{-4} m^2
	1 yd^2	: 8.3613×10^{-1} m^2
	1 acre	: 4.0469×10^3 m^2
	1 mile^2	: 2.5900×10^6 m^2
Calorific value (volumetric)	1 cal/cm^3	: 4.1868×10^6 J/m^3
	1 kcal/m^3	: 4.1868×10^3 J/m^3
	1 Btu/ft^3	: 3.7260×10^4 J/m^3
	1 Chu/ft^3	: 6.7067×10^4 J/m^3
	1 therm/ft^3	: 3.7260×10^9 J/m^3
	1 kcal/ft^3	: 1.4786×10^5 J/m^3
Coefficient of expansion (volumetric)	1 g/cm^3 °C	: 1.0000×10^3 kg/m^3 °C
	1 lb/ft^3 °F	: 2.8833×10 kg/m^3 °C
	1 lb/ft^3 °C	: 1.6018×10 kg/m^3 °C
Density	1 g/cm^3	: 1.0000×10^3 kg/m^3
	1 lb/ft^3	: 1.6018×10 kg/m^3
	1 lb/U.K.gal	: 9.9779×10 kg/m^3
	1 lb/U.S.gal	: 1.1983×10^2 kg/m^3
	1 kg/ft^3	: 3.5315×10 kg/m^3
Diffusion coefficient—see Viscosity, kinematic		
Energy	1 cal	: 4.1868 J
	1 kcal	: 4.1868×10^3 J
	1 Btu	: 1.0551×10^3 J
	1 erg	: 1.0000×10^{-7} J
	1 hp h (metric)	: 2.6477×10^6 J
	1 kW h	: 3.6000×10^6 J
	1 ft pdl	: 4.2139×10^{-2} J
	1 ft lbf	: 1.3558 J
	1 Chu	: 1.8991×10^3 J
	1 hp h (British)	: 2.6845×10^6 J
	1 therm	: 1.0551×10^8 J
	1 thermie	: 4.1855×10^6 J
	1 ft kgf	: 2.9891 J
Power	1 cal/s	: 4.1868 W
	1 kcal/h	: 1.1630 W
	1 Btu/s	: 1.0551×10^3 W
	1 erg/s	: 1.0000×10^{-7} W
	1 tonne cal/h	: 1.1630×10^3 W
	1 hp (metric)	: 7.3548×10^2 W
	1 ft pdl/s	: 4.2139×10^{-2} W
	1 ft lbf/s	: 1.3558 W
	1 Btu/h	: 2.9308×10^{-1} W
	1 Chu/h	: 5.2754×10^{-1} W
	1 hp (British)	: 7.4570×10^2 W
	1 ton refrigeration	: 3.5169×10^3 W

Pressure	1 dyn/cm^2	:	$1 \cdot 0000 \times 10^{-1}$ N/m^2
	1 kgf/m^2	:	$9 \cdot 8067$ N/m^2
	1 pdl/ft^2	:	$1 \cdot 4881$ N/m^2
	1 standard atmosphere	:	$1 \cdot 0133 \times 10^5$ N/m^2
	1 at (1 kgf/cm^2)	:	$9 \cdot 8067 \times 10^4$ N/m^2
	1 bar	:	$1 \cdot 0000 \times 10^5$ N/m^2
	1 lbf/ft^2	:	$4 \cdot 7880 \times 10$ N/m^2
	1 lbf/in^2	:	$6 \cdot 8948 \times 10^3$ N/m^2
	1 tonf/in^2	:	$1 \cdot 5444 \times 10^7$ N/m^2
	1 in water	:	$2 \cdot 4909 \times 10^2$ N/m^2
	1 ft water	:	$2 \cdot 9891 \times 10^3$ N/m^2
	1 mm Hg	:	$1 \cdot 3333 \times 10^2$ N/m^2
	1 in Hg	:	$3 \cdot 3866 \times 10^3$ N/m^2

Reaction rate—see Mass release rate

Shear stress—see Pressure

Specific enthalpy	1 cal/g	:	$4 \cdot 1868 \times 10^3$ J/kg
	1 Btu/lb	:	$2 \cdot 3260 \times 10^3$ J/kg
	1 Chu/lb	:	$4 \cdot 1868 \times 10^3$ J/kg
Specific heat	1 cal/g °C		
	1 Btu/lb °F }	:	$4 \cdot 1868 \times 10^3$ J/kg °K
Specific volume	1 cm^3/g	:	$1 \cdot 0000 \times 10^{-3}$ m^3/kg
	1 ft^3/lb	:	$6 \cdot 2428 \times 10^{-2}$ m^3/kg
	1 ft^3/kg	:	$2 \cdot 8317 \times 10^{-2}$ m^3/kg
Surface per unit mass	1 cm^2/g	:	$1 \cdot 0000 \times 10^{-1}$ m^2/kg
	1 ft^2/lb	:	$2 \cdot 0482 \times 10^{-1}$ m^2/kg
	1 m^2/g	:	$1 \cdot 0000 \times 10^3$ m^2/kg
	1 ft^2/kg	:	$9 \cdot 2903 \times 10^-$ m^2/kg
Surface per unit volume	1 cm^2/cm^3	:	$1 \cdot 0000 \times 10^2$ m^2/m^3
	1 ft^2/ft^3	:	$3 \cdot 2808$ m^2/m^3
Surface tension	1 dyn/cm	:	$1 \cdot 0000 \times 10^{-3}$ N/m
Temperature difference	1 deg F (deg R)	:	5/9 deg C (deg K)
Thermal conductivity	1 cal/s cm^2 (°C/cm)	:	$4 \cdot 1868 \times 10^2$ W/m^2 (°C/m)
	1 kcal/h m^2 (°C/m)	:	$1 \cdot 1630$ W/m^2 (°C/m)
	1 Btu/h ft^2 (°F/ft)	:	$1 \cdot 7308$ W/m^2 (°C/m)
	1 Btu/h ft^2 (°F/in)	:	$1 \cdot 4423 \times 10^{-1}$ W/m^2 (°C/m)
	1 kcal/h ft^2 (°C/ft)	:	$3 \cdot 8156$ W/m^2 (°C/m)
Time	1 h	:	$3 \cdot 6000 \times 10^3$ s
	1 min	:	$6 \cdot 0000 \times 10$ s
	1 day	:	$8 \cdot 6400 \times 10^4$ s
	1 year	:	$3 \cdot 1558 \times 10^7$ s
Force	1 dyn	:	$1 \cdot 0000 \times 10^{-5}$ N
	1 kgf	:	$9 \cdot 8067$ N
	1 pdl	:	$1 \cdot 3825 \times 10^{-1}$ N
	1 lbf	:	$4 \cdot 4482$ N
	1 tonf	:	$9 \cdot 9640 \times 10^3$ N

Heat—see Energy

Heat of combustion, formation, etc.—see Specific enthalpy

Heat capacity—see Specific heat

Heat flow—see Power

Heat flux	1 cal/s cm^2	:	$4 \cdot 1868 \times 10^4$ W/m^2
	1 kcal/h m^2	:	$1 \cdot 1630$ W/m^2

	1 Btu/h ft^2	:	3·1546 W/m^2
	1 Chu/h ft^2	:	5·6784 W/m^2
	1 kcal/h ft^2	:	1·2518 × 10 W/m^2
Heat release rate (mass)	1 cal/s g	:	4·1868 × 10^3 W/kg
	1 kcal/h kg	:	1·1630 W/kg
	1 Btu/h lb	:	6·4612 × 10^{-1} W/kg
Heat release rate (volumetric)	1 cal/s cm^3	:	4·1868 × 10^6 W/m^3
	1 kcal/h m^3	:	1·1630 W/m^3
	1 Btu/h ft^3	:	1·0350 × 10 W/m^3
	1 Chu/h ft^3	:	1·8630 × 10 W/m^3
	1 kcal/h ft^3	:	4·1071 × 10 W/m^3
Heat-transfer coefficient	1 cal/s cm^2 °C	:	4·1868 × 10^4 W/m^2 °C
	1 kcal/h m^2 °C	:	1·1630 W/m^2 °C
	1 Btu/h ft^2 °F		
	1 Chu/h ft^2 °C	:	5·6784 W/m^2 °C
	1 kcal/h ft^2 °C	:	1·2518 × 10 W/m^2 °C
Henry's law constant	1 atm/(g/cm^3)	:	1·0133 × 10^2 (N/m^2)/(kg/m^3)
	1 atm/(kg/m^3)	:	1·0133 × 10^5 (N/m^2)/(kg/m^3)
	1 atm/(lb/ft^3)	:	6·3258 × 10^3 (N/m^2)/(kg/m^3)
	1 atm(kg/ft^3)	:	2·8693 × 10^3 (N/m^2)/(kg/m^3)
Latent heat—see Specific enthalpy			
Length	1 cm	:	1·0000 × 10^{-2} m
	1 ft	:	3·0480 × 10^{-1} m
	1 Ångstrom	:	1·0000 × 10^{-10} m
	1 micron	:	1·0000 × 10^{-6} m
	1 in	:	2·5400 × 10^{-2} m
	1 yd	:	9·1440 × 10^{-1} m
	1 mile	:	1·6093 × 10^3 m
Mass	1 g	:	1·0000 × 10^{-3} kg
	1 lb	.	4·5359237 × 10^{-1} kg
	1 tonne	:	1·0000 × 10^3 kg
	1 grain	:	6·4800 × 10^{-5} kg
	1 oz (avdp)	:	2·8352 × 10^{-2} kg
	1 oz (troy)	:	3·110 × 10^{-2} kg
	1 long ton	:	1·01606 × 10^3 kg
Mass per unit area	1 g/cm^2	:	1·0000 × 10 kg/m^2
	1 lb/ft^2	:	4·8824 kg/m^2
	1 lb/in^2	:	7·0307 × 10^2 kg/m^2
	1 ton/mile^2	:	3·9230 × 10^{-4} kg/m^2
	1 kg/ft^2	:	1·0764 × 10 kg/m^2
Mass flow	1 g/s	:	1·0000 × 10^{-3} kg/s
	1 kg/h	:	2·7778 × 10^{-4} kg/s
	1 lb/s	:	4·5359 × 10^{-1} kg/s
	1 tonne/h	:	2·7778 × 10^{-1} kg/s
	1 lb/h	:	1·2600 × 10^{-4} kg/s
	1 ton/h	:	2·8224 × 10^{-1} kg/s
Mass flux	1 g/s cm^2	:	1·0000 × 10 kg/s m^2
	1 kg/h m^2	:	2·7778 × 10^{-4} kg/s m^2
	1 lb/s ft^2	:	4·882 kg/s m^2
	1 lb/h ft^2	:	1·3562 × 10^{-3} kg/s m^2
	1 kg/h ft^2	:	2·9900 × 10^{-3} kg/s m^2
Mass release rate (volumetric)	1 g/s cm^3	:	1·0000 × 10^3 kg/s m^3
	1 kg/h m^3	:	2·7778 × 10^{-4} kg/s m^3
	1 lb/s ft^3	:	1·6018 × 10 kg/s m^3
	1 lb/h ft^3	:	4·4496 × 10^{-3} kg/s m^3
	1 kg/h ft^3	:	9·8096 × 10^{-3} kg/s m^3

Mass-transfer coefficient, concentration driving force—see Velocity

Mass-transfer coefficient, dimensionless driving force—see Mass flux

Mass-transfer coefficient, pressure driving force	1 g/s cm^2 atm	:	9.8687×10^{-5} kg/s m^2 (N/m^2)
	1 kg/h m^2 atm	:	2.7413×10^{-9} kg/s m^2 (N/m^2)
	1 lb/h ft^2 atm	:	1.3384×10^{-8} kg/s m^2 (N/m^2)
	1 kg/h ft^2 atm	:	2.9507×10^{-8} kg/s m^2 (N/m^2)
Momentum, angular	1 g cm^2/s	:	1.0000×10^{-7} kg m^2/s
	1 lb ft^2/s	:	4.2140×10^{-2} kg m^2/s
	1 lb ft^2/h	:	1.1706×10^{-5} kg m^2/s
Momentum, linear	1 g cm/s	:	1.0000×10^{-5} kg m/s
	1 lb ft/s	:	1.3825×10^{-1} kg m/s
	1 lb ft/h	:	3.8404×10^{-5} kg m/s
Moment of inertia	1 g cm^2	:	1.0000×10^{-7} kg m^2
	1 lb ft^2	:	4.2140×10^{-2} kg m^2

Torque—see Energy

Velocity	1 cm/s	:	1.0000×10^{-2} m/s
	1 m/h	:	2.7778×10^{-4} m/s
	1 ft/s	:	3.0480×10^{-1} m/s
	1 ft/h	:	8.4667×10^{-5} m/s
	1 mile/h	:	4.4704×10^{-1} m/s
Viscosity, absolute (or dynamic)	1 g/cm s (1 poise)	:	1.0000×10^{-1} kg/m s (or N s/m^2)
	1 kg/m h	:	2.7778×10^{-4} kg/m s
	1 lb/ft s	:	1.4882 kg/m s
	1 lb/ft h	:	4.1338×10^{-4} kg/m s
	1 kg/ft h	:	9.1134×10^{-4} kg/m s
Viscosity, kinematic	1 cm^2/s (1 stokes)	:	1.0000×10^{-4} m^2/s
	1 m^2/h	:	2.7778×10^{-4} m^2/s
	1 ft^2/s	:	9.2903×10^{-2} m^2/s
	1 ft^2/h	:	2.5806×10^{-5} m^2/s
Volume	1 cm^3	:	1.0000×10^{-6} m^3
	1 ft^3	:	2.8317×10^{-2} m^3
	1 litre	:	1.0000×10^{-3} m^3
	1 in^3	:	1.6387×10^{-5} m^3
	1 yd^3	:	7.6455×10^{-1} m^3
	1 U.K.gal	:	4.5460×10^{-3} m^3
	1 U.S.gal	:	3.7853×10^{-3} m^3
Volumetric flow	1 cm^3/s	:	1.0000×10^{-6} m^3/s
	1 m^3/h	:	2.7778×10^{-4} m^3/s
	1 ft^3/s	:	2.8317×10^{-2} m^3/s
	1 cm^3/min	:	1.6667×10^{-8} m^3/s
	1 litre/min	:	1.6667×10^{-5} m^3/s
	1 ft^3/min	:	4.7195×10^{-4} m^3/s
	1 ft^3/h	:	7.8658×10^{-6} m^3/s
	1 U.K. gal/min	:	7.5766×10^{-5} m^3/s
	1 U.S. gal/min	:	6.3089×10^{-5} m^3/s
	1 U.K. gal/h	:	1.2628×10^{-6} m^3/s
	1 U.S. gal/h	:	1.0515×10^{-6} m^3/s

Wetting rate (mass)—see Viscosity, absolute

Wetting rate (volumetric)	1 litre/h in	:	1.0936×10^{-5} m^3/s m
	—see also Viscosity, kinematic		

Work—see Energy

1

General Introduction

G. NONHEBEL

1.1 Categories

Processes of gas purification can be readily divided into the following categories:

(i) Removal of gaseous impurities.

(ii) Removal of particulate impurities.

There is also need for sub-division into:

(a) Coarse cleaning for the removal of substantial quantities of unwanted impurity by simple plant.

(b) Fine cleaning for the removal of residual impurities to a degree sufficient for the majority of nominal chemical plant operations, such as catalysis or preparation of normal commercial products; or cleaning to a degree sufficient to discharge an effluent gas to atmosphere through a chimney (Chapters 2 and 19).

(c) Ultra-fine cleaning where the extra expense is only justified by the nature of the subsequent operations or the need to produce a particularly pure product. In rare cases, impurities may have to be reduced below one part per 100 million by weight and the plant required is complex and costly.

A further sub-division, which applies particularly to removal of gaseous impurities, is into chemical and physical processes each of which must be considered in terms of technical efficiency, maintenance of performance and cost. All these categories are described with examples in Chapters 4–17.

Two outstanding examples of gas cleaning are:

(i) The purification of coal gas: crude tarry gases from retorts or coke-ovens are freed from tarry matter, condensable aromatics (such as naphthalene), hydrogen sulphide; in some plants the organic sulphur compounds are partially removed. The gas is then distributed through miles of piping to the fine jets of modern domestic gas burners (Chapters 4 and 8).

(ii) Maintaining the air in a nuclear-powered submarine sufficiently pure for submerged cruises of several months duration (Chapter 17, Part C).

1.2 Specifications for Purified and Unpurified Gas

Time and trouble spent on deciding the specification required for the purified gas is always rewarded by smooth operation of the subsequent operations through which the purified gas passes or by absence of complaint when the gas is discharged to atmosphere.

Specification of the principal impurity which it is required to remove from a gas to be used in subsequent processes is generally easy, but difficulties often arise in specifying trace impurities which may have a serious effect, for example on catalysts, and are sometimes not discovered until a full-scale plant is in operation. Sometimes these difficulties arise through lack of or difficulty of analysis of the unpurified gas, sometimes by changes in raw materials used to prepare the crude gas and sometimes by introduction of impurities from washing solutions or even from nominally distilled water, i.e. from condensed factory steam. Consideration of trace impurities likely to be present in materials used to prepare and treat the crude gas is, therefore, essential and it must not be forgotten that sources of raw materials change for commercial reasons. Moreover, when the raw gas is prepared by combustion in air, oxides of nitrogen are formed in concentrations which are not inappreciable[1]

1.3 Effluents

The impurities removed in a gas purification process must eventually be discarded. They fall into three main categories—solid, liquid, gaseous. It is not always realized, at an early stage of the design of a process, that the disposal of such effluents can raise quite serious difficulties. Cases have arisen, however, where the initial choice of process has been changed because the difficulties, including cost of the actual process together with its effluent disposal, have been reduced by use of a possibly less elegant purification process which has simpler effluent disposal.

1.3.1 Disposal of Solids

In all cases, steps have to be taken to prevent fine dust from the process becoming a nuisance, either during discharge from the plant or when discharged on a tip. With small plants the cost of moisture conditioning plant can sometimes be relatively onerous.

On the large scale disposal of solids to a tip can involve quite considerable problems. The extreme case is the disposal of the fine dust collected from the flue gases of boilers burning coal in pulverized form. One solution in this case is to use combustion chambers designed to discharge most of the coal ash in molten form; another solution adopted is to use the ash for preparation of bricks or to replace aggregate in concrete.

Greater technical difficulty arises when the discarded solid is pyrophoric (cf. colliery spoilbanks) or reacts chemically with CO_2 in the atmosphere with the production of noxious gases such as hydrogen sulphide, or is partially soluble in water with the production of solutions which render rivers toxic to aquatic life, including fish.

1.3.2 Disposal of Liquids

The discharge of liquid effluent to rivers, estuaries and tidal waters is controlled in Great Britain by comprehensive legislation[2]. Most of the technical regulations stemming from this legislation, including specifications of potentially toxic materials, are embodied in conditions by consent of River Boards responsible for the watersheds and estuaries in the country. It is a legal requirement that River Boards be notified of new discharges or alterations in the flow of existing discharges into waters under their supervision.

One result of the legislation on liquid effluents is that factory owners are advised wherever possible to discharge their effluents into Local Authority sewers. The Local Authorities, however, usually require some pre-treatment to render the effluent amenable to final purification in admixture with local sewage and other industrial effluents. A charge may in any case be made by the Local Authority for accepting industrial effluents; this charge may be based on the nature of the contaminants and the total volume per day of the effluent.

A most interesting case of atmospheric pollution, namely a 'cat smell' noticeable over a large industrial area, was ultimately traced to a liquid which had been in contact with a gaseous organic compound. Complaint of the smell was sufficiently vigorous to be mentioned in four annual reports[3] by the Alkali Inspector (Chapter 2). The following is extracted from the 1960 report: 'The cat smell had its origin in a practically odourless aqueous effluent containing amongst other substances an unsaturated aliphatic compound. This effluent was discharged into a polluted river estuary which at times contained no dissolved oxygen. Under certain circumstances dissolved sulphates in the river were converted by anaerobic bacteria to hydrogen sulphide which then reacted with the unsaturated organic compound above-mentioned to produce the malodorous substance responsible for the much publicized smell. The trouble was cured by chlorination of the effluent'.

1.3.3 Gaseous Effluents

The first chemical manufacturers had little or no conscience about the discharge of noxious effluents to atmosphere. It was the discharge to atmosphere of HCl from the saltcake process and the inefficient running of chamber plants for the manufacture of sulphuric acid that led to control of gaseous effluents by successive Acts of Parliament[4], namely the Alkali &c. Works Regulation Acts of 1863 and 1906, the Public Health Acts and lastly the Clean Air Acts, 1956 and 1968. The first effective scrubbing tower for HCl was patented by Gossage in 1836.

As technology improved and the scale of manufacture has increased, recovery processes have produced worthwhile dividends on the capital expended. Thus a large fertilizer plant based on sulphuric acid has grown around the smelter at Trail, British Columbia[5]. Collection of dust (ash) from processes of combustion is unlikely ever to pay dividends. Thus the cost of dust arresting plant for the large pulverized coal boilers of a modern power station is about 10% of the cost of the complete boiler contract[6]. On the other hand the prevention of emission of red iron oxide fume from the CO-rich gases issuing from oxygen-blown steel furnaces has produced a process which collects so much clean combustible gas that modern integrated steel works have become almost self-sufficient in fuel.

In a different context, the natural gas from boreholes at Lacq near the French side of the Pyrenees contains about 15 per cent of H_2S. This has to be removed before the gas can be used for fuel or chemical manufacture (Chapter 7). In 1961 the recovered sulphur amounted to 1·5 million tons and the income derived from its sale was 500 million francs.

1.4 Method Study

1.4.1 Principles

During the past ten years the application of work study techniques to design and operation of chemical processes has substantially reduced capital and running costs.

Work study consists of two associated groups of techniques; method study, the aim of which is to achieve worthwhile objectives by more efficient and more economic means, and work measurement which, quite apart from its better-known role of providing the basis for incentive schemes, is one of the techniques used when comparing rival methods. As the labour content of most gas purification processes is low, work measurement will not be discussed further; it is however of importance in planning and control in construction and maintenance work, and with a few gas purification processes it is valuable for establishing the economic manning of a plant.

Experience has shown that the use of method study can generally effect a saving of at least 10 per cent in the capital cost of chemical plants; the techniques are therefore well worth applying to large projects. The amount of time and effort allocated to any investigation must always be in harmony with the scale of probable improvements.

Method study investigations follow a conventional pattern. After 'selecting' a 'job', which may range from physical work to a proposal to manufacture a product, all the data relevant to the situation are 'recorded', commonly involving the use of simple recording conventions. The main activities are then analysed ('examined') under the five aspects of: 'what is achieved?', 'how?', 'when?' and 'where?', and 'by whom?'. The true reasons for the existing or proposed activity are then established by persistently asking the question 'why?' of each aspect recorded. This is followed by listing all the conceivable alternatives to the present situation and then selecting for 'development' those alternatives which directly or by implication offer some advantage. 'Development' itself consists of evaluating each promising alternative by the use of costing, mathematical or work measurement techniques as is appropriate. This should be done initially in isolation and then in combination with other attractive alternatives. By this means one is left with a limited number of overall methods for one job after making some necessary compromises. The ultimate choice of an operating method is likely to be influenced by such factors as minimum capital or running costs, time for completion, public amenity, or even possibly labour policy.

This 'basic procedure' is usually applied to a problem at a number of levels. Initially, the objective of the study in its broadest terms is 'examined' to establish the desirability of the activity as a whole and to clarify the terms of reference of the investigation. An immediate result from this 'coarse scale investigation' will be to identify the essential activities for subsequent investigation in greater detail. This downward progression into detail will continue with further more detailed studies to the limit set by the terms of reference and the objectives of the investigation.

In the context of gas purification, a method study might well progress as follows. The proposal for a projected plant would be critically examined with

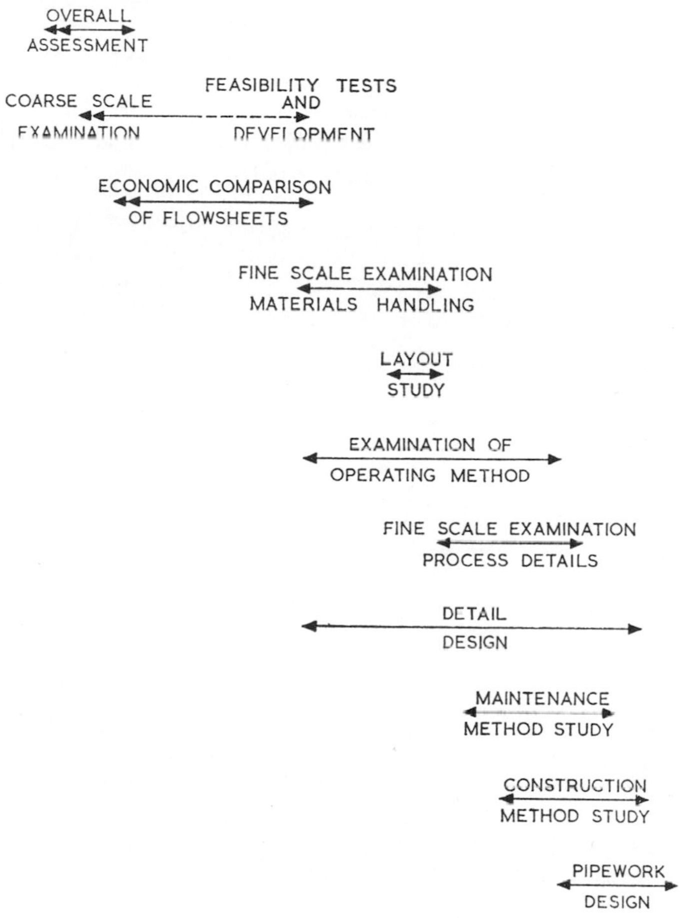

OVERALL
◄◄ ———►
ASSESSMENT

COARSE SCALE   FEASIBILITY TESTS
◄◄ ———————— AND ———————►
EXAMINATION   DEVELOPMENT

ECONOMIC COMPARISON
◄◄ ———————►
OF FLOWSHEETS

FINE SCALE EXAMINATION
◄ ———————————►
MATERIALS HANDLING

LAYOUT
◄ ——►
STUDY

EXAMINATION OF
◄ ————————————►
OPERATING METHOD

FINE SCALE EXAMINATION
◄ ——————►
PROCESS DETAILS

DETAIL
◄ ————————————————————►
DESIGN

MAINTENANCE
◄ ——————►
METHOD STUDY

CONSTRUCTION
◄ ——————►
METHOD STUDY

PIPEWORK
◄ ————►
DESIGN

Figure 1.1 The application of method study to project design

initial emphasis on the specification of the raw and treated gas and the technically favoured processes which convert one to the other. Having established the broad objective of the study, further examination would be made of the individual operations in the conversion process which would provide data for plant design and operating methods. This in turn would form the starting point for further studies in the fields of maintenance, construction and pipework design.

The procedures of method study have been described by Currie[7] and their application to design work have been described by Binsted[8]. Figure 1.1 summarizes Binsted's general approach to project design.

1.4.2 Example of Critical Examination

A good example has been described by Olive[9] of a coarse-scale critical examination of the well-established process of manufacture of sulphuric acid up to 95 per cent concentration from sulphur by the contact process. The savings achieved and the modifications to the process represent the type of gains that can be made by the application of method study techniques, but it must be admitted in this instance that the gains were not (so far as is known) obtained as a result of the application of formal method study techniques. The example shows clearly what can be achieved by critical questioning.

In comparison with the conventional design of plant, the new design contains fewer pieces of equipment, is physically simple, more compact and less costly to build. Operation is less difficult and conversion efficiency is 99 per cent compared with 96–97 per cent by the old process, i.e. sulphur losses are more than halved. In the context of gas purification, in the conventional process, gases from the catalyst chambers are cooled and the sulphuric acid (the make) obtained by absorbing SO_3 in large absorption towers around which is circulated acid held closely to 98 per cent. The gases must be free from SO_3 mist and this entails drying the air to the furnace in which the sulphur is burnt. In the new process, advantage is taken of the capacity of the relatively newly developed Venturi scrubber to remove mist. As a consequence, provided the acid strength required is 95 per cent and not >98 per cent, it is possible to use a simple two-stage horizontal drum absorber in place of a large packed tower. A second function of this absorber is to cool the waste gases by evaporation of water from the absorption acid, thereby substantially eliminating final cooling of the product and in fact reducing cooling water requirement by at least 90 per cent. Moreover, it is not necessary to prevent formation of SO_3 mist in the gases to the absorber and consequently the air to the sulphur burners is not dried. The gases discharged to atmosphere from the Venturi scrubber cyclone contain less SO_2 and H_2SO_4 mist than those from the conventional process (without final electrostatic precipitator); in fact the acid mist content of the chimney plume of steamy gases is so low that the plume rapidly disappears under most conditions of atmospheric humidity.

It will be seen from the above description that critical coarse-scale examination of the conventional process combined with knowledge of newly developed chemical engineering techniques gave substantial savings. Other savings were made in earlier stages of the process.

1.5 The Use of Models in Plant Design

An essential engineering study during design of a large plant consists of a critical examination of the layout of the vessels, pipes and structures of a new plant. The following is a shortened version of a paper by Marsden[10] on the value of models and is reproduced by permission of the author and of the Institution of Mechanical Engineers, see also Farrow[11].

Project work is a team effort at all stages, and, whilst the preparation of models is basically a design office responsibility, all technologists associated with the project can make good use of them.

Originally, three-dimensional models were used to assist management in the visualization of projects. It has been said that the sole use of a model to a design team is to assist those who cannot read drawings with facility. This is sheer technical arrogance. All those associated with the design of plant can very quickly get a clear picture of a proposal by looking at a suitable model. An engineer seeing for the first time a set of 10 arrangement drawings will require at least a day thoroughly to appreciate all the points of the layout. The same man would need some 30 minutes to arrive at a clearer picture from the model. This advantage is much greater still in the case of the medical, safety and fire-prevention officers.

1.5.1 Two types of model

Our practice is to use two main types of models: the layout or preliminary, and the pipework or final model. Each of these plays its part in project management, and each is valuable in cost reduction and speed of completion.

The layout model replaces the traditional general arrangement drawings in the early stages of the project, no layout work whatever being done on the drawing board. The accuracy of modelling required depends on the type and conditions of the plant; for chemical plant, an accuracy of 30 cm actual size is sufficient in most cases. All modelling parts should be available at all times; they are supplemented by cardboard models, tubes, etc., for the odd unusual item. Pipes need only be indicated in special cases, usually when they are of very large diameter. Figure 1.2 illustrates a typical layout model.

The pipework or final model needs a much greater accuracy and takes the place of the traditional final arrangement drawings, as well as of all piping arrangement drawings. It is a true representation of the final plant in all but small details. A typical example is shown in Figure 1.3.

There are other methods of meeting some of the requirements of a model, particularly for single floor projects. Paper cut-out systems have their uses; these developments largely formalize traditional methods, used over many decades in the drawing office, by using a transparent base of flexible gridded plastics sheet, with some means of reproducing the plant outline, which is then stuck on the sheet. Preprinted, pressure-sensitive adhesive strips are used to indicate walls, flow lines, etc., and when all are stuck to the base sheet, prints can be taken in the normal way for engineering drawings.

The basic requirements of model kits are:
  (i) there must be no framework which visually obstructs or confuses;
  (ii) there must be no visible means of fixing the plant item;
  (iii) it must be possible to make up each item quickly from standard parts;

Figure 1.2 The layout model helps in visualizing the spatial relationships between the major plant items

Figure 1.3 The pipework model is prepared with great accuracy and serves instead of arrangement drawings

  (iv) the parts must be capable of firm fixing and easy removal;

  (v) there must be no restrictions to positioning of plant items inherent in the model itself;

  (vi) horizontal planes must be superimposed accurately;

  (vii) provision must be made for adding the structure to the plant; and

  (viii) the model must be capable of showing all the necessary detail.

A model kit developed to meet these requirements is in wide use in our design offices; it costs about £100 per set.

With the successful use of layout models, further savings in design effort may be attempted. The stage can be reached where almost the whole of the pipework is based on a model, and fabrication sketches are prepared direct

Figure 1.4 A final pipework model built with the latest kit looks almost like the real thing

from the model as isometrics. Figure 1.4 shows part of such a model which looks most realistic.

1.5.2 Use and Misuse

The misuse of the layout model can lead to a considerable waste of technical effort and time. A limited number of all the possible arrangements should be pre-selected. In the first place consideration should be given to the vertical layout, that is, to two dimensions only. There are three main groups of plant items to consider which are:

(i) Those with an optimum position, such as heavy items on the ground floor;

(ii) Items depending on one another spatially. On thorough investigation these are usually fewer than one would suppose;

(iii) Independent items.

It is particularly important that items which wholly belong to group (iii) should be excluded from group (ii).

For completely rigorous treatment consideration should be given to all dependent items. To this end we use a correlation chart such as is shown in Table 1.1 on which it is possible to record all decisions and the reasons for them. This last point is particularly important if a game of 'three-dimensional chess' is to be avoided later.

Table 1.1   CORRELATION CHART FOR POSITIONING OF EQUIPMENT

	SOLIDS CHARGING					PRESSURE FILTER				INTERMEDIATE STORAGE				
FLOOR	G	1st	2nd	3rd	4th	1st	2nd	3rd	4th	G	1st	2nd	3rd	4th
REACTION PAN 1st	2	2	4	4	4	4	4	4	X					
REACTION PAN 2nd	2	2	2						X					
REACTION PAN 3rd	2	2	2	2	4	4	4	4	X					
REACTION PAN 4th	2	2	2	2	2	2	2	2	X					
DRIER G							O	O	X	X	O		3	3
DRIER 1st						1		O	X	X	O		3	3
DRIER 2nd						1	1		X	X	O		3	3
DRIER 3rd						1	1	1	X	X	X	X	3	3
DRIER 4th						1	1	1	1	1	1	1	1	1

1, pressure filter; 2, solids charging above reaction pan; 3, intermediate storage in half of building with ground and two floors; 4, keep reaction pan in present position; ×, position not possible when tried on model; ○, alternatives which show slight disadvantage.

Conditions are determined for the possible positioning of equipment and the layout is worked through on the chart. It may then be necessary to try a different set of conditions. There are shortcomings in the chart and it must be used with care. On the other hand, it shows at a glance why certain plant cannot be placed on certain floors.

When the alternatives are reduced to a manageable number, they are tried out on the model. This usually reduces them still further. The final short list can then be tried in a matter of minutes, while all who are concerned are gathered round.

The correlation chart can be applied to the horizontal layout, using any suitable division such as a structural bay as a unit. Without this technique, the time spent in arriving at an agreed layout can extend to weeks, and even then all possibilities may not have been considered. No drawing board work whatsoever is needed in arriving at the agreed plant layout. When this is finally agreed, design work for the building steelwork is put in hand, working directly from the model.

1.5.3 The Piping Model

The skeleton building structure can be started when the layout model is agreed and the plant items prepared from freehand sketches or detail drawings, where they exist, and placed according to the layout model. The piping is then placed on the model working from the engineering flowsheet.

Wires represent the centre line of the pipes and sliding discs on each straight length of wire indicate the outside diameter, including lagging and flanges.

These should be placed by a thoroughly experienced piping engineer as he is virtually piping up the finished plant at this stage. The model is the only complete record and indicates the position of all valves, instrument fittings, etc. On final approval of all aspects of this model, sketch isometrics of all the piping can be finalized and cleared.

It has been found that the best scale for reasonably complicated models to be is 1:24.

The cost of a piping model for chemical plants of the type in which we are interested is from 0·25 to 1·0 per cent of the total cost of the plant. In all recent cases where piping models have been used there has been an overall saving of piping design costs of about 10 per cent in addition to appreciable savings in time.

There is some difference of opinion as to the smallest size of plant for which a pipework model should be used, but a quite small plant is known, worth £10000, which involved a branch into a very complicated pipe bridge carrying about 40 pipes, 30 of which were to be broken. It was found almost impossible to show the changes on a drawing; a simple model costing about £20 was prepared and the whole job was completed from the model, with no drawings. On a normal organic chemical plant the value of the plant, excluding buildings, at which a pipe-work model begins to show directly measurable savings in design costs is in the range of £40000–£80000. This does not allow for the benefit of saved time.

The use of the piping model does not end with design. It is sent to site and constantly used during construction as a reference and also for preliminary training of operating staff. To keep a record in the drawing office, photographs of the model are taken before it leaves. Stereoscopic views are selected to cover all pipework.

1.5.4 Conclusion

To summarize the advantages and disadvantages of the use of models; everybody associated with the plant gets a clear, quick picture at a very early stage of design and agreement can be reached in hours rather than weeks. The project programme is speeded up, design and construction costs reduced. A better standard of layout is achieved and the irritation of last-minute changes with consequent delays is eliminated.

On the debit side, unless close control is exercised, the perfectionist is presented with an ideal tool with which to waste time. Models also take up much space in the drawing office.

There is scope for using photographs of the model in the preparation of instructions to site personnel. The major problem is to add the third dimension without the use of multiple photographs; stereo-photography may be the solution.

1.6 Aerodynamic Design Studies

Although it is obvious that optimum performance of a gas-cleaning plant cannot be obtained if the gas flow to the operating components is not uniform, it is only in recent years that proper attention has been paid to this aspect of plant design by both purchasers and manufacturers of equipment. Poor gas distribution is invariably obtained when the pressure-drop across the cleaning elements is low and the diameter of the gas ducts is high, unless correctly disposed splitter baffles are installed, because the gas has always to turn through a sharp angle. Whenever a plant is large, it is highly desirable to build as large a model as possible in a transparent plastics material and blow air through it at a rate to give the Reynolds number which will apply on the full scale. Air velocities are determined by small Pitot tubes, and visualization of flow can be achieved by fixing 50 mm long brightly coloured, cotton threads to a thin wire grid placed downstream of the bend or by adding smoke to the inlet air. Further information on gas-flow distribution is given by Pope[12] and on models and scaling-up by Patterson and Abrahamsen[13].

When the gas contains grit and dust, such as that from a pulverized fuel boiler, the problem is accentuated by the fact that the dust is not distributed across the flue proportionately to the gas flow. Table 1.2 gives an example of measurement made in the flue from a small pulverized-fuel boiler; the measurements were taken 3·6 m after a right-angled bend which was 6 m ahead of a previous bend[14]. When installing splitter baffles in ducts carrying dusty gas, care must be taken to provide means of cleaning the vanes, e.g. with sootblowers[15].

Final check of the design should always be made whenever possible by drawing air through the plant, making measurements of the gas distribution and adjusting flow distributors as necessary. For low gas velocities where Pitot tubes are not sufficiently accurate, measurements are best made with a suitable anemometer such as that developed for setting gas-cooled nuclear reactors[16].

1.7 The Surface Physics of Small Particles

It is not always appreciated that inter-particle forces become highly significant when the size of the particles is less than 20 μm. These forces are responsible for the tenacity with which small particles adhere to themselves and to a surface and are responsible for many of the difficulties experienced in discharging collected dust from gas purification plants. Lowe and Lucas[17] have calculated these forces for the case of uniform spheres. They assume that the forces of adhesion are molecular forces which become negligible at distances greater than one atomic diameter (10^{-10} m) but inside this

Table 1.2 RELATIVE GAS VELOCITIES AND DUST BURDENS IN FLUE
FROM PULVERIZED FUEL BOILER

Flue dimensions $1 \cdot 5 \times 1 \cdot 8$ m
Average gas velocity   13 m/s
Average dust burden   36 g/s m^2

(The upper figure in each small square is the relative gas velocity, the lower figure the relative dust burden.)

1·6		1·5		1·5		1·6	
	2·0		1·5		1·4		2·2
0·9		0·9		1·0		1·2	
	0·8		0·7		0·8		1·2
0·9		0·7		0·7		0·8	
	0·7		0·6		0·7		0·9
0·8		0·6		0·6		0·6	
	0·8		0·6		0·7		0·7

distance are of the same order as the forces producing the tensile strength of a solid. If two spheres of diameter D_1 and D_2 m are in contact, the area, A, where opposing molecules are within a distance of 10^{-10} m, is:

$$A = \frac{\pi D_1 D_2}{D_1 + D_2} \times 10^{-12} \text{ m}^2 \qquad (1.1)$$

If U is the tensile strength of the material of the particles, the force f opposing disruption is:

$$f = \frac{\pi U D_1 D_2}{D_1 + D_2} \times 10^{-10} \text{ N} \qquad (1.2)$$

For the case of a particle resting on a plane:

$$f = \pi U D \times 10^{-10} \text{ N} \qquad (1.3)$$

The adhesion of spherical particles of fly-ash of density 2000 kg/m^3 and of tensile strength $U = 10^7$ N/m^2 is given in Table 1.3; it will be seen that a 100 μm particle on a plane would not be displaced by an acceleration of the plane of 30 g.

If the plane is contaminated with small particles which separate the main particle of fly-ash from the plane, the forces of adhesion of 100 μm spheres

Table 1.3 FORCES OF ADHESION BETWEEN A FLUE
DUST PARTICLE AND A PLANE

Diameter μm	Force (Newton)	Acceleration (m/s^2)
~ 1	3×10^{-9}	3×10^6
100	3×10^{-7}	3×10^2

resting on one of the smaller particles are given in Table 1.4. In practice the effect is modified because there are usually several small particles between the large particle and the plane.

These calculations explain and emphasize the difficulties of dislodging particles of fine dust from a surface.

Similar considerations can be applied to aggregates of particles such as those collected on the electrodes of electrostatic precipitators. Since the

Table 1.4 FORCES OF ADHESION OF 100 μm
PARTICLES RESTING ON SMALLER PARTICLES
ON A PLANE

Diameter of contaminating particle (μm)	Force (Newton)	Acceleration (m/s^2)
10	3×10^{-8}	30
1	1×10^{-9}	3
0·1	3×10^{-10}	0·3

number of particles per unit area is proportional to D^2 and the molecular force per contact is proportional to D. Consequently small particles can build up larger aggregates than large ones. In an aggregate consisting mainly of large particles but containing smaller ones, the strength of the aggregate will be reduced by the presence of small particles at the points of contact.

2

Legislation on Air Pollution

G. NONHEBEL

2.1 Introduction

The Alkali Works &c. Act 1906,* and the Clean Air Acts 1956 and 1968 have, in combination with the Public Health Act 1936, given Great Britain the most comprehensive national legislation on air pollution in the world. Since the discharge from many gas purification processes is to atmosphere, it is appropriate that a description be given of this legislation and its administration. Table 2.1 summarizes this British legislation. For reasons of space, no attempt has been made to describe the action taken by other countries to limit atmospheric pollution.

2.2 Administration

Legislation dealing with air pollution is the responsibility of the Ministry of Environment (formerly the Ministry of Housing and Local Government) and the Secretary of State for Scotland.

2.2.1 The Alkali Act

The Alkali Act is administered by separate Alkali Inspectorates for England plus Wales and for Scotland. There are minor differences in legal procedure in Scotland from those in England and Wales. In England the Chief Alkali Inspector in London is assisted by about twenty-four Inspectors operating from the larger relevant industrial centres.

In the Alkali Act the only statutory maximum limits for discharges are in respect of HCl and SO_3 from certain operations. For well-established processes, however, the Inspectorate require discharges to be below 'presumptive limits' which they consider to be in conformity with good practice (Section 2.3.4).

All processes registered under the Alkali Act must take the *best practicable means* for preventing the emission of noxious or offensive gases, smoke, grit and dust (defined in Section 2.3.6). Section 27 of the Alkali Act states that

*Also The Alkali Works Regulation (Scotland) Act, 1951.

Table 2.1 MAJOR ITEMS IN ACTS DEALING WITH AIR POLLUTION

Design	Operation	Governing Acts
Processes not scheduled under the Alkali Act (enforcing authority—Local Authority)		
Smoke from Chimneys		
Furnaces to be smokeless as far as practicable. Notification of new furnaces. Approval of design optional.	Smoke to be less than No. 2 Ringelmann except for short stated periods. It may later be compulsory to fit smoke indicators and to send readings to the Local Authority.	Clean Air Acts
Smoke Control Areas		
Furnaces and domestic fireplaces to be completely smokeless or designed to burn approved smokeless fuel.	No smoke at all to be emitted except under locally defined conditions. No proceedings if approved smokeless fuel being burned. Under defined conditions, use of oil-firing and of coal-fired mechanical stokers is permitted.	Clean Air Acts
Smoke Nuisance		
Best practicable means to be taken to prevent nuisance by smoke from chimney or burning of rubbish. Court order may be obtained to improve plant or abate nuisance.	Best practicable means to prevent smoke from chimney. Abatement of other smoke nuisances.	Clean Air Acts Public Health Act, 1936
Grit, Dust and Fumes		
On all plants any practicable means to be used to minimize emission. Dedusters required and prior approval to be obtained on dedusters for new plant burning pulverized fuel or over 1 ton/h solid fuel.	Plant to be properly maintained and used. The Local Authority may require measurements to be made. Minister may prescribe limits on rates of emission (in force 1971).	Clean Air Acts
Chimneys		
Prior approval of height of new chimney which is to be sufficient to prevent smoke, dust, fumes and gases being prejudicial to health or a nuisance.	See also Chapter 19	Clean Air Acts

Design	Operation	Governing Acts

Odours and Fumes

| Best practicable means of collection and destruction. | Good housekeeping. Careful maintenance and operation of collection and destruction plant. Odorous material not to be left lying about. | Public Health Acts |

Processes scheduled under the Alkali Act
    (enforcing authority—Alkali Inspector*)

| Best practicable means to prevent emission of noxious or offensive gases, smoke, grit and dust, and fumes. Inspector may require further instruments or improved plant. | Competent operation. Efficient maintenance. Proper supervision by owner. | Alkali Act as extended by Clean Air Acts |

*The Local Authority may obtain the consent of the Minister to prosecute for dark smoke, smoke nuisances and grit and dust emission.

these means have reference not only to *the provision and efficient maintenance of appliances adequate for preventing such escape, but also to the manner in which such applicances are used and to the proper supervision by the owner of any operation in which such gases are evolved.* Presumably registration, which has to be renewed annually, can be refused if pollution-collecting appliances are not considered to have the required efficiency. The Inspector, it will be noted, can also require the process itself to be operated in such a way as to minimize production of pollutants and he can require provision of necessary instruments and employment of trained operators. Only that part of a process plant which leads to air pollution need be registered.

Proceedings for emission of smoke, etc., can, however, also be taken by Local Authorities, with the consent of the Minister, against operators of processes registered under the Alkali Act, but an additional defence is that best practicable means have been taken. The Clean Air Act empowers the Minister to remove from the list of scheduled processes any for which the special supervision by the Alkali Inspectorate is no longer considered necessary.

The powers behind the Alkali Inspectorate are immense though they have always been used to persuade factory owners to improve processes, and prosecutions have been extremely few. The wide range of problems considered are given in their *Annual Reports*.

The reason for placing numerous non-chemical processes (mainly large emitters of dust—see list in Section 2.3.8) under the supervision of the Inspectorate is that they all present problems of special difficulty and that constant general control under a central control, and with access to information from anywhere in the world, is the only method whereby design and operational methods of plant can be kept up-to-date. If the original design of a large pollution-prevention plant, which might cost over £1 million for a large power station, turns out in practice to be poor, the improvements that can be made at reasonable cost and dislocation to the operation of the plant are usually only marginal: original design is therefore all important.

2.2.2 The Clean Air Acts

The Clean Air Acts which apply to the whole of the United Kingdom are administered by Local Authorities. The only statutory limit in the Act itself prohibits the emission of dark smoke, defined as dark as or darker than shade 2, on the Ringelmann chart. The Acts are primarily enabling acts enunciating general principles on which regulations with considerable technical detail (Section 2.4.4) may be made by the Minister of Environment in respect of England and Wales, and by the Secretary of State for Scotland. These regulations, which are called Statutory Instruments, have the force of law from the date given on them provided they are not annulled by Parliament within 40 days of being laid before Parliament. Frequently the Ministry issue at the same time explanatory circulars and memoranda to Local Authories who administer the Acts apart from those parts reserved for the Alkali Inspectorate. Although there are always strong Parliamentary objections to the principle of 'legislation by reference', it will be appreciated from the review given later of these regulations that control will be more rapid and effective by the issue of regulations which can be readily changed in wording or technical effect to suit experience and present progress in technology.

2.3 The Alkali Act

2.3.1 General

The original Alkali Act was passed primarily to control emissions of HCl from saltcake works and of SO_3 fumes from sulphuric acid chamber processes. There are a few differences between Scotland and England plus Wales. Excellent accounts of the historical development of the Alkali Inspectorate from the first Alkali Act of 1863 until 1959 and of the future plans and philosophy of the Inspectorate have been given by a Chief Alkali Inspector[1].

2.3.2 Definition of Alkali Work (Section 27 (1) of Act)

Alkali works means every works for
  (i) the manufacture of sulphate of soda or sulphate of potash, or
  (ii) the treatment of copper ores by common salt or other chlorides whereby any sulphate is formed, in which muriatic acid gas is evolved.

2.3.3 Registration and Conditions (Section 9 (1))

An alkali works, a scheduled works, a cement works or a smelting works shall not be carried on unless it is certified to be registered.

A certificate of registration shall be in force from one year (expiring on 1 April), and application for subsequent certificates shall be made in January or February. (Applications for registration should be made to the Ministry of Environment or to the Department of Health for Scotland.)

One of the conditions of first registration shall be that the works is furnished with such appliances as appear to the Chief Inspector to be necessary to enable the work to be carried on in accordance with the requirements of the Act (with appeal to the Minister of Environment).

Owners of scheduled works shall use the best practicable means to prevent the escape of noxious or offensive gases to the atmosphere (Section 7 of the Act).

Nothing in the Act shall legalize any act that would be deemed a nuisance (Section 29 of the Act).

2.3.4 Limits for Escape of Noxious Materials in Effluents

Concentrations in gaseous effluents are measured at 60°F (15°C) and 30 in. Hg pressure and before admixture with any air or other diluent gases (1 grain/ft^3 at 60°F = 2·42 g/m^3 at 0°C).

(i) **Statutory limits.** The limits for escape of certain effluents have been fixed by Parliament in the Alkali Act. These are:

Sulphur trioxide (SO$_3$). 4 grains SO$_3$/ft^3 (9·6 g/m^3 n.t.p.) from chamber acid plants (Section 6 (1)); 1·5 grains SO$_3$/ft^3 (3·61 g/m^3 n.t.p.) H$_2$SO$_4$ concentration plants (Section 7 (1)(b)).

Hydrogen chloride (HCl). 0·2 grains HCl/ft^3 (0·48 g/m^3 n.t.p.) (Sections 6 (2) and 7 (1)(a)).

The Inspectors can, however, press for lower limits from some plants today on the grounds that they can be obtained by use of best practicable means.

(ii) **Presumptive limits.** The Inspectorate also fix 'presumptive limits' which are the limits they consider to conform with current best practicable means. These limits are often decided for individual plants according to local conditions including chimney height and, in the case of existing plants, their expected life.

A complete list of 'Standards of Emission under the Alkali Act' was published in the 1966 report by the Chief Inspectors[2]. These standards had not been revised by mid-1970, apart from that for Cement Works emissions given in the 1967 report.

Dusts: For emissions of dusts which are chemically inert and have only a nuisance value, suggested limits vary from 0·1 to 0·5 grains/ft^3 at n.t.p. depending on local conditions including appearance of plume.

2.3.5 Heights of Chimneys

The alkali Inspector includes the height of chimneys for adequate dispersal of gas and dust when considering the design of plants. Thus he has requested chimneys of 200 m for power stations burning several million tons of coal or oil per year.

The policy in respect of emissions of SO_2 from the smaller scheduled works is best indicated by the following quotation from an article by a Chief Alkali Inspector[1].

'The noxious constituent of waste gases most commonly disposed of by discharge at high level is sulphur dioxide. The Alkali Inspectorate has for some years applied a provisional standard correlating actual chimney heights with sulphur dioxide emission whereby heights should be not less than those falling on the curve given by the following table [Table 2.2]. 'Individual discharge points on any given works are normally regarded as one point source. Thus with three chimneys each discharging 2·5 tons SO_2 per day, the height of each chimney should be at least 150 ft (46 m). The heights quoted refer to warm emissions with an appreciable thermal lift. With cold or wet emissions, heights should be greater. In the case of a large number of chimneys, for instance at oil refineries, the actual heights are the result of agreement between the management and the inspectorate. There may be a "bonus" to be applied to calculated heights or an agreement as to minimum height irrespective of the mass of any particular emission. The department's gauge is hence somewhat elastic. Nevertheless, the curve has proved a useful basis for discussion and its application has led to reasonably satisfactory conditions and to freedom from complaint.'

The heights given in Table 2.2 do not apply to large boiler plants scheduled under the Alkali Act because the thermal rise from the large volume of gases is considerable (for further information see Chapter 19, Section 19.3).

Table 2.2 CHIMNEY HEIGHTS REQUIRED BY ALKALI INSPECTORATE FOR REGISTERED CHEMICAL PLANTS

Tons SO_2/day	40	30	21	13	7·5	3·6
Minimum height of chimney (ft)	340	300	250	200	150	100
(m)	104	91	76	61	46	30

A minimum height of 37 m is also applied to chimneys carrying discharges from purely chemical operations, e.g. from granulated fertilizer plants. In his report for 1958 the Chief Alkali Inspector states that in special cases complaint has ceased where chimneys from such plants have been raised to this height.

2.3.6 List of Noxious or Offensive Gases Scheduled by the Alkali Act

The list of noxious or offensive gases in Section 27 of the Alkali Act 1906, as extended by S.I. 1971 No. 1960.

Inorganic Substances
Ammonia and its compounds
Arsenic and its compounds
Carbon monoxide, CO
Carbon bisulphide, CS_2
Cyanogen compounds
Halogens (F, Cl, Br, I) and their compounds
Hydrochloric (muriatic) acid, HCl
Nitric acid and acid forming oxides of nitrogen
Sulphurous acid and SO_2, except those arising solely from the combustion of coal
Sulphuric acid and SO_3
Sulphur chlorides
Sulphuretted hydrogen, H_2S
Fumes from cement works
Fumes containing chlorine or its compounds
Fumes containing the following elements:
    Al, As, Be, Ca, Cd, Cl, Cr, Cu, Fe, K, Mg, Mn, Mo, Na, P, Pb, Sb, Se, Si, Ti, U, V, W, Zn
Smoke, grit and dust

Organic Substances
Acetic acid and anhydride
Acetylene
Aldehydes
Amines
Fumaric acid
Maleic acid and anhydride
Phthalic acid and anhydride
Picolines
Pyridine
Volatile organic sulphur compounds
Products containing hydrogen from the partial oxidation of hydrocarbons
Fumes from benzene works, from tar works and paraffin oil works (oil refineries)
(Added 1971: arylates, di-isocynates, fumes from petroleum works)

2.3.7 List of Non-scheduled Works in the Alkali Act

Works defined in the original Alkali Act are known officially as Non-scheduled Works. They are:
   (i) Alkali works, that is to say, every works for:
      (*a*) the manufacture of sulphate of soda or sulphate of potash, or
      (*b*) the treatment of copper ores by common salt, or other chlorides, whereby any sulphate is formed, in which muriatic acid gas (HCl) is evolved.
   (ii) Cement works, that is to say, works in which aluminous deposits are treated for the purpose of making cement.
   (iii) Smelting works, that is to say, works in which sulphide ores, including regulus, are calcined or smelted.

2.3.8 List of Scheduled Works in the Alkali Act

The first schedule to the Alkali Act 1906, as extended by the Alkali &c. Works Order 1966, gives a list of 56 works (which had not been extended by mid-1970). The list is too long to give here. It includes all works liable to emit the gases and fumes given in Section 2.3.6. Other works include caustic soda works, ceramic works, lime works, chemical incineration works for the destruction by burning of wastes containing combined chlorine, fluorine, nitrogen, phosphorus or sulphur, metal recovery works in which metal is recovered from scrap cable by burning the insulation, all public supply power stations, and private works producing electricity and having boilers of an aggregate capacity not less than 450000 lb/h (400 t/h).

The list was extended by S.I. 1971 No. 960.

2.4 The Clean Air Acts

2.4.1 General

The Clean Air Acts 1956 and 1968 follow closely the recommendations of the Government Committee on Air Pollution appointed after the London smog disaster of 1952 when deaths ascribable to the smog amounted to over 4000 in the Greater London area[4]. The report of the Government Committee[5] is frequently referred to as the Beaver Report.

The Clean Air Act makes it an offence to discharge from a chimney smoke of shade as dark as or darker than No. 2 Ringelmann continuously, or No. 4 Ringelmann for longer than periods specified in detail by regulations. It requires the emission of grit and dust from furnaces to be minimized on all plants above a specified size whether old or new. Also, all new plants of certain types must be fitted with apparatus for arresting grit and dust, the specification of which must be approved by the Local Authority. Similarly, approval of the height of all new industrial chimneys is required. Emission of domestic smoke is covered by permissive powers to Local Authorities to declare districts as Smoke Control Areas, these being a modification of the Smokeless Zones provisions included in the Private Acts of a few Local Authorities since 1947. There are restrictions on the use of coal- and oil-fired industrial equipment in Smoke Control Areas.

Section 17 of the 1956 Act excludes from the provisions of this Act (with certain exceptions) all premises controlled under the Alkali Act.

As this book is concerned with gas purification systems and not with fuel technology, details of the Clean Air Act relating to smoke arising from incomplete combustion will be largely omitted from this chapter.

2.4.2 Technical Groupings under The Clean Air Act

In what follows, 'S' mean sections of the Act and S.I. are dated Statutory Instruments issued under this and related Acts.

(a) *Smoke from industry.* S1, 3, 4 (1956), S2 (1968). S.I. 1958 No. 498 and 878—for Scotland S.I. 1958 No. 1933 and 1934. These control smoke from steam raising and other simple furnaces in general industry, including smoke from ships and railway locomotives.

The Fourth Schedule of the Act repeals the clauses in the Public Health Acts protecting mines, iron and steel works.

(b) *Smoke density meters.* S4, 1956. The Minister may make regulations requiring installation of indicating or recording smoke density meters on any type of specified furnace, using and maintaining the apparatus in pursuance of the regulations, and making available to the Local Authority any results recorded by the apparatus. No regulations had been made by mid-1970.

(c) *Grit, Dust and Fumes.* S6–9 (1956, S2–5 (1968): S.I. 1968 No. 431. The Acts require that new plants burning pulverized fuel or more than 100 lb/h (45 kg/h) of solid fuel or at a rate of liquid or gaseous fuel equivalent to more than $1\frac{1}{4}$ million Btu/h (= 367 kW heat) shall instal arrestment which has been approved by the Local Authority.

In the case of the above size furnaces the Local Authority may require measurements to be made and reported of the grit and dust emission by the method prescribed in Ref. 8—see S.I. 1968 No. 431. In the case of furnaces burning less than one ton/h of solid matter (other than p.f.) or less than a rate of liquid or gaseous fuel equivalent to 28 million Btu/h (8·2 MW heat), the 'occupier' of the building in which the furnace is situate may request the Local Authority to make and record measurements of the grit and dust emission.

The Minister may prescribe limits on the rates of emission of grit and dust from chimneys. These Regulations were issued as S.I. 1971 No. 162. The Ministry has, however, issued a Memorandum[9] which gives charts for recommended maximum levels of emission in terms of boiler sizes expressed as maximum rating of steam per hour (from and at 100°C) from solid and oil-fired plant and in terms of thermal input to furnaces heating the stock directly but where the stock does not contribute to the emission.

(d) *Chimneys.* S10 (1956), S6 (1968). The heights of new chimneys are to be approved by the Local Authority: also of chimneys serving furnaces with enlarged combustion space. The Local Authority shall not approve the height of the chimney unless they are satisfied that the height will be sufficient to prevent, so far as is practicable, the smoke, grit, dust, gases or fumes emitted from the chimney from becoming prejudicial to health or a nuisance having regard to (a) the purpose of the chimney, (b) the position and description of the buildings near it, (c) the levels of the neighbouring ground, (d) any other matters requiring consideration in the circumstances. Conditions may be attached to the approval.

These are the only sections to which reference is made to the discharge of gases, e.g. SO_2.

To assist Local Authorities on heights to be used for chimneys emitting SO_2 from combustion of fuel, the Ministry has issued a Memorandum on Chimney Heights[10] which includes charts for heights of chimneys for SO_2 emission rates for 5 classes of district ranging from undeveloped areas to heavily populated industrial areas; and a chart correcting for heights of adjacent buildings. The Memo gives advice also on combination of effluents to a minimum number of chimneys and on emission velocities.

Heights of chimneys are discussed in Chapter 19.

*Grit consists of particles larger than 76 μm. Fume is liquid or solid particles smaller than dust-size not defined in the Clean Air Acts. Fume is usually taken to mean particles smaller than one μm.

(e) *Processes scheduled under the Alkali Act.* S17 (1956), S11 (1968). The Act extends the Alkali Act to cover smoke, grit, dust and fumes as well as noxious and offensive gases, and now empowers the Minister to make Orders, adding to or removing from the list of works scheduled under the Alkali Act. These Orders can only be made after a public enquiry at which it must be proved to the satisfaction of the Court of Enquiry, and against any opposition by Local Authorities and others, that the industrial processes for which registration is requested present special technical difficulties in respect of emissions of smoke, dust, grit and noxious gases.

(f) *Smoke from houses; smoke control areas.* S11–13. These sections provide for the declaration of 'Smoke Control Areas' by Local Authorities subject to confirmation by the Minister who must hold a public enquiry if objections are raised. No smoke may be emitted in a Smoke Control Area except from defined premises and then only with limitations defined in the Order. The Areas may include industrial and commercial premises. The Act does not repeal those Local Authority Acts for the establishment of 'Smokeless Zones' which are substantially similar to Smoke Control Areas.

2.4.3 Definitions under The Clean Air Act, 1956

Although it is often tedious for the reader, it is almost always better to quote the actual words than to give an abstract of an Act of Parliament when important technical detail is concerned. In this chapter, quotations from the Act are given in italics, together with the Section of the Act or the associated Statutory Instrument.

Smoke—34(1)—*Smoke includes soot, ash, grit and gritty particles emitted in smoke.*

Dark Smoke—34(2)—*Dark smoke means smoke which, if compared in the appropriate manner with a chart of the type known at the date of the passing of this Act as the Ringelmann Chart*, would appear to be as dark as or darker than shade 2 on the chart.*

The Act also states in effect that a prosecution may be brought without there being an actual comparison of the smoke with a Ringelmann chart. A trained smoke inspector can judge whether a smoke is appreciably darker than Ringelmann 2.

Black Smoke

S.I. 1958 No. 498 states that black smoke is as dark as or darker than shade 4 on the chart. This is the first time that black smoke has been legally defined in Britain.

Practicable—34(1)—*Practicable means reasonably practicable having regard, amongst other things, to local conditions and circumstances, to the financial implications and to the current state of technical knowledge.*

Practicable Means—34(1)—*Practicable means includes the provision and maintenance of plant and the proper use thereof.*

---

*The British Standard Chart is published as BS.2742C and a miniature chart as BS.2472M. The method of use of both charts is described in BS.2742.

The Alkali Act 1906, Section 27, uses wording having similar effect, though it and the Public Health Act 1936 omit reference to the current state of technical knowledge—an important clarification in the Clean Air Act.

Fireplace—34(1)—*Fireplace includes any furnace, grate or stove, whether open or closed.*

Oven—34(1)—*Oven includes any form of retort or container used to subject solid fuel to any process involving the application of heat.*

Industrial Plant—34(1)—*Industrial plant includes any still, melting pot or other plant used for any industrial or trade purposes, and also any incinerator used for or in connection with any such purposes.*

Chimney—34(1)—*Chimney includes structures and openings of any kind from or through which smoke or (where the reference is to the chimney serving an oven) grit or dust may be emitted, and references to a chimney of a building include references to a chimney which serves the whole or a part of a building but is structurally separate therefrom.*

Furnaces

No definition is given of furnace, but the following are important interpretations of the word 'furnaces':

S.I. 1958, No. 498—II(3)—*Where a single boiler or unit of industrial plant is fired by more than one furnace discharging to the same chimney those furnaces shall, for the purpose of these regulations, be deemed to be one furnace.*

34(7)—The following definition is in respect of the sections of the Act dealing with grit and dust emission from furnaces:

Any furnaces which are in the occupation of the same person and are served by a single chimney shall, for the purpose of Sections 6–8 of this Act, be taken to be one furnace.

34(1)—*Authorized fuel means a fuel declared by regulations of the Minister to be an authorized fuel for the purposes of this act.* (This definition refers to sections of the Act dealing with Smoke Control Areas.)

2.5 The Factories Act

The Factory Act of 1878 was the first to require fan-induced ventilation for the removal of dust likely to be injurious to health. The problems associated with dust in factory atmosphere has been described by Davies[6] and Drinker and Hatch[7].

Successive Factory Acts were consolidated in the Factories Act, 1937. Part IV, Section 47 of this Act contains the following special provision:

47. *Removal of dust or fumes.* (1) In every factory (*a*) in which, in connection with any process carried on, there is given off any dust or fume or other impurity of such a character and to such extent as to be likely to be injurious (*b*) or offensive to the persons employed, or any substantial quantity of dust of any kind, all practicable measures shall be taken to protect the persons employed against inhalation of the dust or fume or other impurity and to prevent its accumulating (*c*) in any workroom, and in particular, where the nature of the process makes it practicable, exhaust appliances shall be provided and maintained, as near as possible

to the point of origin of the dust or fume or other impurity, so as to prevent it entering the air of any workroom.

The numerous supplementary regulations issued under the 1937 and previous Factories Acts include special provisions for the protection of workers in industries where dust is a special hazard—for example likely to lead to lung damage by silicosis, byssinosis, etc. For a compact statement of these regulations, the reader is referred to Redgrave's Factories Acts[9]: this book also contains abstracts of interpretations by the Law Courts.

3
Instruments

D. M. BISHOP

3.1 Scope

This chapter comprises a summary of the most important factors governing the choice of instruments for the types of process being considered, together with some indication of how they should be applied, what difficulties are likely to be encountered and what may be done to overcome them. As much space as possible has been allotted to the measurement of gas composition because of its importance in the present context, but the more common measurements (pressure, temperature, etc.) since they are so frequently used, have had to occupy a substantial part of the chapter. Automatic control is briefly described, emphasis being placed, as in the sections dealing with measurement, on application rather than description of the devices available on the market.

Any reader wishing to delve more deeply into the subject can do so by consulting the general references[1-3]. In addition to these, literature dealing with particular aspects of the subject is referred to in the relevant sections.

3.2 Temperature Measurement

For instruments mounted near to the point of measurement, expansion and vapour pressure types are usually satisfactory, although the capillaries are vulnerable and awkward to install, and vapour pressure instruments are very non-linear. As the distance between the detecting and measuring elements increases, a transmitter (electric or pneumatic) can be used, and this may also be desirable in order to make use of standard control equipment, or to take advantage of the narrow scale ranges available. Transmission, however, introduces additional errors, and it may be preferable to change to resistance thermometers or thermocouples, the former being the most accurate and stable method of all. These methods are expensive for single points, but it is easy to accommodate a number of them on a multipoint recorder or indicator, thus reducing the cost per point. Instruments are available which convert signals from resistance thermometers and thermocouples to pneumatic or electric signals so that standard control equipment can be used. If a very fast response is required, then a bare thermocouple is ideal, but it may be contaminated and lose its calibration. If a sheath has to be used there is less to choose (in speed) between the best of each type when good installation practice is followed. For very high gas temperatures, a suction pyrometer may be the best solution.

A temperature-sensing device provides a measure of its own temperature and not that of the fluid in which it is immersed. Good installation practice is aimed at reducing to negligible proportions the difference between these two temperatures, i.e. maximizing the heat transfer between the fluid and the bulb, while minimizing heat loss and gain from other sources, e.g. conduction to or from the wall of the vessel, radiation to or from the walls of the vessel or any other surface at a temperature different from that of the bulb. It will usually be necessary to compromise between these requirements and other requirements dictated by the process. Other things being equal, the measurement should be made at a point where the fluid is moving rapidly, the sheath should be a good conductor of heat and as thin as possible and the bulb should be in good thermal contact with the sheath. If radiation is affecting the accuracy (even at the optimum depth of immersion), a radiation shield may be incorporated, or alternatively a suction-type pyrometer may be used.

The errors so far considered apply to steady temperatures. When the temperature of the fluid is varying other errors arise due to failure of the bulb temperature to respond quickly enough. The methods of reducing static errors also help to reduce dynamic errors, an additional need being to keep the heat capacity of the measuring system as low as possible. Static errors do not affect controllability but dynamic errors lead to poor control and also to failure of the controller to show its true performance. Both are discussed in detail by Aikman, McMillan and Morrison[5] who also deal with installation and design of sheaths, etc. The reduction of static errors at high gas temperatures is discussed by Godridge, Jackson and Thurlow[6].

Both static and dynamic errors are liable to change with time if the heat transfer conditions alter, due for example to a build-up of a deposit on the sheath. Thermocouples used at high temperatures must be carefully watched to ensure that the atmosphere in which they are operating does not affect their calibration. In important installations a check point should be installed close enough to the measuring point to ensure identical conditions; this may be either connected up permanently or used intermittently with a test thermometer which must, of course, be properly inserted and given time to stabilize.

The calibration of temperature-measuring devices requires special equipment if high accuracy is required. D.S.I.R. have prepared an excellent guide[7] to this subject, and no trouble should be experienced if the instructions are scrupulously followed.

3.3 Pressure and Pressure Difference Measurement

Bourdon tube pressure gauges are available in a variety of materials and can be used in the range from 0·3 to 700 bar (g.); the minimum requirements for a satisfactory indicating pressure gauge are prescribed in BS. 1780[8] and Budenberg[9] has given an excellent account of the design and use of such gauges. Diaphragm gauges can be used up to 21 bar (g.) and are obtainable with various protective films for corrosive fluids; they can also be applied to lower gauge pressures, using metallic diaphragms down to about 12 mb(g) and slack organic diaphragms below this (and up to about 450 mb(g)). Bellows can be used for the lower range of gauge pressures, and are particularly useful for the measurement of absolute pressures down to 130 mb(a). It is possible to obtain gauges with a better performance than that specified in the British Standard[8] and other more expensive methods can be adopted when necessary. For example, liquid in glass manometers, float-operated manometers and bell-type movements, and for very low gauge pressures, the ring-balance meter may be used. All of them suffer from the disadvantage of relatively slow response to changes in input. For very high pressures strain gauge elements may be preferred.

Differential pressure instruments use the same mechanisms (except that the Bourdon tube is not often used), the two pressures being applied on either side of the measuring element. As the working pressure may be many times the differential pressure being measured it is most desirable to ensure that the instrument will not be damaged by accidental overload to the working pressure; the best instruments will withstand this without even a significant change in zero.

Any of these measuring elements may be attached to pneumatic or electric transmission mechanisms if the distance between the point of measurement and the instrument is long, if it is undesirable to have the measured fluid taken to the point at which indication is required, or if standard control equipment is to be used. Other installation difficulties may also dictate the use of a transmitter, in spite of the loss of accuracy which may occur.

It is generally true to say that most troubles are associated with those parts of the installation which are in contact with the fluid and the way in which they have been installed. Materials in contact with the fluid should be chosen for their resistance to corrosion; if no suitable materials are available, the instrument may be protected by a 'purge' of some gas which will not interfere with the process, or by the use of liquid seals. Connections to vessels and pipes should be at least 12 mm nominal bore at the point of connection if possible. The connection should be on top for gases, and underneath for liquids to facilitate draining and venting. When condensation is expected the lines must slope at least 1 in 12 and suitable collecting points must be installed at low points in the line and provision made for draining them. Alternatively they can be arranged to be always full of condensate, provided the level of condensate is sufficiently controlled to avoid errors due to variation. In liquid installations the lines must slope and must be fitted with vents to release trapped gas which cause errors. The meter should be under the pipe for liquid measurement and over if for gases; this is not mandatory but it simplifies installation and reduces the risk of trouble later. The lower the pressure or differential pressure being measured, the more critical becomes the installation.

Pressure instruments should be calibrated regularly against a test gauge, dead-weight tester or manometer.

3.4 Liquid Level Measurement

Liquid level may be measured most simply by means of a sight glass, but the method is liable to be hazardous and is unsuited to remote reading or control. Most commonly the pressure head due to the contents of a tank is measured: this may be done directly by connecting one side of a differential pressure-measuring instrument to the bottom of the tank and the other to the vapour space above the maximum permissible level (in an open tank, of course only one connection is needed). Alternatively a restricted flow of gas, usually air, may be passed through a dip-pipe extending nearly to the bottom of the tank and also through another restrictor into the vapour space above the liquid. The pressure difference between the two tank connections, downstream of the two restrictors, is equal to the liquid head, provided that there is no other resistance to flow—only the dip-leg 'purge' is required if the tank is open to atmosphere.

A float supported by the surface of the liquid can give an accurate measure of level in an open tank, it being easy to transfer the large motion to the outside where various indicating and transmitting mechanisms can be attached. When the tank is under pressure, however, the large motion makes it more difficult to apply, and it is then mainly used as a very simple and trouble-free actuator for automatic control when close control is satisfactory and the set value can be fixed. The effective weight of a partially submerged cylinder, of mean density greater than that of the liquid, gives a measure of level, the length of the cylinder being chosen to suit the range of measurement. As the movement of the cylinder can be small, the motion can readily be transferred through a bellows or torque tube as pressure seal to actuate indicating or transmitting mechanisms. A change in electrical capacity occurs when the level of liquid in a cylindrical capacitor changes, and this gives a measure of tank contents; this is, however, dependent on the dielectric constant of the fluid, and is therefore particularly susceptible to changes in water content. The rapid change in electrical capacity which occurs when the surface of a liquid or granular solid approaches an insulated probe can be used for alarm and control purposes, and here the dielectric constant is not a significant factor. A very simple form of control, when indication is not required, can sometimes be provided by the electric contact method of detecting the surface of a conducting liquid. For the more intractable problems, there are instruments using radioactive sources, and these can be used for alarm, control, and sometimes measurement, but they are relatively expensive and precautions are essential to ensure the safety of personnel during both operation and maintenance.

Instruments nominally measuring 'level' may be calibrated in terms of volume or weight of contents. Instruments measuring head or the buoyancy of a float are affected by the density of the fluid if they are calibrated in terms of level or volume; if, however, they are calibrated in terms of weight of contents, and if the instrument operates virtually down to zero, the reading will be correct even if the density changes; for tanks with non-linear calibrations the compensation is incomplete. Instruments operated by floats and calibrated in terms of level or volume are accurate, as density has only the second order effect of varying the depth of immersion of the float. The density must, however, be known if the weight of contents is required.

Instruments may be mounted directly in the vessel, but bubbling or stirring interferes and a separate chamber may be necessary. It is usually wise to ignore the bottom 150 mm or so because of the likely presence of sediment, and connections should never be taken from the bottom for the same reason. Buoyancy-type devices have to be carefully installed to ensure that the tubes do not foul the sides of the chambers in which they are mounted. The material of floats must be carefully chosen, as the walls are thin and are soon holed if corrosion takes place.

Precise control of level is generally easy to achieve provided that the inflow or outflow, whichever is used to effect control, may be allowed to vary widely and rapidly. As precise control is seldom necessary, variation in level may be allowed so that unwanted flow changes do not occur; in this case measurement over a wider range may be necessary with consequent complications in the equipment.

3.5 Flow Measurement

Flow measurement may be divided into two categories:
  (1) flow rate measurement;
  (2) total (integrated) flow measurement.

The same device may be used for both purposes: the signal from a flow-rate measuring device may be integrated, and the rate of revolution of a counter in any integrator may be used to indicate flow rate. When control is required, flow rate control is more applicable to continuous processes, and total flow control to batch processes.

The method almost universally used for continuous flow measurement is the orifice plate in conjunction with a differential pressure meter[11,12], and there is no immediate prospect of a change in spite of the numerous disadvantages of the system; the advantages of simplicity, cheapness, ease of installation and replacement, and wide sphere of usefulness, generally outweigh them. First of all, with regard to accuracy, it is important to appreciate that high accuracy is very difficult to attain, and that the majority of orifice plate installations probably exhibit errors up to about ± 5 per cent f.s.d., due chiefly to the effect of the installation and the action of the fluid being measured. Great care in design and regular maintenance are necessary if ± 2 per cent is to be assured; the achievement of ± 1 per cent is possible only in ideal conditions and with the greatest refinements in design, and of course considerable expense. As direct alternatives to the orifice plate, but still using differential pressure, there are the nozzle, Venturi tube and Dall tube, all of which are more expensive: they do not improve accuracy, but they have the advantage that the overall pressure loss is smaller for the same measured differential pressure and this can be most important in large installations where the generation of the extra head may be expensive or even impossible. Installation and replacement are more difficult; the nozzle and Venturi tube are less prone to trouble due to suspended solids in the fluid. Another device which generates a differential pressure but operates on a different principle is the Pitot tube: this has the advantage of presenting a negligible obstruction to the flow, but the accuracy obtainable is low and the presence of even small amounts of solids soon plugs the openings; the chief use is for spot-checks on gas flows in large ducts when other installations are out of the question, and for highest accuracy a 'traverse' of the duct must be made to determine the velocity distribution over the cross-section of the duct. All of the devices described above produce a pressure difference proportional to the square of the flow rate: if therefore, the flow is pulsating due to the use of a reciprocating pump, etc., the average of the fluctuating differential pressure will not give the average of the flow, the discrepancy being greater for rectangular than for sinusoidal variations in flow; the non-linear calibration also reduces the accuracy sharply at flow rates less than $\frac{1}{6}$ f.s.d.

The above types become less accurate at lower flow rates, and then the Rotameter may be preferable. Rotameters have the advantages that their calibration is approximately linear, allowing the measurement of widely varying flow rates, and that there are no special installation requirements. For very small flow rates, metering pumps can be used, but they are prone to interference from minute amounts of solids in suspension.

Magnetic flowmeters[13] are established as accurate though costly devices for liquid flow measurement, and they are capable also of measuring fluids, e.g. slurries, which would be decidedly difficult with orifice plate measurements. They present no obstruction to the liquid, so do not collect or cause pressure loss, and require only that the liquid should have a certain minimum electrical conductivity. These meters are expensive.

For liquids the turbine flowmeter is well established; it is still under development for gases. Care must be taken to protect them from solids.

All the meters mentioned above measure volume, and give a true measure of the mass flow of material only if the pressure, temperature and composition of the material remain constant; discrepancies are greatest in the case of gas flow measurement. It is possible to compensate automatically for such variations, and new meters have become available which directly measure mass flow[13].

When integrated flow is required from a flow rate measuring device, it is usually best to integrate recorded charts manually as mechanical integrators tend to be inaccurate. However, if a pneumatic transmitter is used in conjunction with an orifice plate, it is possible to integrate flow directly from its output and with a high degree of accuracy with a force balance turbine integrator. Integrated flow can be obtained directly, with greater accuracy, by the use of positive displacement meters, which in carefully designed installations can be accepted for transfers of dutiable fluids. These are liquids on which tax is paid, e.g. alcohol, and many petroleum products.

Installation of Rotameters, magnetic meters and positive displacement meters presents no problem. The converse is true of differential pressure-generating devices, as the design of the installation determines the attainable accuracy. The requirements are specified in detail in the literature[11,12], and it is possible only to summarize them here. Any deviation from normal velocity distribution in the vicinity of the device will cause a departure from the established behaviour which has been assumed when the diameter was calculated: thus any fitting (e.g. elbow, valve, etc.) upstream of the device must be followed by a length of straight pipe long enough for the disturbance to be dissipated, as much as 120 times the pipe diameter being required for perfection in some cases (in the case of helical motion only, a reduction can be obtained by the use of 'flow-straighteners; a length equal to a minimum of five pipe diameters downstream is sufficient). The wall of the pipe must be smooth for some distance upstream. Regulating valves cause major disturbances and should if possible be situated downstream. The errors which may result from failure to achieve ideal installation have been determined[10,11,12].

Orifice plates must be carefully made to close tolerance. The upstream edge must be sharp enough not to cause visible light reflection and the face must be smooth and flat; the maximum allowable thickness of the plate is determined by the size of the orifice. It follows that any tendency of the fluid to deposit material on the face (or more particularly the edge) will cause a loss of accuracy, as will any rounding of the edge due to corrosion or erosion. Thus for any installation where high accuracy is required, it is essential that the orifice plate should be installed in such a way that it can be examined regularly. This usually means the installation of a by-pass, which can be an expensive procedure when the pipes are large, due to the fact that the whole straight length of pipe must be by-passed and four valves installed. Because of this, additional straight length may have to be provided.

The practice recommended for the highest accuracy is two complete installations in series, the results of which are compared and must agree to within ± 1 per cent f.s.d.; needless to say, each installation must be separately by-passed to allow maintenance to be done.

When a flow rate must be controlled[14], it is important that the measuring device should have a rapid response to match the almost instantaneous response of flow to changes in conditions which upset it. For this purpose, therefore, differential pressure transmitters are most frequently used, although some bellows-operated instruments are satisfactory in this respect.

Automatic dispensation of fixed quantities of liquid can be performed by positive displacement meters, but they have been developed with water and the products of the oil industry chiefly in mind, so materials of construction are restricted. Like metering pumps, they are susceptible to failure if the fluid contains any suspended solids which prevent valve closure or seize the mechanism. For high accuracy they require frequent calibration.

3.6 Measurement of Composition

3.6.1 Methods Available

Numerous methods are available for the qualitative and quantitative estimation of the composition of a fluid; in fact any physical characteristic which varies from one substance to another by an amount which can be measured is likely to find an application in this sphere (104 distinct methods have been listed by Considine[13]). The following gives some account of the more important instruments with an indication of their usefulness. There is an annual review of the status of the various methods[16].

(i) *Thermal conductivity.* Instruments based on the fact that different gases have different coefficients of thermal conductivity have been in use for many years and are simple, reliable and inexpensive; they are known as katharometers. They are particularly useful for the analysis of binary mixtures by comparison with one pure constituent, and clearly the sensitivity will be dependent on the difference between the conductivities of the constituents; at best the sensitivity is not high, and this tends to limit application. The most common use is in the measurement of CO_2 in flue gases. The katharometer is also used extensively as a detector in vapour phase chromatography. The amount of one gas present in a mixture of other gases can be measured directly if the relative percentages of the others do not vary, or if the others are similar to each other in conductivity; a constituent may be absorbed by or reacted with another component (or an additional one) and then the conductivity measured before and after will give the composition. A similar technique can be used to determine the three components of a ternary mixture. A reaction with an added constituent can be used to analyse a mixture of two gases of similar conductivity.

Hydrogen has a very high thermal conductivity and is therefore readily detected; it will cause large errors if present even in small quantities as a variable impurity in a mixture being analysed for another constituent. Water vapour, because of its ubiquity, also can be troublesome and it may be necessary to dry or to saturate the sample.

(*ii*) *Paramagnetism.* Oxygen, compared with almost all other gases, is highly paramagnetic, and instruments have been designed to measure oxygen concentration by making use of this fact. The minimum span is 0–1 per cent oxygen. The instruments are continuous in operation and are considered to be sufficiently reliable and fast in operation to be used in supervisory control with limits on the effect they have on the process, either by using a wide proportional band, or better by preventing the control signal from deviating far from a predetermined value. The chief use for the instruments has been in the manual or automatic control of combustion processes, but they clearly have other applications.

Nitric oxide and nitrogen peroxide are sufficiently paramagnetic to interfere badly, and they would have to be removed from any sample; otherwise the magnetic susceptibilities of other constituents have a minor effect unless they vary a great deal. As the magnetic susceptibility of paramagnetic materials is reduced as temperature increases, it is necessary to cool hot samples, and to present the sample to the instrument at a steady temperature, the closeness of control depending on the accuracy required. It is preferable to operate the sampling system under pressure, as a small ingress of air has clearly a pronounced effect on the oxygen content of the sample.

Other methods of oxygen measurement, for lower concentrations, are given in Section 3.6.1(vi).

(*iii*) *Gas chromatography.* Chromatography resembles distillation in that it is a method of separating the components of a mixture by taking advantage of the way in which they proceed through a column. The difference is that whereas in a distillation column there is a liquid phase and a phase consisting of its vapour, in gas chromatography the phases may be a finely divided solid or, more usually, a non-volatile liquid supported by an inert finely divided solid or by the walls of a tube, and an inert gas carrying the gas to be analysed. The different components of the gas proceed through the columns at different rates and emerge separately at the other end where they are detected by a suitable detector, and may be collected for further examination by other analytical methods. Further examination may be necessary in order to identify, with certainty, the nature of the component. The component may alternatively be determined by the use of a second sample passed to a chromatograph using a different stationary phase. Quantitative measurements require a knowledge of the sensitivity of the detector to the relevant gases in the presence of the inert carrier. The effect on separation efficiency of column dimensions and temperature, liquid stationary phase content, sample size and flow rate through the column, is complex and not yet fully understood, but it is generally true to say that if separation is incomplete, increasing the column length or decreasing the sample volume will improve it. If, however, the column length is made too great the increase in separation of peaks is more than offset by the reduction in their heights. When high speed is required for repeated quantitative measurement a small stationary phase content and small volume associated with a short column is usually preferable; this is limited by the sensitivity and volume of available detectors. Chromatograph columns of capillary tubes are now becoming established for fast work.

This method of analysis is now very widespread and of increasing value in the laboratory; great advances are continuously being made, so that it is impossible to present an up-to-date picture. Automatic techniques have been devised, and that fast response columns and detectors have reduced the time taken per sample to a few minutes or even seconds with capillary columns. Automatic control of composition using on-line chromatographs is possible in processes where sampling problems are not predominant, and where changes in composition are relatively slow[29]. The method has chiefly been applied to organic compounds, a limit being that they must be volatile at 250°C (this limit will no doubt be raised by the time of publication). Using ionization detectors, detection of impurities of the order of 1 in 10^9 has been achieved.

An excellent practical book on the topic has been written by Nogare and Juvet[17]. A very up-to-date and advanced book has been written by Schuph[18]. BS. 4587: 1970 describes recommended techniques.

(iv) *Mass spectrometry.* These instruments, though expensive, are being increasingly used for the analysis of complex gas streams. The spectrometer plots the number of ions detected against mass, producing what is known as a mass spectrum which under constant conditions is characteristic of the chemical from which it is derived, and the magnitude of which is a measure of the quantity of the chemical in the sample. When spectra overlap, qualitative analysis by another method may be necessary. Quantitative analysis requires prior qualitative analysis and knowledge of n mass values, where n is the number of components of the individual spectra; it then involves the solution of n simultaneous equations. Clearly, for complex mixtures, manual solution becomes tedious and too slow, and a digital computer is an advantage if not a necessity.

Mass spectrometers are particularly suited to the analysis of inert gases, as their spectra do not conflict and no calculations are necessary; detection levels of a few p.p.m. can be attained. Hydrocarbon analysis in the oil and petro-chemical field is another fruitful field of application where the instrument is being used for direct monitoring of plant operation. The demand is leading to the evolution of simpler and cheaper instruments.

Samples are generally discrete, and can be as small as 0·001 ml, but continuous injection is possible.

(*v*) *Absorption of electro-magnetic radiation*[19]. The amount of electro-magnetic radiation absorbed by a pure gas varies with the wavelength of the radiation and the quantity of gas traversed; the effect can be used qualitatively and quantitatively in the spectro-photometer, and quantitatively in non-dispersive analysers; the former finds its uses mainly in the laboratory, but for process monitoring and control the latter has proved to be reliable and of wide application and discussion is restricted to this. The main interest has proved to be in the infra-red and ultra-violet regions, but the absorption of visible light, X-rays, and of radio-frequency waves has been used successfully for analytical purposes. Complex mixtures are sometimes difficult because their absorption spectra overlap; this can be minimized by ensuring that all radiation in the overlapping section is removed e.g. by a filter incorporating the interfering gas or gases, but this reduces sensitivity to the component being measured. Equipments employing more complicated methods of increasing selectivity are available and are being developed. When total impurities are wanted, the instrument can sometimes be made equally sensitive to each so that the sum is recorded. The composition must always be known qualitatively and the range of variation specified before the design can be completed.

Ultra-violet analysers are preferable to infra-red analysers in that they are generally simpler and more sensitive, being capable of detecting a few parts

Table 3.1 COMPOUNDS THAT ABSORB INFRA-RED AND ULTRA-VIOLET RADIATION

Ultra-violet	Infra-red
Aromatic hydrocarbons	Acetylene
Carbon disulphide	Ammonia
Carbonyls	Butane, etc.
Heterocyclic compounds	Carbon dioxide
Halogens	Carbon monoxide
Hydrogen sulphide	Cyclohexane
Ketones	Ethylene
Mercury	Hydrochloric acid
Naphthalene derivatives	Nitric oxide
Ozone	Propylene
Sulphur dioxide	Water

in 10^9 in some cases (compared with 1 in 10^7 for infra-red instruments); they are not, however, as versatile or as selective. Table 3.1 gives an indication of gases that absorb ultra-violet and infra-red radiation; the lists are by no means exhaustive, and do not indicate sensitivity because of its dependence on application.

The use of these instruments is growing fast and they have already reached the stage where they can, if properly applied and carefully maintained, be used for continuous automatic control of plant, although it may be desirable to limit the range of action so that failure cannot be disastrous. A British Standard is in preparation on infra-red analysers for industrial use.

(vi) *Chemical reaction.* If the addition of a reagent to a mixture produces an effect specific to the component required and which can be measured by any of the other methods, then an instrument can probably be based on the reaction, and in some cases an extremely sensitive device results. The effect may be a change in temperature, opacity to electro-magnetic radiation, electrical or thermal conductivity, volume, etc. A catalysed reaction between two constituents can also be used. This general method is clearly of almost unlimited application when the more direct methods fail.

Some examples of the method are: the measurement of very small amounts of sulphur dioxide in air, by passing the air through water with a very little sulphuric acid and hydrogen peroxide to oxidize the sulphur dioxide to sulphuric acid, thus increasing the conductivity of the solution; the measurement of very small amounts of NO in a gas (e.g. water-gas), by oxidizing a measured amount of the gas in a measured amount of oxygen (using butadiene as catalyst), then passing it into a measured quantity of Griess solution to form an azo dye the intensity of which is a measure of the NO in the original gas; the measurement of the heat released in the catalytic combustion of hydrocarbons in air; the heat released on catalytic combustion of oxygen with excess hydrogen added as a measure of oxygen concentration; the measurement of oxygen in a gas (down to less than 1 p.p.m.), by solution in an electrolyte and noting the resultant depolarization of the silver electrode of a silver-cadmium cell owing to adsorption of oxygen which then goes into solution as hydroxyl ions, the current being proportional to the amount of oxygen.

The method generally requires a constant sample rate, errors being directly proportional to any deviation from the correct rate. It is frequently but not always necessary also to control reagent flow rates, and if it is, errors will again usually be proportional to deviation. The automatic handling when discrete samples are used is a source of trouble. It is, of course, essential to ensure that reagent level is maintained, and care must be taken if the installation is to be kept clean.

(vii) *Dew-point measurement*[20]. Dew-point normally refers to the amount of water vapour that is in the atmosphere or other gas, but it can be extended to other vapours. The simplest device is the hair hygrometer, but its accuracy and sphere of application are limited. More accurate is the wet-and-dry bulb measurement. This method has the disadvantage that it does not read directly unless the dry bulb is kept at a constant predetermined temperature (as is usually the case in air-conditioning systems) and requires a substantial flow of air past the wet bulb. The situation in a chemical works may lead to contamination of the wet bulb and so affect the accuracy. Satisfactory instruments have been made which use the properties of a hygroscopic salt to determine the moisture content of the air with which it is in equilibrium.

The method of most general applications is the direct determination of dew-point by cooling a reflecting surface in the gas until condensation occurs; this may be detected visually in manually operated instruments, or automatically by a photocell controlling the coolant to the mirror; it has the advantage that it can operate at the process working pressure, and the limitation that it will, of course, apply only to the first gas to condense. This method has been applied to the determination of SO_3 in flue gases.

Infra-red gas analysis has been used to determine small quantities of water vapour in the p.p.m. range. So also has a more recently developed method which makes use of the hygroscopic nature of phosphoric acid: the rate at which water vapour from a gas passing through the cell is absorbed by the acid is balanced against the rate at which it is electrolysed by the current passing through the cell, the current thus being a measure of the water in the gas. This method cannot be used in the presence of gases which react with phosphoric acid, e.g. ammonia. Oil tends to desensitize the cell, and solids must be removed with particular care.

(*viii*) *pH measurement.* Although pH applies only to aqueous solutions, it is appropriate to mention it in a book dealing with gases because of its great importance in effluent disposal, to which it can be generally applied. The most versatile measuring electrode is the glass electrode; the robust nature of an antimony electrode, however, makes its use worth consideration for the limited number of applications for which it is suitable (it cannot be used in the presence of ions of metals which are electro-positive to antimony, or of strong oxidizing or reducing agents). Electrodes may be obtained for either pipe or tank mounting.

The problems are chiefly associated with maintenance of the electrode system[21], deposition on the surface causing errors, as will any chemical attack. In the case of glass electrodes, a very high insulation is essential between the electrodes, and any condensation is a possible cause of trouble, although recent designs[15] seem largely to have overcome this by ensuring that it does not occur where it would cause a fault; this has also permitted operation at higher temperature.

From the control standpoint, success is very largely based on plant design. It is necessary often to perform neutralization in two or three stages in order to overcome the gross non-linearity of the system; great care must also be taken to ensure adequate mixing and that the electrodes are correctly sited.

(*ix*) *Density.* This is non-specific, but is a useful guide in many cases. An instrument which can be adapted for accurate measurement over a wide range of gas/liquid densities is described by Agar[26].

3.6.2 Sampling

The object of any sampling procedure is to present to the instrument at the optimum rate and with as little delay as possible a sample which is truly representative of the fluid being measured, and from which interfering components have been removed. It is clear that this may constitute a major problem in the design of the installation, and it is further true to say that failure of the sampling system to perform its assigned duty is the most frequent cause of failure of the whole installation.

The position from which the sample is to be drawn must be chosen so that the sample is representative of the gas; if striation is suspected some turbulence may be introduced upstream of the sample point, or alternatively the sample may be drawn from several points and mixed. The sample connection should generally be large and face downstream to minimize solid content in the sample and consequent risk of blockage, unless of course it is the solid that is to be measured.

Having obtained the sample, it must then be reduced to a form in which it is acceptable to the instrument, and to do this the normal methods of purification may be used, including filtering, scrubbing, absorption and adsorption, etc., together with any cooling and pressure let-down that may be necessary. It is essential to remove solids in suspension and chemicals which would interfere with the measurement or adversely affect the instrument, but this must be done without significantly affecting the constituents which are being measured. Nor must there be any leakage of air into the sample, as this may cause serious errors (e.g. if oxygen is being measured); leakage into a pressurized system can occur at points where the geometry of the pipe, in conjunction with the flow along it, causes a reduction in pressure.

The materials of which the sample system is made must be chosen so that there will be a minimum of corrosion which might cause blockages. Corrosion also inevitably changes the composition of the sample by partial removal of constituents and their possible replacement by others. Care must be taken that changes in pressure and temperature do not affect the constituents being measured; the pressure and temperature of the sample may also have an effect on the calibration of the instrument, and pressure is usually limited by the use of a lute to protect the instrument against overload.

The sample line should be arranged to drain to catch-pots at all low points when condensation is likely to occur. Lines should generally be straight with facilities for rodding parts liable to solid deposition.

The rate at which the sample is passed through the instrument may be important and have to be controlled. At the same time, particularly if automatic control is required, the lag between the withdrawal of the sample and the response of the instrument must be as small as possible; further, it may be necessary to site the instrument at some distance from the measuring point for safety reasons, or merely because it is important that it should be readily accessible for maintenance; filtering and other purification equipment may be essential. Another major cause of lag is adsorption on the walls of the lines and equipment; the effect becomes more marked as the amount of impurity is reduced. In order to minimize the time lag it is important to keep the volume of line and equipment as small as possible. It is also possible to reduce the lag still further by increasing the rate of sampling, by-passing the excess round the instrument; then, depending on circumstances, the purification equipment can be either on the whole sample or just that part which is to pass through the instrument, bearing in mind the importance of removing solids as early as possible in the system. Adsorption may be reduced by a better choice of material or finish; and is of course, proportional to the surface area of the line and equipment.

A number of methods are described in detail by Jones[1], but particular installations are covered only when they occur frequently, for example installations for flue gas analysis. General purpose equipment, e.g. absorbers which can be filled with the appropriate chemicals, are usually obtainable from the manufacturers of the analysers, who can also offer considerable advice on special aspects of installation.

3.6.3 Calibration

Next to sampling, calibration is the major problem in analytical instrumentation. It may be done by chemical analysis of the measured gas, or by presenting to the instrument prepared mixtures of known composition. Whichever way it is done, it is frequently the case that the potential accuracy and stability of the instrument are better than those of the method used for checking it; it is most important that this should be realized or the instrument may be unjustifiably condemned. It is not possible to deal with chemical checks here, as they are particular to the application; it is important, however, to say that the rules for sampling outlined in Section 3.6.2 still apply, an ideal sample point being the inlet to or outlet from the measuring instrument.

Gaseous samples of known composition can be prepared in two ways, statically or dynamically, and they both have advantages:

(i) Static. A cylinder is evacuated and filled to a predetermined pressure with gas A, and the gas B is added to increase the pressure further to another predetermined point corresponding to the required percentage. A single mixing like this is sufficient when the dilution of one of the gases is not too great. For lower concentrations the procedure can be repeated using the mixture already obtained as the diluent of a pure gas in another cylinder. The accuracy is dependent on the accuracy of the pressure gauges, the degree of evacuation, effectiveness of mixing, and whether any adsorption occurs on the walls: it should be about ± 2 per cent for 1–50 per cent and up to ± 10 per cent for lower concentrations. The factor in greatest doubt is that of mixing, slow changes with time being experienced; metal balls have sometimes been inserted so that when the cylinder is inverted several times mixing is encouraged. It is generally felt, however, that samples should not be kept for very long before they are used (the actual time depends on the

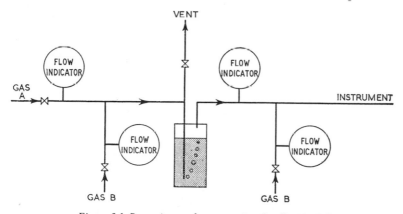

Figure 3.1 Dynamic sample preparation. Small ratio A : B

mixture, and can be estimated from experience). A disadvantage of the method is that several cylinders have to be made up to cover the range of measurement of the instrument.

(ii) Dynamic. Continuous flows of the gases are mixed in the appropriate

ratio, the procedure being repeated to obtain small ratios. The arrangement is shown in Figure 3.1 which applies when a small percentage of gas A in gas B is required. A lute is included between the two mixing points to prevent flow of the second addition of gas B backwards and out through the vent: the liquid must not affect the instrument in any way. The accuracy is dependent on that of the flowmeters (usually Rotameters as the flow rates are very small) and may be varied appreciably during calibration and is generally better than ± 10 per cent. Higher accuracy may be obtained by correcting the meters for the gas being measured, in which case ± 5 per cent may be achieved. More recently accurate gas pumps have become available for this duty, and should be used for critical applications. There are no difficulties due to adsorption (see *(i)*) as equilibrium conditions are reached. Checks over the whole range may be accomplished with one apparatus, and higher degrees of dilution (parts in 10^8) can be achieved, but the method is wasteful of sample gas which may be expensive, and it is somewhat less accurate than the static method.

Because of inaccuracy of all these methods, it is best to do several checks and to treat the results statistically; this will tend to reduce all but systematic errors.

3.7 Automatic Control [22, 23, 29]

The terminology of BS. 1523[24] is used throughout this section, and it is assumed that readers have access to it.

3.7.1 Controller and Plant Interaction

It is important to appreciate the fact that an automatic controller, unlike a device which only measures, must be regarded as part of the plant to which it is fitted: the function of the controller is to maintain at a prescribed value

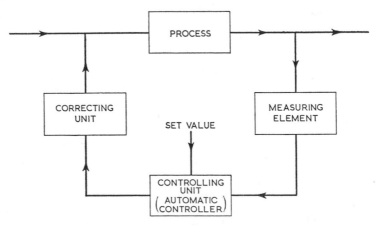

Figure 3.2 Diagram of closed loop process control system

some condition of the process, and in order to do this it must act upon the process. Conversely the effectiveness with which the controller can carry out its function (assuming always optimum adjustment) is dependent on the nature of the process and the physical attributes of the vessels in which it is carried out. This is brought out clearly by the diagrammatic representation of the control system shown in Figure 3.2. The significance of the words 'closed loop' is also clear, each unit affecting the next one and so on until the reaction returns to the originating unit and so on. The behaviour of all the elements will affect the quality of control achieved.

The difficulties met with are due in the main to lags, namely the delays which occur between the application of signals at any point and the response to it at a later point in the loop. These take two forms:

(i) Exponential lag in which the response to a step change in a signal is an exponential. This is characterized by the change in temperature resulting from suddenly increased flow of heat into a simple system.

(ii) Distance/velocity lag in which the response is delayed in time but is otherwise identical to the initiating signal. This is characterized by the finite time taken for fluid to flow along a pipe, the lag being equal to the length of the pipe divided by the velocity along it.

It is possible to split the process further as in Figure 3.3. A, B, C, D and E

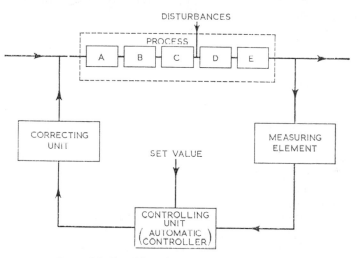

Figure 3.3 Closed loop showing entry of disturbances

are lags occurring in the plant items between the correcting and measuring units (this is greatly simplified).

There are two factors to consider:

(a) Stability of the control system: this is dependent on the nature of the lags which occur in the loop as a whole; and for ease of control it is most desirable to have one dominant exponential lag and any distance velocity lag should be less than $\frac{1}{5}$ of the value of this. It may even be advantageous to arrange this. If so, it is better to do it by decreasing a long lag than by increasing a short one, although the latter may be necessary in some cases.

(b) Ability of the system to minimize the effects of disturbances: this is dependent on the type of disturbances and the point of entry into the plant, but the general case is illustrated in Figure 3.3. The ratio of lags $D+E$ to the total lag round the loop should be as great as possible, which implies that lags in the measuring unit, controller and correcting unit and in the interconnections should be kept as small as possible. Measuring lag is particularly dangerous as deviations occurring in practice are made to appear smaller than they are: the failure of the system is masked by its own weakness. It is bad practice to let disturbances enter at or near the measuring unit.

While it is not possible to enlarge upon these two important factors there are one or two further points which should be emphasized. The effect of measuring lag has been mentioned: when a record is required, and the signal to the recorder has to be damped, then it is important not to damp the signal to the controller as well. The load on the process may affect its characteristics, e.g. distance/velocity lag is increased at low throughputs, and measuring units may have non-linear calibrations, e.g. flowmeters: this can often be compensated automatically by a correct choice of control valve characteristic (Section 3.7.7). It is essential that the required degree of correction should be available: it is not sufficient to ensure, for example, that there is enough heat available for maximum throughput under steady conditions—there must be enough also to correct disturbances with the required performance when on maximum throughput.

3.7.2 Choice of Controller Actions

For level control, two-step controller action will often suffice, and a controller with narrow band proportional action will maintain very constant level without any possibility of instability. Nevertheless level controllers often have to be arranged so that there is no large swing in the outflow from the vessel as this is used as input to the next piece of plant equipment: in this case a controller with wide-band proportional action is always sufficient, the proportional band and vessel depth being decided by the maximum rate at which the outflow may change without causing undesirably large effects. It may be, however, that the addition of integral controller action will be desirable in order that the level is always brought back to the set value (the operator has a better check on performance): in the event of large sustained disturbances this may necessitate a larger vessel to accommodate them.

Similar remarks apply to pressure control, but integral controller action is more often required as pressures tend to be more critical than levels. Derivative controller action can be advantageous but is seldom necessary.

For flow control, provided that the measuring unit is fast in response so that there is a predominant lag in the control valve, narrow band proportional controller action may suffice; wide-band proportional controller action with short integral action time also gives good results and is most frequently used.

It is in thermal operations that derivative controller action provides most benefit, particularly if there is a small number of long exponential lags of the same order of magnitude; it is, however, frequently possible to use two-step controller action when the heat capacity of the heater is small compared with that of the substance being heated and there is only one predominant lag. It is often recommended that as the additional cost of derivative controller action is small and in any case it can be readily removed, controllers incorporating all three actions should be ordered for most temperature control applications.

In addition to the above, if it is found that in spite of the stability of a control loop without derivative controller action disturbances are having an excessive effect, the addition of derivative action may be beneficial; in many controllers this is a simple modification.

3.7.3 Application

Apart from the type of controller action, there are other aspects to be considered in the design of the installation. Generally speaking the size of the plant determines whether transmission is necessary or not. In the case of flow control, however, it is usually the case that satisfactory control can be obtained only when transmitters are used. With transmission lines less than say 75 m or so, the controller can be mounted in the control room; for longer distances it becomes necessary, for flow control at least, to consider mounting the controller near the control valve. This increases costs and four connections instead of two are needed between control room and plant. Local mounting of the controller may also be necessary for other fast-changing variables, but is seldom necessary for thermal processes. Pneumatic transmission can be made satisfactorily fast for all normal purposes and there is seldom the need to consider electric control in order to reduce transmission lags.

The recording instruments can be large or small, the latter being used only with transmitters, and the choice is one based on convenience and expense. Small instruments conserve panel and control room space and it is easy for an operator to assimilate the readings of a large number; large instruments are much cheaper, however, and in a small panel where space is not at a premium, they may be preferable.

3.7.4 Special Control Systems

Only two of the more complex systems are frequently used, 'ratio' and 'cascade' control[25], although there is an increasing tendency to use 'feed-forward' or 'open loop' control systems in order to minimize the effects of disturbances. Ratio control is self-explanatory. Cascade control is used in systems with long lags where unavoidable disturbances occur in the correcting condition: two controllers are used (master and slave) and the master controller output is used as the set value of the slave controller, the arrangement being as in Figure 3.4.

There is only one correcting unit. Lags in Process Unit A should be small compared with those in Process Unit B.

Feed-forward control may be used when unavoidable but measurable disturbances occur at other points in the loop. The signal from the measuring unit is fed directly, or modified to take account of plant dynamic characteristics, to an adding relay in the output line from the controller as in Figure 3.5.

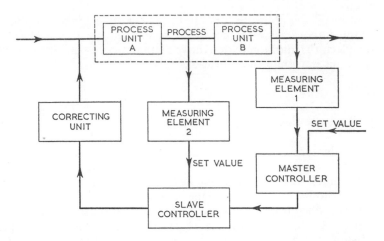

Figure 3.4 Cascade control

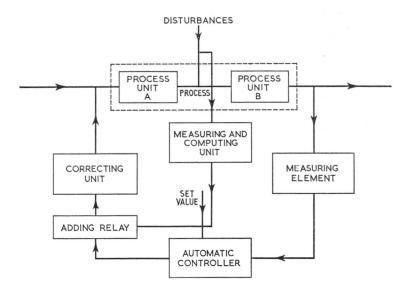

Figure 3.5 Feed-forward control

3.7.5 Adjustment of Controllers

Instructions from manufacturers are usually adequate for this purpose, and it is not necessary to enlarge upon them here.

3.7.6 Time Cycle Control

In some batch processes it is desirable to arrange for the set value to follow a predetermined path. This can readily be achieved by the use of cams in conjunction with otherwise normal controllers.

Alternatively, it is possible to arrange for a sequence of events to take place in a predetermined manner. Equipment is also readily available for this sort of duty, and is frequently used, for example, to control adsorption/ regeneration cycles. A measurement of a process variable may be used to initiate any stage, and normal controllers may also be incorporated.

3.7.7 Control Valve

Control valves are usually operated pneumatically because spring-opposed diaphragm motors are simple and reliable and can generate very large working forces. The effects of friction, hysteresis, and forces due to pressure and flow in the valve can be reduced appreciably by the addition of a valve positioner; a positioner also increases the speed of operation, both because of its high air capacity and because the controller itself does not have to supply and exhaust large volumes of air, perhaps through a long length of pipe. In liquid flow control systems a valve positioner can cause oscillation, and in this case a booster can be used with advantage instead. Electrically operated valves may be satisfactory for some simple duties, but there is always a need to compromise in the design because of the difficulty of including high speed and power together in a small volume. Electric controllers are usually followed, therefore, by electro-pneumatic converters.

The sizing of a control valve is of great importance. It is essential that it should exert some measure of control over its full range of operation, and that its maximum throughput should be sufficient to correct disturbances occurring when the process is operating at its maximum rate. It is also essential that the slope of its flow/opening characteristics should allow operation at the minimum rate at which the plant may be designed to operate. These characteristics depend on the process being controlled and on the presence of other major pressure drops in the system. It is perhaps worth mentioning that the same reasoning applies to the choice of a hand-operated throttling valve; process operators are too often expected to control small rates with quick-opening valves of line size.

The behaviour of the valve on failure of its operating medium is an important consideration. It is a further advantage of the diaphragm motor that it can be arranged to close or open on failure, and with the addition of a small pilot relay it can be made to remain in the position it occupied at the time of failure. It is more difficult to provide these 'fail-safe' characteristics when other operators are used.

Installation is usually straightforward; a by-pass is normally installed so that the control valve may be maintained, but reliability of operation is good, and the by-pass may be omitted in many cases. Steam valves should be preceded by steam traps to reduce the incidence of wire-drawing.

In use, troubles chiefly arise from the fluid, and materials of construction must be carefully chosen. The choice of the correct stuffing box lubricant is also important, as is regular greasing.

3.8 Safety

3.8.1 Fire and Explosion Hazards

When electrical devices are used, the law requires that sufficient care should be taken in the design of the equipment and the installation to reduce the likelihood of fire or explosion to negligible proportions. When inflammable substances are being used in a process the installation must be made flame-proof or intrinsically safe. From the point of view of maintenance and adjustment, the latter is greatly to be preferred, although it may in practice be more difficult to achieve. It neither is possible it may be possible to purge with air or an inert gas.

Flame-proofing generally implies the use of enclosures which are designed to suit the conditions of use, whereas an electrical circuit is intrinsically safe when a spark of sufficient energy to ignite the hazardous atmosphere cannot arise even in fault conditions. It is thus possible to work on intrinsically safe equipment *in situ* with the power on, whereas special precautions must be taken when it is flame-proof.

Should purging be the only way of making the installation safe, then it is important to ensure that a positive pressure is maintained, and it is wise to include a pressure switch to operate when the pressure becomes dangerously low. It is also desirable to arrange that the mains must be switched off before the enclosure can be opened.

Because such hazards are so common on chemical and oil works, most electrical instruments are available in one form or the other. Usually there is a condition that some part of the system must be situated in safe area (e.g. a pressurized control room) and it is essential that the installation instructions be followed precisely. Certification is carried out by the British Approvals Service for Electrical Equipment in Flammable Atmospheres (BASEFA). Instruments must carry a label certifying the conditions under which they may be used. (These U.K. certificates have their equivalent in other countries.)

3.8.2 Electric Shock

Instruments using electricity may present a danger of shock to operators, through inadvertent contact with live terminals. Most manufacturers are aware of this and design accordingly. The main requirements are given by E.E.U.A.[25].

3.9 Maintenance and Repair

Although some reference has been made in earlier sections to the subject of maintenance and repair, its importance is such that a separate section is justified. The instruments are often the only means of knowing what is happening in a plant, and it is essential that they should tell the correct story.

The most common source of trouble is the fluid being measured, trouble being caused by corrosion, deposition of suspended solids, condensation, evaporation, crystallization, freezing, etc. Although these effects can be minimized by good installation practice, regular attention to unavoidable trouble spots is essential. Vents in liquid lines and drains in gas lines should be regularly opened. Pressure connections which tend to block up should be rodded through with a frequency sufficient to avoid closure. Control valves must be regularly inspected for leaks through their glands, and must be regularly lubricated (when lubricant is required) not only for the obvious purpose but also to protect the stem from corrosion which may increase its friction and thus impair control quality.

Regular complete stripping and reassembly of instruments should not be carried out except in special circumstances. Frequent partial stripping may be necessary in some cases because of the effect of the fluid, or because the air supply to a pneumatic instrument falls below the standard of purity required, but this should be kept to a minimum. The other possible excuse for stripping is for the cleaning of lubricated parts and inspection for wear; more and more instruments, however, are being designed so that they do not incorporate bearings of this type. Routine *in situ* checks on calibration are most desirable, the frequency depending on the importance of the application. What must be done in addition to this is often specified in the makers' instruction manuals, and their advice is the best guide available until some experience has been obtained on particular applications.

It is necessary to know the potential accuracy of the instruments used as well as the accuracy required for the application. It is unnecessary to exceed the latter, and foolish to try to exceed the former. The accuracy of the test equipment used should be at least five times as good as that required of the instrument being checked.

The calibration of the control actions of automatic controllers, for example, is usually very inaccurate (± 10 20 per cent of nominal for proportional control action and ± 30–50 per cent of nominal for integral and derivative control action). It is generally unnecessary to strive for anything better than this, although there are some cases where it would be most helpful (electronic controllers may have an advantage here); what is really important in a controller is the alignment of the mechanism so that the measured value always lines up with the desired value.

Maintenance must be carried out by skilled tradesmen suitably trained, and in the case of the more complex installations used for analytical measurements, by personnel educated to Higher National Certificate standard. Many instrument manufacturers organize excellent training establishments. If suitable personnel are not available, it is normally advisable to arrange for maintenance to be done on contract rather than risk failure through ignorance. Routine work which has to be done frequently can usually be done by less skilled men.

3.10 Advanced Techniques

If there is a large number of measurements, it may be possible to reduce the number of recorders and indicators and to simplify the operation by the introduction of an instrument known as an alarm scanner, which is arranged to 'look at' each point in turn and warn the operator if it departs from the preset conditions. Additional features available are automatic logging of values when out of specification or regular logging of some or all values, with logging in red when outside the normal range. These additions increase the complexity and reduce reliability, and unless the records are to be really useful on a continuous basis, logging should not be included. For process investigation, automatically logged results can be a great advantage, particularly in complex processes where treatment of the results would have to be carried out by a digital computer. The log can be taken in suitably coded punched tape form; the readings can be taken very quickly so that they tend to be more nearly simultaneous than is possible with manual logging.

An increasing number of plants are controlled by computer[30]. It is usually necessary for the capital and throughput to be high for this to be justified. The computer may be used for one or more of the following:

(1) Replacement of normal control equipment.
(2) Optimization of plant operation.
(3) Improved dynamic control via normal control set-points.
(4) Data processing.
(5) Scheduling of batch operations.
(6) Rapid emergency shut-down in correct safe sequence.

4

Preliminary Purification of Crude Gases

R. A. MOTT

4.1 Introduction

The crude gases considered in this chapter are those which arise from the carbonization of coal in coke ovens (coke-oven gas) and gasworks retorts (town gas).

The purpose of preliminary purification of these gases in their crude state is the removal of (i) the vapours of tar, water, naphthalene and 'benzole', (ii) mechanically carried solid particles of tar, naphthalene and dust, and (iii) ammonia gas. For the purpose of this chapter 'preliminary purification' does not include the removal of hydrogen sulphide (which is considered in Chapter 8).

Purification of the crude gases is achieved by cooling or washing (usually with water or oil), and by electrostatic precipitation. Since all these procedures are adopted in coke-oven practice, such practice has been selected for consideration of carbonization crude gases, comparison being made with coal-gasworks practice where this is of value.

The principles which have been adopted in the preliminary purification of gases, and the changes which have occurred, may be shown most conveniently by recounting the development of modern practice for the crude gases.

4.2 Historical

The procedures followed in the preliminary purification of crude gases of coal-gasworks and coke-oven plants have much in common since both are concerned with the products of the carbonization of coal and their recovery as by-products. Differences in practice arise from differences in aims; at gasworks the ability to make gas rapidly to meet peak demands is the dominant factor but at most coke-oven plants the dominant factor is regular operation to ensure the optimum quality of coke. For this reason the coal used at gasworks is only coarsely crushed (through 50 mm square apertures) and its free-water content rarely exceeds 2 per cent, but at coke-oven plants the coal is finely-crushed (80 per cent through 3 mm) and consists chiefly of washed smalls (which yields a stronger coke than do larger grades) so that the free-mositure content may be as high as 10 per cent. Since in both types of carbonization practice a further 5 per cent of 'liquor' may be produced from the fixed ('air-dry') moisture of the coal and from the oxygen of the coal, the water-vapour concentration in crude coke-oven gas may be twice that in crude town gas from horizontal retorts, so that the cooling problem for coke-oven gas is the more severe.

The relatively low water content of the coal used in gasworks practice has led to the common practice of cooling the gas to air temperature in one stage (and so removing most of the tar, and the water as ammonia liquor), passing through an exhauster (which raises the temperature which is then reduced in a secondary cooler) and then washing out the ammonia using the weak liquor from the primary and secondary coolers. The strong ammonia liquor thereby produced is then concentrated to a strength of 20–25 per cent, or is distilled, the ammonia being recovered in a 'saturator' containing acid to yield sulphate of ammonia. This outline of common gasworks practice ignores the final removal of tar fog and of naphthalene (when in high concentrations) which must be effected before the ammonia washers to prevent blockages.

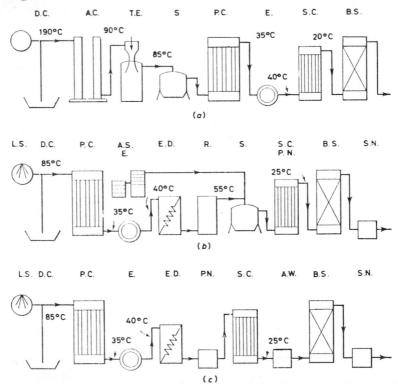

D.C. downcomer, A.C. aircooler, T.E. tar extractor, S. saturator, P.C. primary condenser, E. exhauster, S.C. secondary condenser, B.S. benzole scrubber, L.S. liquor sprays, E.D. electro-detarrer, P.N. primary naphthalene washer, A.W. ammonia washer, S.N. secondary naphthalene washer, A.S. ammonia still, R. reheater

Figure 4.1 Direct (a), semi-direct (b) and indirect (c) ammonia recovery

This system is the *indirect* process of ammonia recovery and until comparatively recently was regarded as being most appropriate when the amount of liquor to be recovered was comparatively low. The term was coined for comparison with the *direct* system of ammonia recovery from crude gases which became popular in coke-oven practice about 1910.

In the direct process of ammonia recovery, practised by the German Otto company, the hot crude gas, after partial cooling in air-coolers, was de-tarred by injection through a Venturi through which hot tar was pumped, the concentration of tar in the gas being reduced to under 1 g/m^3 (Figure 4.1a). The hot de-tarred gas, at about 90°C, was then passed directly through a steam-heated saturator and emerged at about 85°C (above the dew-point of water vapour). It then entered a condenser for the removal of ammonia-free liquor as an effluent or for use in the quenching of the coke.

When this process was applied to British coals, which in certain coal-fields were comparatively high in chlorine (0·3 per cent, that is, as high as the yield of ammonia gas), much of the ammonia was present in the crude gas as ammonium chloride which created difficulties not experienced in German practice. Hot liquor was substituted for the tar sprays to remove both tar and 'fixed' ammonia from the gas before the saturator. Despite these disadvantages, the *direct* process of ammonia recovery was that most commonly adopted in coke-oven practice in the period 1910–1920, centrifugal and other tar extractors also being used to de-tar the crude gas above the dew-point of water vapour (Figure 4.1a).

A further modification, known as the *semi-direct* process of ammonia recovery, was developed by Koppers. This involved cooling the crude coke-oven gas to below the dew-point of water vapour but above the dew-point of naphthalene vapour (say 35°C) to remove most of the tar and liquor. The gas was then passed through an exhauster, a reheater and a saturator to remove the remaining free ammonia, the free and fixed ammonia being removed from the liquor from the condenser by distillation and liming, to re-enter the gas before the saturator.

In the period before the 1914–1918 War there was, in effect, fractional condensation of the tar. The ascension pipes from the ovens were tall and unlined and in the collecting main hot tar was circulated to dissolve the high-boiling pitch fraction which condensed first, the lower-boiling fractions being recovered in the tar extractor and the 'primary coolers' or condensers. With the considerable development of by-product coke-oven practice in the U.S.A. during the 1914–1918 War, this condensation of the pitch in the collecting main became unsuitable for the larger charges in the larger ovens then being built, for even with the 10-ton charge usual in European practice, manual operation of a lever was necessary to aid movement of the pitch along the collecting main. The ascension pipes were therefore reduced in height and lined with brick; then, on entering the collecting main, the crude gas was subjected to shock cooling by powerful sprays of liquor. This reduced the temperature of the gas to near the dew-point of water vapour and condensed the medium-boiling fraction of the tar as well as the pitch so that the tar flowed freely to a catch pot, whence the liquor, with that condensed in the condensers, was recirculated to the liquor sprays. This practice was adopted as the standard in coke-oven practice and made the older direct process of ammonia recovery obsolete. The semi-direct process is now the most widely practised but the indirect process is gaining in popularity with, in some cases, final washing with acid ammonium sulphate liquor in an acid-resistant tower. With the abandonment of the direct process of ammonia recovery the terms 'indirect' and 'semi-direct' have lost some of their significance but are still useful.

The electrostatic precipitator for the removal of tar fog was adopted in the decade before the Second World War. Tar-fog precipitation had previously depended on the passage of gas through perforated plates with impingement on films of tar previously deposited; they could offer considerable resistance. Tar fog, consisting of small bubbles, could even pass through a benzole scrubber where it thickened the wash oil and made it less effective for its purpose. Experience showed that these precipitators works most efficiently on cold gas and they are now sited, in the 'semi-direct' process, after the exhausters (which by their high-speed act also as centrifugal tar-fog extractors) and before the reheater and the saturator (Figure 4.1b). In the 'indirect' process they are sited after the final coolers and before the ammonia washers and benzole scrubbers, though they are also sometimes sited after the exhausters (Figure 4.1c). On cold gas the efficiency of separation of tar fog can exceed 99 per cent with a low back pressure and a low power consumption.

Crude benzole (benzene, toluene and the xylenes, with some carbon disulphide and thiophene) is removed as a standard procedure in coke-oven practice by exposing the gas in tower scrubbers to films of creosote oil or gas oil; the same treatment will remove naphthalene and indene vapours. For efficient recovery the gas must be cooled to near ambient temperature so that the benzole scrubbers are preceded by final coolers or condensers. Until 1958 the favoured procedure for final cooling was to subject the coke-oven gas to direct sprays of water which, after separation of naphthalene scum, was cooled in a water frame or cooler and returned for re-use. This procedure is no longer permitted by the Alkali Inspectorate; new plants were, therefore, designed either for indirect water cooling (like the primary coolers) or for direct cooling with oil subsequently cooled by water in tubular coolers (see also Section 4.5).

Direct water coolers, in cooling the gas from about 45° to 25°C, precipitated naphthalene which was separated as a scum, but the amount of water used had to be high to ensure that the wooden grids in the cooler were flushed free from naphthalene. This led to the development in the U.S.A. of unpacked final coolers with sprays of water at different levels of the gas-cooling tower. Another solution has been to cool the gas to above the naphthalene vapour dew-point by a direct water spray in the lower half of a gas-cooling tower, and in the upper half to wash with warm benzolized wash oil to reduce the naphthalene to below the vapour pressure of the final cooling operation. This is completed in a second tower scrubber by direct water spraying. It will be appreciated that, where nuisance from hydrogen sulphide emission has to be avoided, the direct spray water has then to be cooled in tubular coolers, the cooling water from which can be cooled in a water-cooling tower. The wash oil in this case does not perform a cooling operation and can be recirculated, subject to its concentration of naphthalene being kept low by a purge to the wash-oil stripping plant and a make-up of fresh oil.

The practical problems of naphthalene removal will be considered more fully later but it is necessary in this section to refer to another feature of coke-oven practice in which the naphthalene content of wash oil is controlled. This is the practice of redistillation of wash oil in which the naphthalene is left in a residual fraction. Redistillation is essential for the oil used in a final naphthalene washer to reduce the naphthalene content to the order of 25 mg/m^3 for transmission to Gas Boards; it is of value for benzolized wash oil used in conjunction with a first-stage naphthalene washer where the reduction may be from 1·0 to 0·10 g/m^3.

4.3 Primary Cooling of Coke-oven Gas

4.3.1 Introduction

The gas in the space above the charge in a modern coke oven, say 12 m long and 0·45 m wide, is at a temperature of from 700 to 800°C, tending to rise during the carbonization period. The gas leaves the ascension pipe at approximately 650°C and is subjected to an intense spray of warm liquor as it enters the collecting main. In addition, further liquor sprays are usually fitted to the collecting main at each alternate oven so that a flow of about 270 m^3/h of liquor can be discharged into the collecting main for a plant carbonizing 1000 tonnes of coal per day or 65 m^3/t of coal carbonized. The gas is cooled to about 85°C, approximately 10°C above its dew-point, and the liquor is raised in temperature by about 20°C.

As a result of this rapid drop in temperature most of the tar is condensed, the water vapour from the oven remains as vapour, and the condensed tar, with the liquor flow, is separated at the catch pot before the condensers. As will be shown later, the heat exchange in the collecting main exceeds that in the condensers, to which the erroneous name of primary coolers, which was valid in coke-oven practice 40 or more years ago, is still often given. 'Primary liquor condensers' would be more correct, for there are final condensers before the benzole scrubbers, but the shortened form 'primary condensers' will be used in this chapter.

The difficulty confronting the designer of the primary condensers is that, with a coal containing 10 per cent of free water and yielding 5 per cent of liquor from the fixed water and oxygen of the coal, this total liquor accounts for nearly 95 per cent of the heat exchange in the condensers, but all he knows with certainty is the probable quantity of permanent gas and the probable free and fixed moisture in the coal. It is desirable to show how an estimate can be made of the amount of liquor produced from the coal so that the problem of design can be defined more exactly. Because the major task of the primary condensers is the condensation of the liquor, it is preferable to consider the specific heat of the gases and vapours entering the condensers on a weight basis, i.e. in kJ/kg °C.

4.3.2 Coke-oven Gas

The yield of de-benzolized coke-oven gas per tonne of carbonized coal may be taken as 310 m^3 at n.t.p. (wet gas) (saturated with water vapour) (of calorific value 19·5 MW/m³). Taking the composition to be H_2–54, CH_4–28, CO–7·4, N_2–5·6, C_nH_m (assumed to be C_2H_4) 2·6, CO_2 2·0 and O_2 0·4 per cent by volume[1], the specific gravity would be 0·37 and the weight 157 kg. To this should be added a yield, per tonne of coal, of 0·0132 m³ of crude benzole (11·3 kg calculated as benzene) so that the total yield of benzolized coke-oven gas is 169 kg. Its mean specific heat can be calculated from those of the constituent gases as in Table 4.1.

Table 4.1 SPECIFIC HEATS OF CONSTITUENTS OF BENZOLIZED COKE-OVEN GAS

Range degC	Mean specific heats (kJ/kg °C)		
	Debenzolized coke oven gas	Water vapour	Benzene vapour
650–85 = 565	3·35	2·05	1·93
85–35 = 50	2·85	—	—
35–15 = 20	2·81	—	—

Lowry[2] has shown that, in the 'BM/AGA test', carbonizing 100 lb (45·4 kg) charges of air-dry coal in cylindrical containers at 500° to 1100°C in steps of 100°C, the maximum liquor yield is at 700°C and the mean liquor yield (L) for a series of coals at different temperatures can be expressed in the form:

$$L = a + bV + cW \text{ (per cent)}$$

where V = volatile matter and W = moisture in coal as carbonized, a and b being coefficients. For $V = 24$ and $W = 1$, the mean yields for a series of coals carbonized at 1000°C and 1100°C become 2·7 and 2·0 per cent. Shvarts and Shinkareva[3] found that in coking practice, for such coal charged with 9·7 per cent of total moisture, the liquor yield was 1·7 per cent in excess of the water in the charge or 2·6 per cent above the probable air-dry moisture of the coal, agreeing with Lowry's estimate at 1000°C, which is the common average temperature in the coke on discharge. At 1000°C Lowry's formula is:

$$L = 0·15V + 0·86W \text{ (per cent)} \tag{4.1}$$

and the total liquor yield would be $w_f + (100 - w_f)L$ on the coal as charged, w_f being the free moisture in the charge. On this basis, with 10 per cent of free moisture in the charge, the total yields of liquor would be 12·6 and 15·1 per cent (127–152 kg/t) for coals of 25 and 35 per cent of volatile matter. Thus, although the rank of the coal will influence the results, the dominant factor is the percentage of free moisture in the charge and the higher value should be assumed since it would be attained by a coal of $V = 25$ with 12·5 per cent of free water—a possible contingency.

To the permanent gas and the liquor must be added the tar, the average yield of which is 37·9 kg per tonne of coal carbonized. Values for the specific heat of tar vapour are not available, but since the mean specific heats of liquid tar and pitch (1·47–1·85 kJ/kg °C) are of the same order as that of solid benzene (1·57), the value for solid benzene may be assumed. The heats of vaporization and of fusion of coal tar are also unknown but may be estimated from values of heavy paraffinic hydrocarbons to be, together, 210 kJ/kg.

It is of interest to calculate the volume of tar vapour. For this purpose an estimate of the mean molecular weight is necessary and coke-oven tar can be considered to consist of H_2O 4·0, C_6H_6 2·2, $C_{10}H_8$ 10·6, $C_{14}H_{10}$ 21·4 and pitch 62·0 per cent. Coke-oven pitch may be assumed to have a mean molecular weight of 538 (based on the composition given by Wood and Wilman[4]) and to be represented by the formula $C_{23}H_{27}N$, a nine-ring compound, so that the average molecular weight of coke-oven tar may be taken as 382. From this it can be calculated that 38·6 kg of tar as vapour would occupy a volume of 2·26 m^3 at n.t.p.

4.3.3 Cooling in Collecting Main

The heat to be removed may be calculated as in Table 4.2.

Table 4.2 HEAT OF COOLING OF CRUDE COKE-OVEN GAS

		MJ/t of coal
Benzolized coke-oven gas	$160 \times 565 \times 3·35 \times 10^{-3}$ =	320
Water, vapour	$152 \times 565 \times 2·25 \times 10^{-3}$ =	176
Tar, vapour	$38 \times 565 \times 1·93 \times 10^{-3}$ =	41
Tar, heats of evaporation and fusion	$38 \times 210 \times 10^{-3}$ =	8
Total heat lost by crude coke-oven gas		545

With a liquor flow of 6·55 m^3/t of coal its rise in temperature would be 545/27·4 = 20°C, i.e. if the temperature of liquor at the sprays were 30°C the final temperature would be 50°C.

With a drop in temperature to 85°C most of the tar vapour would condense and be separated at the downcomer before the primary condensers, though some tar fog would pass forward. Per tonne of coal, the constituents of crude coke-oven gas would then be as shown in Table 4.3.

Table 4.3 COMPOSITION OF CRUDE COKE-OVEN GAS

	m^3, n.t.p.	m^3, 85°C
Debenzolized coke-oven gas, 157 kg	319	418
Crude benzole, 11·3 kg	3·3	4·2
Water vapour, 152 kg	(190)	249
		671·2

The water vapour would have a concentration of 0·227 kg/m^3 in the gas at 85°C which is the saturation vapour pressure temperature of air at 73°2; this may be taken as the dew-point of the gases.

4.3.4 Cooling in Primary Condensers

In the primary condensers the crude gas will be cooled to, say, 35°C, and, having passed the dew-point, will usually remain saturated with water vapour throughout the remainder of the plant. The benzole vapours are almost exactly 1·0 per cent of the dry gases. The other important constituents of the gas are ammonia and naphthalene vapour. With a yield of 10·9 kg of sulphate of ammonia per ton of coal, the amount of gaseous ammonia would be 2·7 kg and its volume at n.t.p. 3·6 m³, or slightly over 1 per cent of the permanent gases.

Naphthalene requires special consideration because it can cause so much trouble in the purification plant. Most of it goes into the tar, which may contain 10 per cent. The production of naphthalene per tonne of coal is approximately 4·5 kg, or 0·9 m³ at n.t.p. or 0·2 per cent of the crude gases and vapours in the ascension pipe. Since most of the naphthalene is condensed with the tar, the dominant factor in purification practice is the naphthalene dew-point.

The saturation vapour pressure of naphthalene is shown in Figure 4.2

Richards and Taylor[5] have given concentrations of naphthalene in coke-

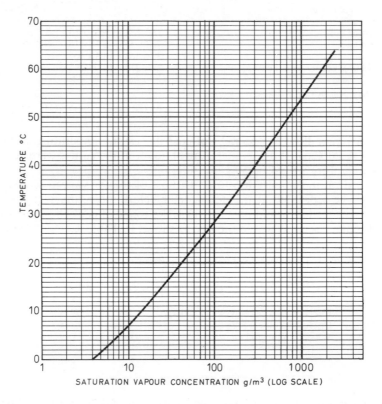

Figure 4.2 Naphthalene saturation pressure, g/m³ gas saturated with water vapour at temperature given: total gas volume reduced to n.t.p. (1 grain/100 ft³ = 0·0228 g/m³)

oven gas at the nearest point usually thought convenient for such a test, namely, after the detarrer; these data are reproduced in Table 4.4.

Table 4.4 NAPHTHALENE PROBLEMS IN PRIMARY CONDENSERS

Location of plant	Midlands	Scotland	Lincs.	S. Wales
Outlet of primary condensers— temperature (°C)	36	27	34	22
Outlet percentage saturation of tar with naphthalene	—	100	100	84
Saturation vapour pressure of naphthalene at these temperatures (g/m³)	1·83	0·78	1·49	0·48
Naphthalene in gas after detarrers (g/m³)	1·67	1·49	1·28	0·82
Naphthalene trouble in primary condensers	Yes	Yes	Yes	No

It will be observed that the naphthalene concentration in the gas was higher than its saturation vapour pressure in the Scottish and Welsh plants. The detarrers were after the exhausters in all except the Lincolnshire plant and the temperature of the gas would be higher than that at the outlet of the primary condensers. Naphthalene (melting point 80°C), would therefore be condensed in the gas in the solid state (a form which in view of the lightness of such a solid may be called naphthalene fog) and carried forward mechanically. The tar deposited in the primary condensers in the Welsh plant was the least saturated with naphthalene and presumably the naphthalene fog was dissolved in it, whereas in the other plants the tar deposited was saturated, or nearly so, and the naphthalene fog caused blockages.

Naphthalene in the solid form is difficult to dissolve in the dilute picric acid used for the determination of naphthalene and the values given in Table 4.4 may be under-estimates. Operators would find it useful to determine naphthalene in gas at the outlet of the primary coolers (and in the tar condensed there) using the B.C.R.A. (British Coke Research Association) thermostatically-controlled bath at a temperature above that of the dew-point of the primary coolers to revaporize such solid naphthalene, and should use a heated tar-fog filter[6]. Should the naphthalene concentration be above the saturation vapour pressure, the temperature of the gas at the outlet should be raised or, if the tar deposited is saturated, it should be supplemented by injection of light tar so that the deposition of solid naphthalene can be prevented. It appears from the figures in Table 4.4 that an outlet temperature below 35°C is likely to give trouble from naphthalene blockages.

4.3.5 Cooling in Condensers (to 35°C)

The heat to be removed may be calculated as shown in Table 4.5.

Table 4.5 HEAT TO BE REMOVED FROM CRUDE COKE-OVEN GAS

	MJ/t of coal	
Benzolized coke-oven gas, sensible heat	$169 \times 50 \times 2\cdot85 \times 10^{-3} =$	24
Water, vapour, heat of evaporation	$137^* \times 2\cdot49$	= 340
Water, liquid, sensible heat	$137 \times 209 \times 10^{-3}$	= 29
		393

The heat removed from the crude gas in the condensers, 394·9 MJ/t of coal, can be expressed in other forms, e.g. for a plant carbonizing 1000 t/day the heat loss is 16585 MJ/h or, for a yield of 317 m^3 (n.t.p.) of debenzolized gas/tonne, 1·18 MJ/m^3.

It should be noted that the heat exchange is dominated by the heat of vaporization of the liquor and that the total heat removed from the liquor accounts for 94 per cent of the total.

4.3.6 Principles of Design of Condensers

The fundamental equation for heat transfer is

$$Q = hA\theta_m \tag{4.2}$$

where Q = quantity of heat transferred in unit time,
  h = coefficient of heat transfer,
  A = area of the cooling surface
and θ_m = mean temperature difference between gas and water.

Although the practical designer describes his condensers in terms of area of water cooling surface, it is desirable to show how the value of h is affected by the velocity of the gas and water and by the disposition of the water tubing.

Silver[7] has shown that, for cooling gas from 71° to 27°C, the effect of variation of velocity (V) of gas (measured at 15°C, 1 atm.) can be expressed as follows:

Horizontal tubes,

$$h_h = 0{\cdot}315V \text{ for values of } V \text{ of } 0{\cdot}46, 1{\cdot}10 \text{ and } 1{\cdot}34 \text{ m/s} \tag{4.3}$$

Vertical tubes,

$$h_v = 0{\cdot}39V^{0{\cdot}8} \text{ for values of } V \text{ of } 1{\cdot}22 \text{ and } 3{\cdot}2 \text{ m/s} \tag{4.4}$$

where h is expressed as MJ/m^{2}h °C.

For a given velocity (1·2 m/s) within the observed range the ratio for the two types of tube is:

$$\frac{h_h}{h_v} = \frac{1{\cdot}88}{1{\cdot}18} = \frac{1{\cdot}6}{1}$$

Moreover, whilst an increase in the velocity of the gas of 50 per cent will increase h_h by 50 per cent, the same increase in velocity only increases h_v by 40 per cent, so that horizontal water tubes are not only more efficient but their conductivity increases *pro rata* with overload.

The effect of water velocity on h is relatively small provided that the flow is always turbulent, i.e. exceeds 0·05 m/s. If the water velocity is doubled from 0·06 m/s, h_h and h_v increase by only one-seventh.

This discussion might lead one to suppose that horizontal water tubing would be generally adopted because of its greater efficiency, so reducing the capital cost. In fact, vertical water tubing is almost universal in coke-oven plants built in Great Britain since 1930; the chief reason for this is that the water supplies used are generally of inferior quality and vertical tubing is easier to brush mechanically to remove scale. On the other hand, in the Ruhr area of Western Germany, where purer supplies of water are common, horizontal tubing is extensively used. Horizontally tubed condensers are favoured in the simple problem of condensation in gasworks in the United Kingdom and in one coke-oven plant built at a gasworks a horizontally and a vertically tubed cooler are used in series and the position of gas entry is reversed when naphthalene blockage is experienced.

One further complication in selecting a suitable value for h should be mentioned. For a given mean temperature difference (θ_m) and given gas and water velocities in a condenser with either horizontal or vertical tubing, h is still variable, depending on the actual range of temperature. It has been shown by Hollings and Hutchinson[8] that, under these conditions, h is proportional to the difference in the partial pressures of the water in the gas and in the condensate at the temperature of the tube wall. Solutions for dealing with this complication have been proposed by Silver[7] and by Colburn and Hougen[9] and have been summarized by Cooper and Priestley[10] and by Pollard[11]. Both methods need laborious calculations and cannot be given here. Suffice it to say that the complication usually leads to a selection of the cooling surface of a vertically tubed condenser based on previous satisfactory practice. It should be noted that h for primary condensers is approximately 1·5 times that for secondary condensers.

The vertically-tubed primary condensers common in Great Britain are O-shaped in plan and have five or six gas passes controlled by vertical baffles. Below and above the gas space the water flows counter-current to the gas flow. When the temperature falls from 85° to 74°C the liquor will condense. The volumes at the entrances and exits of the condensers are shown in Table 4.6.

Table 4.6 VOLUMES AT THE ENTRANCE AND EXITS
OF PRIMARY CONDENSERS

	Inlet 85°C	Outlet 35°C
Coke-oven gas, 317 m³ at n.t.p.	415	357
Water vapour, 152 kg	249	16
Total volume, m³	664	373
Ratio	1·78	1

Condensation of the water vapour at the dew-point (74°C) will reduce the velocity of the gas by 50 per cent and the cooling of the gas will nearly halve the initial velocity if the baffles in the gas space are uniformly distributed. This is sometimes compensated by reducing the free area for gas flow from inlet to outlet in an attempt to maintain the gas velocity on which the rate of heat transfer depends so much.

There is another feature in a multi-pass condenser which can act adversely. The gas is cooling during its passage and its natural flow is therefore downwards; similarly, the water is increasing in temperature and its natural flow is upwards. The relatively fast flow of the gas prevents recirculation in an upward flow but the low velocity of the water may allow its recirculation in its unnatural downwards flow. This can be compensated by increasing the diameter of the water pipes for the downflow and also by restricting the cross-section of the gas upflow so that the sections with downflow of gas and upflow of water are made the essential cooling surface with the other sections as connections, as in Figure 4.3 (Richards and Taylor[5]).

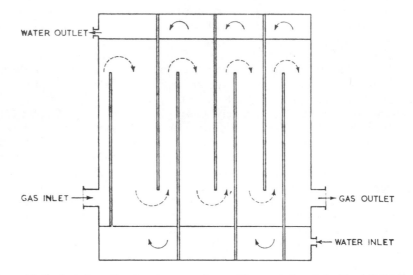

Figure 4.3 Graduated gas flow in primary condenser. (By permission of the Woodall Duckham Construction Co.)

As will be seen later, it is not uncommon in the final coolers or condensers to have to make considerable provision for removal of naphthalene; moreover, this is often associated with direct water-spray coolers which will no longer be built in conjunction with open-frame water-cooling towers. Should the indirect method of ammonia recovery develop, as seems likely, final coolers would be required only to overcome the heat of compression due to the exhausters and some of the load on the final coolers could be transferred to the primary condensers. It is clear that the chief load on the primary condensers is the heat of evaporation of the liquor; below the dew-point conditions are very different as regards velocity of gases, and therefore a different cooling surface is required for a given drop in temperature.

For a plant carbonizing about 1000 tonnes of coal per day, the present British practice is to have three primary condensers; one is a spare and two are in use. The gas stream is split to pass through the condensers in parallel. Each working condenser thus handles in one day the gas from 500 tonnes of coal, and a spare is always available. The primary condenser tubes are commonly 75 mm bore steel tubes $6\frac{1}{2}$–9 m long, the water surface being from

1500 to 2300 m^2 per condenser and the water cooling surface from 2·8 to 4·6 m^2 per ton of coal carbonized per day. In the Ruhr area about 2·8 m^2 of cooling surface per ton of coal carbonized per day is common. The cooling surface is, however, only one factor among three in equation (4.4). The third factor, the specific conductivity, is broadly fixed when vertical or horizontal water tubing is designed, but deterioration can be controlled by scaling the water side. It should be noted that the American Tubular Exchanger Association assign their highest fouling factor for carbonization gases, making of the design factor for the heat transfer coefficient 50 per cent of that for a 'clean' surface. Because of these factors, and increase of duty with increase in free moisture in the coal, operators prefer to have a reserve of cooling surface.

4.4 Detarrers

Persistent tar fog consists of minute particles or bubbles of tar condensed on still smaller particles of pitch or free carbon. The coarser particles (over 5 μm) could be removed by creating a very high velocity (up to 60 m/s) in a cyclone, or by passing through perforated plates, or by centrifugal action. A turbo-exhauster is therefore a detarrer, the efficiency of which is proportional to the speed. Thus, for carburetted water-gas, Badger[12] showed that an increase in speed of the impellor of 500 mm diameter from 2450 to 3200 rev/min decreased the amount of tar fog in the outlet gas at 16°C from 1·5 to 0·75 g/m^3 but a further increase in speed was not very effective. Tar fog is usually condensed in high-speed exhausters and is run to the tar sump.

Detarrers are now invariably of the electrostatic type in which wire electrodes impart a negative charge to the tar fog which is impelled to earthed tubes or sheets where the charge is released and the particles condense to a film which flows by gravity to a sump. An e.m.f. of from 30 to 40 kV, d.c. is required and is most commonly obtained by use of static metal rectifiers.

The rectifying units are mounted on a spindle and immersed in oil, condensation of moisture being prevented by keeping the electrodes warm by a steam coil. The precipitator tubes are of 150–200 mm diameter, 2·75 m long, or form a series of cells, wire electrodes being stretched tautly between the walls. The gas passes downwards at a speed of about 1·8 m/s. The discharge is a cold corona or brush discharge with sparking not usually occurring until the e.m.f. exceeds 40000 V.

The efficiency of tubular electrostatic detarrers may be related to the current discharge and the gas velocity by the expression[13]

$$n = 1 - e^{-ki/v} \tag{4.5}$$

where n = the efficiency of removal of particulate matter,
$\quad i$ = the current discharge,
$\quad v$ = the velocity of the gas in the tubes,
$\quad e$ = 2·718,
$\quad k$ = constant.

The chief value of equation (4.5) is in emphasizing the need to increase the current discharge (providing that electrical stability, or prevention of sparking can be maintained) if the velocity is increased. For wire-in-plate systems the effective velocity is half that in a tubular type but, since the effective area for gas passage in the casing in which the tubular type is installed is nearly half that if the plate type, the effective ground space required does not differ much for the two types.

The design velocity of the gas is usually chosen to give 99 per cent efficiency of the detarrer, but the tar content of the outlet gas will obviously vary with that of the inlet gas. If the detarrer is placed after an exhauster of the high-speed type the latter will reduce the tar fog to about 1.1 g/m^3, even with an inlet of 11 g/m^3 (3.8 kg/t coal), and the detarrer will then give an outlet gas containing 0.01 g/m^3. If, on the other hand, the exhauster is of the slow-speed Beale or Rootes type, and the inlet gas has the high concentration of 11 g/m^3, a design efficiency of 99 per cent is insufficient, at least 99.5 being desirable.

The resistance of an electrostatic detarrer is very small, say 0.5 mb, in contrast with the earlier perforated-plate types with high induced velocities in which considerable back pressure was created. For 28000 m^3 of gas per day the current used is between 8 and 16 mA or, allowing for rectification of a.c., the power consumption, on the same basis, is 0.35–0.7 kW, or 0.1–0.2 kW per tonne of coal.

If an electrostatic precipitator has been designed for maximum electrical stability it may not be possible to increase the current consumption and an overload of 100 per cent will cause the efficiency to fall to 90 per cent and possibly to a lower value because the current will probably have to be reduced; since the overload will rarely exceed 30 per cent, the efficiency will not normally fall to below about 97 per cent. To maintain the design efficiency, the main suspension insulators require cleaning at regular intervals and must, of course, be maintained above the dew-point of the gas.

4.5 Final Cooling of Coke-oven Gas and Naphthalene Removal

Final coolers are required to compensate for the increase in temperature of the gas on passing the exhausters and before entering the benzole scrubbers. If the semi-direct system of ammonia recovery is used, the temperature of the gas entering the final coolers will be higher (say 55°C) than when the indirect system of ammonia recovery is practised, when it may only be 40°C, 5°C higher than at the outlet of the primary condensers. Moreover, for the semi-direct process the gas is almost resaturated with water at its higher temperature but for the indirect process the water vapour saturation temperature is the temperature of the outlet of the primary condensers.

The old system involved direct cooling with water sprays, with circulation of the water to a cooling frame and return for re-use. Since with direct water sprays on gas containing hydrogen sulphide in concentration up to 16 g/m^3 some hydrogen sulphide would be dissolved and released to the air above the water-cooling towers, this practice is now regarded with disfavour by the Alkali Inspectors who have stated[14]: '... as a long-term policy we can see no alternative to asking for the abolition of the technique of recirculation in open frame coolers of water which has been used for the shock cooling of crude coke-oven gas. So far as new coke-oven plants are concerned, the industry has readily agreed, but has pointed out that there could be space and other difficulties regarding its application to existing plants. It has been 'agreed that as a general rule existing plant will only require consideration if it is the subject of complaint or if extensions are being considered. Every case will be considered carefully by the district inspector and treated on its merits.'

In new plants one solution will be the use of indirect coolers with cooling towers for the water and a naphthalene washer with circulation of the wash oil to a stripping still. Alternatively, wash oil may be used for direct cooling with indirect cooling of the wash oil and tower cooling of the water used in the indirect coolers. Both these systems will be discussed and compared with the older system of direct cooling.

Semi-direct System: cooling from 55° to 25°C; water saturation temperature 55°C (Figure 4.1*b*, p. 52):

$$MJ/t \ of \ coal$$

Benzolized coke-oven gas, sensible heat	$168.7 \times 30 \times 2.81 \times 10^{-3}$ =	14.2
Water vapour, heat of cooling	$46.4 \times 30 \times 1.85 \times 10^{-3}$ =	2.6
Water vapour, heat of condensation	38.4×2.49 =	95.1
Water, liquid, sensible heat	$38.4 \times 30 \times 4.18 \times 10^{-3}$ =	4.8
		117.2

Indirect System: cooling from 40° to 25°C; water saturation temperature 35°C (Figure 4.1*c*):

$$MJ/t \ of \ coal$$

Benzolized coke-oven gas, sensible heat	$168.7 \times 15 \times 2.81 \times 10^{-3}$ =	7.11
Water vapour, heat of cooling	$10.5 \times 15 \times 1.85 \times 10^{-3}$ =	0.29
Water vapour, heat of condensation	7.14×2.49 =	17.78
Water, liquid, sensible heat	$7.14 \times 10 \times 4.18 \times 10^{-3}$ =	0.30
		25.5

Thus for the semi-direct process the heat exchanged in cooling to 25°C is one-third of that exchanged in the primary condensers, but θ_m, the mean difference between the temperatures of water and gas, is only about one-third of that in the primary condensers and the coefficient, h, is reduced. Thus the cooling surface required for indirect vertical coolers is about the same as that of the primary condensers and direct cooling has been favoured.

For the indirect process the final exchange required is much less, say one-sixteenth of that in the primary condensers, but since θ_m is reduced to about one-third and h is less, the cooling surface required in indirect coolers is roughly one-third that of the primary condensers.

However, final cooling cannot be considered as a simple heat-exchange problem since the practical problems of naphthalene removal may be said to dominate the design. As previously noted the gas leaving the primary condensers is probably saturated with naphthalene vapour and carries solid naphthalene in suspension; some of this is removed in the electrostatic detarrer but on passage of the gas through the exhauster the temperature rises and any naphthalene fog vaporizes and the naphthalene saturation temperature may exceed 35°C. In final cooling after semi-direct ammonia recovery it has been common recent practice to use direct water sprays to cool to the naphthalene dew-point, to wash the gas with wash oil to remove naphthalene and to use a final water spray to cool to as low as temperature as is practicable.

The theory of oil washing is that of absorption which is discussed in

Chapter 5. Here it is only necessary to say that to meet Silver's minimum requirement ($qk = 1$) the minimum flow of wash oil at 25°C to remove naphthalene is 5·9 litres/1000 m³ of gas compared with 154 litres/1000 m³. On a plant carbonizing 1000 tonnes of coal per day this minimum rate would be only 82 litres/hour. This low flow would be insufficient to meet an essential requirement of packed tower scrubbers for which a minimum irrigation rate of 3·8 m³/h m² of tower area is recommended by Silver and Hopton[15]. A naphthalene washer is therefore usually a multi-stage static washer filled with shallow grid packing, pumps being used to supply each section with the appropriate amount of oil to give a good irrigation of the packing. Fresh oil is supplied to the gas outlet bay, the overflow from the gas inlet bay passing to a naphthalene-stripping plant and, after cooling, returning to the first bay.

Alternatively, warmed benzolized wash oil from the final benzole scrubber may be used for naphthalene removal in the upper half of a packed tower scrubber. One other solution practised on a plant treating 51000 m³/h was the use of a tower scrubber with shallow grid packing of a small surface area per cubic metre (49 instead of the common 82 m³); this gives a suitable minimum wetting rate, namely 3·9 m³/h m² of tower area, the actual oil flow being 1·3 times this minimum rate. The oil was sprayed to the packing in series at three levels and reduced the naphthalene saturation temperature to 18°C. A bleed of 0·46 m³/h wash oil was fed to a naphthalene-stripping plant to keep the naphthalene content of the oil to a low level.

A method of final cooling which conforms to modern requirements involves direct cooling by oil in a tower scrubber, separation of the oil and the water which also condenses, passage of the oil through the tubular coolers (the cooling water passing to a cooling tower) and return for re-use. The specific heat of gas oil is about 1·84 kJ/kg °C (weight basis) so that oil of rather more than twice the amount of water has to be used for the same cooling duty, but the use of oil also serves to reduce the naphthalene content below 0·1 g/m³. Part of the oil has to be bled to a wash-oil still with, preferably, an oil-redistillation unit on the return to keep the naphthalene (and sludge) to a low concentration. This system is illustrated diagrammatically in Figure 4.6 (Richards and Taylor[5]).

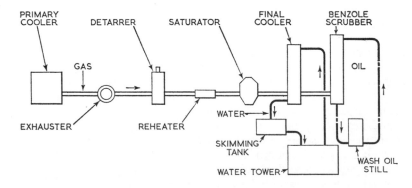

Figure 4.4 Direct water final condenser (cooler), and water-cooling tower, semi-direct process. (By permission of the Woodall Duckham Construction Co.)

Figure 4.4 shows the common old method using a direct final cooler with skimming of the condensed naphthalene from the liquor. Figure 4.5 shows an acceptable modern method, using, with indirect ammonia recovery, an

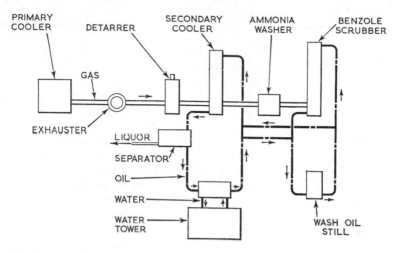

Figure 4.5 Direct oil final condenser (cooler) with tubular heat exchanger and water tower, indirect process. (By permission of the Woodall Duckham Construction Co.)

indirect final cooler preceded by a naphthalene washer. In the system shown in Figure 4.6, where the ammonia washer follows the final cooler, the condensing liquor is ammoniacal and must be separated to avoid corrosion of the wash-oil still, a step which is not necessary with semi-direct ammonia recovery in which the ammonia is removed in the saturator preceding the final cooler.

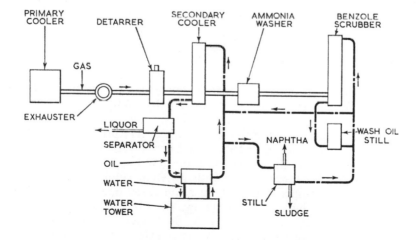

Figure 4.6 Direct oil final condenser (cooler) heat exchanger and water tower with wash oil indirect process. (By permission of the Woodall Duckham Construction Co.)

For the heat exchange of 117 MJ/t of coal, or 4880 MJ/h for a 1000 tonne/day plant, the amount of oil (sp.gr. 0·85) entering at 22°C and leaving at 52°C (a rise of 20°C) would be

$$\frac{4880 \times 10^3}{1·84 \times 20} = 132000 \text{ kg/h} = 155 \text{ m}^3/\text{h}$$

To cool this oil over the same temperature range in tubular coolers would require 353 m^3/h of water which would then be circulated to a tower cooler to cool to, say, 20°C. A minimum irrigation rate recommended by Morris and Jackson[16] for tower scrubbers with a packing of 82 m^2/m^3 is 6·5 m^3/m^{2}h of free tower area; for the oil flow required this necessitates a tower of 24 m^2 maximum area. Since the use of oil overcomes problems of naphthalene blockage, it would appear to be useful to increase the surface area of the packing per cubic metre of tower to 168 m^2/m^3 (small graded coke or stacked small stoneware rings) when the minimum irrigation rate would rise to 8·6 m^3/m^{2}h. A cooling tower of 3·5 m diameter as might be used for the adjacent benzole scrubbers, would then give a flow of 16 m^3/m^{2}h.

It is appropriate to mention here that whatever steps are taken to remove the naphthalene from the gas in the final cooling before the benzole scrubbers, such steps will not in all circumstances reduce the naphthalene concentration to the low value required to meet the specification of the Gas Boards, particularly, if the gas has to be boosted to high pressures (2 atm. gauge or more) for supply as town gas. The gas comes into contact with benzole wash oil which, if it is fresh creosote oil, is rich in naphthalene, and in the summer, when higher primary and final cooling temperatures obtain, the naphthalene content of the gas entering the final coolers is high. It is therefore usually necessary to have a final naphthalene washer at the end of the purification system despite the fact that the use of oil in the final cooler and the use of benzole wash oil of low naphthalene content could, under winter cooling conditions, leave the gas after the benzole scrubbers with only 35 mg/m^3 (Richards and Taylor[5]), a value which would be suitable for gas supply up to 1 atm gauge pressure.

4.6 Ammonia Recovery

In the historical portion of this chapter reference is made to the different methods of ammonia recovery and to the fact that, in the semi-direct system, an acid bath or saturator will precede the final cooler; in the indirect system the ammonia washer will succeed the final cooler. The principles of ammonia absorption are dealt with in Chapter 5 and here it is necessary to refer only to certain practical details of carbonization practice.

Ammonia gas, because it reacts with water or sulphuric acid, which is used to absorb ammonia from carbonization gases, does not obey Henry's law; it is not very soluble in hot water and therefore it dissolves only in the water deposited in the condensers in the final stages. In the usual indirect method practised in gasworks and now being extensively practised in newer coke-oven plants, the aim is to obtain an ammonia liquor as strong as possible to minimize the cost of its further concentration. In gasworks it is usual to recover 0·13 m³ of liquor per tonne of coal. That which condenses above about 50°C is weak liquor and is used, after cooling, in the ammonia washers where it becomes strong liquor. The ammonia which is removed first in the condenser is the 'fixed' ammonium chloride; the 'free' ammonia which is subsequently removed is, in fact, combined with weak acids, carbon dioxide and hydrogen sulphide, the salts of which readily dissociate with the loss chiefly of CO_2 and H_2S. Since the final ammonia content of the gas after the ammonia washers is dependent on the concentrations of ammonia and carbon dioxide in the liquor, a low final concentration of ammonia in the gas is favoured by recarbonating the liquor supplied to the ammonia washer. This can be achieved by circulating the liquor first to the third bay from the gas outlet, circulating co-currently with the gas to the gas outlet, then re-circulating to the fourth bay from the gas outlet, and then in turn to each of the bays towards the gas inlet, counter-current with the gas flow.

The multi-stage static washer with packings of wooden grids, metal sheets, or fibres is commonly used in gasworks for the amount of liquor required for overall circulation (i.e. the overflow from bay to bay) is low, but the re-circulation within a bay is high enough to ensure a suitable bay efficiency. Priestley[17] has shown how the design of a 12-bay ammonia washer may be calculated to reduce the ammonia in gas from 7 to 1 g/m³ for 170 000 m³/day, the total gas/liquid interface surface required being 1400 m² and the liquor volume 0·76 m³/h with a bay circulation of 5·5 m³/h to give a liquor containing 6·95 per cent ammonia by weight.

In coke-oven practice the volume of gas for a plant carbonizing 1000 tonnes of coal per day would be twice the above amount and two streams could be adopted. For a plant carbonizing 2000 tonnes of coal per day two streams with three washers in series have been used. For a plant carbonizing 3000–4000 tonnes per day tower scrubbers have been used, each scrubber being a two-stage unit, the tendency in large plants being to build upwards rather than horizontally. An alternative introduced into a plant of this size is the use of ammonium sulphate liquor containing 1 per cent of acid in acid-resistant towers, which reduces the scale of the washing plant; the liquor is subsequently concentrated in a vacuum evaporator.

The majority of coke-oven plants built during the period 1950–1970 in the United Kingdom have used indirect ammonia recovery, many with the subsequent production of sulphate of ammonia. Ammonia recovery is no longer a source of profit but remains a technical necessity in carbonization practice; a saturator in the main stream of gas, as in the semi-direct process, is a source of variable pressure-drop which makes it more difficult to maintain uniform and standard pressures on the plant.

4.7 Benzole Recovery

The principles of benzole recovery are those of absorption discussed in Chapter 5. Here it is necessary to refer only to the practical problems which arise at coke-oven plants (where benzole recovery is invariably practised). The common practice is the use of tower scrubbers with the gas and wash oil in counter-current flow.

The essential practical problem is the maintenance of irrigation of the tower packing to give a uniform gas/liquid interface. The factors which influence performance are: (1) temperature; (2) ratio of the volume of the gas and oil; and (3) quality of the oil.

The temperature of the gas has been considered in the discussion of final coolers, which are designed to bring the gas to a temperature as close to ambient as possible. With direct water or oil coolers it is possible to bring the gas to the temperature of the coolant; with indirect coolers to within 5°C. The final temperature of the gas is therefore a function of the cooling which can be obtained in the water-cooling towers, which will be considered later. With recirculation of water and natural-draught cooling towers it may be possible to cool the gas only to 25°C in the summer and to 15°C in the winter. To compensate for the difference in temperature it would be necessary to circulate about 50 per cent more oil in summer than in winter to maintain the same slip of benzene in the gas. For a 5 per cent slip of benzene (which accounts for about 80 per cent of the crude benzole) at 25°C, Silver *et al.*[15] showed that the circulation of 2 m^3 of petroleum wash oil was required per 1000 m^3 of gas, or 0·67 m^3 per tonne of coal carbonized. This wash oil was of specific gravity 0·85; drop point 270°C, 50 per cent distilling at 331°C; and had a viscosity of 67 sec Redwood at 20°C. The recommended oil flow was 3·8 m^3/h per m^2 of free tower area.

The quality of wash oil can be assessed in a number of ways. The two chief wash oils used are creosote oil and gas oil from petroleum; in either case the 'drop point' (this is the temperature at which, on distillation, the first drop appears in the receiver) should be above 200°C, a boiling range of 200–300°C being preferable. Fresh creosote oil will contain naphthalene and if used directly would pass some of this to the gas and some would doubtless be a cause of blockages; it should be passed slowly through the benzole still to remove as much naphthalene as possible, the crude oil from the benzole dephlegmator (which is rich in naphthalene) not being returned to the wash oil.

Gas oil has a specific gravity of about 0·85 at 20°C compared with about 1·00 for creosote oil. Creosote oil has a lower effective molecular weight than gas oil and should therefore have a greater absorptive power for benzole, values given by the Joint Benzole Research Committee being of the order of 4·0–4·5 per cent by weight for light creosotes compared with 3·0 for gas oil. The viscosity of both these wash oils is 30–35 sec Redwood at 20°C. On the other hand, absorption from the coke-oven gas of tar fog, and of unsaturated hydrocarbons (e.g. indene) which polymerize, tends to increase the viscosity of creosote in which these products are soluble; they are much less soluble in gas oil and tend to form a sludge which can be a source of trouble in forming deposits in the benzole plant but which do not affect the viscosity of the gas oil seriously.

Thus, in practice, the efficiency of creosote oil tends to fall with use but the efficiency of gas oil tends to rise because of the solution of some aromatic compounds. Viscosity is, therefore the most important characteristic of wash oils in use; it is of obvious importance in the gas/liquid interface on the scrubber boards where the solution of benzole vapours from the gas occurs.

A considerable improvement in the performance of creosote wash oils has followed the use of electrostatic precipitators to remove tar fog from the gas before the final coolers. Bradley[18] compared records of two periods, each of 12 months, for the viscosity of creosote wash oils with and without such a detarrer in use. With no detarrer the viscosity varied from 65 to 72 sec Redwood at 20°C in a series of waves; with a detarrer in use the viscosity after the first two months was uniform at 62 sec. At the same time Buckley[19] gave records for 12 months of the specific gravity of creosote wash oil with and without a detarrer in use. Without the detarrer the specific gravity rose from 0·929 to 0·934, then decreased to 0·926 and re-increased to 0·950; with a detarrer in use the mean specific gravity was 0·900 with a maximum increase of 0·005 and an average monthly change from the mean of 0·0015. For these two periods the average consumption of wash oil per m³ of 65 per cent benzole made was 0·087 and 0·030 m³ without and with the precipitator in use respectively. Moreover, with the precipitator in use, the crude benzole production increased by 0·6 litres per tonne of coal and the scrubbing slip was constant at 5 per cent.

A further step is the redistillation of a portion of the wash oil to remove all material boiling above 300°C, the fraction of highest molecular weight, viscosity and specific gravity. This became common practice immediately before the Second World War. The universal employment of electrostatic detarrers of high efficiency on the cold gas has overcome most of the thickening of wash oil due to tar fog, but thickening by the polymers of unsaturated hydrocarbons may still occur. With a primary naphthalene washer or with a direct oil cooler, unsaturated hydrocarbons are removed with the naphthalene and the need for regeneration of a creosote oil may not occur, though even in such circumstances it is still practised at some plants. Without an oil-washing stage before the benzole scrubbers, indene is removed in the benzole scrubbers, as the values given in Table 4.7 show.

Table 4.7 STAGES IN THE REMOVAL OF
NAPHTHALENE AND INDENE

	Naphthalene g/m³	Indene
Before benzole scrubbers	0·24	1·06
After benzole scrubbers	0·12	0·02
After naphthalene washer	0·03	0·007

Residual tar fog does not dissolve in gas oil but forms a sludge which is liable to be deposited in the heat exchangers of the benzole plant or in the scrubbers. This can be removed by the redistillation of part of the wash oil, the sludge being conveniently disposed of by adding it to the coal charged to the ovens, as part of the oil which it is convenient to add to control the bulk density.

With a wash oil of constant viscosity and specific gravity (and therefore of constant effective molecular weight) the maintenance of a constant slip of benzole at the scrubbers becomes a problem of reaction-temperature control. This is shown clearly in Figure 4.7. It is usual to keep the wash oil temperature a few degrees above that of the gas to prevent deposition of moisture in the

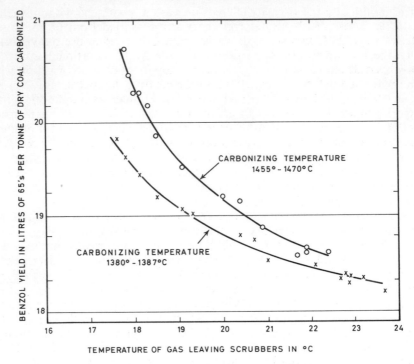

Figure 4.7 Effect on benzole yield of temperature of gas leaving scrubbers, for two ranges of carbonizing temperature (Ruddy[20]).

wash oil and the effective reaction temperature is dominated by the temperature to which the cooling water for the final gas coolers and the wash oil
coolers can be reduced.

5

Gas Absorption Towers

The following table shows the symbols and abbreviations used in Parts A and B of this chapter.

NOTATION (PART A)

a	specific area dry packing material	m^2/m^3
a_e	effective area for mass-transfer	m^2/m^3
a_e^*	effective area for mass-transfer on trays	m^2/m^2
a_w	wetted area of packing material	m^2/m^3
A_{an}	total annular area per tray	m^2
A_b	bubbling area per tray, $(A_c - 2A_d)$	m^2
A_c	cross-sectional area of column	m^2
A_d	area of one downcomer	m^2
A_f	area available for vapour flow, $(A_c - A_d)$	m^2
A_h	total hole area per tray	m^2
A_r	total riser area per tray	m^2
A_{rev}	total reversal area per tray	m^2
A_s	total slot area per tray	m^2
A_{ud}	minimum area under downcomer	m^2
b	tray thickness	m
b_s	slot width (bubble-caps)	m
c_L	specific heat of liquid	J/kg.°C
c_G	specific heat of gas	J/kg.°C
C	concentration	$kgmole/m^3$
C^o	concentration in bulk	$kgmole/m^3$
C^i	concentration at interface	$kgmole/m^3$
C_g	liquid gradient correction factor	—
C_s	coefficient in maximum slot capacity formula	—
C^*	'equilibrium' concentration (fictitious)	$kgmole/m^3$
d_b	diameter of gas bubble	m
d_c	outside diameter of cap	m
d_{ci}	inside diameter of cap	m
d_d	diameter of a liquid drop	m
d_e	diameter of an equivalent sphere	m
d_h	hole diameter (sieve tray)	m
d_p	nominal packing size	m
d_r	diameter of riser	m
D_{AB}	molecular diffusivity	m^2/s
D_c	column diameter	m
$D_g(D_l)$	diffusion coefficient in gas (liquid)	m^2/s
e	entrainment rate	kg/s
E_D	'dry' plate efficiency (without entrainment) on a consistent basis (E_{MV} or E_p^o)	—
E_T	absorption efficiency of tower	—
E_P	plate efficiency	—

E_0	overall plate efficiency	—
E_{MV}	Murphree vapour efficiency	—
E_p^o	point efficiency	—
E_w	'wet' plate efficiency (with entrainment) on a consistent basis	—
f_B	association parameter	—
$f_g(f_l)$	multicomponent mass-transfer factors in gas (liquid)	—
f_e	cost of power	MU/kWh
F	packing factor	m^{-1}
g	gravitational acceleration ($= 9.81$)	m/s^2
G	gas load per cross-sectional area	$kg/m^2.s$
G^*	total gas load	kg/s
G_{max}^*	maximum gas load per tray	kg/s
G_b	gas load per cross-sectional area related to bubbling area	$kg/m^2.s$
h	height (general)	m
h_a	pressure drop caused by the presence of froth	m tray liquid
h_{ci}	pressure drop of cap internals	m tray liquid
h_d	dynamic submergence	m
h_{dc}	'height' of clear liquid in the downcomer (see Figure 5.22)	m
h_f	height of gas–liquid layer on tray	m
h_{hd}	pressure drop of dry sieve tray	m tray liquid
$(h_{hd})_{iw}$	pressure drop of dry sieve tray at incipient weepage	m tray liquid
h_l	clear liquid height	m
h_n	depth of notches in weir	m
h_o	slot opening (bubble-caps)	m
h_{ow}	height of liquid crest over weir	m
h_{pd}	pressure drop of dry plate	m tray liquid
h_s	slot submergence (bubble-caps)	m
h_{sc}	skirt clearance of a bubble cap	m
h_{ss}	static seal (lowest height of weir minus highest point of slot)	m
h_t	pressure difference between two trays	m tray liquid
h_{ud}	head loss caused by liquid flow under the downcomer apron	m tray liquid
h_w	height of weir	m
H	dimensionless hydraulic parameter	—
H_e	solubility coefficient (Henry)	$\dfrac{kgmole}{m^3.bar}$
H_s	slot height	m
H_T	height of tower	m
HTU	height of a transfer unit	m
I	ionic strength	$kgmole/m^3$
J_A	mass-flux by eddy-diffusion	$kgmole/m^2.s$
k_{AB}	reaction rate constant	various
$k_g(k_l)$	partial mass-transfer coefficient in gas phase (liquid phase); physical absorption	m/s
$k_{mg}(k_{ml})$	partial generalized mass-transfer coefficient in gas phase (liquid phase)	m/s
$K_g(K_l)$	overall mass-transfer coefficient based on driving force in gas phase units (liquid phase units)	m/s
K_C	capital cost of a tower section of unit height (1 metre) and a diameter of one metre	monetary unit
l	length of tray parallel to direction of liquid flow	m
l_p	pitch of contacting device	m
l_T	average width of tray in a direction normal to liquid flow	m
l_w	length of weir	m
L	liquid load per cross-sectional area	$kg/m^2.s$
L^*	total liquid load	kg/s
M	molecular weight	
m_g	mass-transfer factor (trays)	—
MU	monetary unit (1 MU $\approx$ £1) (1970)	
n_p	number of packing per unit of volume	m^{-3}
N_A	mass-flux of component A	$kgmole/m^2.s$

N_c	number of caps per tray	—
N_h	number of holes per sieve tray	—
N_r	number of rows of caps normal to flow	—
N_s	number of slots per bubble-cap tray	—
N_t	number of theoretical plates	—
NTU	number of transfer units	—
p	partial pressure (1 bar $= 10^5$ N/m^2 $= 14{\cdot}504$ lb/in^2)	bar
P	total pressure	bar
Q_S	heat of solution	J/kgmole
Q_R	heat of reaction	J/kgmole
r_g	slope equilibrium line/slope operating line	—
r_l	$= 1/r_g$	—
r_{wd}	ratio of wall thickness to (nominal) diameter of ring-packing	—
R	gas-constant $= 83{\cdot}144 \times 10^{-3}$	$\dfrac{\text{m}^3.\text{bar}}{\text{kgmole.}^\circ\text{K}}$
R_s	trapezoidal slot shape factor	—
R_v	vapour distribution ratio	—
s	rate of surface renewal $=$ fraction of total surface area per unit time	s^{-1}
t	time	s
t_{dc}	residence time of liquid in downcomer	s
T	temperature	$^\circ$K
T_s	tray spacing	m
u	velocity (general)	m/s
u_b	gas velocity based on bubbling area	m/s
u_f	gas velocity based on area available for vapour flow	m/s
u_0	superficial velocity based on cross-sectional tower area	m/s
v	molar volume at normal boiling point	m^3/kgmole
V	dimensionless hydraulic parameter	—
w_h	gas velocity in hole (sieve-tray)	m/s
w_s	gas velocity in slot (bubble-cap)	m/s
w_{ss}	slot velocity, based on fully opened slots	m/s
w_w	weepage rate based on total hole area	m/s
x	distance in direction of diffusion	m
y	molar fraction	—
z	film thickness	m
α	thermal diffusivity of liquid	m^2/s
β	general constant	—
β_a	aeration factor	—
γ	solubility according to Oswald	—
Δ	liquid gradient	m
Δ_1	liquid gradient at $u_0 \rho_g^{\frac{1}{2}} = 1{\cdot}34$	m
ε_D	eddy-diffusivity	m^2/s
ε_g	gas fraction in gas–liquid layer on tray	—
ε_l	liquid hold-up in packed towers	m^3/m^3
ε_p	plate porosity (sieve trays)	—
ε	voidage fraction of packing	—
η	efficiency of fans and motors	—
θ	stoichiometric constant	—
$\mu_g \ (\mu_l)$	viscosity of gas (liquid)	kg/m.s
ρ_f	specific mass of froth	kg/m^3
$\rho_g \ (\rho_l)$	specific mass of gas (liquid)	kg/m^3
σ	surface tension	J/m^2
τ	exposition time	s
ϕ	chemical acceleration factor	—
ϕ_A	ratio of mass flux of component A to total mass flux, regarding direction of flux	—
Φ	mass flux ratio	
ψ	entrainment expressed as fraction of gross downflow	—

Dimensionless numbers

Sherwood number $= Sh = \dfrac{\text{mass diffusivity}}{\text{molecular diffusivity}}$

Reynolds number $= Re = \dfrac{\text{inertial force}}{\text{viscous force}}$

Schmidt number $= Sc = \dfrac{\text{kinematic viscosity}}{\text{molecular diffusivity}}$

Galilei number $= Ga = \dfrac{\text{gravitational force}}{\text{viscous force}} \times$ Reynolds number

Eötvös number $= E\ddot{o} = \dfrac{\text{gravitational force}}{\text{surface tension force}}$

Froude number $= Fr = \dfrac{\text{inertial force}}{\text{gravitational force}}$

    log = logarithm to base 10

    ln = natural logarithm to base $e = 2{\cdot}71828\ldots$

    lm = log mean

$\exp(x) = e^x$

index l = liquid   superscript: i = at interface

    g = gas o = in bulk of gas (liquid)

ADDITIONAL SYMBOLS USED IN PART B

C_a	nitric acid capacity	tonnes HNO_3 as 100 per cent per 24 h
C_1	cost of installed tray	monetary units per tray
C_2	cost of erected column shell	monetary units per metre height
C_i	molar concentration of ionic species i	kgmole/m^3
C_N	nitric acid concentration	wt.% HNO_3
D	diffusion coefficient	m^2/s
F_N	molar fraction of nitrous-N in tail gas	—
F_O	molar fraction of oxygen in tail gas	—
K	equilibrium constant (see 5.8.3)	bar^x (x is a varying number)
k	reaction-rate constant for a first-order reaction	s^{-1}
k_1	rate constant of Bodenstein equation	bar^{-2}.s^{-1}
k_g	gas phase mass transfer coefficient	m/s
k_l	liquid phase mass transfer coefficient	m/s
N_g	total gas flow	kgmole/s
N_x	rate of absorption of component x per unit area	kgmole/m^2.s
p_x	partial pressure of component x	bar
p_x^o	partial pressure of component x in gas-bulk	bar
p_x^i	partial pressure of component x at interface	bar
Q_3	heat of reaction of nitric acid formation	J/kgmole
V_a	absorption volume	m^3
X_O	molar percentage of oxygen in tail gas	%
Y	optimal tray spacing	m
Z_O	ratio of oxygen over nitric oxide	—
Z_i	ionic charge of species i	—
β_0	ratio of NO-content after oxidation over NO-content before oxidation. See equations 5.187 and 5.188.	

β^i pressure 'ratio' at interface, equation (5.185); the same
        dimension as K_2. bar^{-2}
β_a factor in equation (5.191)   —
η_a absorption efficiency $(0 \leqslant \eta_a \leqslant 1)$ —
ξ degree of oxidation = 4-valent nitrous-N over total
        nitrous-N $(0 \leqslant \xi \leqslant 1)$. See equation (5.173).   —

   log = logarithm to base 10
   ln = natural logarithm to base e = 2·71828 ...

$\exp(x) = e^x$

index : l = liquid   superscript : i = at interface

     g = gas o = in bulk of gas (liquid)

PART A GENERAL

F. J. G. KWANTEN AND J. HUISKAMP

5.1 Physical Basis of the Process

5.1.1 Introduction

The removal of unwanted gaseous contaminants by gas-absorption is effected
by bringing the gas into contact with a liquid in which the impurities alone
are soluble. The components to be absorbed have to be transferred from the
bulk of the gas to the bulk of the liquid. The force producing this movement
of the molecules of the soluble component, or the driving force, as it is called,

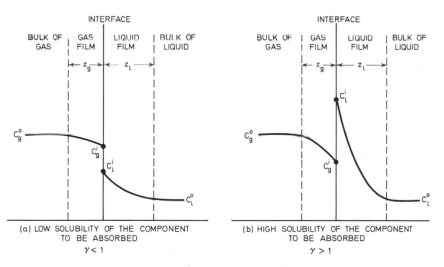

Figure 5.1 Concentration profile near the interface in gas–liquid absorption

is caused by the non-equilibrium of the concentration of the component in
the gas-phase (C_g^0) with that in the liquid-phase (C_l^0). The concentration
profile near the interface is shown in Figure 5.1.

The gas and liquid phases can be regarded as offering resistance to the passage of the component to be absorbed, while in general it can be assumed that the interface itself offers no such resistance. The phase which contributes the major resistance to mass transfer is said to be controlling or to be the limitation.

This introductory Section 5.1 reviews the literature up to 1970 on the general factors basic to absorption of gases.

5.1.2 Diffusion

DIFFUSION IN GASES

Absorption is a diffusional process. The molecules to be transferred can move either by molecular diffusion, which is a slow process, or by 'eddy-diffusion', a much faster process in which appreciable amounts of the gas or liquid move as a whole. Diffusion is more complicated than viscous flow or heat conduction because we have to deal with mixtures.

All widely used diffusion 'laws', for both liquids and gases, depend primarily upon the assumption of a linear homogeneous relation between diffusional mass fluxes and the driving forces tending to produce mass movement. For the simplest case of molecular diffusion in binary systems this assumption is usually expressed as 'Fick's first law' of diffusion:

$$J_A = -D_{AB}\frac{dC_A}{dx} \tag{5.1}$$

This equation states that species A diffuses (moves relative to the mixture A, B) in the direction of decreasing molar concentration of A.

D_{AB}, the diffusion coefficient, is the proportionality-factor between flux and concentration-gradient. Of special importance is the form of Fick's first law in terms of N_A, the total molar flux of A relative to stationary co-ordinates:

$$N_A = \frac{C_A}{C_A+C_B}(N_A+N_B)-D_{AB}\frac{dC_A}{dx} \tag{5.2}$$

This equation states that the molar flux N_A relative to stationary co-ordinates is the resultant of two vector quantities:

$$\frac{C_A}{C_A+C_B}(N_A+N_B),$$

which is the flux of A resulting from the bulk motion of the fluid, and

$$J_A = -D_{AB}\frac{dC_A}{dx},$$

which is the flux of A resulting from the diffusion superimposed on the bulk flow.

In many cases gas and liquid are in turbulent motion, it may be imagined that 'eddies' or small chunks of fluid, suddenly and erratically move from one place in a fluid to another where they lose their identity by blending with the fluid. If such an eddy moves from one place to another, it must interchange with a similar eddy that moves in the opposite direction to take its place. If the concentration of component A is not the same in the two places, the interchange results in a net transport of A, the rate of which is proportional to the difference in concentration and the volume rate of interchange. The flux of mass-transfer resulting from this mechanism is expressed in equation (5.3):

$$J_A = -\varepsilon_D \frac{dC_A}{dx} \qquad (5.3)$$

in which ε_D is the eddy-diffusivity. We have little information about ε_D, but it is known that, in a fully turbulent fluid, ε_D is many orders of magnitude larger than the molecular diffusivity D_{AB}.

For first estimates the following formulae can be used:

gas phase
$$D_g \approx 4 \cdot 3 \times 10^{-9} \frac{T^{3/2} \left(\frac{1}{M_A} + \frac{1}{M_B} \right)^{1/2}}{P(v_A^{1/3} + v_B^{1/3})^2}$$

liquid phase
$$D_l \approx 0 \cdot 12 \times 10^{-15} \frac{T \cdot M_B^{1/2} \cdot f_B}{\mu_l \cdot v_A^{0 \cdot 6}}$$

(f_B = association parameter: 1·6 for water, 1·4 for methanol, 1·2 for ethanol and 1·0 for unassociated liquids; index B is for second component or mixture when considering gas phase or for solvent when considering liquid phase)

The present lack of diffusivity data on most mixtures of interest makes it necessary to use estimated or extrapolated values of D_{AB} in most calculations[1,2,3]. Measured data are also available[4,5,6,11].

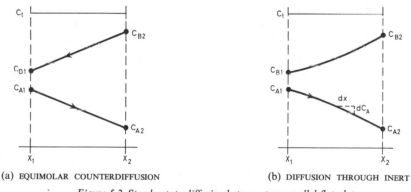

(a) EQUIMOLAR COUNTERDIFFUSION   (b) DIFFUSION THROUGH INERT

Figure 5.2 Steady-state diffusion between two parallel flat plates

In the following we shall proceed with some particular cases of molecular diffusion, assuming steady state conditions and rectangular co-ordinates in one direction, i.e. we shall consider the diffusion between two parallel flat planes of reference (x_1 and x_2), Figure 5.2.

Case A: Equimolar counterdiffusion

If in a binary mixture the components diffuse in opposite directions, the process is called counterdiffusion. The molar flux of A is given by:

$$N_A = -\frac{D_{AB}}{x_1 - x_2}(C_{A1} - C_{A2}) \qquad (5.4)$$

while that for component B is:

$$N_B = -\frac{D_{BA}}{x_1 - x_2}(C_{B1} - C_{B2}) \qquad (5.5)$$

As $N_A + N_B = N_t = 0$ it follows that $D_{AB} = D_{BA} = D$.

Case B: Diffusion of one component through another inert component

This case is very common since it appears in all the processes in which one component A of a binary gas mixture is absorbed, while component B does not participate in the diffusional process, i.e. behaves inertly.

For this case, Fick's law leads to:

$$N_A = -\frac{D_{AB}}{x_1 - x_2} C_t \left(\frac{C_{A1} - C_{A2}}{C_{Blm}} \right) \qquad (5.6)$$

in which

$$C_{Blm} = \frac{C_{B1} - C_{B2}}{\ln \dfrac{C_{B1}}{C_{B2}}} \qquad (5.7)$$

and

$$C_t = C_A + C_B \qquad (5.8)$$

The concentration profile is given in Figure 5.2(b). Note that component A is transported while B remains stationary. If the gas obeys the perfect gas law we may introduce partial pressures instead of molar concentrations

$$C_A = \frac{p_A}{RT}, \qquad C_B = \frac{p_B}{RT} \qquad \text{and} \qquad C_t = \frac{P}{RT}$$

So equation (5.6) can be written in the form in which it is very often used in gas-absorption problems

$$N_A = -\frac{D_{AB}}{x_1 - x_2} \cdot \frac{P}{RT} \left(\frac{P_{A1} - P_{A2}}{P_{B1} - P_{B2}} \right) \left\{ \ln \left(\frac{P_{B1}}{P_{B2}} \right) \right\}^{-1} \qquad (5.9)$$

Comparing equimolar counterdiffusion, equation (5.4), with diffusion of one component through an inert one, equation (5.6), it follows that equimolar counterdiffusion proceeds at a slower rate than the diffusion of one component in an inert gas.

Case C: Diffusion of one component through an inert multi-component mixture

This is the case that is most frequently encountered in industrial practice, as a mixture rarely contains only two components. The molar flux of the diffusing component is expressed here in the same way as stated by equation (5.6).

$$N_A = -\frac{D_{AM}}{x_1 - x_2} C_t \left\{ \frac{C_{A1} - C_{A2}}{(C_{inert})_{lm}} \right\} \tag{5.10}$$

in which

$$(C_{inert})_{lm} = \frac{(C_t - C_A)_1 - (C_t - C_A)_2}{\ln \dfrac{(C_t - C_A)_1}{(C_t - C_A)_2}} \tag{5.11}$$

The value of the mass diffusivity D_{AM} is an equivalent value and is calculated from

$$D_{AM} = \frac{1 - y_A}{\dfrac{y_B}{D_{AB}} + \dfrac{y_C}{D_{AC}} + \dfrac{y_D}{D_{AD}} + \dots + \dfrac{y_N}{D_{AN}}} \tag{5.12}$$

in which y is the molar fraction of any component in the gas mixture and $D_{AB}, D_{AC}, \dots$, etc., are the binary coefficients of A in B, A in C, ..., etc.

Case D: Multi-component diffusion in various directions

In many cases not only one but two or more components diffuse in one or various directions. Some particular cases are described in the literature[1,7,8]. For the time being there is, however, no general exact and at the same time direct method of computation, which would be suitable for use in practical engineering calculations. Hence approximate solutions have to be used. Wilke[9] has presented two such methods. The simple one can be generally applied in practice. We can start by writing down the fluxes of all components in a way analogous to equation (5.2).

$$N_A = y_A N_t - D_{AM} \cdot C_t \frac{dy_A}{dx} \tag{5.13}$$

$$N_B = y_B N_t - D_{BM} \cdot C_t \frac{dy_B}{dx} \tag{5.14}$$

etc.

The total flux of all components is defined as

$$N_t = N_A + N_B + N_C + N_D + \dots + N_N \tag{5.15}$$

Note that N is a vector with magnitude and direction.

Introducing the factors $\Phi_A = N_A/N_t$, $\Phi_B = N_B/N_t$, etc., we can write equation (5.13) in the following way:

$$N_A = y_A \frac{N_A}{\Phi_A} - D_{AM} \cdot C_t \frac{dy_A}{dx} \tag{5.16}$$

Assuming Φ_A to be constant over the diffusion distance $z = x_2 - x_1$, integration leads to:

$$N_A = C_t \cdot \Phi_A \frac{D_{AM}}{z} \ln \frac{\Phi_A - y_{A2}}{\Phi_A - y_{A1}} \qquad (5.17)$$

This formula leads to the following set of six formulae with which we are able to solve practical multi-component diffusion problems.

$$N_A = C_t \frac{D_{AM}}{z} \left(\frac{y_{A1} - y_{A2}}{f_A} \right) \qquad (5.18)$$

$$f_A = -\left(\frac{y_{A1}}{\Phi_A} - \frac{y_{A2}}{\Phi_A} \right) \left\{ \ln \left(\frac{1 - y_{A1}/\Phi_A}{1 - y_{A2}/\Phi_A} \right) \right\} \qquad (5.19)$$

$$\Phi_A = \frac{N_A}{N_t} \qquad (5.20)$$

$$N_t = N_A + N_B + N_C + \ldots + N_N \qquad (5.21)$$

$$D_{AM} = \frac{1 - y_A}{\dfrac{y_B}{D_{AB}} + \dfrac{y_C}{D_{AC}} + \ldots + \dfrac{y_N}{D_{AN}}} \qquad (5.22)$$

$$y_A = \frac{y_{A1} + y_{A2}}{2} \qquad (5.23)$$

To a first approximation it is tentatively assumed that all components except A behave inertly, i.e. $N_B = 0$, $N_C = 0$, etc., so that $\Phi_A = 1$.

So we may start by computing N_A from equation (5.18); after this we repeat the same procedure for B, C, etc. As a result we are now able to calculate more precise values for Φ_A, Φ_B, etc., and the fluxes. It should be noted that $D_{AM} \neq D_{BM} \neq D_{CM}$, etc., must be calculated separately. Hereafter a second approximation would consist of repeating the computation cycle. Usually the first approximation will be sufficient, in particular when the values of Φ are close to 1. More information on multi-component diffusion may be found in literature[1,10,12].

DIFFUSION IN LIQUIDS

Present understanding of diffusion in liquids is far from satisfactory, and reliable estimates of diffusion coefficients are possible only for self-diffusion and for very dilute binary mixtures. No methods are available for predicting the behaviour of multicomponent systems or the concentration dependence of binary diffusivities. This situation results in large part from the lack of a usable kinetic theory of liquids and consequent dependence on simplified physical models. In spite of this, the same formulae and terms as given for diffusion in the gas-phase are applied to diffusion in the liquid phase.

5.1.3 Mass Transfer Concept

GENERAL

The molecules to be absorbed encounter three mass-transfer resistances: the gas phase resistance, the resistance of the interface and the liquid-side resistance. A basic tool for the design and analysis of interphase mass-transfer in gas-absorption is the concept of additivity of the gas-phase resistance and the liquid-phase resistance, assuming that the interfacial resistance can be neglected. This conception, originally stated by Lewis and Whitman[13] as the 'two-film theory', leads to an expression which will enable us to calculate 'point-values' of the rate of absorption

$$N_A = k_g(C_g^o - C_g^i) = \phi . k_l(C_l^i - C_l^o) = \frac{\gamma . C_g^o - C_l^o}{\dfrac{\gamma}{k_g} + \dfrac{1}{\phi . k_l}} \qquad (5.24)$$

The solubility of the component to be absorbed is defined by factor $\gamma = C_l^i/C_g^i$, while factor ϕ is the so-called 'chemical acceleration factor' which takes into account the influence of a chemical reaction between the component to be absorbed and a reactant already present in the absorbing liquid. (For physical absorption $\phi = 1$, for chemical absorption $\phi > 1$; note that ϕ is never smaller than 1.)

As can be seen from equation (5.24), the individual mass-transfer coefficients (k_g and $\phi . k_l$) are defined in terms of mass fluxes and driving forces. The theory expressed in this equation is simple; however, in any realistic mass-transfer device there will be local and time dependent, often stochastic, variations in γ, k_g, ϕ, k_l and the concentrations. Such behaviour is predicted both by the penetration theory, the surface renewal theory and by boundary-layer theories.

Consequently the two-film equation for the addition of individual phase resistances will be subject to several stringent conditions: γ and ϕ must be constants, there must be no significant resistance present other than those represented by k_g and $\phi . k_l$, the individual phase resistances of gas and liquid must not interact[14]. Although the physical base of the 'two-film theory', using additive mass-transfer resistances is not correct, it still is the main tool in solving technical absorption problems.

The use of mass-transfer coefficients is in fact derived from the basic knowledge about diffusion. If we compare equation (5.24) with equation (5.10) it follows that for the case of diffusion of one component through an inert multicomponent mixture the value of k_g can be given as:

$$k_g = \frac{D_{AM}}{z_g} \frac{C_t}{(C_{\text{inert}})_{lm}} = \frac{D_{AM}}{z_g} . \frac{P}{RT(p_{\text{inert}})_{lm}} \qquad (5.25)$$

For the case of equimolar counterdiffusion this leads to:

$$k_g = \frac{D_{AB}}{z_g} \qquad (5.26)$$

Similar equations can be written for the liquid side transfer coefficient k_l. Apart from conditions on constancy of D, z_g and C_t it follows from equation

(5.25) that for a given absorption tower the values of k_g and k_l are not constants along the absorption path as $(C_{inert})_{lm}$ will change from one place to another. But, as we are dealing with gas purification (low concentrations), the assumption that k_g and k_l are constants along the total tower length is correct. The film thickness z and various other factors are rarely known, so it is common practice to correlate measured values of k_g and k_l in a logical way with physical (diffusivity, density, viscosity, etc.); hydrodynamic (flow rate of liquid and gas load) and geometric (scale of equipment, size of packing material, etc.) factors.

In most cases the correlations are given as a relationship between the Sherwood-number and the Reynolds and Schmidt numbers:

$$(Sh) = \text{const } (1) + \text{const } (2) \times (Re)^n (Sc)^m \tag{5.27}$$

Many of these relations, in most cases dealing with very specific and non-technical circumstances, will be found in the literature; a critical survey on packed towers has recently been given by Semmelbauer[15].

INTERFACIAL RESISTANCE

Resistance on the interface itself is still a controversial point. According to some investigators[16-20] interfacial resistance could be the reason for rather low rates of absorption in some cases. Others[21-23] have pointed out that only in the case of very high absorption rates or very low gas-pressure will this resistance be a determining factor in gas-absorption. For most common situations we can assume that the resistance of the interface may be neglected so that there is physical equilibrium between gas and liquid.

This may be expressed with the equations:

$$\frac{C_l^i}{C_g^i} = \gamma \qquad \text{according to Oswald, or} \tag{5.28}$$

$$\frac{C_l^i}{p_g^i} = H_e \qquad \text{according to Henry.} \tag{5.29}$$

When the gas-phase may be assumed to behave as an ideal gas then it follows

$$\gamma = H_e . RT \tag{5.30}$$

The value of the solubility coefficient is a very important factor in gas-absorption. Two factors may greatly influence the solubility: temperature and ionic strength. In general the solubility will decrease with increasing temperature (T_{abs}) and increasing ionic strength (I) of the solution:

$$H_e \sim \exp\left(\frac{\text{const}}{T_{abs}}\right),$$

$$H_e \sim \exp(-\text{const} \times I).$$

The numerical value of the solubility determines to a great extent whether the resistance of the gas-phase is of any importance. For a quick estimate the next formula, derived from the penetration-theory concept, is recommended

$$\frac{\text{rate of absorption without gas-phase resistance}}{\text{rate of absorption with gas-phase resistance}} = 1 + H_e.RT\left(\frac{D_l}{D_g}\right)^{1/2} \qquad (5.31)$$

MASS TRANSFER AT THE LIQUID SIDE

The rate of mass-transfer in practically all gas–liquid contacting systems is controlled by the liquid phase resistance. Theories based on three distinct hypotheses about the behaviour of the liquid will be considered in short for the case of physical absorption.

(a) Whitman film model

This model was proposed by Whitman[24] in 1923 in analogy with heat-transfer concepts. The liquid at the surface is assumed to be in laminar flow parallel to the surface, while liquid below the film boundary is in turbulent motion. The rate of absorption is determined mainly by molecular diffusion in the surface layer ('liquid film'). Although the relative importance of transport by molecular diffusion and by turbulence will presumably vary continuously with depth below the gas–liquid interphase, it is convenient to take as a model a completely stagnant layer of effective thickness z_l, overlying liquid of uniform composition. The film thickness is assumed to be so small that the absorption process can be treated as a process of steady-state diffusion through the stagnant 'film'. The liquid-film transfer coefficient is defined by

$$N_A = k_l(C_l^i - C_l^o) = \frac{D_l}{z_l}(C_l^i - C_l^o) \qquad (5.32)$$

(b) Higbie systematic surface renewal (penetration theory)

In 1935 Higbie[19] proposed a model that was derived from the concept of unsteady transfer of heat by conduction as stated by Fourier (though in 1877 von Wroblewski[25] was the first to apply this concept experimentally for the case of gas-absorption). Higbie pointed out that this theory could be used in solving industrial gas-absorption problems.

In this theory each element of liquid surface is assumed to be exposed to the gas for the same length of time and to absorb gas during this time at the same changing rate as though it were a stagnant layer of infinite depth. The mean liquid-side mass transfer coefficient is defined by:

$$N_A = k_l(C_l^i - C_l^o) = 2\left(\frac{D_l}{\pi.\tau}\right)^{\frac{1}{2}}(C_l^i - C_l^o) \qquad (5.33)$$

Note that k_l is defined here as the mean value of the mass transfer coefficient during the time interval from $t = 0$ up to $t = \tau$, while the time dependent value of k_l is given by:

$$(k_l)_t = \left(\frac{D_l}{\pi.t}\right)^{\frac{1}{2}}$$

This concept of mass-transfer has been proven by numerous experiments.

(c) Danckwerts' random surface renewal

This model was described by Danckwerts in 1951[26], the paper in which it was presented belongs to the classics in mass-transfer. Like in Higbie's model it is assumed that all elements of liquid are behaving as stagnant layers of infinite depth during the time of exposure to the gas. A further, and crucial assumption is that there is no correlation between the time for which an element of surface has been exposed and its chance of being remixed. Instead of the exposure time τ now the rate of surface renewal s is introduced. This very sound physical theory leads to the following expression for k_l:

$$N_A = k_l(C_l^i - C_l^o) = (D_l.s)^{\frac{1}{2}}(C_l^i - C_l^o) \qquad (5.34)$$

The physical significance given to k_l is different in each of these three models as can be seen from Figure 5.3. Other models of mass-transfer, for instance Kishinevsky's 'effective diffusion model'[27] and Toor and Marchello's 'film-penetration model'[28], will not be described here.

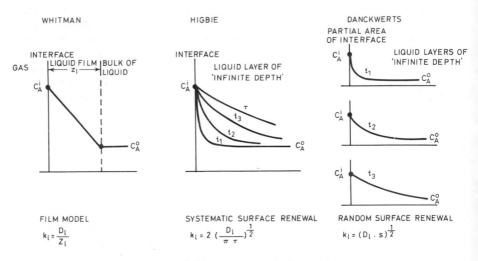

Figure 5.3 Mass transfer at the liquid side

All three models lead to the same prediction concerning the effect of the driving force on the absorption rate. The models of Higbie and Danckwerts, which are more in accordance with physical reality, predict that k_l is proportional to $\sqrt{D_l}$, which agrees well with many observations. Apart from this it may be stressed that each model contains an empirical constant: effective film thickness z_l (Whitman); effective exposure time τ (Higbie); effective rate of surface renewal (Danckwerts); effective coefficient of diffusion (Kishinevsky).

Consequently, when predicting the rate of absorption in the case of purely physical absorption under technical conditions, the more refined models give no better results than the empirical mass-transfer coefficient as defined by

Lewis and Whitman. Nevertheless, the more refined theories are valuable tools in solving complex problems in which chemical absorption is important.

ABSORPTION WITH CHEMICAL REACTION

Although most publications dealing with absorption accompanied by chemical reaction are theoretical, many can be used to predict the rate of absorption of a chemical absorption process starting from knowledge on the microkinetics of the reaction and the rate of physical absorption in the apparatus to be used[24-39].

The main purpose of chemical absorption in gas purification is to enlarge the capacity of the liquid. Important papers concerning fundamentals of chemical absorption are summarized as follows:

Reaction order	Film model Steady conditions	Penetration model Unsteady conditions
First order	Hatta[29] 1935	Danckwerts[30] 1950
Second order	van Krevelen, Hoftyzer[31] 1948	Pigford[32] 1953 Brian, Hurley, Hasseltine[33] 1961
General order		Brian [34] 1964, Astarita[35] 1967

The type of chemical system which has received most attention is that in which the dissolved gas (component A) undergoes an irreversible second-order reaction with a reactant (component B) dissolved in the liquid, Figure 5.4.

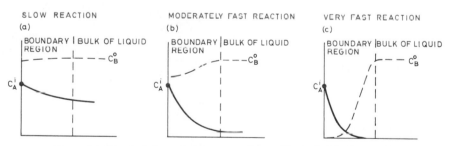

Figure 5.4 Chemical absorption–concentration profiles in the boundary region

Figure 5.4a refers to the case where the reaction between A and B is relatively slow. Most of the conversion takes place in the bulk of the liquid, and the drop in concentration of A over the boundary region is mainly due to diffusional resistance. Should the ratio of bulk volume and interfacial area be increased, the concentration drop of A would become greater since more A would have to be supplied per unit area for the reaction proceeding in the main body of the reaction phase.

Figure 5.4b gives the concentration profile for a moderately high chemical reaction velocity. Here, a great deal of A is already converted within the boundary layer; this can be seen from the concentration distribution of B which has to be supplied by diffusion from the bulk of the liquid. In this case the surface area of the interface has become more important for the total conversion rate relative to the volume of the reaction phase. Finally, profiles shown in Figure 5.4 will be found when the reaction is very fast, i.e. it occurs entirely within the boundary layer in a rather narrow reaction zone towards which A and B have to be transported. The total conversion rate is proportional to the interfacial area. The position of the small reaction zone depends on the ratio C_B^o/C_A^i.

Three important parameters play a role in mass-trasnfer with a reaction between A and B. These are:

    (i) the ratio of surface to liquid volume of the reaction phase;
    (ii) the ratio of chemical reaction velocity and maximum mass-transfer rate;
    (iii) the ratio C_B^o/C_A^i

As a chemical reaction may accelerate the rate of absorption we are interested in the numerical value of ϕ, the 'chemical acceleration factor'. In many cases the chemical reaction is irreversible and of second order.

The stoichiometric reaction equation is defined by:

$$A + \theta.B \rightarrow C.$$

Microkinetics are given by

$$\frac{dC_A}{dt} = -k_{AB}.C_A.C_B \tag{5.35}$$

Further assumptions are that the concentration of reactant in the bulk of the solution is C_B^o and the concentration at the interface of the component to be absorbed is C_A^i. Studies by van Krevelen and Hoftyzer[31] led to the conclusion that factor ϕ can be expressed as a function of two dimensionless parameters:

$$Ha = \frac{(k_{AB}.D_A.C_B^o)^{\frac{1}{2}}}{(k_l)_{\text{physical}}}, \tag{5.36}$$

the Hatta-number and

$$Z = \theta \frac{D_A.C_A^i}{D_B.C_B^o}, \tag{5.37}$$

the concentration–diffusion parameter,

in which D_A and D_B are the coefficients of diffusion in the liquid.

The relation between ϕ, Ha and Z is given in Figure 5.5, and is mathematically expressed by:

$$\phi = \frac{Ha\{1-(\phi-1)Z\}^{\frac{1}{2}}}{\tanh\left[Ha\{1-(\phi-1)Z\}^{\frac{1}{2}}\right]} \tag{5.38}$$

Although these results are based on an approximate solution to the film theory, Figure 5.6, their accuracy was demonstrated by Peaceman[36], while more refined solutions for this case, based on the penetration theory[32,33] confirm the usefulness of the van Krevelen–Hoftyzer graph. A theoretical study by Brian[34] leads to the conclusion that even for reactions of general order Figure 5.5 will give reasonably correct values for ϕ in many more

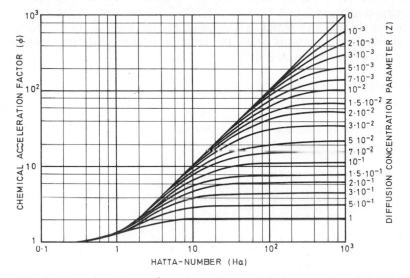

Figure 5.5 The chemical acceleration factor ϕ as a function of the Hatta number and the diffusion-concentration parameter. (After van Krevelen and Hoftyzer[31])

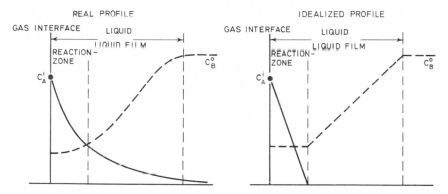

Figure 5.6 The basic model of van Krevelen and Hoftyzer for chemical absorption

complicated cases. For the case that the kinetics of the reaction are of general order

$$\frac{dC_A}{dt} = -k_{AB} \cdot C_A^n \cdot C_B^m \tag{5.39}$$

it has been shown by Brian that the 'chemical acceleration factor' ϕ is a function of the factor Z and a generalized definition of the Hatta-number

$$Ha = \frac{\{2/(n+1)k_{AB}(C_B^o)^m(C_A^i)^{n-1}D_A\}^{\frac{1}{2}}}{(k_l)_{\text{physical}}} \tag{5.40}$$

When the concentration of B varies negligibly throughout the liquid phase species A will undergo a pseudo nth-order reaction and for small values of Z it is permitted to use the van Krevelen–Hoftyzer graph for reaction orders in A ranging from 0 to 3.

In conclusion, two simple expressions for the rate of absorption in the many common situations where the reaction is of second order (first order in A and first order in B) are

(a) Relatively rapid reaction

$$N_A = C_A^i (k_{AB} C_B^o D_A)^{\frac{1}{2}} \tag{5.41}$$

This equation is valid for practical purposes when $\phi > 2$ and $Z < (0 \cdot 1/\phi)$. Note that N_A is independent of $(k_l)_{\text{physical}}$.

(b) Infinitely fast reaction

In this extreme case the reaction takes place in a plane parallel to the interface.
The rate of absorption is given by:

$$N_A = C_A^i \cdot (k_l)_{\text{physical}} \left\{ 1 + \frac{1}{Z} \right\} \tag{5.42}$$

This equation is valid when $\phi > (10/Z)$.

Most of the studies of simultaneous mass transfer and chemical reaction have been developed for simple reaction mechanisms. In practice the mechanisms of simultaneous chemical reactions are complex, as in various commercially important absorption systems, such as the absorption of H_2S in amine or alkali solutions; absorption and partial hydrolysis of SO_2 in water; absorption of CO_2 in activated potassium carbonate solutions; absorption of nitrous oxides in water, see Chapter 5B. The rate of absorption in these cases cannot be expressed by simple equations, but is represented by complex functions of the concentration of the dissolved gas at the interface and the concentration of the reactants in the bulk of the liquid[37-39].

EXPERIMENTAL INVESTIGATION OF MASS TRANSFER

In the foregoing it was shown that the theoretical fundamentals of gas absorption are well developed. In many cases of practical absorption problems, however, there is a lack of principal data, such as the mechanism of absorption accompanied by chemical reaction; the key components that are being transferred; the magnitude of the reaction rate constant; the value of the diffusivity coefficient in the liquid; the question whether the absorption is controlled by the liquid phase or by the gas film, etc. Very often these data can be obtained by simple experimental investigation on laboratory scale. Various devices have been introduced in the past and have proven their practical utility. Some of them are: the laminar jet[40-45]; the wetted wall column[22,46]; the stirred cell[47,48]; the standard disc-tower[49]; the small scale packed tower; the small scale plate column; the stirred gas–liquid contactor; and the rotating drum[18,20], Figure 5.7. The laminar jet, wetted wall column and the stirred cell, are very useful in investigation of gas absorption as with these devices the interfacial area is known with great

	LAMINAR JET	WETTED-WALL COLUMN	STIRRED CELL	STANDARD DISC TOWER	ROTATING DRUM	STIRRED GAS-LIQUID CONTACTOR
TIME OF EXPOSURE OF FRESH LIQUID ELEMENTS TO GAS (MILLI-SECONDS)	1-100	100-2 000	1 500-10 000	100-2 000	0.2-100	50-2 000
EFFECTIVE INTERFACIAL AREA	KNOWN WITH HIGH PRECISION	KNOWN WITH HIGH PRECISION	KNOWN WITH PRECISION	KNOWN WITH MODERATE PRECISION	KNOWN WITH HIGH PRECISION	NOT KNOWN ACCURATELY

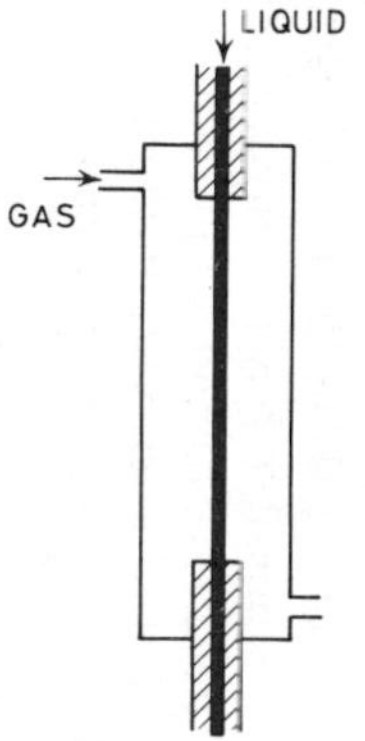

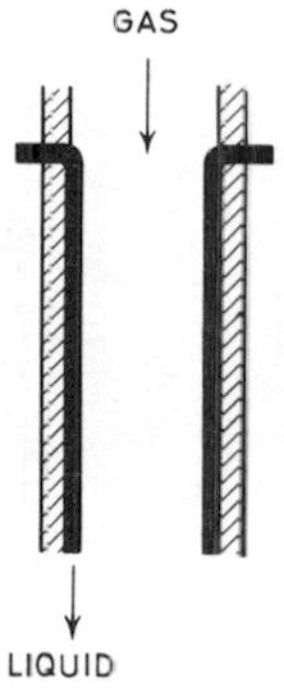

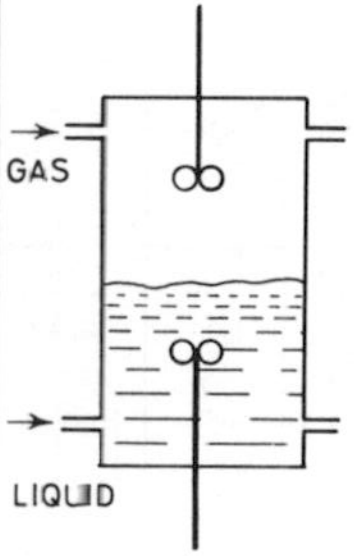

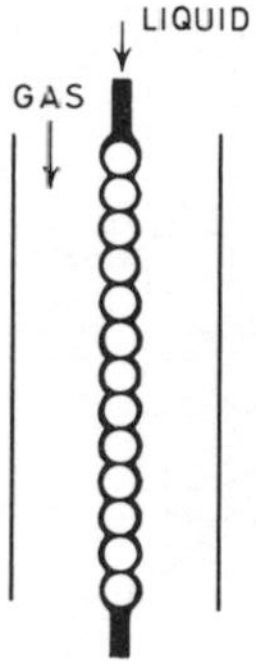

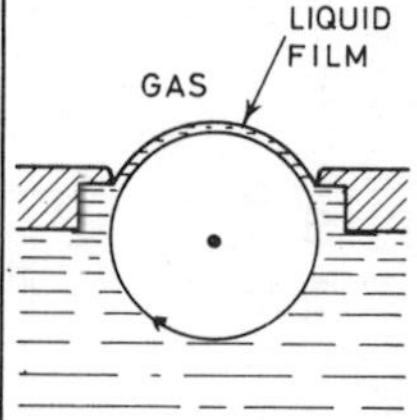

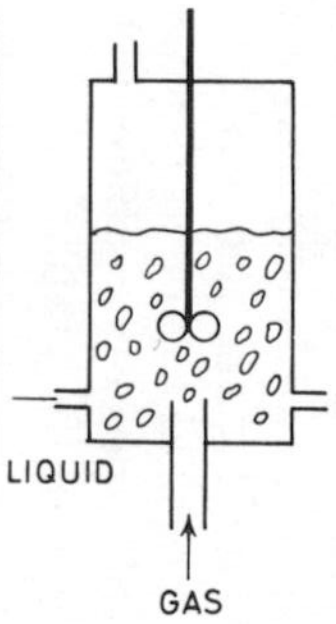

Figure 5.7 Experimental investigation of gas absorption on the laboratory scale

accuracy. The physical exact penetration theory can be applied directly to the wetted wall column and the laminar jet, as it is very easy with these devices to vary the time of exposure of the liquid to the gas.

When the absorption is purely physical a plot of the rate of absorption against the square root of time of exposure enables us to calculate the coefficient of diffusion from the slope of the graph.

When we have to deal with chemical absorption a plot of the rate of absorption against the exposition time will lead to a direct determination of the constants $(k_{AB}.D_A)^{\frac{1}{2}}$ and k_{AB}, the reaction rate constant for chemical reactions with a first order or a pseudo first order reaction mechanism, Figure 5.8.

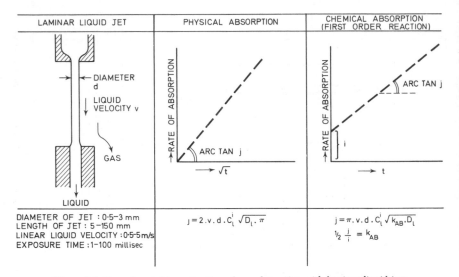

Figure 5.8 Experimental investigation of gas absorption with laminar liquid jets

The authors consider that the laminar jet, introduced in 1930 by Dirken and Mook[40], and the stirred cell, introduced by Whitman and Davis[47] in 1924, are still the most powerful tools to be used when investigating the fundamental principles of complex absorption systems. Scaling up gas absorption processes from the laboratory scale to the full industrial scale (a factor of 10^4–10^5 for the gas-load), is possible but can involve large errors. In order to reduce these errors it is necessary to understand both the physical and chemical aspects of the absorption process both on the laboratory scale and on the full scale. For more information on this the reader is referred to a paper by Andrew[50].

5.2 Mass Transfer Calculation of Gas Absorption Towers

5.2.1 Operating Line and Equilibrium Line

In *packed towers*, used for gas absorption, gas and liquid are in continuous contact throughout the tower. The two streams, contacting each other, will not reach equilibrium, and the point to point relationship between co-existing gas and liquid concentrations of the two streams is extremely important in establishing driving forces that determine the rate of mass transfer. This is in direct contrast to *stage contactors*, where gas and liquid are brought together, interact and then separate: the two streams leaving the 'ideal stage' approach equilibrium. The relationship between the phase concentrations throughout the tower is the *operating line* which is established by a mass balance.

The relation between the phase concentrations under conditions of equilibrium is represented in Figure 5.9 as the so-called *equilibrium line*. Taking

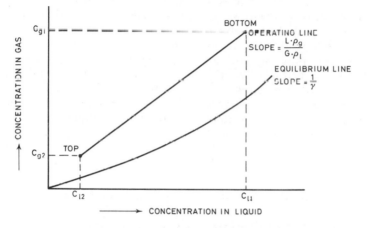

Figure 5.9 Operating line and equilibrium line

a material balance on the component to be absorbed from the bottom of the tower, concentrations C_{g_1} and C_{l_1}, to any plane, where the concentrations are C_g and C_l, and assuming G, L, ρ_g and ρ_l to be constant, we have for unit area of cross section

$$C_g = C_{g_1} - \frac{L \cdot \rho_g}{G \cdot \rho_l}(C_{l_1} - C_l) \tag{5.43}$$

If G, L, ρ_g and ρ_l are constants throughout the column, which will be the case in many gas absorption processes, this is the equation of a straight line, which passes through the points C_{g_1}, C_{l_1} (bottom of the column) and C_{g_2}, C_{l_2} (top of the column).

With packed towers (continuous contact) every point on the operating line has a physical meaning. With tray towers (discontinuous contact) the operating line has significance only with respect to stream compositions to or from a particular tray.

In general L, G, ρ_l and ρ_g are not constants throughout the tower, thus the operating line is not a straight line. In such cases we will not refer the concentrations to the variable quantities ρ_g, G and ρ_l, L. When the fluids contain inert components, the mass flow of these becomes a convenient reference quantity.

In most cases the use of concentration ratios (mass, molar or volumetric) referring to the flow of inert components allows us to set up a simple and correct balance of the tower, resulting in a straight operating line. In cases where the fluids do not contain inert components, but where the mass exchange is equimolar, i.e. the molar flow from phase A to phase B equals the flow from phase B to phase A, the total number of moles in the flows serves as constant reference quantity. We see, that if we want to balance an absorption tower by an operating line of the linear type given above, we cannot avoid the application of different expressions for the concentration. The equilibrium line is, in contrast with the operating line, very often curved. Only for the case that Henry's law is strictly valid throughout the tower, will the equilibrium line be straight. In practice this situation is met for moderate concentrations, low partial pressures and not too low temperatures and when the component to be absorbed reacts irreversibly with another component present in the liquid. (Note that in the last case the equilibrium concentration in the gas is zero.) Solubility data will be found in References 4, 5, 6 and 51.

When solving practical problems, drawing a graph with operating and equilibrium lines can be of great help. Operating line and equilibrium line may not touch or cross between top and bottom of the column. In many cases the equilibrium line is more or less fixed beforehand, depending on temperature, composition of liquid, etc., so the only thing we can do is to adjust the operating line by choosing a sound value for the ratio of liquid load to gas load. Very often the choice of the best liquid/gas ratio depends on economic considerations, see Section 5.6.6.

5.2.2 General Mass Transfer Concept and Basic Design Equations

BALANCE EQUATIONS AND MASS TRANSFER EQUATIONS

For a small differential element of mass transfer volume, either in a packed column or in a plate tower, the equations defining mass transfer can be presented in a general way. Let us consider such a small element in a packed tower (Figure 5.10). The gas is flowing upwards while the liquid passes in downwards direction through the tower and some component is being transferred from the gas to the liquid. The concentration of this component will decrease with increasing height of the tower. Under steady conditions the rate of change of mass of the gas phase has to be equal to the rate of change of the liquid mass. Consequently

$$dG = dL \tag{5.44}$$

Also the rate of change of a specific component in the gas phase has to be equal to the rate of change of the same component in the liquid.

$$d\frac{G}{\rho_g}C_g = d\frac{L}{\rho_l}C_l \tag{5.45}$$

As the rate of change of a component within a phase has to be equal to the rate of transfer to or from the phase, the basic design equations for a small element of tower volume, height dh, can be denoted by the equations

$$d\frac{G}{\rho_g}C_g = -d(N_A.a_e.h) \tag{5.46}$$

$$d\frac{L}{\rho_l}C_l = -d(N_A.a_e.h) \tag{5.47}$$

N_A may be replaced by one of the various expressions in use for calculation of the mass transfer flux.

By making use of film coefficients this leads to:

$$\mathrm{d}\,\frac{G}{\rho_g}C_g = -\mathrm{d}\{k_{mg}.a_e(C_g^o - C_g^i)h\} \qquad (5.48)$$

and

$$\mathrm{d}\,\frac{L}{\rho_l}C_l = -\mathrm{d}\{\phi.k_{ml}.a_e(C_l^i - C_l^o)h\} \qquad (5.49)$$

In these equations k_m is a generalized partial mass transfer coefficient for physical absorption, while a_e is the effective area for mass transfer per unit of volume.

In many cases of gas purification, L, G, ρ_l, ρ_g, k_m, ϕ and a_e may be taken as constants throughout the tower and thus may be put before the differential symbol. When this is not the case the computation can become complicated, a difficulty that nowadays can be overcome by using computers. So far the given equations are meant for countercurrent flow of gas and liquid.

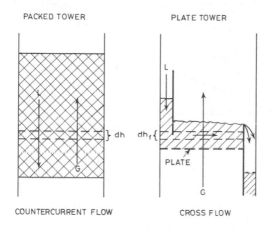

Figure 5.10 Differential element of mass transfer volume

In a plate tower, however, we have to deal with a cross flow pattern on the plates, see Figure 5.10. For a small element of gas–liquid dispersion on the plates the rate of change of the gas concentration in the vertical direction is related to the mass transfer to the liquid by

$$\frac{\pi}{4}.\frac{D_c^2}{A_b}\mathrm{d}\,\frac{G}{\rho_g}C_g = -\mathrm{d}(N_A.a_e.h_f) \qquad (5.50)$$

in which D_c is the column diameter, A_b the bubbling area and h_f the height of the gas–liquid dispersion on the plate.

The rate of change of the liquid concentration in relation to the transfer of mass is approximately given by:

$$\frac{\pi}{4}.\frac{D_c^2}{h_f.l_T}\mathrm{d}\,\frac{L}{\rho_l}C_l = \mathrm{d}(N_A.a_e.l) \qquad (5.51)$$

In this equation l_T is the average width of the tray in a direction perpendicular to the direction of liquid flow on the plate and l is the length of the tray parallel to the direction of liquid flow. (Various other forms of the equations for plates are possible, depending on the liquid flow pattern that results from the plate construction.)

In equations (5.48) and (5.49) the driving forces are expressed as concentration differences between the interface and the bulk of the liquid or gas. Several other ways of expression are possible, see Figure 5.11.

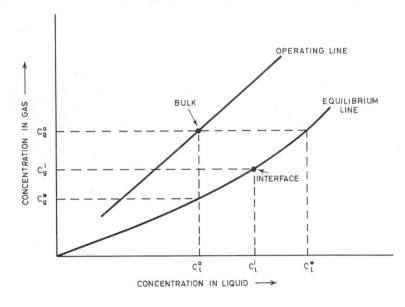

Figure 5.11 *Driving forces*

Based on the partial real driving forces the absorption flux is expressed by:

$$N_A = k_{mg}(C_g^o - C_g^i) = \phi . k_{ml}(C_l^i - C_l^o) \tag{5.52}$$

while the absorption flux based on the overall fictitious driving forces is defined by:

$$N_A = K_g(C_g^o - C_g^*) = K_l(C_l^* - C_l^o) \tag{5.53}$$

Concentrations, marked by an asterisk, are fictitious equilibrium concentrations, i.e. a gas-concentration assumed to be in equilibrium with the liquid bulk or a liquid concentration assumed to be in equilibrium with the gas bulk.

$$C_g^* = \frac{C_l^o}{\gamma} = \frac{C_l^o}{H_e . RT} \tag{5.54}$$

$$C_l^* = \gamma . C_g^o = H_e . RT . C_g^o \tag{5.55}$$

From equations (5.52) to (5.55) the following relations between partial

Table 5.1 DRIVING FORCE AND MASS TRANSFER COEFFICIENT

Driving force		Mass transfer coefficients k_{mg} and k_{ml}			
Expression for driving force	Units of driving force	Equimolar counter diffusion	Transfer of one component through an inert mixture	Multicomponent mass transfer	Units of mass transfer coefficient
$C_g^o - C_g^i$	kmole/m³	k_g	$k_g \dfrac{C_t}{(C_{\text{inert}})_{lm}}$	$\dfrac{k_g}{f_g}$	m/s
$p_g^o - p_g^i$	bar	$\dfrac{k_g}{RT}$	$\dfrac{k_g}{RT} \cdot \dfrac{P}{(p_{\text{inert}})_{lm}}$	$\dfrac{k_g}{f_g \cdot RT}$	kmole/m² s bar
$y^o - y^i$	mole fraction	$\dfrac{k_g P}{RT}$	$\dfrac{k_g}{RT} \cdot \dfrac{P}{(y_{\text{inert}})_{lm}}$	$\dfrac{k_g \cdot P}{f_g \cdot RT}$	kmole/m² s
$C_l^i - C_l^o$	kmole/m³	k_l	$k_l \dfrac{C_t}{(C_{\text{inert}})_{lm}}$	$\dfrac{k_l}{f_l}$	m/s
$x^i - x^o$	mole fraction	$k_l \dfrac{\bar\rho_l}{M_l}$	$k_l \dfrac{\bar\rho_l}{M_l} \cdot \dfrac{1}{(x_{\text{inert}})_{lm}}$	$k_l \cdot \dfrac{\bar\rho_l}{M_l} \cdot \dfrac{1}{f_l}$	kmole/m² s

transfer coefficients (k_{mg} and $\phi.k_{ml}$) and the overall mass transfer coefficients (K_g, K_l) can be derived:

$$\frac{1}{K_g} = \frac{1}{k_{mg}} + \frac{1}{\gamma.\phi.k_{ml}} \tag{5.56}$$

$$\frac{1}{K_l} = \frac{1}{\phi.k_{ml}} + \frac{\gamma}{k_{mg}} \tag{5.57}$$

In deriving these equations use is made of the fact, see Figure 5.11, that for relatively small changes in concentration the following holds:

$$\gamma \approx \frac{C_l^i - C_l^o}{C_g^i - C_g^*} \approx \frac{C_l^* - C_l^i}{C_g^o - C_g^i} \tag{5.58}$$

Until the late 1960s the precise definitions of the generalized partial mass transfer coefficients k_{mg} and k_{ml} remained somewhat vague; they were presented as simple proportionality constants between mass flux and driving force. Various rather different expressions of mass transfer are possible: equimolar transfer, transfer of one component through an inert multicomponent mixture, multicomponent transfer in various directions and multicomponent mass transfer at high mass transfer rates. Besides this, the fact that the driving force can be expressed in various units, such as molar concentration (kgmole/m^3), partial pressure (bar), mole fraction (kgmole/kgmole total) or mole ratios (kgmole/kgmole inert), leads to a number of ways in which the basic equations of mass transfer can be expressed, see Table 5.1

For the case of multicomponent transfer factors f_g and f_l are introduced in accordance with the theory given in paragraph 5.1.2, bearing in mind that for the gas phase the relations between mole fraction, concentration and partial pressure are given by

$$y = \frac{C_g}{C_{tg}} = \frac{p}{P} \tag{5.59}$$

while for the liquid phase the relation between mole fraction and concentration follows from

$$x = \frac{C_l}{C_{tl}} \tag{5.60}$$

The multicomponent mass transfer factors are defined by the equations:

$$f_g = -\left(\frac{y^o}{\Phi} - \frac{y^i}{\Phi}\right) \ln\left\{\frac{1-(y^o/\Phi)}{1-(y^i/\Phi)}\right\}^{-1} \tag{5.61}$$

$$f_l = -\left(\frac{x^i}{\Phi} - \frac{x^o}{\Phi}\right) \ln\left\{\frac{1-(x^i/\Phi)}{1-(x^o/\Phi)}\right\}^{-1} \tag{5.62}$$

The mass flux ratios Φ, specific for each component, are defined by:

$$\Phi_A = \frac{N_A}{N_t}, \ \Phi_B = \frac{N_B}{N_t}, \ \text{etc.,}$$

while the total mass flux follows from:

$$N_t = N_A + N_B + N_C + \ldots + N_N$$

The expressions for the overall mass transfer coefficients may become very complex, because in the expressions for K_g and K_l the quantities $C_t/[(C_{inert})_{lm}], f$ and γ appear, which cannot be determined without knowing the conditions at the interface. Thus the mass transfer coefficients K_g and K_l, which are most commonly used, remain somewhat indefinite. By replacing $C_t/[(C_{inert})_{lm}]$ and f by the extreme values $(C_t/C_{inert})_{bulk}$ and $f = 1$, we obtain some approximation at the cost of accuracy, which may lead sometimes to large errors.

Owing to the presence of the terms $(C_{inert})_{lm}$ and f, the coefficients K_g and K_l often vary much along the path of the gas flow through the tower. If, for example, we want to absorb a large amount of some component from a gas stream, the partial pressure of the inert components at the top of the column may be many times higher than its pressure at the bottom.

In the case of multicomponent absorption f is only approximately equal to 1 for low concentrations of the components to be absorbed. These facts are not stressed strongly enough in literature and even escape our attention in many cases owing to the notation K_g and K_l. When one uses data taken from the literature it is therefore necessary to be critical. In most cases the values given for K_g, K_l, k_g and k_l are values found at very low concentrations and for vanishing small mass transfer rates, when $C_t/(C_{inert})_{lm}$ is approximately constant over the tower length or even equal to 1, and f is approximately equal to 1, i.e. the absorption of one component in a multicomponent mixture is not influenced by the simultaneous absorption of other components. At high concentrations and for high mass transfer rates such data cannot be used directly but require some correction. So in the case of absorption of one component from an inert mixture one has to take account of the logarithmic mean concentration difference of the inert components.

In multicomponent absorption problems, especially at high mass transfer rates, one must take account of the fact that the total flow of gas into the absorbing liquid can be many times the rate of absorption of one specific component by diffusion alone[10,52]. Computation of the correction factors $C_t/(C_{inert})_{lm}$ and f may be performed by proceeding with some sort of trial and error method. For instance in the case of multicomponent gas absorption at high mass transfer rates one could start by calculation of the various approximate overall mass transfer coefficients K_g from

$$\frac{1}{K_g} = \frac{1}{k_{mg}} + \frac{1}{\gamma . \phi . k_{ml}}$$

assuming tentatively that k_{mg}, ϕ and k_{ml} may be taken as the limiting values (k_g, k_l) for small mass transfer rates. After this one proceeds by calculation of the various absorption fluxes from

$$N_A = K_g(C_g^o - C_g^*).$$

Now that the approximate values of N_A, N_B, N_C, etc., are known (bearing in mind that the fluxes are vectors: positive when the flux is directed into the absorbing liquid and negative when the flux is directed out of the absorbing liquid) we are able to calculate the approximate value of the total flux, N_t, absorbed by the liquid. Thus the approximate concentrations of the various species at the phase boundary, C_g^i and C_l^i, are calculated from:

$$\gamma = \frac{C_l^* - C_l^i}{C_g^o - C_g^i} = \frac{C_l^i}{C_g^i} \quad \text{and} \quad k_{mg}(C_g^o - C_g^i) = \phi . k_{ml}(C_l^i - C_l^o)$$

Next the various approximate ratios of the specific fluxes over the total flux, i.w. Φ_A, Φ_B, Φ_C, etc., are calculated. Insertion of the values for C_g^o, C_g^i, C_l^o, C_l^i and Φ into equations (5.59) to (5.62) leads to the first approximate values for f_g and f_l. Hereafter one proceeds by recalculation of more precise values of the overall mass transfer coefficients from:

$$\frac{1}{K_g} = \frac{f_g}{k_g} + \frac{f_l}{\gamma . \phi . k_l} \tag{5.63}$$

Note that the new values of the partial mass transfer coefficients k_g and k_l are now given by k_g/f_g and k_l/f_l, and that the chemical acceleration factor ϕ depends on the Hatta-number, which does have to contain the corrected value of k_l in the denominator, paragraph 5.1.3. After this we may proceed by repeating the computation cycle, which may be stopped when N_t tends to approach an asymptotic value. Repeated computations of this rather tedious kind preferably have to be computer programmed.

Before treating the actual mass transfer design of absorption towers it is necessary to deal with the information from which the partial mass transfer coefficients k_g and k_l and the effective specific interfacial area a_e can be derived. Though many data are available in the literature, reliable equations for general purpose design are still lacking, partly because many equations are derived from experiments in rather small scale (laboratory, semi-technical) towers. In particular the fact that various ways of expressing the transfer coefficients are in use is a cause of confusion. The following equations from which k_g, k_l and a_e can be calculated will be helpful.

MASS TRANSFER COEFFICIENTS AND SPECIFIC MASS TRANSFER AREA IN PACKED TOWERS

Very often the products $K_g.a_e$ and $K_l.a_e$ are simply correlated with gas load G, liquid load L and the nominal size of the packing material. A large number of correlations of the kind $K_m.a_e = \text{constant} \times G^m.L^n$ can be found in literature[6,53-58]. In most cases these are not applicable for general design.

The object of more recent investigations is:
(a) to determine K_m and a_e separately, and
(b) to obtain general correlations from which the individual coefficients k_g and k_l and the effective interfacial area can be calculated.

The individual mass transfer coefficients are obtained from experiments with systems known to have either a negligible liquid film resistance (e.g., highly soluble gases, ammonia/water system, etc.) or a negligible gas film resistance (e.g., oxygen/water system). Measurement of the effective interfacial area is difficult[51]. The best method of measuring interfacial areas and interphase mass transfer coefficients separately seems to be the 'chemical method'; this is based on the theory of gas absorption accompanied by chemical reaction, section 5.1.3. By suitably choosing the solubility, the concentration of reactant and the rate of reaction, either the interfacial area or the individual mass transfer coefficients can be deduced from the experimental determined overall rate of absorption[59]. The order of magnitude of the various factors in packed columns is as follows:

$$k_g \approx 10^{-3}\text{--}10^{-1} \text{ m/s}$$
$$k_l \approx 10^{-6}\text{--}10^{-4} \text{ m/s}$$
$$a_e \approx 10\text{--}100 \text{ m}^2/\text{m}^3$$

From the many existing correlations on mass transfer in packed towers a limited choice has been made as follows using dimensionless parameters defined in the Notation at the beginning of this chapter.

Gas side mass transfer coefficient k_g

For general purpose the following correlation[15] is recommended:

$$(Sh)_g = \beta.(Re)_g^{0.59}.(Sc)_g^{0.33} \qquad (5.64)$$

in which $\beta = 0.69$ for Raschig rings, and $\beta = 0.86$ for Berl saddles. The equation is valid for $100 < Re_g < 10000$ and $0.01 < d_p$ (metres) < 0.05. The scatter is about 20 per cent.

The dimensionless parameters are defined by:

$$(Sh)_g = \frac{k_g.d_p}{D_g}, \quad (Re)_g = \frac{G.d_p}{\mu_g}, \quad (Sc)_g = \frac{\mu_g}{\rho_g.D_g}$$

The same type of equation was presented earlier by van Krevelen and Hoftyzer[60,61] and used by Hobler[51] for the design of large scale towers.

Liquid side mass transfer coefficient k_l

From the study by Semmelbauer[15], the following equation is put forward:

$$(Sh)_l = \beta.(Re)_l^{0.59}.(Sc)_l^{0.5}.(Ga)^{0.17} \qquad (5.65)$$

Here $\beta = 0.32$ for Raschig rings, and $\beta = 0.25$ for Berl saddles. This equation is valid for:

$$3 < Re_l < 3000 \quad \text{and} \quad 0.01 < d_p \text{(metres)} < 0.05.$$

In the authors' opinion the limits of confidence are about 50 per cent. The various dimensionless parameters are defined as follows:

$$(Sh)_l = \frac{k_l.d_p}{D_l}, \quad (Re)_l = \frac{L.d_p}{\mu_l}, \quad (Sc)_l = \frac{\mu_l}{\rho_l.D_l}, \quad (Ga) = \frac{d_p^3.g.\rho_l}{\mu_l}$$

It will be seen that, in contrast with the correlation for the gas side mass transfer coefficient, the liquid side mass transfer coefficient for Berl saddles is about 30 per cent smaller than for Raschig rings, and furthermore, that the value of the exponent on the Schmidt number is in accordance with the penetration theory and the surface renewal theory; see also reference 62.

It has to be remarked that the equation recommended here, and all other existing equations proposed in the literature, cannot result in very reliable values for the liquid side mass transfer coefficient in large scale towers.

Hence somewhat large safety factors are necessary when designing completely new absorption systems.

Effective interfacial area a_e

In general three kinds of area can be distinguished: dry area, a; wetted area, a_w; effective area for mass transfer, a_e.

Very often the assumption is made that a_e is identical with a_w and that the effective interfacial area for physical absorption is the same as for chemical absorption. The last assumption seems to be a rough one as de Waal and Beek[63] have shown that the interfacial area in the case of chemical absorption can be about 25 per cent greater than for purely physical absorption.

Table 5.2 EFFECTIVE INTERFACIAL AREA IN PACKED TOWERS

Case	Relative area
Dry area of packing	1·0
Wetted area (irrigated)	0·7
Chemical absorption	0·5
Physical absorption (liquid phase controlled)	0·45
Physical absorption (gas phase controlled)	0·4

A sequence of interfacial areas for conditions between the loading point and the flooding point may be encountered in many cases, as shown in Table 5.2. Correlations from which the effective interfacial area may be calculated incorporate large uncertainties, nevertheless one has to rely on them when designing completely new absorption systems.

According to Semmelbauer[15], the effective interfacial area in packed towers follows from:

$$\frac{a_e}{a} = \beta.(Re)_l^{0.46}.(E\ddot{o})^{0.5} \tag{5.66}$$

in which $\beta = 0.0061$ for Raschig rings, and $\beta = 0.0076$ for Berl saddles. The equation is claimed to be valid for water and organic liquids below the flooding point for:

$$1 < Re_l < 1000 \quad \text{and} \quad 0.01 < d_p \text{(metres)} < 0.05,$$

and is to be used in combination with k_g and k_l.

Other limiting conditions are:

$$2.5 < \frac{\text{tower diameter}}{\text{packing diameter}} < 25, \quad \text{and}$$

$$10 < \frac{\text{packing height}}{\text{packing diameter}} < 100.$$

The scatter is about 40 per cent.

The dimensionless numbers are defined by:

$$Re_l = \frac{L.d_p}{\mu_l} \quad \text{and} \quad E\ddot{o} = \frac{d_p^2.\rho_l.g}{\sigma}$$

It follows that for the same conditions and nominal packing size the effective area for Berl saddles is approximately 60 per cent larger than for Raschig rings.

Table 5.3 EFFECTIVE INTERFACIAL AREA IN PACKED TOWERS (PHYSICAL ABSORPTION) AS A FUNCTION OF LIQUID-LOAD

Liquid load, L (kg/m².s)	Effectiveness (%)
0·1	5–15
1	15–30
5	30–60
10	40–70
20	55–85
30	70 90
40	80–100

The higher values are for conditions near the flooding point.

In theory it is possible that equation (5.66) may lead to values for the effectiveness greater than 1; when this is the case it will be sensible to fix the effectiveness by definition equal to some value between 0·8 and 1, but never exceeding 1. In fact the whole problem of effectiveness of interfacial area in packed towers is, in spite of a great deal of information, still very obscure. Teutsch[65] found that for conditions 70 per cent below the flooding point the effectiveness for various sorts of packing material, ranging in size from 25 to 50 mm, was about 30 per cent.

For conditions near the flooding point he found values of approximately 60 per cent effectiveness. In most cases towers are designed about 30 per cent below flooding, so a rule of thumb value seems to be 50 per cent effectiveness for mass transfer. From our own experience with industrial absorbers and from literature, Table 5.3 is presented as a guide for preliminary estimates. The order of magnitude of the various coefficients is shown in Figure 5.12. Recent up-to-date information about mass transfer coefficients and interfacial area in absorbers may be found in the regularly appearing reviews edited by Springe and Schmidt[57].

MASS TRANSFER COEFFICIENTS AND SPECIFIC MASS TRANSFER AREA IN PLATE TOWERS

The order of magnitude of the various coefficients in plate towers is

$k_g \approx 10^{-2}–10^{-1}$ m/s;

$k_l \approx 10^{-4}–10^{-3}$ m/s;

$a_e \approx 50–300$ m²/m³   (related to the volume of gas liquid dispersion);

$a_e^* \approx 5–50$ m²/m²   (related to the bubbling area of the plate).

In most cases the methods of measurement and the ways of correlation are identical to those mentioned for packed towers. It should be noted that for plates the whole interfacial area is active and furthermore that the range of

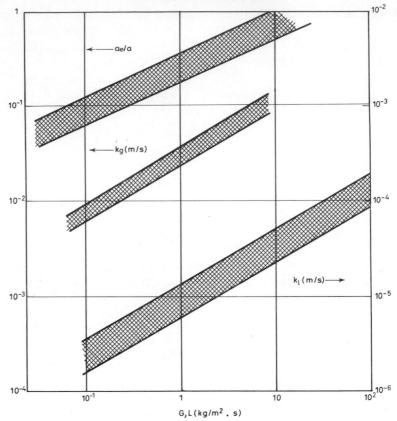

*Figure 5.12 Mass transfer coefficients and interfacial area in packed towers
(carbon dioxide–air–water, 25°C, 1 bar, 25 mm Raschig rings)*

the various coefficients is smaller for plates than for packing material. It is necessary also to distinguish between two expressions for the gas load: G is the gas load related to the overall area $[(\pi/4)D_c^2]$ of column cross section, while G_b is the value of the gas load related to the bubbling area A_b. The precise value of the ratio G/G_b depends on column construction, in most cases the ratio is approximately equal to 0·75.

Gas-side mass transfer coefficient k_g

In general the gas-side mass transfer coefficient is proportional to the square root of the diffusion coefficient and more or less independent of the liquid load. For bubble cap traps the following simple equation has been put forward by Andrew[66]:

$$k_g \approx 2 \cdot 2 \left(\frac{G_g}{\rho_g}\right)^{\frac{1}{4}} \left(\frac{D_g}{h_s}\right)^{\frac{1}{2}} \tag{5.67}$$

For other kinds of plates we propose tentatively to use $\frac{1}{2}h_f$, half the height of the gas liquid layer on the plate, instead of h_s.

Asano[68,69] put forward equations, in which the various geometrical dimensions of the plate are incorporated. For bubble cap plates he proposes

$$\left(\frac{k_g \cdot b_s}{D_g}\right) = 4\cdot7\left(\frac{\mu_g}{\rho_g \cdot D_g}\right)^{\frac{1}{2}}\left(\frac{w_s \cdot b_s \cdot \rho_g}{\mu_g}\right)^{0\cdot63}\left(\frac{b_s}{h_o + h_d}\right)^{0\cdot60} \tag{5.68}$$

For sieve trays the correlation takes the following form:

$$\left(\frac{k_g \cdot d_h}{D_g}\right) = 1\cdot0\left(\frac{\mu_g}{\rho_g \cdot D_g}\right)^{\frac{1}{2}}\left(\frac{w_h \cdot d_h \cdot \rho_g}{\mu_g}\right)^{\frac{3}{4}}\left(\frac{d_h}{h_l}\right) \tag{5.69}$$

It is interesting to notice that Dytnerskii[70] put forward an equation that correlated at the same time the mass transfer coefficients in gas and liquid and the heat transfer coefficient regardless of the tray type. Regarding the practice of industrial design of new systems it is our opinion that no special preference can be given to any equation. Very often the theoretical background of the correlations is related to some model of the behaviour of the gas liquid dispersion; especially the idea of round gas bubbles flowing upwards in the liquid in a regular pattern is encountered in many studies.

By using the penetration theory it can be deduced that, for a completely stagnant round gas bubble, the value of the gas side mass transfer coefficient follows from

$$\frac{k_g \cdot d_b}{D_g} = \frac{2}{3}\pi^2 \tag{5.70}$$

The hydraulic conditions on large scale plates are far away from the conception of nice round gas bubbles: the bubbles are deformed to a great extent, the gas enclosed in them mixes with the gas from other bubbles and the process is accompanied by liquid spraying and foaming. Consequently equation (5.70) can be used only for an estimation of the limiting lower value of the transfer coefficient.

Liquid side mass transfer coefficient k_l

A great deal of information concerning the liquid-side transfer-coefficient on plates has been published in literature[71-79]. A summation of the effects on k_l shows that k_l seems to be rather independent of the operating conditions, i.e. column height, gas flow rate, bubble diameter and mixing intensity. This fact allows one to assume that for all practical purposes the volumetric transfer coefficient $k_l \cdot a_e$ depends only on the variation of the specific area with the operating conditions. A careful analysis of the experimental evidence, published in the literature mentioned, led us to the conclusion that for the standard case, i.e. absorption of carbon dioxide in an aqueous solution at 25°C and 1 bar, all values of k_l lie within the rather narrow range of 2.10^{-4} to 6.10^{-4} m/s. A rule of thumb value of 4.10^{-4} m/s, for this standard case seems to be a very good first estimate, so it is tentatively suggested that k_l is estimated from the simple equation

$$k_l \approx 8(D_l)^{\frac{1}{2}} \tag{5.71}$$

This result is not unexpected because most plates, regardless of the type, are designed within a rather narrow range of hydrodynamic and aerodynamic conditions, see for instance Smith[80].

The following more complicated equations must be mentioned. For bubble cap trays Andrew[66] gives:

$$k_l \approx 3.5 \left(\frac{G_b}{\rho_g}\right)^{\frac{1}{4}} \left(\frac{D_l}{h_s}\right)^{\frac{1}{2}}$$ (5.72)

When we compare this equation with that given for the gas side transfer it follows that:

$$\frac{k_l}{k_g} \approx 1.6 \left(\frac{D_l}{D_g}\right)^{\frac{1}{2}}$$ (5.73)

For other kinds of plates we propose to insert $\frac{1}{2}h_f$, half the active height of the gas liquid layer on the plate, instead of the slow submergence h_s. Asano[69] proposed two equations, in which the various geometrical dimensions of the plate are incorporated. For bubble cap trays his equation takes the following form:

$$\frac{k_l . b_s}{D_l} = 100 \left(\frac{\mu_l}{\rho_l . D_l}\right)^{\frac{1}{2}} \left(\frac{L . D_c}{\mu_l}\right)^{\frac{1}{2}} \left(\frac{b_s}{h_o + h_d}\right)$$ (5.74)

For sieve trays Asano calculates k_l from the equation

$$\frac{k_l . d_h}{D_l} = 100 \left(\frac{\mu_l}{\rho_l . D_l}\right)^{\frac{1}{2}} \left(\frac{L . D_c}{\mu_l}\right)^{\frac{1}{2}} \left(\frac{d_h}{h_l}\right)$$ (5.75)

From the model of stagnant gas bubbles, diameter d_b, rising upwards into the liquid layer (gas fraction ε_g) it follows by using the penetration theory that:

$$k_l \approx \frac{4}{(3\pi)^{\frac{1}{2}}} \left(\frac{G . D_l}{\rho_g . \varepsilon_g . d_b}\right)^{\frac{1}{2}}$$ (5.76)

Effective interfacial area a_e, a_e^*

The interfacial area on plates is the most important variable in mass transfer calculations of plate towers.

In literature two kinds of mass transfer area may be encountered:
a_e = effective interfacial area per unit of volume of gas liquid dispersion, and
a_e^* = effective interfacial area per unit of bubbling area.

Defining h_f as the effective height of the gas liquid layer on the plate, sometimes called 'foam height', it follows that

$$a_e^* = h_f . a_e$$ (5.77)

For technical columns the values of a_e and a_e^* will be in the following ranges

$$50 < a_e < 300 \text{ m}^2/\text{m}^3 \quad \text{and}$$

$$5 < a_e^* < 50 \text{ m}^2/\text{m}^2.$$

Some higher values, up to 1000 m^2/m^3 for a_e and 1000 m^2/m^2 for a_e^*, have been quoted in the literature. It seems, however, that these larger values have only been obtained in rather small scale laboratory towers.

The most important variable influencing the value of the interfacial area is the gas load. From experimental evidence[71-75,81] it follows that the interfacial area is proportional to the superficial gas velocity raised to a power ranging from 0·2 to 0·8.

Correlations, proposed in literature, are very often rather complicated, while the values of the exponents are given in many cases with an accuracy of three decimals (!), but a direct check on technical plates is seldom attempted. For bubble cap trays Andrew[66] proposed the following simple equation for the interfacial area per unit of bubbling area

$$a_e^* \approx 320 \left(\frac{G_b}{\rho_g}\right)^{\frac{1}{2}} (h_s)^{\frac{2}{6}}$$ (5.78)

Asano[68] put forward two rather complicated equations, in which the constructional factors are incorporated. For bubble cap trays the equation is as follows:

$$a_e^* \approx 7.N_s^{\frac{2}{3}} \left\{\frac{G}{(g.\rho_g.\rho_l.D_s)^{\frac{1}{2}}}\right\}^{0·34} \left(\frac{h_d+h_o}{D_c}\right)^{1·15} \left(\frac{b_s^2.g.\rho_l}{\sigma}\right)^{0·1}$$ (5.79)

Notice that the interfacial area is proportional to the number of slots per bubbling area raised to the $\frac{2}{3}$ power and proportional to the 0·34 power of the gas load. Surface tension seems to have little influence as the power on the Eötvös number is small. For sieve trays the interfacial area per unit of bubbling area follows from:

$$a_e^* \approx 8.N_h^{\frac{2}{3}} \left(\frac{G}{(g.\rho_g.\rho_l.D_c)^{\frac{1}{2}}}\right)^{0·34} \left(\frac{h_l}{D_c}\right)^{1·15} \left(\frac{d_h^2.g.\rho_l}{\sigma}\right)^{0·1}$$ (5.80)

The number of holes per tray is approximately given by:

$$N_h \approx \tfrac{3}{4}\varepsilon_p \left(\frac{D_c}{d_h}\right)^2$$ (5.81)

From equations (5.79) and (5.80) it follows that the most important variables are: gas load, number of holes per bubbling area, tray porosity and hole diameter. Experimental evidence, published by Atroshchenko[82], on the absorption of nitrous oxides in water leads to the conclusion that smaller holes will result in a higher plate efficiency, i.e. tend to produce a larger interfacial area.

The design of most plates is mainly determined by hydraulic conditions, for which the value of the kinetic pressure of the gas is of paramount importance. So from our own experience on large scale technical absorption towers, and sustained by experimental data in literature[72,74,76,83,84], we came to the conclusion that for large industrial plates, regardless of the type, the interfacial area per unit of tray area is given by:

$$a_e^* \approx 30.G^{\frac{1}{2}}.\rho_g^{-\frac{1}{4}}$$ (5.82)

The accuracy is about 30 per cent.

EFFECT OF TEMPERATURE—HEAT EFFECTS

In some absorption processes, the gas being treated or the absorbing liquid may be hot, or there may be an appreciable heat of solution of the gas in the liquid; effects due to large heats of solution or heat of reaction are not likely to be important in gas purification processes, where the proportion of soluble gas in the gas mixture is small.

On the gas side, the effect of temperature on the gas phase coefficient is incorporated mainly in the physical constants μ_g, ρ_g and D_g. The gas phase transfer coefficient thus increases as the temperature is increased. On the liquid side, the effect is more complicated. The mass transfer coefficient increases quite rapidly with increase in temperature. On the other hand, the solubility of gases in liquids decreases with increasing temperature. The liquid temperature also affects the equilibrium partial pressure of the soluble gas, and thus the position of the equilibrium line in the driving force diagram, Figure 5.11. Since higher liquid temperatures correspond to increased equilibrium partial pressures, the effect is to reduce the mean driving force, and so to reduce the rate of absorption.

Further complications are introduced if the absorption is accompanied by chemical reaction between the dissolved gas and some component of the absorbing liquid. Here, the effect of a rise in temperature leads to an increase of the reaction rate, and this increase, together with that in the liquid phase transfer coefficient, may be more than sufficient to outweigh the negative effects mentioned above. Advantage is taken of this fact, for example, in the process developed for the removal of carbon dioxide from synthesis gas by means of hot potassium carbonate solutions. Where the absorbed gas is subsequently to be regenerated, the use of a hot absorbing liquid has other economic advantages, apart from those resulting from the increased rate of absorption. Thus less heating steam is required for the stripping process.

Assuming gas and liquid to be perfectly mixed so far as heat transfer is concerned, the effects of heat of solution Q_S and heat of reaction Q_R on the temperature of gas and liquid may be calculated from

$$\frac{dT}{dh} = \sum \frac{K_g(C_g^o - C_g^*)a_e}{(\pi/4)D_c^2(L.c_L + G.c_G)}(Q_S + Q_R) \tag{5.83}$$

This formula may be used for calculation of the interfacial temperature when the heat of absorption proceeds rather uniformly over the reaction phase, i.e. for rather slow reactions or for small heat effects.

With rapid chemical reactions, the heat production is concentrated near the interface from which appreciable local temperature differences may result. When this is the case equation (5.83) may be used only as a heat balance but may not be used for the calculation of the interfacial temperature. The rise in temperature of the interphase itself during absorption follows from References 85 and 86.

$$\Delta T_i = \frac{Q_S(C_l^i - C_l^o)}{\rho_l.c_L}\left(\frac{D_l}{\alpha}\right)^{\frac{1}{2}} \tag{5.84}$$

to be used for purely physical absorption, and

$$\Delta T_i = \frac{Q_S + Q_R}{\rho_l.c_L}(C_l^i - C_l^o)\frac{4}{\pi}.\frac{D_l}{k_l}\left(\frac{k_{AB}}{\alpha}\right)^{\frac{1}{2}} \tag{5.85}$$

to be used for moderately fast or very fast first order reactions. In some cases the solubility data have to be taken at the precise temperature of the interface, which itself depends on the rate of absorption and thus on the solubility; a problem that can be solved by trial and error.

5.2.3 Methods of Mass Transfer Design for Packed Towers

When designing packed gas absorption towers various methods of calculation may be used, such as integration of balance equations and mass transfer equations, the transfer unit method and the graphical method. In fact, all these different methods are basically identical.

Before an absorption tower can be designed the following information is necessary:
(a) The flow rate of the gas to be purified.
(b) The initial amount of impurity in the gas, and the desired amount at the exit.
(c) The composition and the physical properties of the gas mixture, such as ρ_g, μ_g, D_g, etc., for the conditions of temperature and pressure at which the process is to be operated.
(d) The physical properties of the absorbing liquid, such as ρ_l, μ_l, D_l, σ, etc., and the reaction rate constants when the absorption is accompanied by a chemical reaction.
(e) Equilibrium data, solubility constant H_e or γ, preferably as a function of temperature and liquid composition.

INTEGRATION OF MASS TRANSFER EQUATIONS AND BALANCE EQUATIONS

It is convenient to observe the following sequence of computation:
(a) First we start by setting up a trial mass balance, expressed in concentrations or some other suitable concentration parameter but corresponding to the process involved.
(b) By using equilibrium data $(C_l^i/C_g^i) = \gamma =$ function (temperature, liquid composition, etc.) we may set up in a concentration diagram the equilibrium line. Thereafter the operating line is drawn in the same diagram by using the mass balance equation, which in its simplest form is expressed by

$$\frac{G}{\rho_g}(C_{g_1} - C_{g_2}) = \frac{L}{\rho_l}(C_{l_1} - C_{l_2}) \qquad (5.86)$$

where 1 = bottom of tower; 2 = top of tower.

C_{g_1}, the initial amount of impurity in the gas and C_{g_2}, the desired amount at the exit (required by process conditions or demands on pollution control) are known beforehand. In most cases also C_{l_2} is known or else a sensible assumption has to be made.

The operating line is drawn by connecting the points (C_{g_1}, C_{l_1}) and (C_{g_2}, C_{l_2}). Note that when the amount of impurities is high, the factor $(\rho_g . L)/(\rho_l . G)$ is not a constant over the whole tower height, and the operating line is curved. When this is the case it is more convenient to choose another concentration parameter, for instance moles/moles inert.

From the diagram of the operating line and the equilibrium line we can see clearly whether the tentative assumptions of the mass balance are true. The operating line and the equilibrium line must neither intersect nor touch each other. The diagram will also give us an approximate idea about the magnitude of the driving forces in the tower. If the driving forces seem to be very small the mass balance should be correspondingly corrected, i.e. by choosing another liquid load.

(c) When we have decided on the packing material to be used and given the values of the gas flow rate and the liquid flow rate, we tentatively determine the tower diameter from equation (5.127) and Figure 5.24.

Thereafter the degree of wetting is estimated as outlined in 5.4.1, equations (5.123), (5.124). It may prove that the wetting is unsatisfactory and leads to values of a_w/a that are too low. If by diminishing the tower diameter or by choosing another kind or size of suitable packing no acceptable degree of wetting can be attained it becomes necessary to increase the liquid load.

In some cases we may resort to circulation of the liquid over the tower. If all these means fail or are not advisable from an economic point of view, the idea of using a packed tower has to be given up, and one has to consider the use of another type of tower, e.g. the bubble cap column, which is not so sensitive to low liquid loads.

(d) After gas load, liquid load, tower diameter, packing material, etc., are fixed we are able to calculate the height of the tower from one of the following equations, for instance equations (5.88, 89, 90, 93).

For a small element dh of tower height the generalized design equation is written as:

$$d\left(\frac{G}{\rho_g}C_g\right) = -d(N_A . a_e . h) \tag{5.87}$$

This equation has to be integrated between the boundary conditions:

$$h = 0, C_g = C_{g_1} \text{ for the bottom, and}$$

$$h = H_T, C_g = C_{g_2} \text{ for the top}$$

Instead of N_A we now have to introduce one of the equations from 5.2.2, so for the case that the absorption flux is given by:

$$N_A = K_g(C_g - C_g^*)$$

the height of the packing in the tower follows from:

$$H_T = \int_{C_{g_2}}^{C_{g_1}} \frac{G . dC_g}{\rho_g . K_g . a_e(C_g - C_g^*)} \tag{5.88}$$

(Note that the symbol C_g^o, denoting the concentration in the gasbulk, for matters of convenience is replaced by C_g.)

The same kind of equation can be written when the driving force is based on the liquid side concentrations:

$$H_T = \int_{C_{l_2}}^{C_{l_1}} \frac{L . dC_l}{\rho_l . K_l . a_e(C_l^* - C_l)} \tag{5.89}$$

In general L, G, ρ_l, ρ_g, K_g, K_l and a_e may not be taken constant throughout the tower, while further C_g^* and C_l^* depend on the changing concentrations in liquid and gas along the flow path in the tower.

Moreover the solubility is seldom a constant throughout the tower. So it follows that calculation of the packing height for the general case of multicomponent absorption complicated by heat effects, without making any simplifying assumptions for the various factors, may become very complex. By using computers, however, there seems to be no real objection to complicated mathematical models for the design of packed towers.

The imaginative engineer can build his model from the equations given. A sound guide line seems to be: try to sort out first the real determining factors by sound common sense reasoning, before starting with the building of a highly complex model. Such models can be tricky; for instance when large heat effects are to be expected, the main influence is on equilibrium and chemical kinetics of reactions and only secondary effects have to be expected from partial mass transfer coefficients like k_y and k_l and interfacial area. For these we already know that the correlations to be put into the model will have no great accuracy.

When the proportion of the impurities is small, equation (5.88) can be simplified to a great extent.

Assuming G, ρ_g, K_g and a_e to be constant over the total height of packing the packed tower height follows from:

$$H_T = \frac{G}{\rho_g . K_g . a_e} \int_{C_{g2}}^{C_{g1}} \frac{dC_g}{C_g - C_g^*} = \frac{G}{\rho_g . K_g . a_e} \times \frac{C_{g1} - C_{g2}}{(\Delta C_g^*)_m} \qquad (5.90)$$

$(\Delta C_g^*)_m$ is the mean driving force.

For the exceptional case that the driving force is approximately constant over the tower height (which might be seen from the diagram of operating line and equilibrium line) the mean driving force is given by:

$$(\Delta C_g^*)_m = C_{g1} - C_{g1}^* = C_{g1} - \frac{C_{l_1}}{\gamma} = C_{g2} - \frac{C_{l_2}}{\gamma} \qquad (5.91)$$

When operating line and equilibrium line are both straight, but not parallel, which will be the case when Henry's law is followed, the mean driving force follows from:

$$(\Delta C_g^*)_m = (\Delta C_y^*)_{lm} = \frac{(C_g - C_g^*)_1 - (C_g - C_g^*)_2}{\ln \dfrac{(C_g - C_g^*)_1}{(C_g - C_g^*)_2}} \qquad (5.92)$$

Now as this is always approximately true for a small element of tower height, the total height for the general case where operating line and equilibrium line are curved, may be found in good approximation from:

$$H_T = \sum \Delta h = \sum \frac{G}{\rho_g . K_g . a_e} \times \frac{(C_g)_h - (C_g)_{h+\Delta h}}{(\Delta C_g^*)_{lm}} \qquad (5.93)$$

When the driving force is expressed in other units, such as pressure, mole fraction, etc., the same methods of computation may be used.

(e) For totally new absorption systems, the height of the packed bed should be increased by a safety margin which takes into account the inaccuracy of the equations and parameters. This margin will usually amount to about 30 per cent depending on the existing uncertainties.

TRANSFER UNIT METHOD

What has been treated in literature as a seemingly distinct alternate approach to sizing packed absorption towers, referred to as the transfer unit method, is actually a variation of the mass transfer coefficient approach, in which the inaccuracies in K_g, K_l and a_e are simply invested in the values of the so-called HTU or height of a transfer unit. The number of transfer units in a given operation was defined by Chilton and Colburn[87]:

$$NTU_g^* = \int_{y_2}^{y_1} \frac{dy}{y - y^*} = \int_{C_{g2}}^{C_{g1}} \frac{dC_g}{C_g - C_g^*} \tag{5.94}$$

and

$$NTU_l^* = \int_{x_2}^{x_1} \frac{dx}{x^* - x} = \int_{C_{l2}}^{C_{l1}} \frac{dC_l}{C_l^* - C_l} \tag{5.95}$$

which are the extreme right-hand terms of equation (5.90)

The transfer unit approach states that the required height of packing is equal to the number of transfer units times the height of a transfer unit

$$H_T = NTU \times HTU \tag{5.96}$$

From equation (5.90) it follows that the height of the overall transfer unit, based on the overall driving force in the gasphase, is given by

$$HTU_g^* = \frac{G}{\rho_g . K_g . a_e} \tag{5.97}$$

while the overall transfer unit, based on the liquid phase is defined by:

$$HTU_l^* = \frac{L}{\rho_l . K_l . a_e} \tag{5.98}$$

In cases where the equilibrium line and the operating line are straight, the number of transfer units may be found from

$$NTU_g^* = \frac{\ln\left[(1 - r_g)\left(\frac{\gamma . C_{g_1} - C_{l_2}}{\gamma . C_{g_2} - C_{l_2}}\right) + r_g\right]}{1 - r_g} \tag{5.99}$$

where index 1 is for the concentrated end (bottom), index 2 is for the dilute end (top) and factor r_g is defined by

$$r_g = \frac{1}{r_l} = \frac{G . \rho_l}{\gamma . L . \rho_g} = \frac{\text{slope equilibrium line}}{\text{slope operating line}}$$

The same equation can be derived for NTU_l^*.

It is also possible to define the separate film transfer units

$$HTU_g = \frac{G}{\rho_g . k_g . a_e} \tag{5.100}$$

and

$$HTU_l = \frac{L}{\rho_l . \phi . k_l . a_e} \tag{5.101}$$

The relations between overall transfer units and film transfer units are given by:

$$HTU_g^* = HTU_g + r_g.HTU_l \qquad (5.102)$$

$$HTU_l^* = HTU_l + r_l.HTU_g \qquad (5.103)$$

The number of transfer units, defined by equations (5.94) and (5.95) and the corresponding height of a transfer unit, when taken from literature, have to be treated with caution. In some cases the f factors, for multi-component absorption, and the factors $C_t/[(C_{inert})_{lm}]$ for absorption from a gas containing inert components, are already incorporated in the HTU and NTU values. If in all probability the value of the mass transfer correction factors deviate to a great extent from 1, we propose to use a more rigorous method for calculation than the transfer unit approach. A considerable amount of information on the performance of packings is available in published literature[6,88,89] in the form of curves, showing the variation of the height of a transfer unit for a given packing material with various factors, and for different systems. This information can, of course, be used in the design of towers for the systems covered, thus avoiding the need to use the rather lengthy mass transfer coefficient method.

A common method of presenting information on heights of transfer units is to plot HTU_g^* against the gas rate, with the liquid rate as a parameter. The curves thus plotted tend to rise to a maximum in the region of the loading point, as shown in Figure 5.13.

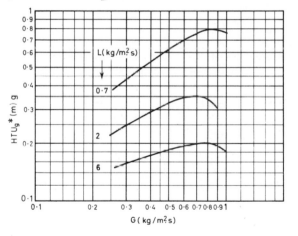

(Absorption of ammonia in water, 25mm Raschig rings; Ref. 88)

Figure 5.13 Heights of a transfer unit.

For preliminary design both HTU_g and HTU_l (for physical absorption only, i.e. $\phi = 1$) can be regarded as constants, and are given in Table 5.4 for grids, Raschig rings and solid packings.

Semmelbauer[15] reworked his correlations for physical absorption of k_g, k_l and a_e and proposed to calculate the values of the film transfer units HTU_g and HTU_l from the following set of equations. (Notice that HTU_l is only valid for purely physical absorption, i.e. $\phi = 1$.)

Table 5.4a HEIGHT OF A TRANSFER UNIT FOR VARIOUS PACKINGS (after Morris and Jackson[56])

Material	Size in millimetres			Height of a transfer unit (m)	
Grids	Pitch	Height	Thickness	HTU_g	HTU_l
Plain grids					
Metal	25	25	1·6	1	0·5
	25	50	1·6	1·2	0·6
Wood	25	25	6·4	0·9	0·5
	25	50	6·4	1·2	0·6
Serrated grids					
Wood	100	100	13	6·8	0·7
	50	50	9·5	1·8	0·6
	38	38	4·8	1·6	0·6
Solid material	nominal size				
Coke	75			0·7	0·9
	38			0·25	0·8
	25			0·2	0·7
Quartz	50			0·5	0·8
	25			0·16	0·8

Table 5.4b HEIGHT OF A TRANSFER UNIT FOR VARIOUS PACKINGS (after Morris and Jackson[56])

Material	Size (mm)			Height of a transfer unit (m)	
Raschig rings	Diameter	Height	Thickness	HTU_g	HTU_l
Stacked	100	100	9·5	1·8	0·7
	75	75	9·5	1·1	0·6
Stoneware	75	75	6·4	1·4	0·6
	50	50	6·4	0·7	0·6
	50	50	4·8	0·8	0·6
Random	50	50	1·6	0·5	0·6
Metal	25	25	1·6	0·2	0·5
	13	13	0·8	0·1	0·5
	75	75	9·5	0·8	0·7
	50	50	6·4	0·5	0·6
Stoneware	50	50	4·8	0·5	0·6
	38	38	4·8	0·3	0·6
	25	25	2·5	0·2	0·5
	19	19	2·5	0·15	0·5
	13	13	1·6	0·1	0·5
Carbon	50	50	6·4	0·5	0·6
	25	25	4·8	0·2	0·5
	13	13	3·2	0·1	0·5

$$HTU_g = \frac{G}{\rho_g . k_g . a_e} = \beta \frac{G^{0 \cdot 41} . \mu_g^{0 \cdot 26} . \mu_l^{0 \cdot 46} . \sigma^{0 \cdot 5}}{L^{0 \cdot 46} . \rho_g^{0 \cdot 67} . \rho_l^{0 \cdot 5} . D_g^{0 \cdot 67} . d_p^{0 \cdot 05}} \qquad (5.104)$$

in which $\beta = 65$ for Raschig rings, and $\beta = 33$ for Berl saddles.

$$HTU_l = \frac{L}{\rho_l . k_l . a_e} = \beta \frac{\mu_l^{0 \cdot 88} . \sigma^{0 \cdot 5}}{L^{0 \cdot 05} . \rho_l^{1 \cdot 33} . D_l^{0 \cdot 5} . d_p^{0 \cdot 55}} \qquad (5.105)$$

in which $\beta = 30$ for Raschig rings, and $\beta = 21$ for Berl saddles.

These equations are valid in the following ranges:

L	0·1–10	kg/m² s
G	0·1–1	kg/m² s
d_p	0·006–0·06	m
ρ_l	600–1400	kg/m³
ρ_g	0·4–4	kg/m³
D_l	$0 \cdot 3 \times 10^{-9}$–3×10^{-9}	m²/s
D_g	$0 \cdot 3 \times 10^{-5}$–3×10^{-5}	m²/s
μ_l	$0 \cdot 2 \times 10^{-3}$–2×10^{-3}	kg/m s
μ_g	$0 \cdot 5 \times 10^{-5}$–3×10^{-5}	kg/m s
σ	20×10^{-3}–200×10^{-3}	J/m²
γ	0·4–4	

Notice that for $\gamma > 4$ there is chemical absorption in most cases, while for $\gamma < 0 \cdot 4$ the absorption is controlled by the liquid phase.

Temperature 0–100°C.

$$2 \cdot 5 < \frac{\text{tower diameter}}{\text{packing diameter}} < 25$$

$$10 < \frac{\text{packing height}}{\text{packing diameter}} < 100$$

Equations (5.104) and (5.105) could, apart from the superficial velocity terms L/ρ_l and G/ρ_g, also be expressed by way of dimensionless numbers.

The results show that when the liquid side is rate controlling, the HTU_l values for Raschig rings is about 25 per cent greater than for Berl saddles, while for the situation where the gas side is rate controlling this factor amounts to a 100 per cent. This advantage of Berl saddles over Raschig rings is annulled in most cases because the price of Raschig rings is about 30–40 per cent below the price of Berl saddles.

In some cases it can be useful to have an expression for the efficiency of an absorption tower, for instance when comparing various alternatives. This tower efficiency is defined by

$$E_T = \frac{\left(\frac{G}{\rho_g} C_g\right)_1 - \left(\frac{G}{\rho_g} C_g\right)_2}{\left(\frac{G}{\rho_g} C_g\right)_1 - \left(\frac{G \, C_l}{\rho_g \, \gamma}\right)_2} \approx \frac{C_{g1} - C_{g2}}{C_{g1} - C_{g2}^*} \qquad (5.106)$$

The efficiency is a function both of NTU_g^* and r_g. In the case of dilute gas systems (straight equilibrium line and operating line) this relation is expressed by

$$NTU_g^* = \frac{\ln\left(\frac{1-r_g}{1-E_T}+r_g\right)}{1-r_g} \tag{5.107}$$

Notice that for the case where $r_g = 1$ it follows that

$$NTU_g^* = \frac{E_T}{1-E_T} \tag{5.108}$$

GRAPHICAL METHOD

An illustrative and at the same time quick method of design is the graphical method[90], this gives the course of the driving force as a function of the composition of gas and liquid. By plotting the reciprocal value of the driving force versus the concentration (partial pressure, mole fraction, etc.) and by graphical integration the number of transfer units can be found.

Physical absorption

In its application to physical absorption the graphical method is well known; it is shown in Figure 5.14.

The construction is based on the equation for physical absorption:

$$N_A = k_g(C_g^o - C_g^i) = k_l(C_l^i - C_l^o) \tag{5.109}$$

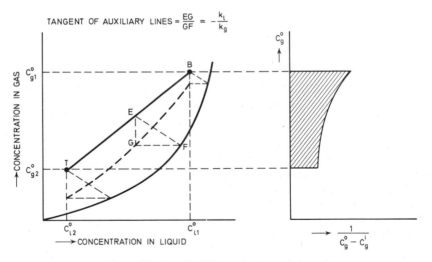

Figure 5.14 Graphical design for physical absorption

From various points on the operating line, auxiliary lines are drawn to the equilibrium line at an inclination $= -k_l/k_g$. The auxiliary line from E reaches the equilibrium line at F, the point F gives the conditions at the interface, where a gas of concentration C_g^i is in equilibrium with the interfacial liquid having a concentration C_l^i.

The driving force in the gas is $C_g^o - C_g^i = EG$; the driving force in the liquid is $C_l^i - C_l^o = FG$. The same construction can be performed for other points of the operating line.

The line through point G connects all the points defining the partial driving forces throughout the tower. The number of transfer units, based on the gas film, may be found by graphical integration, see the right-hand part of Figure 5.14.

Very fast chemical reaction

For absorption combined with a very fast reversible reaction $A + \theta B \rightleftharpoons AB_\theta$, in which case the rate of absorption is determined by the rate of transport of B from the bulk of the liquid to the interface, the graphical method of design is analogous to that for physical absorption.

In Figure 5.15 the concentration of A in the gasphase is plotted along the vertical axis, the concentration of the reaction product AB_θ in the liquid being plotted along the horizontal axis. The concentration of B may be plotted in the opposite direction along the same axis. Notice that $C_B = C_{B_2} - \theta . C_{AB_\theta}$, in which index 2 is for the top of the tower and θ expresses the stoichiometric factor of the chemical reaction.

Also here an equilibrium line may be drawn, giving the equilibrium concentration of A in the gas over solutions containing the reaction product AB_θ. The construction is the same as the one used for physical absorption. It is to be noted that the auxiliary lines must now be drawn at an inclination $= -k_l/\theta . k_g$.

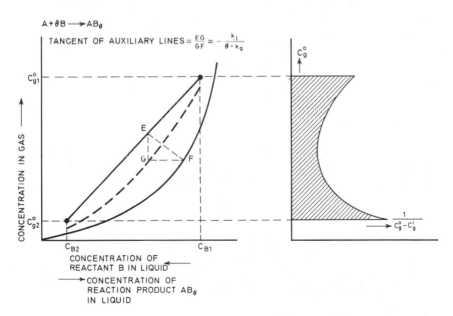

Figure 5.15 *Graphical design for absorption with fast reversible reaction*

A special case may present itself if the equilibrium concentration of A in the gas over the liquid is nil or very low, which will be the case for very fast irreversible reactions. This situation is illustrated in Figure 5.16.

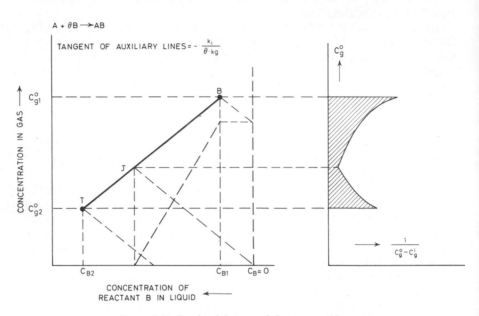

Figure 5.16 Graphical design with fast irreversible reaction

In this case the equilibrium line is absent and coincides with the horizontal axis. The auxiliary lines are drawn now at an inclination $k_l/\theta.k_g$ up to the abcissa. For points on the operating line between J and B the auxiliary lines cannot be produced as far as the abcissa, because the concentration of B at the interface cannot fall below zero. From point J on we have to draw the auxiliary lines up to the vertical through point $C_B = 0$. Point J corresponds to the node in the diagram of the graphical integration.

Moderately fast irreversible reaction

In this case the graphical construction has to be performed by trial and error, as ϕ, the chemical acceleration factor, depends on the concentration diffusion parameter Z (see paragraph 5.1.3). This parameter is defined by:

$$Z = \theta \frac{D_A . C_A^i}{D_B . C_B^o}$$

in which C_A^i is the interfacial concentration of A at the liquid side. C_A^i is not known beforehand, so for a certain point on the operating line we tentatively assume a value for C_A^i and are able to calculate a first approximate value of Z. Thereafter the first approximate value of ϕ is determined from Z and the Hatta number by way of the van Krevelen–Hoftyzer diagram, Figure 5.5.

From $N_A = k_g(C^o_{Ag} - C^i_{Ag}) = \phi \cdot k_l(C^i_A)$ and the equilibrium relation it follows that a check value of C^i_A can be calculated from

$$C^i_A = C^o_{Ag}\left(\frac{1}{\gamma} + \phi\frac{k_l}{k_g}\right)^{-1}$$

The concentration of A in the bulk of the liquid is zero. If the check value of C^i_A is approximately equal to the value assumed, ϕ is correct and the auxiliary line can be drawn at an inclination

$$-\frac{\phi \cdot C^i_A \cdot k_l}{\theta \cdot k_g \cdot C^o_B}$$

The constructional method is the same as outlined for the case of irreversible infinitely fast reactions, Figure 5.16.

5.2.4 Methods of Mass Transfer Design for Plate Towers

As with packed towers, the essential results of design are the column diameter and the column height, but these are determined in different ways. The general methods of design regarding mass transfer, however, are not basically different from the principles used for packed towers. An important feature in the design of all types of plate towers is the determination of the number of theoretical plates or stages. A stage may be defined as a unit of equipment in which two dissimilar phases are brought into intimate contact with each other and then separated. With gas absorption various diffusing components are transferred during the contact of gas and liquid. The resulting two phases approach equilibrium and therefore have compositions different from the initial phases. By successive countercurrent contact and separation of gas and liquid (a multistage operation) large changes in the compositions of the phases are possible. For a theoretical plate, it is assumed that gas and liquid are so well mixed for a sufficient time that thermodynamic equilibrium between the phases leaving the stage is established; no real plate, of course, achieves this ideal performance.

Efficiency

In industrial gas absorption towers it is not practical to allow sufficient time, with thorough mixing to attain equilibrium. Therefore an actual plate does not accomplish as large a change in composition as a theoretical plate. The degree of approach to theoretically perfect contacting is expressed conveniently in terms of the plate efficiency, which may be defined in a number of ways.

(a) The *plate efficiency* is defined as the ratio of a change in concentration on an actual plate to that in an equilibrium stage. For the equilibrium stage it is assumed that gas and liquid are perfectly mixed, i.e. the concentration in the liquid leaving the plate is identical with the concentration on the plate; the same is assumed for the gas phase. Assuming L, G, ρ_l, and ρ_g to be constants the plate efficiency based on gas-concentrations is expressed by:

$$E_p = \frac{C_{g_1} - C_{g_2}}{C_{g_1} - (C^*_{g_2})_E} \tag{5.110}$$

index 1 = flowing to the plate, index 2 = flowing from the plate, $(C_{g_2}^*)_E$ = fictitious gas-concentration, assumed to be in equilibrium with the liquid leaving an equilibrium stage.

(b) The *overall plate efficiency* E_0 is defined as the ratio of the number of theoretical plates required for a given absorption process to the number of actual plates: $E_0 = N_t/N_P$.

(c) The *Murphree vapour efficiency* E_{MV} of a single plate is the ratio of the actual concentration change in the thoroughly mixed gas flow accomplished by the plate to the change that would occur if the gas leaving the plate reached equilibrium with the uniformly mixed liquid stream flowing downwards from the plate. Thus for dilute gas liquid systems

$$E_{MV} = \frac{(C_{g_1})_{avg} - (C_{g_2})_{avg}}{(C_{g_1})_{avg} - (C_{g_2}^*)_{avg}} \tag{5.111}$$

$(C_{g_2}^*)_{avg}$ is not identical with $(C_{g_2}^*)_E$, because $(C_{g_2}^*)_E$ is based on the assumption that the liquid in an equilibrium stage is perfectly mixed in the stage, which is not the case for an actual tray.

While for E_p holds $0 < E_p \leqslant 1$, the Murphree efficiency may be greater than 1, because an actual plate may consist of a number of imperfect mixers which in its total effect may have an efficiency greater than the efficiency of one equilibrium stage. The overall efficiency E_0 and the Murphree efficiency E_{MV} are equal if the equilibrium line and the operating line are straight and parallel. In the case where the operating line and the equilibrium line are straight (but not parallel), the relation between the overall efficiency and the Murphree efficiency is given by

$$E_0 = \frac{\ln\left[1 + E_{MV}(r_g - 1)\right]}{\ln r_g} \tag{5.112}$$

As already stated it follows that for $r_g = 1$: $E_0 = E_{MV}$. Notice that the Murphree plate efficiency can be determined by direct measurement.

(d) The *point efficiency* E_p^0 is defined by

$$E_p^0 = \frac{C_{g_1} - C_{g_2}}{C_{g_1} - C_{g_2}^*} \tag{5.113}$$

In this case the concentrations are point values at a single point on the plate. The fictitious equilibrium concentration $C_{g_2}^*$ is now related to the average value of the liquid concentration in the discrete element of liquid layer considered, i.e. it is assumed that the liquid is perfectly mixed in vertical sense. The relation of the point efficiency to mass transfer is given by the equation

$$E_p^0 = 1 - \exp\left(-\frac{K_g \cdot \rho_g \cdot a_e^*}{G_b}\right) = 1 - m_g \tag{5.114}$$

The relation between the Murphree efficiency and mass transfer can be based on several assumptions. For instance let us assume the following conditions:

The gas is well mixed before and after the plate: mean concentrations $(C_{g_1})_{avg}$ and $(C_{g_2})_{avg}$;
The flow pattern of the gas during passage through the active liquid layer is perfect plug flow, i.e. no mixing during passage;

The flow pattern of the liquid over the plate is perfect plug flow in horizontal direction, while at the same time the liquid is perfectly mixed in vertical direction;
Gas and liquid are flowing relative to each other with the simplest kind of cross flow.

It can be shown that for the conditions stated the Murphree efficiency is related to mass transfer by:

$$E_{MV} = \frac{e^{r_g(1 - m_g)} - 1}{r_g} \tag{5.115}$$

In the limiting situation where the liquid on the plate is perfectly mixed over the whole plate area, i.e. the liquid concentration on each part of the plate is equal and identical to the concentration in the liquid leaving the plate, the Murphree efficiency is equal to the point efficiency and may be calculated from $E_{MV} = E_p^0 = 1 - m_g$. Hence it follows that the Murphree efficiency for the case where perfect liquid mixing is assumed will always be lower than for ideal cross plug flow. The two cases described may be considered as the limiting situations.

Kirschbaum[91] introduced the concept of mixed pools, describing the liquid mixing on plates in terms of a number of perfectly mixed pools. In this way the relationship between point efficiency and plate efficiency can be expressed by the equation

$$E_{MV} = \frac{1}{r_g}\left[\left(1 + r_g \frac{E_p^0}{n}\right)^n - 1\right] \tag{5.116}$$

where n is the number of mixing pools.

In the case of complete mixing $n = 1$, while for the case of perfect plug flow $n = \infty$. The following variables affect the number of mixing pools:

(a) *The length of the liquid path on the tray*: Obviously the longer the liquid path, the greater the number of mixing stages, i.e. large tower diameters tend to result in higher values of n and thus higher values of the Murphree efficiency.

(b) *The liquid rate*: If the liquid flows across the plate unmixed, there will be an infinite number of mixing pools. The general conclusion is that with high liquid rates the less mixing occurs and thus the greatest number of mixing stages is found.

(c) *The gas load*: The vapour rate through the slots or holes affects the turbulence and thus the degree of mixing. The number of mixing pools tends to diminish with increasing gas velocity.

(d) *The design of the tray*: Any tray design which minimizes mixing will increase the number of mixing stages.

The number of mixing pools follows from[69]:

$$(n)_{\text{bubble caps}} \approx \left(\frac{L.\mu_g}{G.\mu_l}\right)^{0.2}\left(\frac{L}{\mu_l}\right)^{0.14}(0.46 + 2D_c) \tag{5.117}$$

and

$$(n)_{\text{sieve trays}} \approx \left(\frac{L.\mu_g}{G.\mu_l}\right)^{0.2}\left(\frac{L}{\mu_l}\right)^{0.14}\left(\frac{\varepsilon_p}{d_h}\right)^{0.2}(0.53 + 0.19\,D_c) \tag{5.118}$$

These equations are valid for the most common type of cross flow tray, in which the liquid flows across the whole tray surface from the inlet to the outlet weir.

When the number of mixing pools calculated becomes smaller than one, n must be taken as unity, this being the lower limit and we have one perfect mixer. More information on these matters may be found in literature[67,69,92,93].

Number of plates

The number of theoretical plates N_t can be determined graphically by the well-known construction shown in Figure 5.17. The equilibrium line represents the relation between the gas and liquid composition, while the operating line gives the relation between the composition of the gas flowing upwards from a given plate and the composition of the liquid flowing downwards from the plate above. A series of steps is drawn between the

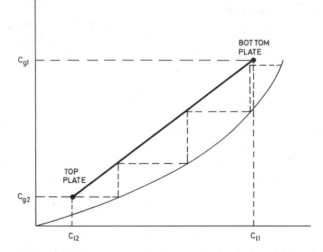

Figure 5.17 Graphical construction for determining the number of theoretical plates

equilibrium line and the operating line, each step corresponding to a theoretical plate.

When the proportion of soluble components in the gas is small, the equilibrium line can be regarded as a straight line, and the number of theoretical plates can then be calculated from the following equation:

$$N_t = \frac{\ln\left[(1-r_g)\left(\frac{\gamma . C_{g_1} - C_{l_2}}{\gamma . C_{g_2} - C_{l_2}}\right) + r_g\right]}{\ln(1/r_g)} \tag{5.119}$$

The number of actual plates then follows from

$$N_P = \frac{N_t}{E_0} \tag{5.120}$$

5.3 Types of Tower

This section deals with the most widely used types of tower which are the counterflow packed tower with random packings and the crossflow plate column. For special services counterflow packed towers with regular packings such as grids or stacked rings, spray towers and counterflow trays (splash decks, grid trays without downcomers) find application.

Until 1960 the packed tower was mainly used for gas absorption purposes whereas in the field of distillation the plate column was predominant. This can be ascribed to the circumstance that in gas absorption mainly dilute watery solutions are used as solvent, for which at that time reasonably reliable theory was only available for the design of packed towers. In normal distillation practice, where usually the whole range of concentration of organic liquids occurs, these relations failed to predict the necessary column height for the desired separation. For plate columns, the situation was not much better; the predictability of the plate efficiency was based on purely empirical relations[96-98], derived from measurements on existing towers.

The results of the A.I.Ch.E. research programme on bubble tray efficiencies[67] made prediction of the efficiency with a higher degree of confidence possible, so that the plate tower gradually came into use also for absorption purposes. The choice between a packed column or a plate column is now largely determined by economic considerations rather than from technological considerations, such as: gas load, liquid load, foaming, liquids depositing solid material, temperature effects (cooling), pressure drop, corrosion, etc.

5.3.1 Packings

In large scale apparatus the most commonly used types of packing are Raschig rings, Berl saddles, Intalox saddles and Pall rings, Figure 5.18, in size ranging from 6 mm to 75 mm for Raschig rings, 6 mm to 50 mm for Berl saddles and Intalox saddles and 16 mm to 90mm for Pall rings. Depending on the corrosion characteristics of the system the packings can be chosen from a variety of materials. The ring type of packing is available in stoneware, porcelain, carbon, plastic (polyethylene, polypropylene, p.v.c., polystyrene) and metal (mild steel, stainless steels, aluminium, and other more rarely used metals). The saddle type is in consequence of its shape only available in stoneware/porcelain and plastic. Other kinds of packing sometimes used for special duties are lumps of coke or quartz and grids of wood, carbon, metal, glass, plastic.

5.3.2 Plates (Trays)

The three main types of plates used for mass transfer purposes are the bubble cap plate, the sieve plate and the valve plate. These plates are of the type with forced liquid flow, i.e. the liquid from the plate above descends through a downcomer and flows in horizontal direction across the plate to an outlet downcomer where the process is repeated. The quantity of

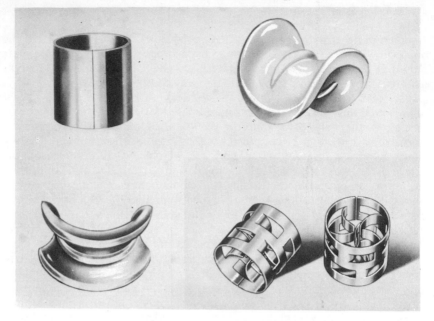

Figure 5.18 Some types of packing
(Top left) Metal Raschig ring. (Top right) Berl saddle. (Bottom left) Intalox saddle. (Bottom right) Metal pall ring. (Courtesy Norton Co. Ltd)

liquid on the plate is controlled by the weir height of the outlet downcomer above the tray floor. On the plate the gas is led into the aerated mass through an array of 'contacting devices'. With the bubble cap plate this device consists of a riser over which a cap is placed. If low gas loads occur, the lower edge of the caps are provided with slots to ensure an even distribution of the gas, Figure 5.19. The sieve tray, Figure 5.20, has its floor perforated with a large number of round holes. Hole diameters of 2·5 to 20 mm are used. The

Figure 5.19 Typical bubble cap tray (Courtesy Fractionation Research, Inc)

125

Figure 5.20 Typical sieve tray. (Courtesy Fractionation Research, Inc)

Figure 5.21 Valve tray with rectangular valves equipped with legs. (Courtesy Nutter Engineering Co.)

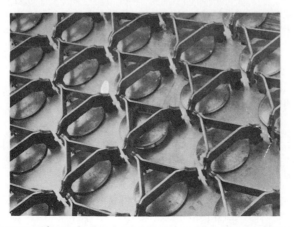

Figure 5.22 Valve tray with round valves housed in spiders. (Courtesy N. V. Metawa and Shell)

valve plate is a perforated tray with the holes covered by movable circular or rectangular 'valves' either equipped with legs, Figure 5.21 (rectangular valve), or housed in 'spiders', Figure 5.22 (round valve). The position of the valve will be either totally open or closed; with low gas loads the number of open valves adjusts itself to the load.

In recent years the sieve tray with large holes and the valve tray have displaced the bubble cap plate. The sieve tray is extremely simple to manufacture and is therefore the cheapest type of tray available. A drawback of this tray is the low flexibility (ratio of maximum and minimum applicable load). The advantages of the valve tray lie in the relatively simple construction and in its high flexibility as a result of the self positioning valves. It is less expensive than the bubble cap plate.

With high gas loads on all types of trays a violent interaction between liquid and gas takes place, resulting in a jetting of liquid towards the plate above. The spacing of the plates must also be large enough as to avoid massive entrainment of liquid in the ascending gas stream.

5.3.3 Choice between Packed and Plate Towers

The relative advantages and disadvantages of packed and plate towers may be summarized as follows:

Pressure drop: When pressure drop has to be low, the packed tower seems to be a better choice than the plate tower.

Capital cost: The capital cost of packed towers is low, particularly in the smaller sizes (< 0·5 m). For large diameters, however, plates are cheaper than packings.

Construction: The construction of a packed tower is simple.

Availability of packings and plates: Packing material is available in a great variety of corrosion-resistant materials, while plates are available only in a limited range of corrosion-resistant materials. Of course special demands can be met for plates and trays, but these specialities, e.g. titanium, glass-lined, monel, etc., are never cheap.

Side-streams: In plate towers it is easy to introduce or withdraw side-streams.

Liquid hold-up: In packed towers the liquid hold-up is relatively small.

Absorption efficiency: The efficiency of packed towers is very susceptible to mal-distribution, particularly in the larger sizes. The efficiency of packed towers varies with the liquid and gas flow rates, while the efficiency of plates is constant for a wide range of liquid and gas rates.

Distribution of liquid: In packed towers there may be places where the gas has no contact with the liquid because of bad distribution of the liquid. In the case of a well-installed plate tower there is no such shortcoming.

Liquid feed rate: The plate column can stand any arbitrarily low liquid feed and permits a higher feed than the packed column.

Fouling liquids: Plate towers may be preferred when the operation involves liquids that deposit small amounts of solid material that must be removed periodically.

Heat effects: In absorption processes, accompanied by considerable heat effects, cooling or heating the liquid is much easier in the plate column. Cooling coils can be immersed in the liquid layer on the plates, and the heat is removed or supplied directly to the gas–liquid layer in which the absorption process is taking place. The cooling coils preferably have to be installed in a pattern staggered in the direction of gas flow. The overall heat transfer coefficient between the gas–liquid dispersion on the tray and the cooling medium in the coils is usually in the range 500–2000 W/m^2 °C. The lower value holds for low superficial gas velocities, near 0·1 m/s, and the higher values may be found at high gas rates, near 1–1·5 m/s. Information on these matters in the literature is very scarce although a great deal of data must have been accumulated by firms specializing in this field. Some guidance is given by Poll and Smith[94].

With packed towers it is necessary to divide the towers into a number of compartments for which the cooling or heating takes place in coolers placed externally. When cooling water quality is bad, so that it tends to build up dirt or scale on heat-transfer surfaces, packed towers with externally placed coolers may be preferred to plate towers with internal placed cooling coils.

It is a matter of economics to decide between an adiabatic absorption tower or an isothermal tower which has fewer theoretical (and practical) plates but provisions for effective cooling. A computer program to calculate the number of theoretical stages for adiabatic absorption and for absorption with the interstage coolers has been put forward by Coggan and Bourne[95].

Tower diameter: Plate towers tend to have a larger diameter (about 25 per cent) than packed towers for the same system and conditions of gas and liquid load.

Economic considerations: The choice between packed and plate columns will be chiefly determined by economic considerations. Therefore in every case calculations must be made in order to determine which design will be the most profitable. A good example of the way the problem can be attacked is given by Billet[99, 100]

Total weight of tower: The total weight of a plate tower is usually less than that of a packed tower designed for the same duty. The limited crushing strength of packing material may make it impossible for one packing-support plate to bear the weight of a tall column of packing.

Number of transfer units (theoretical stages): Absorption processes for which a large number of transfer units or theoretical stages are required are preferably performed in plate towers, because of the lesser extent of channeling and mixing of gas and liquid, compared with packed towers.

Chemical absorption: Plate towers are advantageous for absorption processes with an accompanying chemical reaction (in particular when it is not very rapid) as the process is favoured by a long residence time of the liquid in the column and by easier control of the reaction.

Foaming liquids: Packed towers are to be preferred in the case of liquids that tend to foam.

5.4 Hydraulic Design of Packed Towers

5.4.1 Properties of Packing

DRY AREA OF PACKING

The duty of a packed bed is to create an active area for mass transfer. Depending on the type of packing this area will, in one way or another, be related to the dry area of the packing. In the case of dumped packings it will be influenced by the method used for filling because the number of packings per unit volume will slightly differ whether the tower has been filled dry or wet. If the mechanical strength of the tower and its support is sufficient, wet filling is to be preferred. Normally, the tower will be filled dry; in this case care must be taken to distribute the packings in random position across the area of the tower. The number of packings per unit of volume n_p, and in consequence the dry area and the fractional voidage ε, will vary with each filling.

It is obvious, that for geometrically similar packings the product $n_p d_p^3$ is a constant. As the dry area of the packings is approximately proportional to $n_p d_p^2$, the product da will also be constant.

The voidage ε (free gas space) is more or less constant for the saddle type of packings; with the ring type it will depend on the ratio r_{wd} of wall thickness to nominal diameter of the ring. The number of packings per unit volume is not influenced by this ratio so that the following relation (valid for Raschig rings and Pall rings, with height equal to diameter) can be derived from the equation

$$(1-\varepsilon) = 2\cdot5 r_{wd}(1 - r_{wd}) \tag{5.121}$$

The constant 2·5 represents the product $\pi n_p d_p^3$. Average values of the various constants are given in Table 5.5 in which the density of some packing materials ρ_p is also given. Consequently the approximate weight of the packed bed can easily be calculated.

WETTABILITY OF PACKINGS

When the liquid is evenly distributed over the top of the packed bed, there exist preferential flow paths[101,102] along which the liquid flows downwards in the column. These flowpaths are mainly dependent on the filling; packing the column anew will lead to other flow paths. Stopping the liquid flow and starting it again results in the same flow paths.

Table 5.5 PACKING CONSTANTS

Type of packing	$n_p d_p^3$	ad_p	ε	$\rho_p\,(kg/m^3)$
Stoneware Raschig rings		4·9		2450
Metal Raschig rings	0·8	5·0	See equation (5.121)	7860 mild steel
Carbon Raschig rings		4·7		1650
Porcelain berl saddles	1·25	6·0	0·68	2650
Porcelain intalox saddles	1·3	6·0	0·74	2650
Stoneware pall rings		5·9		2450
Metal pall rings	0 8	5·4	See equation (5.121)	7860 mild steel
Carbon pall rings		5·9		1650
Plastic pall rings		5·3		900 polypropylene
				1500 PVC
				950 polyethylene

The liquid in the interstices of the wetted area a_w of the packing will be slowly replenished, so that in the case of physical absorption only that part of the packing on which liquid is actually flowing will be effective. An important factor regarding this effective area a_e is the minimum wetting rate, at which breakdown of the liquid film occurs and a stable dry patch on the irrigated surface is formed. Ponter et al.[103] have shown that on a vertical tube surface in the laminar flow regime this phenomenon can be described by the following equation

$$\left(\frac{\Gamma}{\pi}\right)_l = 1\cdot12\,(1-\cos A)^{0\cdot6}\left(\frac{\rho\sigma}{\mu^4 g}\right)^{0\cdot2} \tag{5.122}$$

It is to be expected that the same variables will govern the degree to which a packing will be wetted.

In practice the important variable contact angle (A) is not known. It depends to a great deal on the nature and condition of the surface; surface roughness and (with metals) oxide layers play an important role[104]. The influence of the surface tension, as shown by Ponter's formula, is furthermore complicated by local changes in surface tension due to mass transfer to or from the liquid. Zuiderweg and Harmens[105] have given an adequate qualitative picture of the so-called Marangoni effect. In the flowing liquid films there

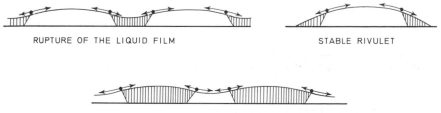

RUPTURE OF THE LIQUID FILM   STABLE RIVULET

STABILIZATION OF THE LIQUID FILM

Figure 5.23 Schematic illustration of the Marangoni effect[105]. Shaded areas correspond with liquid of lower surface tension

exist 'thin' spots. Then differences between these spots and their environment arise as a result of mass transfer concentration. If the surface tension of the liquid film markedly increases with the change in concentration, the film will be stabilized (a positive system). In case of a decrease of the surface tension (a negative system), the film contracts and ruptures with the formation of rivulets. If the change in surface tension $\Delta\sigma$ is less than 3×10^{-3} J/m^2, the system is called neutral. Figure 5.23 gives a picture of the effect. It is clear that the direction of mass transfer governs the outcome of the effect, as Zuiderweg and Harmens have aptly shown. With the same physical system both stabilization or break up of the film can be obtained, depending on the transferred component being absorbed or desorbed. In practice fairly large concentration differences are required for the appearance of the phenomenon, so that it can only be expected with the right combination of gas and solvent (a highly soluble gas and a sufficient large $\Delta\sigma$), for instance ammonia/water and hydrogen chloride/water[106].

DEGREE OF WETTING

In absence of Marangoni effects the wetted area, provided normal contact angles exist, will depend on the liquid rate and the physical properties of the liquid. Research has, however, shown that the active area of a packed column is only a fraction of the total area of the packing material. Hoftyzer[101] came to the following striking conclusion: more than half the amount of liquid flows over 5 per cent of the surface, while on the other hand, 50 per cent of the surface is hardly irrigated at all.

Below a certain liquid rate the wetted area decreases; the gas load seems to have no influence on the wetted area until the loading point is reached. A very thorough survey on the effectiveness of wetting has been given by Hobler[51]. Of the numerous equations, which relate the wetted area to the variables, the equations given by Semmelbauer[15] are chosen here.

$$\text{for Raschig rings } \frac{a_w}{a} = 0.0061.(Re_l)^{0.46}.(E\ddot{o})^{0.5} \qquad (5.123)$$

$$\text{for Berl saddles } \frac{a_w}{a} = 0.0076.(Re_l)^{0.46}.(E\ddot{o})^{0.5} \qquad (5.124)$$

Very often the wetted area a_w is set equal to the effective area a_e; see also paragraph 5.2.2.

For quick estimates a rule of thumb is

$$a_w = (a)^{0.45} \qquad (5.125)$$

For Pall rings no data are available.

When the calculated value of a_w/a exceeds 1, a_w must be taken equal to a.

FLOODING AND PRESSURE DROP

In an irrigated tower the pressure drop per unit height of packing will depend on gas rate, the liquid rate and packing size. If at constant liquid rate the gas rate is increased, the pressure drop will rise with a growing power of the gas velocity. This is due to an increase of the liquid hold-up caused by the friction between gas and liquid streams. With low liquid rates this increase is hardly perceptible and the pressure drop tends to be proportional to the square of the gas velocity (turbulent flow regime). As the gas load is further increased, the effect on the liquid hold up becomes more and more pronounced (loading zone) with an accompanying growing increase in pressure drop, until a point is reached where the column floods.

Numerous equations have been proposed, which relate this flood point to the relevant variables. For design purposes the generalized pressure drop correlation of Eckert[107], corrected by Prahl[108] is chosen. Based on work by Sherwood et al.[109] and Leva[89] the flooding line and lines of constant pressure drop are represented in a diagram with

$$V = \frac{G^2 F}{g \cdot \rho_g \cdot \rho_l} \left(\frac{\rho_w}{\rho_l}\right)\left(\frac{\mu_l}{\mu_w}\right)^{0.2}$$

as ordinate and

$$H = \frac{L}{G}\left(\frac{\rho_g}{\rho_l}\right)^{\frac{1}{2}}$$

as abcissa, Figure 5.24. (ρ_w = specific mass of water.)

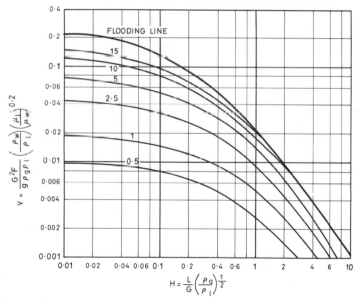

Figure 5.24 Generalized pressure drop correlation. Prahl[108] suggests that when the ratio ρ_w/ρ_l differs to a great extent from unity the following factors should be used

Ordinate: $V = \dfrac{10^{-3} G^{2'} F}{g\,\rho_g}\left(\dfrac{\mu_l}{\mu_w}\right)^{0.1}$

Abscissa: $H = \dfrac{L}{G}\left(\dfrac{\rho_g}{\rho_l}\right)^{\frac{1}{2}}$

The dimensionless ordinate originally contained a kind of Froude number

$$\frac{(u/\varepsilon)^2 a}{g.\varepsilon} = \frac{u^2 a}{g.\varepsilon^3}$$

in which a/ε^3 is determined by the packing. It is obvious that this packing constant by itself is not sufficient to correlate the hydrodynamic behaviour of different types of packing, so that Lobo et al.[110] replaced it by a packing factor F. Table 5.6 gives a survey of the packing factor for various types of packing[111]. With high liquid gas ratios the calculated values of the column diameter are on the conservative side. It appears that Pall rings and plastic Intalox saddles possess the lowest F-value and have therefore the highest capacity, while Raschig rings show the opposite behaviour.

The lines for constant pressure drop in Figure 5.24, originally proposed by Leva[89] have been corrected by Prahl[108]. The pressure drop per metre of packed height can be calculated from the ordinate V and the abcissa H by way of the following relation, valid for H ranging from 0 to 1:

$$\Delta P = \frac{V(0.114H + 0.049)}{1 - V(35H + 3)} \tag{5.126}$$

with ΔP in bar/metre packed height.

LIQUID DISTRIBUTION IN PACKED BEDS

Due to the spreading tendency of the packings part of the liquid accumulates on the wall of the column until a point is reached where the rate of liquid spread to the wall equals the rate at which liquid returns to the packing. The height of the packed bed at the equilibrium point and the proportion of wall flow to the total flow depend on the type and size of the packings and on the diameter of the column.

It has been shown that Raschig rings give the highest ratio wall/total flow and Pall rings the lowest; Berl saddles and Intalox saddles are intermediate[112,113]. This means that the rate of liquid return shows the opposite picture, viz. a small rate with Raschig rings and a high rate with Pall rings. Furthermore this rate decreases with higher ratios of column diameter D_c to packing diameter d_p. In view of this Eckert recommends a minimum value of D_c/d_p for Raschig rings of 30, for Intalox and Berl saddles of 15 and for Pall rings of 10–15[107]. Redistribution of the wall flow should be considered at each $2\frac{1}{2}$–3 D_c, 5–8 D_c and 5–10 D_c respectively or each 6 metres column height, whichever is the smaller[107]. The point must be stressed that with high D_c/d_p ratios the proportion of the liquid, which flows along the wall, is small[112,114].

5.4.2 Area of Cross Section

In ordinary design practice the gas load and liquid load are fixed beforehand. If the total pressure drop can be disregarded, a gas rate of about 70 per cent of the flooding rate, is chosen. This gas rate corresponds to about half the value of the flooding line ordinate at the appropriate abscissa of Figure 5.24.

Table 5.6 PACKING FACTORS—F

Nominal packing size (mm)		6	10	13	16	19	25	32	38	51	76	89
Type of packing	Material	Packing factor—m^{-1}										
Raschig rings	Ceramic	4590/8*	3280/6	2100/5·3	1250/6·7	855/8	525/8	410/6·7	310/8	215/8	120/8	—
0·8 mm wall	Metal	2300	—	985	625	510	375	—	—	—	—	—
1·6 mm wall	Metal	—	—	1115	950	755	475	360	270	185	105	—
3·0 mm wall	Metal	—	—	—	—	—	—	—	—	—	125	—
Berl saddles	Ceramic	2950	—	785	—	555	360	—	215	150	—	—
Intalox saddles	Ceramic	1970	—	655	—	475	320	—	170	130	—	—
Pall rings	Plastic	—	—	—	320	—	170	—	105	82	—	52
Pall rings	Metal	—	—	—	235	—	155	—	92	66	—	—

*The second number indicates the ratio packing size/wall thickness $= \frac{1}{t_{wd}}$

As the type and size of the packing are generally known, the column diameter can easily be calculated from

$$D_c = 1{\cdot}35 \, (G^*)^{\frac{1}{2}} \left\{ \frac{F(\rho_w/\rho_l)(\mu/\mu_w)^{0{\cdot}2}}{V_{fl} \cdot g \cdot \rho_g \cdot \rho_l} \right\}^{\frac{1}{4}} \tag{5.127}$$

in which G^* is the total gas load (kg/s) and V_{fl} the value of the gas-load parameter at flooding conditions.

If the total pressure drop of the column is an important factor in the design, then the situation becomes more complicated. The superficial gas and liquid velocities (determined by the tower diameter) influence the total height necessary for the desired separation. In this case both the required pressure drop and the demands on gas-purification must be met, so that repetitive calculations will be required.

5.5 Hydraulic Design of Plate Towers

5.5.1 Plate Types

The most common plate-type is the cross flow tray (see Figure 5.25(a)) with the liquid flowing in horizontal direction from inlet side to outlet weir. This liquid flow gives rise to a liquid gradient Δ, which depends among other things on the type of contacting device and on the length of the horizontal flowpath. The clear liquid height on the tray will therefore decrease in the direction of the liquid flow and there will be an increase of the vapour flow

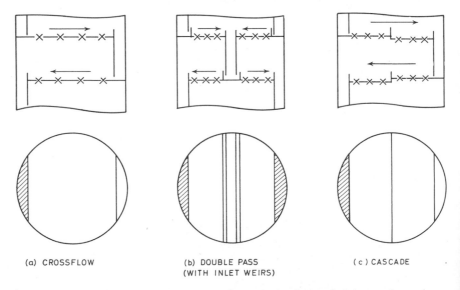

    (a) CROSSFLOW   (b) DOUBLE PASS   (c) CASCADE
                             (WITH INLET WEIRS)

Figure 5.25 General tray types. X represents the contacting device, shaded areas denote down-flow of liquid

in the same direction. With high gradients the liquid at the inlet side of the tray will pour through the contacting device (dumping), thus by-passing two trays. This can be prevented by shortening the length of the flowpath, either by using a double pass tray, by employing one or more intermediate weirs (cascade tray), or by a combination of both, Figure 5.25(b) and (c).

With intermediate weirs care must be taken to ensure an equal clear liquid height on all aerated parts of the tray by use of different weir heights, Figure 5.26 assists in a tentative selection of the type to be used.

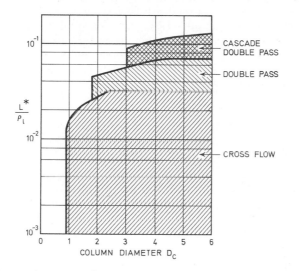

Figure 5.26 Diagram for tentative selection of tray-type absorption tower

In case of large column diameters and high liquid loads the use of three or more passes is often recommended; however, an unequal distribution of the liquid between the passes can arise, resulting in highly different vapour–liquid ratios across the tray. Here the installation of a number of relatively small circular or rectangular downcomers, which are evenly distributed across the tray, is recommended. Each of these downcomers discharges into a pan which is situated at a distance of one third to one half times the tray spacing above the tray below. This construction has the additional advantage that the area, otherwise needed for the outlet downcomer, is used as bubbling area. On the other hand, the use of this relatively short downcomer promotes downcomer flooding.

5.5.2 General Hydraulic Characteristics

The way in which the liquid and vapour interact depends for a well-loaded tray only to a minor degree on the type of contacting device, provided the area available for vapour passage into the aerated mass is adequate and evenly distributed. The vapour stream, issuing from the apertures, disintegrates, thereby causing a well-agitated gas–liquid mass. Above this pulsating froth a zone of liquid slugs and droplets is present. This zone gradually becomes a mist of very small droplets, which is carried away by the vapour to the tray above.

When the vapour load is decreased, the devices exhibit different hydraulic characteristics as a result of their construction, for instance intermittent bubbling with bubble caps and weeping with sieve trays.

Due to the passage of the vapour through the apertures of the contacting device and through the froth a pressure difference h_t exists between two trays. This pressure difference is made up of the dry plate pressure drop h_{pd} depending on construction of the contacting device and the pressure drop h_a, caused by the presence of the froth. Referring to Figure 5.27, the pressure drop h_a depends on the length of gas travel through the aerated mass and, thus on the difference between weir height and the highest exit point of the contacting device; in addition on the height of the liquid crest over the weir h_{ow}, the mean value of the liquid gradient $\frac{1}{2}\Delta$ and aeration factor β_a (defined by equation (5.137)).

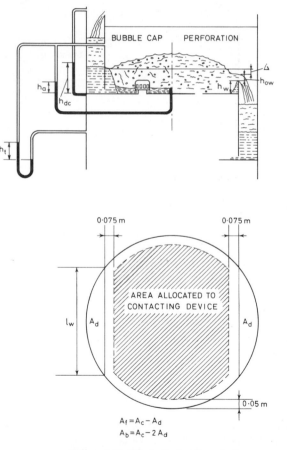

Figure 5.27 Schematic drawing of a tray

The clear liquid height in the downcomer is equal to $h_w + h_{ow} + \Delta + h_{ud} + h_t$, with h_{ud} representing the head loss caused by the liquid flow under the downcomer apron. If an inlet weir is used, $h_w + h_{ow}$ must be replaced by the corresponding heights valid for the inlet weir. The frothy liquid, which enters the downcomer gives rise to a higher actual height of aerated liquid. The residence time of the liquid must therefore be sufficiently large to allow for escape of entrained bubbles, otherwise the downcomer will soon be choked.

ENTRAINMENT FLOODING

It has already been stated that adequate distribution of the vapour results in an aerated mass (froth) having properties which depend only to a minor degree on the type of contacting device. With increasing vapour load the froth expands and tray liquid will finally reach the tray above, either by jetting or by expansion of the froth itself. Some of the liquid will be entrained by the vapour, thereby narrowing the passage available for vapour flow, which results in a sharp increase of the pressure drop. This, together with the increased liquid load raises the level in the downcomer and leads to choking of the tray.

This flooding phenomenon can be described[115] by a load factor $u_f (\rho_g/(\rho_t - \rho_g))^{\frac{1}{2}}$ and a flow parameter $(L^*/G^*)(\rho_g/\rho_l)^{\frac{1}{2}}$; and depends furthermore on the tray spacing, the surface tension and the foaming tendency of the liquid. The load factor originates from the ratio of the forces, acting on a suspended liquid drop, namely,

$$(u^2 \rho_g . \pi/4\, d_d^2)/[g(\rho_l - \rho_g) . \pi/6\, d_d^3]$$

It appears that the diameter term can be set proportional to the tray spacing T_s and to the 0·4 power of the surface tension. With small tray spacings

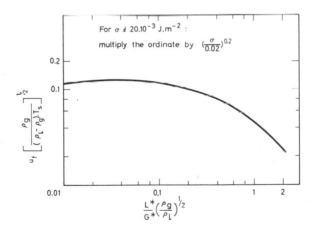

Figure 5.28 Correlation for entrainment flooding

($<0·2$ m) it is better to use the distance between the top of the weir and the plate above $(T_s - h_w)$ instead of the tray spacing. Figure 5.28, derived from literature data[116, 117, 80], shows the relation between $u_f [\rho_g/(TS.(\rho_l - \rho_g))]^{\frac{1}{2}}$ and $(L^*/G^*)(\rho_g/\rho_l)^{\frac{1}{2}}$ for non- to low-foaming systems and $\sigma \approx 20 \times 10^{-3}$ J/m².

For values of the flow parameter larger than 0·05 the curve can be described by the following equation

$$u_f \left[\frac{\rho_g}{(\rho_l - \rho_g) . T_s} \right]^{\frac{1}{2}} = \frac{20 - 3H}{218 H + 148} \qquad (5.128)$$

with $H = (L^*/G^*)(\rho_g/\rho_l)^{\frac{1}{2}}$.

Sieve trays having a ratio of hole area/bubbling area smaller than 0·10 show a lower permissible flooding velocity than that calculated from equation (5.128). The calculated velocity should be corrected by means of the factor[117] given in Table 5.7. With foaming systems the flooding velocity is also reduced. The factors given by Glitsch[119] are suggested, Table 5.8.

Table 5.7 FLOODING VELOCITY CORRECTION (NON-FOAMING SYSTEMS) FOR RATIOS OF HOLE AREA/BUBBLING AREA SMALLER THAN 0·1

Hole area/bubbling area	Factor
0·10	1·0
0·08	0·9
0·06	0·8

Table 5.8 FLOODING VELOCITY CORRECTION (FOAMING SYSTEMS) FOR RATIOS OF HOLE AREA/BUBBLING AREA SMALLER THAN 0·1

System	Factor	Example
non-foaming	1·00	
moderate foaming	0·85	oil absorber, amine and glycol regenerator
heavy foaming	0·73	amine and glycol absorber
severe foaming	0·60	solvent (methyl ethyl ketone/aromatic) fractionator in de-waxing of lubricating oil
foam-stable	0·30–0·60	caustic regenerators

DOWNCOMER FLOODING

When the level of the aerated liquid in the downcomer passes the top of the weir, the froth height on the tray and thus the pressure drop will rise, finally resulting in flooding of the tray. This can be caused by:

(a) too short a residence time of the liquid in the downcomer. The entrained vapour cannot disengage from the liquid. A residence time t_{dc} of 3 sec, based on the clear liquid height is regarded as a minimum for non-foaming systems[120]. With foaming systems this residence time should be divided by the same factors as given in Table 5.8.

(b) A pressure drop, h_t, which is too high. In this case the height of the aerated liquid exceeds the sum of tray spacing + weir height. This height depends on the relative density of the froth ρ_f/ρ_l which varies from a value of approximately 1 at the bottom of the downcomer to a much lower value at the froth–vapour interface up in the downcomer. A conservative average value of 0·5 for ρ_f/ρ_l is generally assumed with both foaming and non-foaming systems[120]. This corresponds to a maximal allowable clear liquid height equal to half the height of the downcomer.

DOWNCOMER PROPERTIES

Under this heading both the height of the liquid crest over the weir, h_{ow}, and the head loss due to passage of the liquid under the downcomer apron, h_{ud}, are discussed.

(a) Height of the liquid over the weir

The height of the liquid crest over a straight weir is calculated by means of the Francis weir formula

$$h_{ow} = 0.66 \left(\frac{L^*}{\rho_l l_w} \right)^{\frac{2}{3}} \tag{5.129}$$

A minimum value of 0·006 m for h_{ow} is recommended. Should this not be the case, then a notched (sawtooth) weir with a maximum depth of the notches of 0·01 m should be used.

With notches not running full h_{ow} is given by[121]:

$$h_{ow} = 1.16 \left(\frac{L^* . h_n}{\rho_l . l_w} \right)^{\frac{2}{5}} \tag{5.130}$$

When the height over the weir exceeds the depth of the notches h_n, then h_{ow} must be calculated by trial and error from[121]:

$$\frac{L^*}{\rho_l} = 0.195 \frac{l_w}{h_n} [h_{ow}^{\frac{5}{2}} - (h_{ow} - h_n)^{\frac{5}{2}}] \tag{5.131}$$

(b) Head loss due to flow under the downcomer apron

This loss is calculated from the following equation[120]:

$$h_{ud} = 0.165 \left(\frac{L^*}{\rho_l A_{ud}} \right)^2 \tag{5.132}$$

In order to avoid vapour passing up through the downcomer some apron seal (weir height minus clearance under apron) is necessary. Taking in account possible departures from true level of the tray, the amount of apron seal is set dependent on the length of the flowpath, i.e. the distance between

Table 5.9 APRON SEAL

Length of flow path (m)	Apron seal (mm)
< 1·5	10
1·5–3	25
> 3	40

downcomer apron and outlet weir. The values given in Table 5.9 are recommended[120]. If these values cannot be met, for instance with extremely high liquid loads, then an inlet weir must be installed.

5.5.3 Properties of Bubble Cap Plates

DIMENSIONS

Although a great variety of bubble caps are in use, round standardized caps seem to be preferable[122,123]. These caps are available in three or four diameters, ranging from 75 mm to 150 mm. In view of the area losses between the capped field and the tower wall the cap to be used depends on the column diameter, Table 5.10. Under certain circumstances, for instance if a low vapour pressure drop of the column is required, special constructions are advised[124]. The properties of these types of caps belong to the manufacturer's know-how. We shall confine ourselves to the plain slotted type of cap as sketched in Figure 5.29

Table 5.10 RECOMMENDED BUBBLE CAP DIAMETERS

Column diameter (m)	Cap diameter (mm)
0·5–2·0	75–100
1·5–4·5	100–125
3·0–6·0	125–150

In this context it is worth noting that caps without slots show the same efficiency and capacity as slotted caps[125,126]. With regard to the various dimensions and geometrical layout refer to Table 5.11 and Figures 5.27

Table 5.11 GEOMETRICAL DIMENSIONS

General			
A_d/A_c	ratio of downcomer area to column area	0·05–0·15	—
l_w/D_c	ratio of weir length to column diameter	0·60–0·80	—
h_w	weir height	40–100	mm
h_n	height of notches in weir	10	mm
T_s	tray spacing	300–900	mm
Bubble cap trays			
d_c	cap diameter	75–150	mm
$(l_p - d_c)$	distance between caps	25–75	mm
d_r/d_c	ratio of riser diameter to cap diameter	∼ 0·7	—
A_{rev}/A_r	ratio of reversal area to riser area	1·0–1·35	—
A_s/A_r	ratio of slot area to riser area	1–1·8	—
h_{ss}	static slot seal	15–40	mm
H_s	slot height	20–30	mm
h_{sc}	skirt clearance	10–30	mm
Sieve trays			
d_h	hole diameter	4–20	mm
l_p/d_h	ratio of hole pitch to hole diameter	2·5–4	—

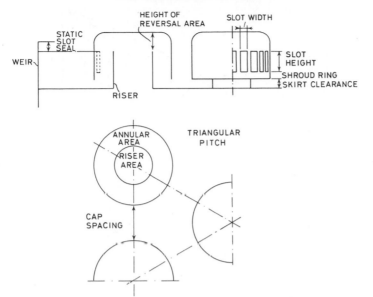

Figure 5.29 Schematic drawing of a bubble cap

and 5.29. Although different downcomer types may be employed (sloped apron downcomer, envelope downcomer, circular downcomer) only the segmental downcomer with vertical apron will be considered here.

PRESSURE DROP OF THE CAP

The pressure drop of the cap is made up from two parts: the pressure drop as a result of vapour flow through riser, reversal and annular area and the pressure drop through the slots in the presence of liquid. The pressure drop of the cap internals can be described by an equation, derived by Bolles[122]

$$h_{ci} = \frac{0 \cdot 18}{\rho_g(\rho_l - \rho_g)} \cdot \frac{G^{*2}}{A_{an} \cdot A_r} \tag{5.133}$$

The equation is valid for a reversal area of $1 \cdot 35 \times$ the average of annular and riser area. The pressure drop in the slots is generally set equal to the height of the slot opening h_0. For rectangular, triangular and trapezoidal slots the maximum vapour load of fully opened slots is calculated from[122]

$$G^*_{max} = C_s[H_s \cdot \rho_g(\rho_l - \rho_g)]^{\frac{1}{2}} \cdot A_s \tag{5.134}$$

Factor C_s is a function of the ratio

$$R_s = \frac{\text{slot width at top of slots}}{\text{slot width at bottom of slots}},$$

R_s varies from 0 for a triangular slot to 1 for a rectangular slot. The ratio of the actual vapour load and the calculated maximum vapour load determines the percentage over which the total slot height is opened, see Figure

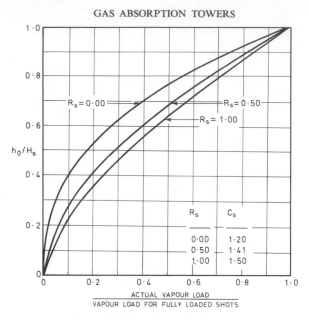

Figure 5.30 Correlation for slot opening

5.30. For caps that are not slotted it is advised to use the following formula, principally valid for rectangular slots[127]:

$$h_0 = 0.354\left[\frac{1}{\rho_g(\rho_l-\rho_g)}\cdot\left(\frac{G^*}{N_c d_c}\right)^2\right]^{\frac{1}{3}} \tag{5.135}$$

PRESSURE DROP DUE TO THE HYDROSTATIC HEAD OF THE AERATED MASS

The pressure losses as a result of flow through the liquid consist of the loss due to formation of 'bubbles' and the loss due to flow through the aerated mass. The loss due to surface tension (bubble formation) can generally be neglected. Pressure drop h_a can be described by

$$h_a = \beta_a(h_{ss}+h_{ow}+\tfrac{1}{2}\Delta) \tag{5.136}$$

An approximate value of the aeration factor β_a is calculated from

$$\beta_a = \frac{u_b\rho_g^{\frac{1}{2}}+2}{2u_b\rho_g^{\frac{1}{2}}+2} \tag{5.137}$$

PRESSURE DROP OF THE WET TRAY

The total pressure drop is acquired by addition of the cap pressure drop and pressure drop due to the presence of the aerated mass.

$$h_t = h_{ci}+h_0+\beta_a(h_{ss}+h_{ow}+\tfrac{1}{2}\Delta) \tag{5.138}$$

LIQUID GRADIENT

The liquid gradient is the difference between the clear liquid heights at the inlet side and at the nearest weir and is the result of the liquid flow through the aerated mass. Based on fluid hydraulics Davies[128] developed a relation between the relevant variables, which was simplified by Mittelstrass and Hoppe[129]. For bubble caps with an annular area equal to riser area, placed on equilateral triangular pitch the equation has the following form:

$$\Delta_1^{\frac{1}{2}}\left\{\Delta_1(1\cdot5\,N_r - 1\cdot4) + 3\,N_r\left[h_w + h_{ow} + h_{sc}\left(\frac{d_c - d_r}{l_p - d_c}\right)\right]\right\} =$$

$$0\cdot06\left(\frac{L^*}{\rho_l.l_l}\right)^{\frac{1}{2}}.\frac{N_r^{\frac{3}{2}}.l_p}{l_p - d_c} \tag{5.139}$$

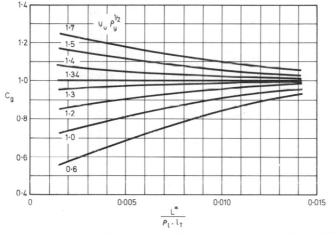

Figure 5.31 Liquid gradient correction factor for vapour load and liquid load

The value of Δ_1 is valid for a flow factor $u_0\rho_g^{\frac{1}{2}}$ equal to $1\cdot34$; for other flow factors the liquid gradient Δ is obtained by means of a correction factor C_g for Δ_1, which depends on the liquid load, Figure 5.31.

CLEAR LIQUID HEIGHT IN THE DOWNCOMER

As already stated in paragraph 5.5.2 the clear liquid height in the down-comer corresponds to

$$h_{dc} = h_w + h_{ow} + \Delta + h_{ud} + h_t \tag{5.140}$$

ENTRAINMENT

The disengagement of the vapour from the aerated mass is accompanied with the formation of droplets. Part of this liquid, called entrainment, is carried with the vapour to the tray above and causes a lowering of the tray efficiency.

This effect can be described by means of the Colburn relation[130]

$$E_W = \frac{E_D}{1+(eE_D/L^*)} \qquad (5.141)$$

The entrainment rate e depends largely on the vapour velocity, the system properties and the tray spacing, and to a lower degree on the liquid load. Fair and Matthews[117] developed a correlation between the fractional entrainment ψ and the percent flood in dependence of the flow parameter $(L^*/G^*)(\rho_g/\rho_l)^{\frac{1}{2}}$, Figure 5.32.

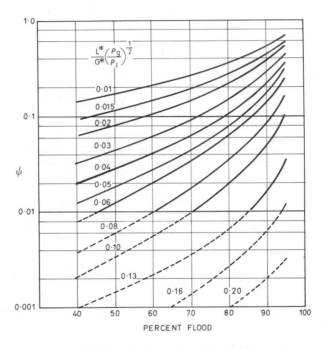

Figure 5.32 Fractional entrainment from bubble cap trays

The fractional entrainment is defined as follows

$$\psi = \frac{e}{L^* + e} \qquad (5.142)$$

The percent flood ratio is expressed as the ratio of the actual gas load and the gas load at flooding conditions for the same value of the flow parameter, taking into account the foaming tendency of the system (see 5.5.2). Combining equations (5.141) and (5.142) leads to

$$\frac{E_W}{E_D} = \frac{1}{1 + E_D\psi/(1-\psi)} \qquad (5.143)$$

In design practice the value of the percent flood is usually taken as 80 per cent. At normal gas absorption conditions the value of the flow parameter is rather high, to say 0·1 and higher. Hence it follows from Figure 5.32 and equation (5.143) that the effect of entrainment under these circumstances can be neglected. The accuracy of the predicted ψ-values amounts for $\psi > 0.10$ to ± 20 per cent. For ψ-values < 0.1 the accuracy is smaller.

LIMITING HYDRAULIC CONDITIONS

(a) Vapour pulsation

With very low vapour rates the vapour will occasionally escape from the caps. This pulsating flow results in a lowering of the plate efficiency due to insufficient contacting of vapour and liquid.

Bolles[122] recommends a minimum slot opening of 12 mm to avoid vapour pulsation. It is clear that with smooth caps low vapour velocities will sooner give rise to pulsating vapour flow. In these circumstances the use of this type of cap has to be avoided.

(b) Coning

With low slot submergences and high vapour velocities the vapour issuing from the slots forms a channel or cone, giving rise to very short contact times, thereby lowering the efficiency. Lockhart and Leggett[58] suggest that a clear liquid height above the top of the slots of 12 mm or more will be sufficient to provide for well aerated liquid.

(c) Dumping and vapour distribution

High liquid gradients and a low vapour pressure drop of the cap may cause dumping of the liquid through the risers due to the fact that the kinetic energy of the vapour is not sufficiently large to 'penetrate' into the liquid layer. This will occur where the liquid layer is high, also at the inlet side of the tray. A less extreme difference between liquid head and velocity head leads to serious maldistribution of the vapour flow, accompanied with considerable cross flow of the vapour in the vapour space between the positions of the lowest liquid heights, i.e. the near outlet sides of the tray. A measure for this is formed by the vapour distribution ratio R_v, formulated as the ratio of liquid gradient and mean cap pressure drop. The maximum acceptable value of R_v, at which the cross flow of vapour is tolerable is given by Bolles[122]

$$R_v = \frac{\Delta}{h_{ci} + h_0} \leqslant 0.5 \tag{5.144}$$

THE PERFORMANCE DIAGRAM

For a given tray it is possible to calculate the various hydrodynamic properties in terms of vapour load and liquid load. Plotted in a diagram with these loads as axes the various hydrodynamic limits enclose an area, in which the tray will perform well, Figure 5.33.

This diagram offers a valuable visual aid in design. In such a case the gas and liquid load are generally known beforehand. The position of the load point in the diagram is also fixed. The area of stable operation (which is determined by the tray variables) must now be 'shaped' around the load point in such a manner that the desired hydrodynamic requirements are met. The customary safety factors should of course be taken into account.

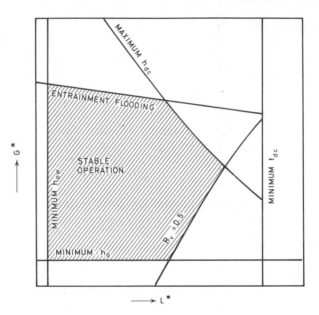

Figure 5.33 Performance diagram of a bubble cap tray

If, for instance, the smallest column diameter must be obtained, then the highest permissible vapour velocity (at the chosen tray spacing) should be applied; here entrainment flooding will be the limiting condition.

5.5.4 Properties of Sieve Trays (Perforated Trays)

DIMENSIONS

When first introduced, sieve trays were only hesitatingly used, because the tray was thought to be very sensitive to load variations. The improvement in design methods, however, combined with the low cost have made it extremely popular. Meanwhile it was found that the formerly used hole diameters of 2–4 mm could be increased to values up to 20 mm without significant loss in capacity or efficiency[125]. A further advantage of the use of large hole diameters is the prevention of hole-blocking crusts with dirty absorption liquids, a drawback for which small holes were very sensitive.

Normally the holes are placed in an equilateral triangular pattern with a pitch-hole diameter ratio ranging from 2·5 to 4. For the perforated area this corresponds to a fraction hole area varying between 0·15 and 0·06, see Table 5.11. With regard to the dimensions of the tray variables not specific for the contacting device proper, the values given in Figure 5.27 and Table 5.11 should also be used with sieve trays.

PRESSURE DROP OF A SIEVE TRAY

The total pressure drop is calculated as for bubble cap trays.

The dry sieve tray pressure drop can be described by the following equation[131]:

$$h_{hd} = \frac{0 \cdot 051}{\rho_g \cdot \rho_l} \left[\left(1 - \frac{A_h}{A_f} \right)^2 + 0 \cdot 21 \left(\frac{d_h}{b} \right)^{1 \cdot 27} \right] \cdot \left(\frac{G^*}{A_h} \right)^2 \tag{5.145}$$

PRESSURE DROP DUE TO THE HYDROSTATIC HEAD OF THE AERATED MASS

The calculation of this pressure loss differs in no way from the procedure followed with bubble caps. Equation (5.136) adapted for sieve trays states:

$$h_a = \beta_a (h_w + h_{ow} + \tfrac{1}{2}\Delta) \tag{5.146}$$

PRESSURE DROP OF THE WET TRAY

Adding the dry tray pressure drop and the share of the aerated mass leads to:

$$h_t = h_{hd} + \beta_a (h_w + h_{ow} + \tfrac{1}{2}\Delta) \tag{5.147}$$

LIQUID GRADIENT

Due to the absence of parts of the contacting device projecting above the tray floor the liquid gradient on sieve trays is much smaller than on bubble cap trays. In this context it is worth noting that choice of the tray type according to paragraph 5.5.1, Figure 5.26, is only advised, because sufficient data on sieve tray columns are lacking. If desired, the value of Δ can be calculated by the relation of Hughmark and O'Connell[132], modified by Fair[133]:

$$\Delta = 4 \times 10^3 \; \mu_l \cdot \frac{L^*}{\beta_a} \cdot \frac{l}{l_T} \left(\frac{2}{l_T} + \frac{2\beta_a - 1}{\beta_a} \cdot \frac{1}{h_w + h_{ow}} \right)^2 \tag{5.148}$$

CLEAR LIQUID HEIGHT IN THE DOWNCOMER

Addition of all the head losses gives for h_{dc}:

$$h_{dc} = h_w + h_{ow} + \Delta + h_{ud} + h_t \tag{5.149}$$

The entrainment characteristics of sieve trays differ somewhat from those of bubble caps, especially in the region of low percentages flood ratios.

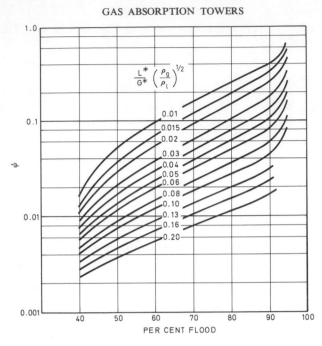

Figure 5.34 Fractional entrainment from sieve trays

This can be seen by comparing Figure 5.32 and Figure 5.34, the latter being given by Fair[117].

The conclusions, drawn in paragraph 5.5.3, are also valid for sieve trays.

LIMITING HYDRAULIC CONDITIONS

(a) Weeping and dumping

With low vapour velocities excessive flow of liquid through the holes sets a lower limit to stable tray operation. Just as it is the case with entrainment the fraction of the total liquid flow that passes the holes will lower the efficiency. This is especially the case when high gas–liquid ratios are encountered. Normally a fairly large amount of weepage, for instance 25 per cent of the nominal liquid load may be tolerated. An absolute lower limit to stable operation is formed by dumping. According to Chase[134] dumping occurs when the total liquid flow passes the holes instead of the weir. For incipient weepage the formula given by Hoppe and Mittelstrass[118] is used. This formula relates the minimum dry tray pressure drop at incipient weepage to the clear liquid height on the tray:

$$(h_{hd})_{iw} = 5 \cdot 1 \times 10^{-3} + 0 \cdot 10 \, \beta_a (h_w + h_{ow}) \tag{5.150}$$

According to Zenz and co-workers[135] the amount of weepage can be calculated from the difference between the value of $w_h \rho_g^{\frac{1}{2}}$ at incipient weepage, equations (5.148) and (5.145), and the actual value of $w_h \rho_g^{\frac{1}{2}}$, both taken at the same submergence $h_w + h_{ow}$. From their data the following formula is derived:

$$w_w \rho_l^{\frac{1}{2}} = 6 \times 10^{-4} \left[(w_h \rho_g^{\frac{1}{2}})_{iw} - w_h \rho_g^{\frac{1}{2}} \right]^3 \qquad (5.151)$$

The value of h_{ow} to be used for the calculation of $(w_h \rho_g^{\frac{1}{2}})_{iw}$ depends on the quantity of liquid flowing over the weir, equation (5.129). This quantity is on its turn determined by the amount of weepage. This necessitates a trial and error solution for w_w.

(b) Coning

Application of the same criterion as given in section 5.3 shows that coning will not occur on a sieve tray, unless the static liquid height is smaller than 12 mm, which will seldom be the case.

(c) Vapour distribution ratio

The condition for ensuring a good vapour distribution as given in section 5.5.3 for bubble caps is also used here, on the understanding that the dry hole pressure drop must be used

$$R_v = \frac{\Delta}{h_{hd}} \leqslant 0.5 \qquad (5.152)$$

PERFORMANCE DIAGRAM

Identical with the bubble cap tray (5.5.3), the performance diagram serves as a guide in designing a sieve tray. The various hydrodynamic conditions given in the foregoing paragraphs lead to a diagram as given in Figure 5.35.

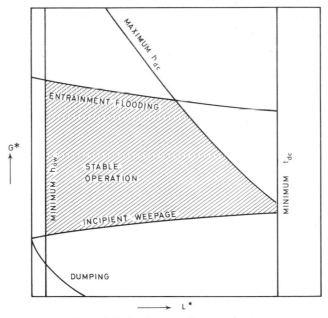

Figure 5.35 Performance diagram of a sieve tray

5.5.5 Valve Trays

The application of valve trays has increased enormously due to the circumstance that the valve tray, though more expensive than a sieve tray, has a high flexibility with regard to the vapour flow. With low vapour loads a part of the valves on the tray is closed, thus limiting the amount of weepage whilst maintaining a high efficiency of the tray. It is claimed by the manufacturer that a turndown ratio (i.e. the ratio maximum/minimum load) of 5 can easily be acquired.

Being a proprietary contacting device, available in different valve forms (round, rectangular, square) and valve weights, general information about the hydrodynamic characteristics cannot be given except on the limit set by entrainment flooding, paragraph 5.5.2.

The usual dimensions for the valves are 40–50 mm for the diameter of round valves and the side of square valves. Rectangular valves as shown in Figure 5.21 have a length of 125 mm and a width of 28 mm. The maximum clearance above the tray deck varies from 6 mm to 11 mm depending on the valve type. The centres of the round valves are generally placed in an equilateral triangular pattern with a pitch-diameter ratio varying from 1·5 to 3. Square valves are placed in square array with a pitch-diameter ratio of 1·3–1·5 while for rectangular valves the distance between the valves amounts to circa 30 mm.

To minimize the tendency to stick the valves, when in the closed position, rest on tabs or dimples in the valve rim of about 1–2·5 mm. The holes in the tray deck are a few mm smaller than the valve.

5.5.6 Summary of Hydraulic Design Considerations

In the foregoing, a number of hydraulic limits set to a satisfactory operating range have been mentioned; a survey, with reference to the relevant paragraphs, is given in Table 5.12.

Table 5.12 GENERAL DESIGN CONSIDERATIONS

General			Paragraph
% flood	$\leqslant 80$	—	5.5.2, 5.5.3
h_{ow} = height over weir	0·006–0·035	m	5.5.2
h_{dc} = 'height' of clear liquid in downcomer	$\leqslant 0\cdot5\,(T_s + h_w)$	m	5.5.2
t_{dc} = residence time of liquid in downcomer	$\geqslant \dfrac{3}{\text{foaming factor}}$	s	5.5.2
Bubble cap trays			
h_0 = slot opening	$\geqslant 0\cdot012$	m	5.5.3
$R_v = \dfrac{\Delta}{h_{ci} + h_o}$ = vapour distribution ratio	$\leqslant 0\cdot5$	—	5.5.3
Sieve trays			
$\dfrac{\text{amount weepage}}{\text{nominal liquid load}}$	$\leqslant 0\cdot25$	—	5.5.4
$R_v = \dfrac{\Delta}{h_{hd}}$ = vapour distribution ratio	$\leqslant 0\cdot5$	—	5.5.4

5.6 Practical Aspects

Various practical aspects of the construction, operation, maintenance, instrumentation, liquid–gas ratio and economics will now be discussed briefly.

5.6.1 Construction

PACKED TOWERS

The construction of packed towers is relatively straightforward. The packed bed rests on a support plate; redistributors are installed when maldistribution occurs. It is advisable to instal the redistributing plates at bed depths of $2.5–3$ D_c with Raschig rings, $5–8$ D_c with Intalox and Berl saddles and $5–10$ D_c with Pall rings, with an overriding maximum bed depth of 6 m[107]. The redistributor plate also can serve as support plate in case of a large packed height with fragile packings.

Hold-down plates are desirable to confine the pieces of packing, especially with ceramic, carbon and plastic packings. Without a hold-down plate movement of the bed (as a result of surges at high loads) will cause the packing to chip or wear. The free space will gradually be lessened and the tower capacity falls off, making a more frequent clean-out necessary. With plastic packings floating of the packing at the top of the bed will be prevented if a hold-down plate is used.

At the top of the bed a liquid distributor with an adequate number of distribution points provides for an even irrigation of the packing. Various kinds of liquid distributors are illustrated in Figures 5.36 and 5.37.

The support plate should have at least 75 per cent free area. As a portion of this area will be blocked off by the packing, supports with a lower percentage free area will cause flooding at the support. The simplest support consists of a grid with relatively widely spaced bars on which a few layers of large partition rings or Raschig rings are stacked. Partition rings are Raschig rings, carrying one (Lessing rings) or two (cross partition rings) webs in their diameter.

A larger fraction free area is obtained with the 'gas injection' support plate[89]. This plate is essentially a perforated base on which cylindrical or beam-type risers are placed, see Figure 5.38. The sides and sometimes the tops of the risers are slotted. It is obvious that the beam-type construction has a much greater load-bearing capacity than the plate with cylindrical risers. The support plates mentioned above also serve well as redistributors in cases where it is necessary to split up the packed bed in two or more sections.

The use of wall wipers (flat or conical rings, attached to the shell) in the packed bed is not recommended as the restricted area will give rise to premature flooding.

Hold-down plates are constructed as a simple grid or as a heavy wire mesh, fastened to a grid with widely spaced bars. Both types rest on the packing; with fixed plates the possibility exists that due to settling of the bed packing units are blown against the grid and crushed by impact.

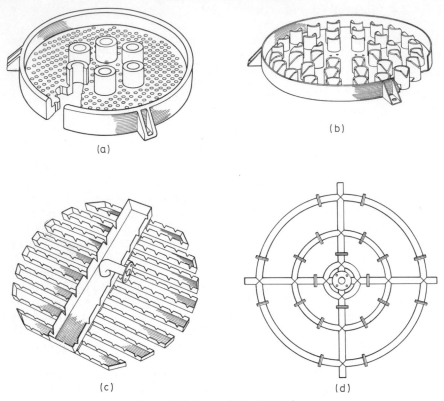

Figure 5.36 Types of Liquid Distributor

(a) A simple orifice type. This type gives very fine distribution but must be correctly sized for a
     particular duty and should not be used where there is any risk of the holes plugging
(b) Notched chimney type of distributor, which has a good range of flexibility for the medium and
     upper flow rates, and is not prone to blockage
(c) Notched trough distributor which is specially suitable for the larger sizes of tower. Because
     of its large free area it is also suitable for the higher gas rates
(d) Perforated ring type of distributor for use with absorption columns where high gas rates and
     relatively small liquid rates are encountered. This type is especially suitable where pressure
     loss must be minimized. For the larger size of tower where installation through manholes is
     necessary, it may be made up in flanged sections
                              (Courtesy Hydronyl Ltd)

A high degree of evenness in the initial liquid distribution is of utmost
importance. Although with dumped packings an irregular distribution
becomes increasingly regular as the liquid flows downwards, this equalization
of the liquid distribution is only achieved at the cost of a loss in effective
column height. With large diameter towers ($D_c > 1$ m) good distribution
means at least forty distribution points per square metre of cross-sectional
tower area; with smaller towers this number should be increased[107].
It is evident that for both the trough type or perforated plate type of
liquid distributors and for the support plates when used as redistributors

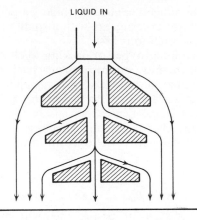

Figure 5.37 Distributor for dirty liquids

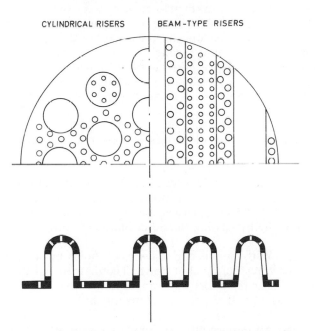

Figure 5.38 Schematic drawing of a 'gas injection' support plate

accurate levelling is necessary. With exception of the perforated ring type distributor the column internals are (in a more or less modified form) available in ceramic, metal and plastic.

Various packings, ranging in size from 10 to 150 mm, are used. In large-scale equipment rings of a diameter smaller than 15 mm are very seldom used. An important factor is the behaviour of the packing material under the operating conditions of the process. If a very large amount of packing is going to be used under difficult conditions (high temperature, corrosion, etc.) it is advisable to perform experiments with a small amount of the packing material under similar conditions first.

Besides the more common types of packing, such as Raschig rings, Berl saddles and Pall rings, there are a number of new packings such as cylindrical pads of corrugated knitted wire gauze strip, made up to any desired diameter and combining a large surface area, up to 2000 m^2/m^3, with a high free gas space, up to 95 per cent. In most cases they ensure a lower pressure drop and higher mass-transfer rates but at a much higher cost. The attitude of industrial engineers towards all these new varieties is still rather conservative.

PLATE TOWERS

Accessibility. The tower shell can be provided with manways of 0·6 m o.d. to give easy access for inspection and maintenance. If the diameter of the column is large enough ($> 1·5$ m) the trays are generally equipped with a removable section (internal manway). In this case the tray spacing should be at least 0·6 m to permit workmen to move between the trays. The maximum number of trays to be installed between column man-holes amounts to 10. Metal trays made up in sections are preferred to welded trays because they can be installed and removed through the column manholes.

The tray sections should be easily detachable with a minimum of bolts or clamps, which must be accessible from the topside of the tray. Tray thicknesses of 2–4 mm are in use. Sufficient tray support members should be provided.

Levelness. With large tray diameters a maximum difference of 6 mm is permissible.

Outlet weir. Sometimes overflow weirs can be vertically adjusted to facilitate initial levelling of the tray. The ratio weir length–column diameter should not be too small ($> 0·6$ m) otherwise the liquid will flow through the centre of the tray, thereby by-passing the outer bubbling area.

Drainage holes. With bubble-cap trays weep holes must be provided for drainage of the trays during shut-down. The diameter of the holes, which must be placed near the outlet weir ranges from 6 to 15 mm. The total hole area should amount to 0·03 per cent of the tray area.

Standardization. An important factor in plate tower fabrication is standardization as the cost of standardized equipment is always less than the cost of specialties. Tower diameters, plate spacing, sizes of bubble caps, weir lengths, etc., can be standardized to a large extent without giving up the great variety of demands required by mass-transfer and hydraulic factors in industrial practice. According to Schulz[136] the following standardized diameters are recommended: 0·5; 0·6; 0·8; 1; 1·2; 1·4; 1·6; 2·0; 2·4; 2·8; 3·2; 3·6; 4·0; 5·0; 6·3; 8·0 m. Four types of bubble-caps are recommended: 75; 100; 125; 150 mm while the ratio of weir length to tower diameter should be in the range of 0·60–0·80.

5.6.2 Liquid Hold-up

Special attention should be given to the dimensioning of the bottom part of the tower. It should be remembered that when a pump is shut off or when the gas-flow is taken back, the entire liquid suspended on the packing or on the plates, will trickle downwards. With packed towers this can amount to about 10–15 per cent of the packed volume.

For water the liquid hold-up in *packed towers* is approximately given by Leva[89] as

$$(\varepsilon_l)_w = \text{m}^3 \text{ liquid/m}^3 \text{ tower volume} \approx 2\cdot3 \times 10^{-3} \left(\frac{L}{d_e}\right)^{0\cdot6} \qquad (5.153)$$

where d_e is the diameter of an equivalent sphere. For Raschig rings and Berl saddles: $d_e \approx 0\cdot85\,(d_p)^{0\cdot95}$. (Subscript w = water).

Equation (5.153) is valid below the loading point and for a packing dumped at random. The effect of the nature of the liquid upon the hold-up is given by[137]

$$\frac{(\varepsilon_l)}{(\varepsilon_l)_w} \approx \left(\frac{\mu_l}{\mu_w}\right)^{0\cdot1} \left(\frac{\rho_w}{\rho_l}\right)^{0\cdot8} \left(\frac{\sigma_w}{\sigma_l}\right)^n \qquad (5.154)$$

where exponent n depends on the liquid load and $n = 2\cdot1 - 1\cdot4^{10} \log L$.

The liquid hold-up in plate towers may be calculated from the clear liquid-height h_l. For bubble-caps[67]

$$h_l = 0\cdot042 + 0\cdot19\,h_w - \frac{\pi}{4}D_c^2 \left(0\cdot014\frac{G}{A_b\sqrt{\rho_g}} - 24\cdot6\frac{L}{\rho_l \cdot l_T}\right) \qquad (5.155)$$

For perforated trays[138]

$$h_l = 0\cdot025 + 0\cdot22\,h_w - \frac{\pi}{4}D_c^2 \left(0\cdot011\frac{G}{A_b\sqrt{\rho_g}} - 45\cdot4\frac{L}{\rho_l \cdot l_T}\right) \qquad (5.156)$$

Regarding the lack of appropriate data the last formula should also be used with valve trays.

5.6.3 Operation and Maintenance

There should be no difficulties with the initial start-up of packed towers. With bubble-cap towers, waste material may be left in the downcomers during construction, and thus may cause premature flooding on start-up. Flooding has also been caused on occasion by a bubble-cap which has become detached on start-up and then lodged in a downcomer.

Various faults may develop in the operation of packed towers. Thus distributors may become silted up, and require cleaning, or may become out of level. Packings may also be fouled in operation, and have to be removed for cleaning; with ceramic packings, this may result in a large amount of breakages. Breakages of packing units during operation can cause the packing to sink in the tower, and this may interfere with the operation of distributors. If fouling takes place, the voidage of the packing will be effectively reduced, and thus the pressure-drop across the tower will increase; the pressure-drop can thus be used as a guide to indicate when cleaning of the packing is required. Plate towers, of course, do not suffer from distribution difficulties, but, like packed towers, are liable to become fouled; as before, fouling is indicated by an increase in the pressure-drop across the tower. Plate towers can be cleaned chemically, or by hand if man-holes have been provided.

5.6.4 Instrumentation

Absorption towers are generally controlled manually and comparatively little instrumentation is required. Apart from the analyses of the exit gas, it is usual to measure the following:

The gas temperature at inlet and exit.

The inlet gas flow rate.

The liquid flow rate.

The pressure-drop across the tower; this gives an indication of whether the packing is fouled, or whether flooding is taking place.

Control and adjustment of the liquid rate is simple as in most cases this is usually set to a rather safe margin. With gas purification the exit gas concentration is important, regular analysis by 'continuous' measurement or probably from snap tests will be necessary.

5.6.5 Safety

Safety in the operation of absorption towers depends largely, of course, on the character of the absorption process. Where a highly toxic gas is being absorbed, it may be necessary to site the towers in cubicles which are maintained under reduced pressure. The vent gases from the cubicles can then be sent under forced draught up a chimney. Automatic devices should be provided to detect any escape of the gas in question.

A different kind of hazard may arise when a corrosive or otherwise objectionable liquid is used as the absorbent. Any fault in the distribution system which causes the liquid to splash on to the packing will then result in a spray of the liquid being carried out of the tower by the gas. This can happen, for example, where some of the packing in the tower has been broken, so that the rest of the packing has settled down at a lower level; liquid from the distributor, instead of running on to the packing, then falls on to it from a height and causes splash.

In connection with questions of safety, it must be remembered that pressure absorption towers are regarded as pressure vessels, and are therefore inspected regularly. The prescribed interval between two inspections varies from country to country but two years seems to be a normal time-span for pressure vessels in the chemical industry. It is advisable, therefore, in pressure towers, for the tower internals to be easily removable without damage. Ceramic packings are particularly liable to suffer damage in this way.

5.6.6 Economic Liquid–Gas Ratio

The design factor of first importance is the liquid–gas ratio L/G, which determines to a great extent the slope of the operating line.

The choice of the liquid–gas ratio often is based on economic factors. From equations (5.102) to (5.105) it can be seen that the height of a transfer unit in packed towers strongly depends on the ratio L/G: when the resistance to mass-transfer is dominantly at the gas side it follows that

$$HTU_g^* \sim \left(\frac{L}{G}\right)^{-0\cdot4},$$

while for the case that the liquid-side resistance is large the influence of the liquid–gas ratio is even greater

$$HTU_g^* \sim \left(\frac{L}{G}\right)^{-1}$$

For plate towers it follows from equation (5.119) that the number of theoretical plates becomes smaller for large values of the liquid–gas ratio

$$N_t \sim \left(\ln\frac{L}{G}\right)^{-1}$$

Thus with increasing value of L/G the height of the tower and thus the capital costs will be less. This is offset to some degree because of the fact that the tower diameter will increase. On the other hand, with large values of L/G more liquid has to be circulated over the tower, leading to a greater energy consumption and also more of the absorbing liquid will be lost in the exit gases.

In general for each specific absorption system there exists an economic optimum for the liquid–gas ratio[99,100].

5.6.7 Economic Gas Velocity

With packed towers the tower diameter is selected by considering first a safe operating velocity with respect to flooding, for instance 70 per cent of the flooding velocity, and second the optimal velocity calculated from an economic balance between column costs and power costs. Data on capital costs of columns are given in Figures 5.39 to 5.41, they are approximates for Western European conditions in 1970. Generalized cost data are never precise, so for accurate results one has to use up-to-date information, which is very often time dependent and can fluctuate a great deal depending on local circumstances. The capital cost of an installed absorption tower, integrated in a chemical plant, i.e. with allowances for piping, concrete, instruments, insulation, paint, erection, setting, transport, labour, overheads, etc., may be calculated from

capital cost of installed tower $\approx$ 3 × Base Cost + Cost of Tower Shell +
Cost of Packing (or Plates)

where Base Cost = Cost of Tower Shell made of carbon steel.

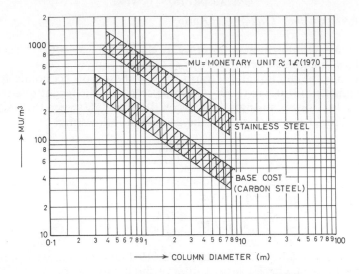

Figure 5.39 Approximate cost of tower shell

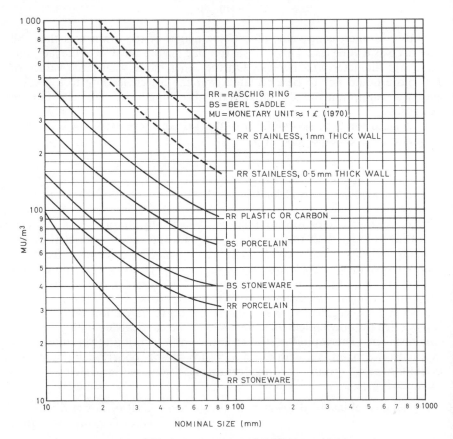

Figure 5.40 Approximate cost of various tower packings

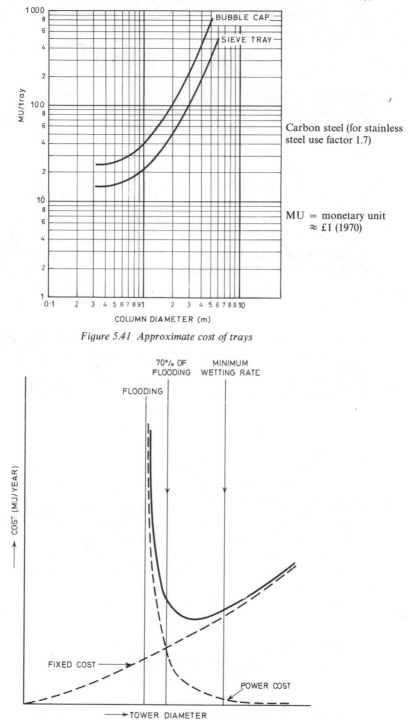

Figure 5.41 Approximate cost of trays

Figure 5.42 Economic column diameter (packed column)

From the data given it can be derived that the capital cost per unit height of tower (1 m) can be expressed by

$$\text{capital cost} = \left(\frac{\pi}{4}\right)^{\frac{1}{3}} : K_c \left(\frac{G^*}{G}\right)^{\frac{2}{3}} \tag{5.157}$$

in which K_c is equal to the capital cost of a tower section with unit height (installed) and a diameter of 1 m, while G^* is the total gas load in kg/s. Very often the fixed costs are taken as a certain percentage of the capital costs, allowing for depreciation (technical or economical?), maintenance, overheads, interest, etc.

Let F_f be this fraction of capital costs (usually this is taken as 0·25) then the fixed costs per year are given by

$$\text{fixed costs/year} = F_f \left(\frac{\pi}{4}\right)^{\frac{1}{3}} . K_c \left(\frac{G^*}{G}\right)^{\frac{2}{3}} = 0\cdot23\, K_c \left(\frac{G^*}{G}\right)^{\frac{2}{3}} \tag{5.158}$$

The variable costs per unit height of tower, which are mainly power costs are related to pressure drop and given by

$$\text{power costs/year} = 800 \times 10^3 \times \frac{f_e}{\eta} \times \frac{G^*}{\rho_g} \Delta P \tag{5.159}$$

in which f_e is the cost of power (MU/kWh) and η is the efficiency of fans and motors, while it is assumed further that the operation time is equal to 8000 h/year. The pressure drop per unit height of packing is given in paragraph 5.4.1, equation (5.126) and Figure 5.24. For each case the value of G, and thus the tower diameter

$$D_c = \left(\frac{4}{\pi} \frac{G^*}{G}\right)^{\frac{1}{2}},$$

for which the sum of power costs and fixed costs is a minimum may be found by computation of the total annual costs as a function of G or D_c. An illustration is shown in Figure 5.42.

Notice that the economic diameter preferentially must lie in between two technical limiting values: the flooding diameter (small) and the minimum wetting diameter (large). In most cases the economic diameter is near the diameter based on 70 per cent of flooding. It is interesting to observe that the economic optimum usually is associated with the velocity at which the fixed costs exceed three times the power costs. For quick estimates the optimal gas velocity may be found from:

$$G_{\text{opt}} \approx 0\cdot012\, C^{3/8} (G^*)^{-1/8} \tag{5.160}$$

in which:

$$C = \frac{K_c}{f_e}\eta \left\{ \frac{1 - 0\cdot5\, V_{fl}(35H+3)}{H+0\cdot43} \right\} \frac{\rho_l \rho_g^2}{F} \left(\frac{\rho_l}{\rho_w}\right) \left(\frac{\mu_w}{\mu_l}\right)^{0\cdot2}$$

The value of V_{fl} at flooding conditions is found from factor H by way of the flooding line of Figure 5.24.

Further simplification of formula (5.160) leads to

$$G_{opt} \approx 0.16 \left(\frac{K_c}{f_e} \eta . \frac{\rho_g^2}{F} \right)^{3/8} (G^*)^{-1/8} \qquad (5.161)$$

and

$$(D_c)_{opt} \approx 2.8 \left(\frac{f_e}{K_c . \eta} . \frac{F}{\rho_g^2} \right)^{3/16} (G^*)^{9/16} \qquad (5.162)$$

It follows that when power is expensive and for small sizes of packing material (factor F is large) the optimal diameter will increase. Notice further the influence of pressure: $(D_c)_{opt} \sim P^{-\frac{1}{4}}$.

With plate towers pressure drop is mainly determined by the height of the liquid layer on the plate while the dependence of pressure drop on gas velocity is only slight.

From this it follows that an economic tower diameter based on a balance between investment and power cost will be hardly perceptible. Narsimhan[139], however, has presented a paper in which pressure drop and capital costs are balanced against each other. One could also tackle the problem of economic tower diameter for plate towers by weighing tower diameter and plate spacing against each other on a minimal fixed cost basis; however, this will not lead to a sharp minimum in fixed costs.

5.7 Worked Examples

To reduce the concentration of sulphur dioxide from 5 per cent by volume to 0·05 per cent in a stream of dry-cleaned gas from a lead smelter. The gas is to be taken as 95 per cent nitrogen and 5 per cent sulphur dioxide. The washing liquor to be used is dimethylaniline (see E. P. Fleming, T. C. Fitt, Use of Dimethylaniline as Absorbant, *Ind. Eng. Chem.*, **42**, 2253 (1950)); the lean solvent recycled from the stripping section of the plant will contain not more than 0·1 wt.% of sulphur dioxide.

As the heat of solution is not to be neglected because a low temperature is favourable in preventing loss of solvent it is proposed to use a bubble-cap column (lead plated) provided with externally placed coolers, maintaining the column temperature at 20°C.

The working pressure will be about 1 bar abs.

Data	Gas	Liquid
Flow rate (m³/h)	30000 (standard)	30
Specific mass (kg/m³)	1·36	956
Viscosity (kg/m s)	1.8×10^{-5}	1.5×10^{-3}
Diffusivity SO_2 (m²/s)	1.1×10^{-5}	1.7×10^{-9}
Surface tension (J/m²)		37×10^{-3}
Specific heat (J/kg °C)		2200
Molecular weight	28–29·8	121
Thermal diffusivity (m²/s)		95×10^{-9}

The absorption process may be taken as physical dissolution of SO_2; the solubility follows Henry's law: at 20°C $H_e = 82$ kgmole/m³ bar. The heat of solution is 20×10^6 Jkg mole SO_2.

1. Mass-balance

From considerations outlined in paragraphs 5.2.1 and 5.2.3 the conditions at the top and the bottom of the column follow as:

	Bottom	Top
Gas load (kg/s)	11·1	9·9
Liquid load (kg/s)	9·2	8·0
Gas concentration (kgmole/m³)	$2·05 \times 10^{-3}$	$0·02 \times 10^{-3}$
Liquid concentration (kgmole/m³)	2·22	0·015

Check if at top $C_l < \gamma \times C_g$? (0·015 < 0·04).

2. Hydraulic design

(a) COLUMN DIAMETER (BASED ON CONDITIONS AT BOTTOM)

$L^*/\rho_l = 9·5 \times 10^{-3}$, thus from Figure 5.26 type of flow = cross flow. Flooding velocity: flow parameter $(L^*/G^*)(\rho_g/\rho_l)^{\frac{1}{2}} = 0·03$, thus from Figure 5.28 load factor:

$$u_f \left\{ \frac{\rho_g}{(\rho_l - \rho_g)T_s} \right\}^{\frac{1}{2}} = 0·126.$$

With tray spacing $T_s = 0·6$ (to be chosen freely within the limits of Table 5.11), a foaming factor of 0·73 (Table 5.8) and at 80 per cent of flooding, it follows that the superficial velocity is equal to $u_f = 1·9$ m/s. With a downcomer area at $A_d/A_c = 0·1$ (Table 5.11), column diameter follows from

$$u_f \times 0·9 \times \frac{\pi}{4} D_c^2 = G^*/\rho_g \text{ as } D_c = 2·50 \text{ m.}$$

(b) TRAY DESIGN

From Table 5.10 the cap diameter is taken at 0·10 m. The manufacturer's data gives: 24 rectangular slots per cap, slot width $b_s = 0·008$ m, slot height $H_s = 0·0325$ m, skirt clearance $h_{sc} = 0·010$ m, no shrouding. With a tri-angular equilateral pitch of 0·1375 m a total number of 199 caps can be placed on the tray. Total annular area per tray $A_{an} = 0·71$ m², riser area $A_r = 0·57$ m², reversal area $A_{rev} = 0·86$ m², slot area $A_s = 1·24$ m². It is recommended (Table 5.11) that a straight weir be used with a height $h_w = 0·075$ m. The clearance under the downcomer apron is to be taken at 0·04 m and the slot opening $h_0 = 0·031$ (equation (5.134), Figure 5.30).

(c) PRESSURE DROP (METRES LIQUID)

The pressure drop of cap internals $h_{ci} = 0·044$ (equation (5.133)), height of liquid crest over weir $h_{ow} = 0·020$ (equation (5.129)), static seal $h_{ss} = h_w - H_s - h_{sc} = 0·0325$, liquid gradient $\Delta = 0·034$ (from equation (5.139)).

$\Delta_1 = 0.24$, while from Figure 5.31 factor C is set equal to 1.4 which follows from the extrapolated value of $u_0 . \rho_g^{\frac{1}{2}} = 3.10$, pressure drop of froth $h_a = 0.040$ (equations (5.136) and (5.137)) and total pressure drop per tray $h_t = 0.119$ (equation (5.138)).

(d) DOWNCOMER PROPERTIES

The height of clear liquid in the downcomer $h_{dc} = 0.251$ (equation (5.140)). Check (Table 5.12) if: $h_{dc}/T_s + h_w \leqslant 0.5$ ($0.37 \leqslant 0.5$) and if: $t_{dc} \geqslant 3$/foaming factor ($12.7 \geqslant 4.1$).

(e) FRACTIONAL ENTRAINMENT

At 80 per cent from flooding and for $(L^*/G^*)(\rho_g/\rho_l)^{\frac{1}{2}} = 0.030$ it follows from Figure 5.32 that $\psi - 0.14$ and thus from equation (5.143):

$$E_W = \frac{E_D}{1 + 0.16 \times E_D}$$

(f) LIMITING HYDRAULIC CONDITIONS

Checks are: vapour pulsation (Table 5.12): $h_0 \geqslant 0.012$? ($0.031 \geqslant 0.012$), coning (paragraph 5.5.3): $h_a \geqslant 0.012$? ($0.040 \geqslant 0.012$), vapour distribution ratio (equation (5.144)(: $R_v \leqslant 0.5$? ($0.45 \leqslant 0.5$).

3. Number of theoretical plates

The equilibrium line is straight and the operating line is nearly straight; thus with $r_g = 0.43$ (equation (5.99)) it follows from equation (5.119): $N_t = 5.4$.

4. Plate efficiency

Slot submergence $h_s \approx h_d = h_{ss} + h_{ow} = 0.053$ m, bubbling area $A_b = 80$ per cent of column cross section; then from equation (5.67): $k_g = 3.7 \times 10^{-2}$ m/s and from equation (5.72): $k_l = 7.3 \times 10^{-4}$ m/s.

From equation (5.56) a first value for the overall mass-transfer coefficient is found: $K_g = 3.6 \times 10^{-2}$ m/s (gas side resistance dominates).

From equations (5.61) to (5.62) the correction factors for mass-transfer are found: $f_g = 0.99$, $f_l = 0.98$ (top); $f_g = 0.96$, $f_l = 0.78$ (bottom). After inserting the mean values of f_g and f_l in equation (5.63) it follows that: $K_g = 3.7 \times 10^{-2}$ m/s. Hence the correction is very small. From equation (5.82): interfacial area $a_e^* = 40.5$ m²/m².

The point efficiency follows from equation (5.114): $E_p^0 = 0.54$; the number of mixing pools from equation (5.117): $n = 4.2$ and thus the Murphree efficiency: $E_{MV} = 0.58$ (equation (5.116)).

The overall 'dry' plate efficiency is given by equation (5.112): $E_0 = 0.48$. Correcting for entrainment (equation (5.143)) the overall 'wet' plate efficiency is found to be $E_0 = 0.44$.

5. Actual number of trays

$N_P = N_t/E_0 = 5\cdot4/0\cdot44 = 12\cdot3$. Adding 20 per cent for uncertainty the actual number of trays will be 15.

6. Interfacial temperature

Check if real interfacial temperature is near 20°C. From equation (5.84) it follows for the bottom plate: $\Delta T_i = 0\cdot06$°C. This is acceptable.

PART B. ABSORPTION OF NITROUS GASES

P. J. HOFTYZER AND F. J. G. KWANTEN

5.8 A Typical Absorption Process

Nitrogen compounds must be absorbed in several chemical and related processes, the most important of which is the absorption of nitrogen peroxide in water for the manufacture of nitric acid. Absorption of nitrous gases also takes place in the lead-chamber process used for the production of sulphuric acid, in the metallurgical industries where metals are treated with nitric acid, and in the purification of several tail gases.

The example given here deals with the absorption of nitrogen peroxide for the production of nitric acid. Reasons for the choice of this example are:
  (i) The manufacture of nitric acid is of economic importance.
 (ii) This process has received much attention in the literature and the mechanism of the absorption of nitrogen peroxide has been the object of many investigations.
(iii) The example demonstrates that an absorption process can become very complicated if the absorption rate depends on chemical reactions. It will be shown that the design of an installation for this absorption process is the work of a specialist.

5.8.1 Composition of Nitrous Gas Mixture

The present discussion is limited to the absorption of nitrous gases, produced by the catalytic oxidation of ammonia with air. This reaction proceeds according to the equation:

$$NH_3 + \tfrac{5}{4}O_2 \rightarrow NO + \tfrac{3}{2}H_2O \qquad (5.163)$$

Complete conversion of the ammonia yields a mixture of NO, H_2O, O_2 and N_2. There exists an optimum value for the ammonia/air ratio (about 1:9) for this reaction, and thereby the composition of the gaseous mixture obtained is determined. The oxygen content of the resulting mixture is too low, however, for the conversion of NO to HNO_3 according to the equation

$$NO + \tfrac{3}{4}O_2 + \tfrac{1}{2}H_2O \rightarrow HNO_3 \qquad (5.164)$$

Therefore more air (so-called secondary air) is added before the gases enter the absorption system. The mixture thus obtained has approximately the following composition: NO 8·5 per cent; O_2 8·5 per cent; N_2 70 per cent; H_2O 13 per cent.

In several plants, part of the air is replaced by oxygen if this is available at a low price. In this case a mixture with a somewhat higher NO content is produced.

Reaction (5.163) is the main reaction of the ammonia oxidation. Part of the ammonia, however, is converted to N_2 or N_2O, whereas another part remains unconverted. For our purpose the small quantities of NH_3 and N_2O in the mixture can be left out of consideration. The gas mixture is cooled before entering the absorption system. During and after the cooling step nitric oxide is oxidized, yielding a number of nitrogen oxides, among which nitrogen peroxide (NO_2) is the most important.

5.8.2 Reaction Equations

In the gas phase nitric oxide is oxidized to nitrogen peroxide according to the reaction

$$2NO + O_2 \leftrightharpoons 2NO_2 \tag{5.164}$$

Dimerization of nitrogen peroxide gives nitrogen tetroxide, N_2O_4. Upon combination of nitrogen peroxide and nitric oxide, nitrogen trioxide, N_2O_3, is formed. Finally, in the presence of water vapour nitrogen trioxide can be hydrated to nitrous acid, HNO_2. The gross reaction equation of nitric acid formation may be written as

$$3NO_2 + H_2O \leftrightharpoons 2HNO_3 + NO \tag{5.165}$$

This reaction proceeds in the gas phase as well as in the liquid phase. Under normal conditions of nitrous gas absorption liquid phase reaction is dominant. The mechanism of this reaction was studied by Abel[140] who found that the first step consists of N_2O_4 formation by dimerization. After absorption of N_2O_4 in the liquid phase, N_2O_4 reacts with water according to:

$$N_2O_4 + H_2O \leftrightharpoons HNO_3 + HNO_2 \tag{5.166}$$

In acid solutions and if nitric oxide can escape freely into the gas phase, HNO_2 is decomposed[171,172]

$$3HNO_2 \leftrightharpoons HNO_3 + 2NO + H_2O \tag{5.167}$$

As nitrous acid is a weak acid, the acid-base equilibrium

$$HNO_2 \leftrightharpoons H^+ + NO_2^-$$

is shifted predominantly to the right side when the absorbing solution is alkaline. So in alkaline solutions reaction (5.167) will not proceed to any great extent. However, from our experiments on nitrous gas absorption in strong alkaline laminar jets, it followed that reaction (5.167) always will proceed to some extent. Decomposition of HNO_2 in alkaline solutions depends for a great part on mass transfer conditions (liquid phase transfer of HNO_2, liquid- and gas-phase transfer of NO). Since the original work of Abel many studies have been made of this reaction but the microkinetics are still not fully known.

It must be emphasized that reaction (5.165) is essentially reversible, i.e.

when nitric oxide is contacted with concentrated nitric acid the reaction will proceed from right to left. The NO formed as a result of the absorption of NO_2 or N_2O_4 is desorbed into the gas phase where it must be reoxidized to NO_2.

The most important reactions in describing nitric acid formation are

oxidation of nitric oxide in the gas phase

$$2NO + O_2 \rightarrow 2NO_2 + 115 \cdot 5 \times 10^6 \text{ J/kg mole} \tag{5.168}$$

and

formation of nitric acid

$$3(NO_2)_g + (H_2O)_l \rightarrow 2(HNO_3)_l + (NO)_g + Q_3 \tag{5.169}$$

For conditions prevailing in nitric acid absorption columns, the heat of absorption, Q_3, may be calculated from

$$Q_3 = 138 \cdot 6 \times 10^6 - 1047 \times (\text{wt.\% } HNO_3)^{2 \cdot 5} \text{ J/kg mole}$$

If all components of reaction (5.169) are in the gaseous state heat of reaction may be taken as:

$$Q_3 = 35 \cdot 8 \times 10^6 \text{ J/kg mole.}$$

5.8.3 Equilibria

The most important equilibrium for the nitric acid absorption system is given in equation (5.165). The equilibrium conditions of this reaction determine the maximum nitric acid concentration that can be obtained at a given composition of the nitrous gases. The equilibrium constant is defined as

$$K_1 = \frac{p_{HNO_3}^2 \cdot p_{NO}}{p_{NO_2}^3 \cdot p_{H_2O}} \tag{5.170}$$

The same definition may be applied to the heterogeneous equilibrium; in that case p_{NO} and p_{NO_2} are the partial pressures of NO and NO_2 in the gas phase and p_{HNO_3} and p_{H_2O} are the vapour pressures of HNO_3 and H_2O over the liquid phase.

Under normal absorption conditions, ideal behaviour of the gas phase may be assumed; in that case K_1 is independent of the gas composition, so that K_1 depends on the temperature only. The most reliable K_1-values have been calculated from thermodynamic data by Forsythe[141] and Giauque[142], Table 5.13; a review of existing data is given in literature[165].

Table 5.13 NITRIC ACID FORMATION EQUILIBRIUM CONSTANT

Temperature (°C)	K_1 (bar^{-1})
0	0·0444
25	0·0130
50	0·0030

It is common practice to split the equilibrium constant K_1 into two factors:

$$K_2 = \frac{p_{NO}}{p_{NO_2}^3}$$ (5.171)

$$K_3 = \frac{p_{HNO_3}^2}{p_{H_2O}}$$ (5.172)

The factor K_3 contains the vapour pressures of water and nitric acid over the solution.

For binary mixtures of HNO_3 and H_2O the vapour pressures of HNO_3 and H_2O are a function of nitric acid concentration and temperature only. Some of the gaseous components (N_2O_4, N_2O_3, HNO_2) are soluble in nitric acid solutions; presence of these in the liquid phase can have a marked influence on activities of HNO_3 and H_2O. However, for nitric acid concentrations up to 65 wt.% and total nitrous-N pressures up to 1 bar, vapour pressures of HNO_3 and H_2O over nitric acid solutions, in contact with nitrous gases, may be taken from the data for the binary system HNO_3/H_2O. Now as the equilibrium constant K_1 is only depending on temperature, factor K_2 is, in good approximation a function of temperature and nitric acid strength only. Values of K_2 are of great practical importance for the design of a nitric acid absorption plant, as they immediately give the relation between the gas composition and the strength of acid obtainable. Direct determinations of K_2 values have been made by several investigators[143-146,166,190]. These measurements involve many experimental difficulties which cause a considerable spread in the results.

Another way to obtain values of K_2 is by calculation from K_1 and K_3. The thermodynamic K_1 values mentioned above are reliable. The factor K_3 can be calculated from the available data of p_{HNO_3} and p_{H_2O} over nitric acid. The older vapour pressure values, compiled by Taylor[147], were not very accurate; they did not obey the thermodynamic rules for binary mixtures. The measurements of Aunis[148] and Vandoni[149] are more reliable. Figure 5.43 gives a summary of these data. K_2 values calculated from the data mentioned[141,142,148,149] have been plotted against the nitric acid concentration in Figure 5.44.

Favourable conditions for the production of strong nitric acid comprise high partial NO_2 pressure, low partial NO pressure and low temperature. Calculation shows that at normal gas composition and medium absorption pressure (5 bar) a nitric acid strength of 60–65 per cent by weight is the maximum value practically attainable.

The question may arise whether it is permissible to use the equilibrium constant K_1, containing the partial pressures of NO and NO_2, for a system in which NO is continuously oxidized to NO_2. The oxidation reaction is so slow, however, that for the calculation of the equilibrium constant the partial pressures of NO and NO_2 may be assumed to be independent of each other.

The concentrations of the other gaseous components can be calculated from the equilibrium constants given in Table 5.14.

It is common practice to express the composition of nitrous gases by means of the degree of oxidation:

$$\xi = \frac{NO_2 + 2N_2O_4 + N_2O_3 + \frac{1}{2}HNO_2}{NO + NO_2 + 2N_2O_4 + 2N_2O_3 + HNO_2} = \frac{\text{4-valent nitrous-N}}{\text{total nitrous-N}}$$ (5.173)

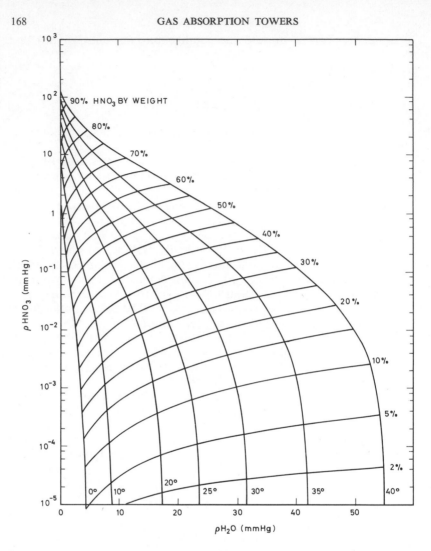

Figure 5.43 Vapour pressures of HNO_3 *and* H_2O *over nitric acid*
$(1 \text{ mm Hg} = 133 \cdot 3 \text{ N/m}^2 = 1 \cdot 33 \text{ mb})$

According to this definition: $0 \leqslant \xi \leqslant 1$; other definitions can be encountered in literature, for instance:

$$\xi = \frac{\Sigma \text{ valency N} \times \text{nitrous-N}}{\text{total nitrous-N}} \text{ for which } 1 \leqslant \xi \leqslant 5.$$

In most cases we may assume the liquid phase to consist of the binary mixture HNO_3/H_2O. Gas phase components are: NO, NO_2, N_2O_3, N_2O_4, HNO_2, HNO_3, H_2O and inerts (note that oxygen may be taken as inert). For quick calculations it may be assumed that only NO, NO_2 and N_2O_4 are present as nitrous-N carriers.

Four variables are sufficient to describe the heterogeneous system;

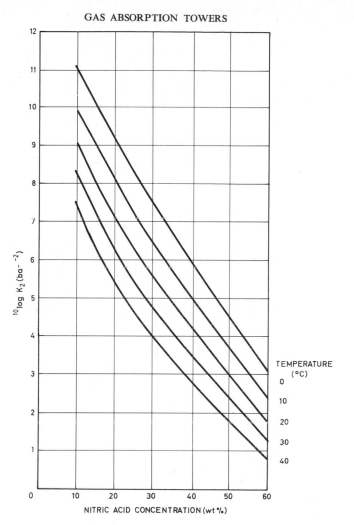

Figure 5.44 K_2 as a function of nitric acid strength and temperature

temperature (T), nitric acid concentration (C_N), degree of oxidation (ξ) and nitrous-N pressure (P_N). For convenience effective nitrous-N pressure is defined as

$$P_N = p_{NO} + p_{NO_2} + 2p_{N_2O_4} + 2p_{N_2O_3} + p_{HNO_2} + p_{HNO_3} \qquad (5.174)$$

Knowledge of reliable relationships between T, ξ, C_N and P_N are of great importance in nitric acid technology.

An interesting graph, calculated by means of one of the computer programs in use by Stamicarbon (a subsidiary of DSM, Holland), is given in Figure 5.45. As can be seen, for attaining high nitric acid concentration ξ

Table 5.14 EQUILIBRIUM CONSTANTS

Equilibrium	Equilibrium constant	Source	Dimension
$3NO_2 + H_2O \leftrightarrows 2HNO_3 + NO$	$K_1 = p_{HNO_3}^2 \cdot p_{NO}/p_{NO_2}^3 \cdot p_{H_2O}$ $= 1 \cdot 29 \times 10^{-9} \times \exp\left(\dfrac{4376}{T}\right)$	Forsythe and Giaque[141,142]	Bar^{-1}
$2NO_2 \leftrightarrows N_2O_4$	$K_4 = p_{N_2O_4}/p_{NO_2}^2$ $= 0 \cdot 698 \times 10^{-9} \times \exp\left(\dfrac{6866}{T}\right)$	JANAF[151,165]	Bar^{-1}
$NO + NO_2 \leftrightarrows N_2O_3$	$K_5 = p_{N_2O_3}/p_{NO} \cdot p_{NO_2}$ $= 65 \cdot 3 \times 10^{-9} \times \exp\left(\dfrac{4740}{T}\right)$	Beattie and Bell[167]	Bar^{-1}
$NO + NO_2 + H_2O \leftrightarrows 2HNO_2$	$K_6 = p_{HNO_2}^2/p_{NO} \cdot p_{NO_2} \cdot p_{H_2O}$ $= 0 \cdot 185 \times 10^{-6} \times \exp\left(\dfrac{4723}{T}\right)$	Wayne and Yost[152] Waldorf and Babb[168] Ashmore and Tyler[169] Karavaev[170]	Bar^{-1}

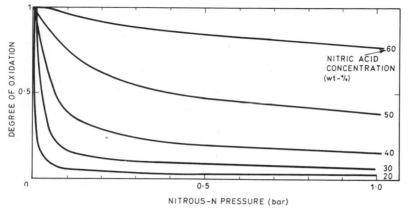

Figure 5.45 Equilibrium of heterogeneous nitric acid reaction at 30°C

and P_N must be high; on the other hand temperature must be as low as possible.

5.8.4 Mechanism of $NO_2(N_2O_4)$ Absorption

Many investigators[153-161,173-176] have studied the absorption of NO_2 and N_2O_4 in water or nitric acid. However, the absorption mechanism only became clear by 1965.

If a pure NO_2–N_2O_4 mixture is brought into contact with water, both NO_2 and N_2O_4 dissolve physically at the liquid surface. From experimental evidence, however, it follows that only N_2O_4 is readily soluble in water and that NO_2 may be neglected when considering mass transfer in the liquid phase. After physical dissolution, N_2O_4 reacts with water according to the second order reaction:

$$N_2O_4 + H_2O \rightarrow HNO_3 + HNO_2 \qquad (5.175)$$

As the molar quantity of water is in great excess, decrease of water concentration near the gas–liquid interface may be neglected; so the chemical reaction may be taken as pseudo first order in N_2O_4.

In accordance with the theory relating to a process of absorption combined with a chemical reaction, section 5.1.3, the absorption rate can be described by the equation:

$$N_{N_2O_4} = H_{N_2O_4} \cdot p^i_{N_2O_4} (k_{N_2O_4} \cdot D_{N_2O_4})^{\frac{1}{2}} \qquad (5.176)$$

If the gas phase contains only NO_2, N_2O_4 and inerts, and assuming the gas phase mass transfer resistance to be negligible, $p^i_{N_2O_4}$ is approximately equal to the partial N_2O_4 pressure in the gas phase.

It must be emphasized that this statement is correct only if the degree of oxidation is equal to one. Values of $H_e(kD)^{\frac{1}{2}}$ and k may be derived from measurements of rates of absorption in laminar jets and wetted wall columns. Some data, taken from experiments at DSM with laminar jets (nitrous-N pressures ranging from 0·05 bar up to 1·7 bar) are given below. Note that $H_{N_2O_4}(k_{N_2O_4} \cdot D_{N_2O_4})^{\frac{1}{2}}$ is abbreviated in $H_e(kD)^{\frac{1}{2}}$.

$$H_e(kD)^{\frac{1}{2}} = (0.921 \pm 0.015) \times 10^{-3} \, \text{kgmole/m}^2 \, \text{s bar} \, (25°C)$$

$$k = 670 \pm 110 \, \text{sec}^{-1} \, (25°C)$$

$$\log H_e(kD)^{\frac{1}{2}} = -0.53 - \frac{760}{T} \, (3-75°C) \tag{5.177}$$

$H_e(kD)^{\frac{1}{2}}$ is only slightly dependent on the temperature, this is caused by two opposing factors: decrease of H_e and increase of k and D with rising temperature.

From published experimental data it may be concluded that numerical values for $H_e(kD)^{\frac{1}{2}}$ are known with fair accuracy. On the other hand measurements of reaction rate constant k still do show a rather large spread. From more direct kinetic measurements by Moll[177], injection of liquid N_2O_4 in water and measurement of temperature profiles, k can be derived from

$$\log k = 7.12 - \frac{1375}{T} \, (2-20°C) \tag{5.178}$$

Decrease of $H_e(kD)^{\frac{1}{2}}$ with increasing nitric acid concentrations is caused by a decrease of H_e (Henry coefficients tend to decrease for increasing ionic strength) and a decrease of k as the molar concentration of 'free' water tends to become relatively small in concentrated nitric acid[178]. It may be remembered that k, as defined in this text, does incorporate the molar concentration of water.

Influence of a decrease of H_e is dominant. In the tail of the absorption system, which is mainly used as a device for purification of the stack gases, nitric acid concentration is low. Still the decrease of H_e is in comparison to pure water remarkable. In connection with this it may be noted that one of the results of our experiments with laminar jets was that neither alkalinity nor acidity of the absorbing solution is important but only ionic strength. So quite different solutions of NaOH, Na_2SO_4, NaCl, HNO_3, K_2SO_4, $Al_2(SO_4)_3$ in water all showed the same decrease of $H_e(kD)^{\frac{1}{2}}$ for the same ionic strength. As a first approximation one could use the factor: $\exp(-0.075.I)$, where

$I =$ ionic strength $(\text{kgmole/m}^3) = \frac{1}{2} \sum_{i=1}^{n} Z_i^2 . C_i$, to correct for the influence of nitric acid strength on the solubility.

For practical calculations on absorption systems, however, $H_e(kD)^{\frac{1}{2}}$ is more important than k. In more precise calculations and experiments one has to take account of the fact that the value of $p_{N_2O_4}^i$ depends on the rate of mass transfer in the gas phase. As the equilibrium between NO_2 and N_2O_4 is established very rapidly[184], the consumption of N_2O_4 by the liquid is supplied by the transport of both NO_2 and N_2O_4 in the gas phase. The rate equation for this transport is

$$N_{N_2O_4} = \frac{1}{2}\frac{k_{gNO_2}}{RT}(p_{NO_2}^0 - p_{NO_2}^i) + \frac{k_{gN_2O_4}}{RT}(p_{N_2O_4}^0 - p_{N_2O_4}^i) \tag{5.179}$$

Using equations (5.176), (5.179) and the value of K_4, see Table 5.14, $p_{N_2O_4}^i$ and the rate of absorption $N_{N_2O_4}$ can be calculated.

According to Andrew and Hanson[162], the mechanism of N_2O_4 absorption described above predominates at high concentrations of NO_2 and N_2O_4 in the gas phase. According to dimerization the ratio $p_{N_2O_4}/p_{NO_2}$ at lower concentrations is smaller. The rate of physical absorption of NO_2 may then exceed the rate of chemical absorption of N_2O_4. In that case the formation of nitric acid takes place in the bulk of the liquid. This type of absorption mechanism will not be of great practical importance because in those parts of the absorption system where the ratio $p_{N_2O_4}/p_{NO_2}$ is small the partial pressure of NO is generally of the same order of magnitude as p_{NO_2}. The absorption mechanism to be described in the next section will then become predominant.

Much has been written about the formation of HNO_3 in the gas phase. Some authors assumed that a large part of the nitric acid obtained is produced by reaction between the components of the gas mixture. A number of arguments, however, can be raised against this assumption. Carberry[153] concluded that no HNO_3 is formed from NO_2 and water vapour in the absence of a liquid phase. Production of nitric acid in a gas would therefore require the formation of liquid drops. In several experiments described in literature[155], the formation of a mist has, however, been observed. Mist formation may be caused by the release of the heat of reaction at the liquid surface. In industrial absorption systems the gas phase formation of nitric acid will not be of much importance.

5.8.5 Simultaneous Absorption of NO and NO_2

It is well known that the absorption rate of NO_2 (N_2O_4) increases upon addition of NO[154,158,160]. This can be readily explained by the absorption of HNO_2 or N_2O_3 present in the gas phase. The equilibrium concentrations of these components can be calculated with the data given in section 5.8.3. Multiplication of the equilibrium partial pressures by the mass-transfer coefficient k_g gives the maximum absorption rate of HNO_2 and N_2O_3. Whether this absorption rate is reached depends on the partial pressure of the component to be absorbed at the liquid surface, i.e. on the solubility. Little is known about the solubility of N_2O_3, but HNO_2 is readily soluble in aqueous solutions. In the liquid, HNO_2 is decomposed at the prevailing acidity as shown in equation (5.167). Only $\frac{1}{3}$ mole of HNO_3 is formed per mole of HNO_2 absorbed.

The first quantitative description of this absorption mechanism was published by Andrew and Hanson[162]. It may be stressed that HNO_2 is much more soluble than N_2O_4, and as for degrees of oxidation below 0·9 the partial pressure of HNO_2 in the bulk of the gas and especially at the phase boundary is not low, it follows that the HNO_2 absorption mechanism can never be neglected. It appears that the absorption of HNO_2 plays an important part at the end of the absorption system where low partial N_2O_4 pressures and relatively high partial NO pressures prevail. Here, the partial pressure of N_2O_3 is negligible compared with that of HNO_2.

For the purpose of technical calculations it will be sufficient in most cases to base absorption models only on NO, NO_2 and N_2O_4 for gas-phase transport and on N_2O_4, HNO_2 and NO for liquid-phase transport.

A model describing mass-transfer and chemical reactions near the gas–liquid interface is given in Figure 5.46. Nitrous-N mass-transfer can be described as follows:

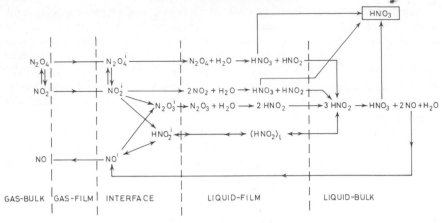

Figure 5.46 Absorption model

(a) 4-valent nitrous-N transfer from the bulk of the gas to the gas–liquid interface is equal to the sum of the transfer of species NO_2 and N_2O_4:

$$(N_4)_g = \frac{k_{gNO_2}}{RT}(p^0_{NO_2} - p^i_{NO_2}) + 2K_4\frac{k_{gN_2O_4}}{RT}\left\{(p^0_{NO_2})^2 - (p^i_{NO_2})^2\right\} \quad (5.180)$$

(b) 4-valent nitrous-N transfer from the interface to the liquid-bulk is expressed as the sum of the liquid-phase transfer of the 'soluble' species N_2O_4 and HNO_2:

$$(N_4)_l = H_e(kD)^{\frac{1}{2}} \cdot 2K_4(p^i_{NO_2})^2\left\{1 - \left(\frac{\beta^i}{K_2}\right)^{\frac{2}{3}}\right\} +$$

$$\tfrac{1}{2}H_{HNO_2} \cdot k_{lH}{}^N{}_{O_2}(K_6 \cdot p^i_{NO} \cdot p^i_{NO_2} \cdot p^i_{H_2O})^{\frac{1}{2}}\left\{1 - \left(\frac{\beta^i}{K_2}\right)^{\frac{1}{6}}\right\} \quad (5.181)$$

(c) The transfer of 2-valent nitrous-N from the interface to the gas-bulk is incorporated in the transfer of species NO:

$$(N_2)_g = \frac{k_{gNO}}{RT}(p^i_{NO} - p^0_{NO}) \quad (5.182)$$

The mathematical model describing absorption in nitric acid plants is expressed by means of the following equations:

$(N_4)_g = (N_4)_l$,   continuity of 4-valent nitrous-N transfer   (5.183)

$(N_2)_g = \tfrac{1}{3}(N_4)_g$,   stoichiometry of equation (5.165)   (5.184)

which have to be solved for the 'unknowns' p^i_{NO} and $p^i_{NO_2}$. Note that $p^i_{H_2O}$ is known, as it is a function of nitric acid concentration and temperature, Figure 5.43.

In equation (5.181) the liquid-bulk concentrations, see section 5.1.3, equation (5.24), of species N_2O_4 and HNO_2 are denoted by factor β^i/K_2. The equilibrium constant K_2, equation (5.171), is a function of nitric acid concentration and temperature, see Figure 5.44.

Factor β^i is defined by:

$$\beta^i = \frac{p_{NO}^i}{(p_{NO_2}^i)^3} \qquad (5.185)$$

The introduction of the liquid-bulk concentrations of N_2O_4 and HNO_2 by way of factor β^i/K_2 is based on the assumption that a nitric acid solution which has been in contact with a nitrous gas for a relatively long time, as is the case in nitric acid plants, is nearly saturated with NO.

The mass-transfer coefficients k_{gNO}, k_{gNO_2}, $k_{gN_2O_4}$ and k_{lHNO_2} may be calculated from the equations given in section 5.2.2: equations (5.64) and (5.65) for packed towers and equations (5.67) to (5.75) for plate towers. Information on the liquid-side mass-transfer coefficient of N_2O_4 (chemical absorption), denoted as $H_e(kD)^{\frac{1}{2}}$ in equation (5.181), is given in section 5.8.4. The relative importance of the N_2O_4 and HNO_2 liquid-phase transport mechanisms in high pressure plants is given in Figure 5.47.

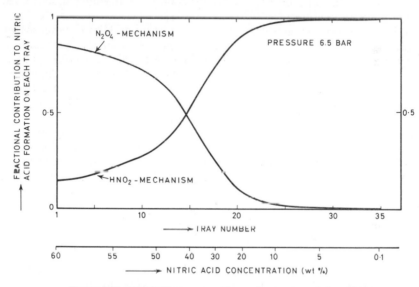

Figure 5.47 Liquid-side mass transfer mechanism in a nitric acid plant

The model described has been used with fair success by one of the authors (F.K.) for the design and recalculation of Stamicarbon-DSM large-scale plants.

5.8.6 Favourable Conditions for the Absorption of Nitrogen Oxides

Whether the absorption conditions will be favourable depends on the following quantities:
(a) partial pressures of nitrogen oxides—should be high,
(b) degree of oxidation of nitrogen oxides—should be high,
(c) temperature—should be low,
(d) gas–liquid interface—should be large.

(a) The attainment of high partial pressures of the nitrogen oxides is promoted by high contents of these compounds in the gas mixture as well as by a high total pressure. As outlined in section 5.8.1, the nitrogen oxide content of the gas produced by oxidation of ammonia is limited by the nitrogen present in the air used. The concentration of 4-valent nitrogen oxides can be increased by the use of oxygen instead of part of the air.

The favourable effect of a high total pressure is generally employed in industrial absorption systems.

(b) The degree of oxidation has previously been denoted as the fraction of 4-valent nitrous-N over total nitrous-N. In the first part of the absorption system, where the partial pressures of the nitrogen oxides are high, the absorption of N_2O_4 predominates. The partial pressure of N_2O_4 is roughly proportional to the square of the degree of oxidation; in consequence a high degree of oxidation is very favourable. Towards the end of the absorption system, a large part of the absorption occurs by the transfer of HNO_2 from the gas phase, the concentration of which is only slightly dependent on the initial degree of oxidation.

(c) The equilibrium concentrations of both N_2O_4 and HNO_2 increase with decreasing temperature. The physical transport rate in the gas phase is nearly independent of the temperature. The rate of chemical N_2O_4 absorption is proportional to the group $H_e(kD)^{\frac{1}{2}}$, which is also nearly independent of the temperature. This means that at a given total content of nitrogen oxides in the gas phase, and at a given degree of oxidation, the absorption rate will always increase with decreasing temperature.

(d) The absorption rate of N_2O_4 as well as that of HNO_2 is proportional to the area of the gas–liquid interface. For most absorption processes this is so evident that in the construction of any type of absorption apparatus the provision of a large interfacial area is a very important consideration. This is especially important for high pressure absorption.

5.8.7 Oxidation of Nitric Oxide

The oxidation of nitric oxide is such an essential step in the production of nitric acid that a discussion of this process would be incomplete if no data were given about the oxidation rate. In addition to the NO present in the feed gas which has to be oxidized prior to the absorption, the NO liberated during the process according to equations (5.165) and (5.167) must also be oxidized. Especially at the end of the absorption system, where the partial NO pressures and the NO_2/NO ratios are low, the rate of acid production is strongly dependent on the rate of oxidation of the NO. The oxidation of nitric oxide to nitrogen peroxide

$$2NO + O_2 \rightarrow 2NO_2$$

is one of the few examples of a third-order reaction. According to the classical work of Bodenstein[163,185], at constant temperature and volume the kinetics of the process can be described by:

$$\frac{dp_{NO_2}}{dt} = k_1 p_{NO}^2 p_{O_2} \tag{5.186}$$

Values for the reaction rate constant k_1 are given in Table 5.15. (Note that k_1 decreases with increasing temperature.) The reverse reaction can be neglected at the temperatures prevailing in the absorption system.

Table 5.15 REACTION RATE CONSTANT FOR NO OXIDATION

Temperature °C	k_1 $(bar)^{-2}.(s)^{-1}$
0	36·6
25	23·6
50	16·4

$$k_1 = 0.2166 \times \exp \frac{1399}{T}$$

Source: Bodenstein and Lindner[185]

For more recent investigations of this reaction, especially on mechanism and kinetics when concentrations are in the p.p.m. range (this is of great importance in view of air pollution control), the reader is referred to recent literature[179-182].

To calculate the amount of nitric oxide oxidized in a given apparatus, equation (5.186) must be integrated. Bodenstein gave the integrated formula for a static process, using the stoichiometric relationship between p_{NO} and p_{O_2}. In the absorption system this stoichiometric relation is not valid as nitric oxide is released during the absorption of higher oxides. Moreover, the static integration formula may under continuous operating conditions be used only in the case of plug flow, but this does not invariably occur in practice. As, for reactions of an order higher than one, 'piston flow' is more favourable from a time–volume point of view than 'perfect mixing', design must be aimed at 'piston flow' (i.e. avoid mixing of incoming and outgoing gas flows). In practice flow conditions will be somewhere in between 'piston flow' and 'perfect mixing'. The following formulae, derived from equation (5.186) for constant temperature and constant volume, may be useful in solving practical problems.

Piston flow.

$$(p_{NO}^0)^2 . k_1 . t = \frac{1 - \beta_0}{\beta_0(z_0 - \frac{1}{2})} - \frac{\ln \frac{z_0 - \frac{1}{2}(1 - \beta_0)}{\beta_0 . z_0}}{2(z_0 - \frac{1}{2})^2} \tag{5.187}$$

Perfect mixing.

$$(p_{NO}^0)^2 . k_1 . t = \frac{1 - \beta_0}{\beta_0^2(z_0 - \frac{1}{2} + \frac{1}{2}\beta_0)} \tag{5.188}$$

where $\beta_0 = p_{NO}/p_{NO}^0$ and $z_0 = p_{O_2}^0/p_{NO}^0$ (p^0 is for time t = zero).

Fortunately the alteration of the partial NO and O_2 pressures in one stage of the absorption system is generally small. Therefore it is permissible to use mean values of the partial pressures. Equation (5.186) is then modified into

$$\Delta p_{NO} = -k_1(\overline{p_{NO}})^2(\overline{p_{O_2}}) \, t \tag{5.189}$$

in which Δp_{NO} is the alteration of the partial NO pressure due to the oxidation; t is the mean residence time of the gas and $\overline{p_{NO}}$ and $\overline{p_{O_2}}$ are the mean values of the partial pressures of NO and O_2. Favourable conditions for the oxidation of NO are: high partial pressure of NO; high partial pressure of O_2; low temperature; long residence time, i.e. a large gas volume. It appears that a high total pressure and a low temperature favour both the absorption of nitrogen oxides and the oxidation of nitric oxide. The two requirements, of a large interfacial area for the absorption and a large gas volume for the oxidation, determine the shape of the absorption vessels.

5.8.8 Absorption Equipment

(i) Requirements and general flow sheet. The purpose for which the absorption system is to be used is to produce, from a feed gas mixture of a given composition, nitric acid of the desired concentration with minimum stack losses and at minimal cost. These conditions therefore give the following requirements which the absorption system should satisfy:

- (a) the passage of the gas through the apparatus should approach piston flow; homogenization of the gas phase should be avoided;
- (b) the liquid should pass through the apparatus in countercurrent to the gas stream;
- (c) the heat of reaction should be removed as it is evolved;
- (d) a large gas–liquid interface;
- (e) a large volume of the gas phase.

With regard to (a) both the absorption rate and the rate of NO oxidation increase with increasing partial pressures. Therefore, the mean values of the partial pressures should be as high as possible. This is achieved with piston flow of the gas. Referring to (b), nitric acid of maximum concentration can be produced only if the gas entering the system has a high degree of oxidation to NO_2.

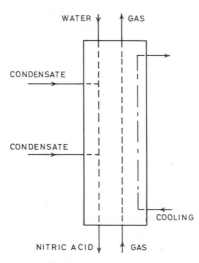

Figure 5.48 General scheme of absorption system

On the basis of these requirements the ideal flow scheme of the absorption system is fixed as shown in Figure 5.48. However, one complication, caused by the condensates, should be included in the scheme. When the gaseous mixture produced by the oxidation of ammonia is cooled, most of the water formed by the reaction condenses in the cooler–condenser. Nitrogen oxides are absorbed in this condensate, forming nitric acid. Although a discussion of the problems related with the cooling system is beyond the scope of this survey, the correct position for the introduction of the condensates has been indicated in the scheme of the absorption system. As a general rule the condensates are introduced in that part of the absorption system where nitric acid of the same concentration is found. (Nowadays condensate concentration and place of introduction can be calculated with fair accuracy by means of computer programs.)

It is advantageous to keep the nitric acid concentration of the condensates as low as possible in order to produce nitric acid of a high concentration in the absorption system.

(ii) Types of absorption tower used for nitric acid manufacture. The majority of absorption systems for the nitric acid manufacture can be divided into two types, packed columns and tray columns. The usual construction in the U.S.A. was a plate tower with bubble caps which contains the whole absorption system. This has become possible by the use of a high working pressure of about 8 bar.

In this type of absorption tower countercurrent piston flow of gas and liquid is approached reasonably well, the homogenization of gas and liquid being restricted to one stage only. The heat of reaction is carried off by cooling coils passing through the liquid layer on each plate. A large contact surface between gas and liquid is provided by the bubbles forming at the caps. The space between the plates provides the volume necessary for NO oxidation. As sieve trays do have some advantages (lower capital cost, better installation of cooling coils) over bubble caps, most modern nitric acid absorption columns are designed for sieve trays. Hole diameters may range from 1 to 13 mm, plate porosities from 3 to 15 per cent. In connection with tray design detailed information is given by Atroshchenko[82] and Kadlas and Vesely[183].

Absorption towers of this construction contain 30 to 50 plates (height 18–40 m). Diameters range from 1·5 m for small capacities to 5 m for modern large plants. The towers can produce up to about 1500 tons HNO_3 per 24 h. Progress in capacity, using only one tower, has been tremendous:

1930. 25 tons per 24 h
1950. 50 tons per 24 h
1960. 300 tons per 24 h
1970. 1500 tons per 24 h

This type of absorption system has the advantage of a compact construction, necessitating only a relatively small investment of stainless steel. A serious disadvantage is the high power consumption, caused by the relatively large pressure drop over the trays. On the other hand the number of nitric acid pumps is very small in comparison to a packed column absorption system, so the electric power consumption is small. The relative importance of the power expenses depends on the local circumstances. A constructional difficulty is the insertion of the cooling coils in the plates, especially in the base of the tower.

The second type of absorption system consists of a series of packed towers. In principle, countercurrent flow of gas and liquid can be closely approached in such a system. In practice this is not possible, however, owing to the very small liquid–gas ratio of the process. If at normal gas velocity the liquid were to pass through each absorption tower only once, the liquid rate would by no means suffice for ensuring satisfactory distribution over the packing. Therefore, the liquid is recycled in each tower. As a result, the composition of the liquid remains nearly constant during passage through each compartment of the tower. The countercurrent effect can be realized merely by the relative arrangement of the towers.

The recirculation system of the liquid is used to carry off the heat of reaction by passing the circulating liquid through coolers, see Figure 5.49.

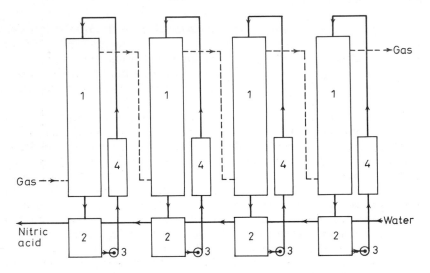

Figure 5.49 Scheme of an absorption system with packed towers
1. Absorption columns. 2. Tanks. 3. Pumps. 4. Coolers

Absorption systems of this type have been constructed for operation at atmospheric as well as at elevated pressures (generally about 3 to 4 bar gauge). In atmospheric pressure systems the gas leaving the system is usually passed through some additional absorption towers through which an alkaline solution is circulated whereby a further reduction of the nitrogen oxide content of the stack gases is effected. The advantage of using packed absorption towers lies in the very low pressure drop in the towers. The plant becomes more complex, however, by the installation of many acid circulation pumps and coolers. These do consume a great deal of electric power.

When cooling water quality is bad, so that it tends to build up dirt or scale on heat-transfer surfaces, packed towers with plate-type coolers (placed outside the absorption columns) may be preferred over tray columns (where cooling coils are placed inside the tower).

An absorption system for operation at atmospheric pressure may consist of six towers of 3·5 m in diameter and 20 m in height. Such an installation gives a daily production of 50 tons of HNO_3; the acid has a concentration of 50 per cent by weight. A system of the same dimensions operating at about 3 bar gauge would produce 250 tons of HNO_3 daily with a nitric acid concentration of 60 per cent.

(iii) Packed towers. Of the two types of absorption equipment mentioned in the preceding section, packed towers are still used most frequently for nitric acid production in Europe. Therefore a further discussion will be devoted to this type of absorption system. A modern packed tower absorption system is shown in Figure 5.50.

The principles of the design of packed towers have already been given in sections 5.2–5.6 and need not be repeated here. Neither will the construction of the towers be discussed. It should only be mentioned that it is essential to design a good device for the distribution of the liquid at the top of the towers.

(a) *Diameter of the column.* At a given feed rate the tower diameter is determined by the admissible gas velocity. This gas velocity is usually kept below the value derived from loading correlations so as to provide sufficient residence time for the oxidation of NO. A normal gas velocity is about 1 m/s.

(b) *Height of the column.* The height should be adapted to the diameter of the column. The maximum value of the dimensions will often depend on practical considerations.

(c) *Packing material.* The dimensions of the packing elements should correspond to the diameter of the tower. The type of packing material is determined by the demand of a large free space. Normal Raschig rings have proved to be suitable.

(d) *Liquid velocity.* The velocity of the circulating liquid is determined by the requirement of a sufficient degree of wetting of the packing material. Moreover, the liquid velocity should be high enough to restrict the temperature rise per pass to a few degrees.

(e) *Absorption in the first tower.* The mean nitric acid concentration in the first tower is approximately equal to that of the acid produced. On the basis of the above assumptions the absorption rate of N_2O_4 per unit active surface area can be calculated. Assuming a given active fraction of the total surface area of the packing material, the total absorption effect of the column can be determined.

When too great a value has been chosen for the height of the tower the calculated partial pressures of the nitrogen oxides in the gas leaving the tower are so low that the corresponding equilibrium nitric acid concentration is lower than the concentration of the acid circulating in the tower. The calculation should then be repeated for a smaller tower height. From a constructional point of view it may be preferable to choose a larger tower height and to divide the tower into two or more parts equipped with separate liquid circulation systems.

(f) *The next tower.* The acid concentration in the next tower can be calculated with the aid of a material balance. Then, the whole calculation can be repeated for this tower. In this way the calculation can be extended to the

Figure 5.50 Modern packed tower absorption system. Height 26 m, diameter 3·8 m, pressure 5 bar, capacity 450 tonne HNO_3/24 h. As cooling takes place outside the towers, the small pipes are for acid circulation between the plate heat-exchangers and the absorption compartments. (Courtesy Stamicarbon-DSM)

Figure 5.51 Nitric acid absorption column with sieve trays. Height 22 m, diameter 3 m, pressure 7 bar, capacity 185 tonne HNO_3/24 h. The cooling water pipes can be clearly seen. (Courtesy Humphreys and Glasgow Ltd and A.C.C.)

whole absorption system. Usually, a number of such calculations are carried out in which some quantities are varied, e.g. the number of towers, the working pressure, the strength of the acid produced, etc. If sufficient economic data are available, the most advantageous situation can be chosen. The design of the absorption system then becomes an optimization problem.

(iv) Plate towers. Modern high pressure plants use only one plate tower (see Figure 5.51), though for very large capacities, high nitric acid strength, or high absorption efficiencies, there may be two columns. Plate towers are essentially composed of a number of the same units. Each unit consists of: a tray, for gas–liquid mass transfer; cooling coils, installed on the tray for transfer of heat of reaction, although there may be trays (top section) without, and gas-volume for oxidation of NO to NO_2.

It will be obvious that cooling surface and tray spacing are not equal for all trays. A rule of thumb states that about 1 m^2 of cooling surface per ton HNO_3 produced in 24 hours has to be installed in the absorption column. Most of the expensive cooling coils are installed in the lower parts of the column. The reason for this is obvious: heat load is greatest in the bottom sections and central part of the tower. Optimal division of the cooling surface (installing minimal number of cooling coils on the right tray) can be calculated only by specialists in this field. Although computer programmed optimization will be of great help, know-how and skill derived from long years of practice are still needed.

As stated earlier, tray spacing is not the same for all trays. Roughly stated, tray spacing, or division of total column volume in discrete parts, will increase when going from the lower section to the tail of the absorption column.

Some details on this subject have been discussed in literature[186,187]. Optimal tray-spacing in the top of the tower is very important, especially in view of optimal absorption efficiency (lowest cost-price) and air pollution control. For preliminary studies optimal tray-spacing in the tail of the absorption system, which does comprise a large part of the tower, may be calculated from a formula, derived by one of the authors (F.K.):

$$Y_{opt} = \left[\frac{4 . N_g . R . T . C_1}{\pi . D_C^2 . F_0 . F_N . P^3 . k_1 . C_2} \right]^{\frac{1}{2}} \tag{5.190}$$

Note that the optimal tray-spacing is inversely proportional to the square root of the nitrous-N content of the tail gas (F_N).

A method of calculation that leads to optimal tray spacing in the lower parts of the tower cannot be explicitly given as too many factors are involved; so optimization for a specific case can be done only by computerized calculation. It may be added that optimization of tray-spacing in the lower part of the column is of minor importance in comparison to optimization of cooling surface distribution.

5.8.9 *Absorption—Volume related to Pressure and Absorption Efficiency*

A somewhat simplified picture of design problems has been given in the above discussion, and in practice, many complications may arise. Obviously, the complete design of an absorption system for the production of nitric acid requires an intricate set of calculations. Main factors to take account of in design of nitrous gas absorption systems are: mass transfer, heat transfer, kinetics of reactions proceeding in gas and liquid and equilibrium conditions. So a nitric acid absorption column is in fact a very complicated chemical reactor.

Although even a badly designed absorption column will produce nitric acid, nitric acid strength, capacity and absorption efficiency (pollution control) may deviate to a great extent from the desired technical and economical optima. Especially in view of rigorous demands on air pollution control installation of sufficient absorption volume must be of utmost importance.

As a conclusion to the discussion on design problems of nitric acid plants a formula, derived by one of the authors (F.K.) from theory and amplified with data from Stamicarbon designed plants, will be given. The formula relates absorption volume (V_a) to capacity (C_a), pressure (P) and absorption efficiency (η_a).

$$V_a = \beta_a . C_a \left[\frac{22}{P^2} + \frac{8 \cdot 7}{P^3} \frac{T}{k_1 . x_0} \left(\frac{\eta_a - 0 \cdot 97}{1 - \eta_a} \right) \right] \qquad (5.191)$$

where for plate towers: $\beta_a = 1$, and for packed columns: $\beta_a = \frac{4}{3}$.

The formula is valid for: $\eta_a \geqslant 0 \cdot 97$, $x_0 \sim 3$ mol.%, $T \sim 303$ °K, while nitric acid strength of produced acid may range from 55 to 60 wt.%.

A graphical presentation of formula (5.191) is given in Figure 5.52.

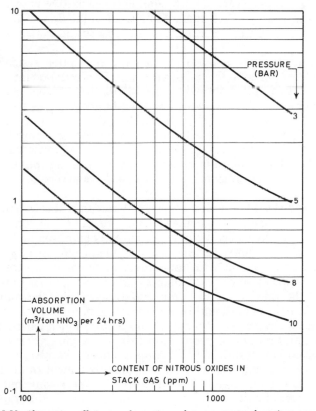

Figure 5.52 Absorption efficiency–absorption volume–pressure chart (see equation 5.191)

5.8.10 Construction and Operation of Industrial Plant

(i) Materials of construction. The depreciation cost of the equipment is one of the main elements of the cost price of nitric acid, and hence a proper choice of the construction materials is very important.

Long ago, all the absorption systems consisted of large towers constructed of blocks of granite and were operated at atmospheric pressure. Since stainless steel has become available at a reasonable price, however, this is the only construction material used nowadays. As a result, it has become possible to perform the absorption at elevated pressures. The type of stainless steel generally used is austenitic with 18 per cent chromium, 8 per cent nickel and a low carbon content; it is usually stabilized, e.g. with niobium, tantalum or titanium. The packing rings are usually made of acid-proof porcelain. The gaskets may be made of any type of suitable acid-resistant material.

Several types of corrosion may be observed in the stainless steel equipment. It is remarkable that a large part of the corrosion events relate to the water-side of the acid coolers. Sometimes pitting is observed there; this is caused by the deposition of dirt (calcium carbonate, rust or algae) which prevents the formation of the protective oxide layer. The remedy lies in preventing formation of deposits by suitable conditioning of the water and avoiding dead corners in the coolers[164,191]. Another type of corrosion observed on the water-side of the coolers is weld-corrosion. This is caused by chloride content of the water in excess of 100 mg/l. Finally, accumulation of hydrochloric acid in the nitric acid in some part of the absorption system may cause corrosion.

Chlorides must not be allowed to enter the absorption system with the make-up water supplied to the tail of the tower. Concentrated nitric acid and chlorides will react at the bottom of the column to give hydrochloric acid and nitrosylchloride (NOCl), which is volatile and tries to work its way back upward. However, as it is hydrolyzed by water in the top sections (low nitric acid concentration) it will flow downwards as chloride. Vapour pressure of hydrochloric acid is too low to be carried out with the gases. Consequently it builds up in intermediate sections of the column and as it tends to penetrate the protective layer it may have a very corrosive effect.

(ii) Purchase of plant. It is not customary to build an absorption installation for nitrous gases under direct management. Orders for the complete nitric acid plant are usually placed with a specialized engineering and contractor firm, which will give some guarantees concerning proper operation. For the acid coolers and the liquid distributing devices patented constructions are often used. The acid pumps are available in standard construction. Packing material for the towers is also commercially available; the filling of the packings into the towers should be done very carefully.

Design and manufacture of plate towers require much care. Reviews of data concerning capital and production costs of varying nitric acid plants have been given in literature[188,189]. Main points of discussion, nowadays, are: design for optimum energy economy and abatement of air pollution. Expensive rotating machinery (compressors, turbines) contribute a great deal to total capital cost; so energy optimization is very important.

As to air pollution, there seem to be only two ways of abatement: installation of sufficient absorption volume or catalytic conversion of nitrogen oxides to nitrogen. If a content of 500 p.p.m. of nitrous oxides in the tail gas is tolerable, installation of sufficient absorption volume is more favourable. When demands on content of nitrous oxides are below 500 p.p.m., or when a nitric acid plant will be used as a power production unit, catalytic treatment of tail gas must be considered. Capital costs of catalytic treatment will amount to about 10 per cent of total plant cost. For most existing plants, however, installation of catalytic treatment devices does not seem feasible from an economic point of view, particularly as catalytic treatment is strongly inter- woven with total energy conception of the plant.

As there is still no well devised cheap remedy for reduction of air pollution from old plants, stress must be laid on design of all new plants. Most new plants are high-pressure plants. For these it is remarkable that the extra cost to lower the nitrous oxides content of the tail gas from 500 to 100 p.p.m. by installation of sufficient absorption volume will only amount to about 1 per cent of nitric acid cost. Installation of one extra tower, which will be an almost empty shell with some well spaced trays and some small cooling coils, would be sufficient.

All considerations concerning the purchase of a new plant may be narrowed down to nine main factors:

1. *capacity*;
2. *nitric acid strength* (58, 60, 65 or 70 per cent?);
3. *absorption efficiency* (tail gas content of nitrous oxides);
4. *pressure* (medium, high, atmospheric/medium or medium/high?);
5. *temperature* (cooling water, new cooling systems);
6. *absorption volume* (one column, two columns?);
7. *total cooling area* (waste-heat boiler, cooler condenser, absorption column; how much and where?);
8. *energy recovery* (no export energy, catalytic tail-gas treatment, export steam or generation of electricity?);
9. *cost-price* (which is more important: fixed costs or variable costs?).

It will be obvious that these factors do not encompass all points of con- sideration, for instance reliability and time of start up have been left out. Still, we do think that when factors 1–3 are given, main points of consideration should be factors 4–9. As has been shown, all factors are strongly interwoven, so optimal design and realization can be reached only when client and a company specialized in nitric acid plants, are willing to co-operate together in the preliminary stages of design.

ACKNOWLEDGMENTS

One of the authors (F. J. G. Kwanten) would like to acknowledge the experimental assistance given to him in preparation of section 5.8.4 by M. J. J. Kusters of Central Laboratory DSM and by A. Gany of Technion- Institute of Technology, Haifa.

6

Centrifugal Gas Absorbers

G. NONHEBEL

6.1 Introduction

Conventional gas absorption towers containing packings or bubble plates are bulky and also are unsuitable for use with the absorbing liquids of high viscosity or which tend to froth.* Absorption vessels in which the gas is brought into vigorous contact with droplets of liquor by means of an impellor overcome the above disadvantages; the advantages are probably more pronounced when the liquid film coefficient governs the rate of absorption and when the operation is conducted under pressure; there would also be a great advantage when the liquid is thermally unstable. It is somewhat surprising, therefore, that, so far as is known, there are no industrial plants in operation which use this principle despite higher capital cost.

The main technical disadvantage is the difficulty of removing fine entrained spray from the stripped gas; loss of valuable absorbent and contamination of the gas might only be overcome by additional plant for spray removal which would reduce the space advantage. Greater power consumption is also a disadvantage.

The principal published work on centrifugal absorbers is to be found in three papers[1,2,3] contributed to a Symposium on Gas Absorption held by the Institution of Chemical Engineers and in an account[4] of a Bureau of Mines investigation on agitated absorbers for the removal of acid-gas impurities from synthesis gas made from coal. The British and American pilot plant studies were on the absorption of carbon dioxide by mono- and di-ethanolamine respectively.

6.2 Apparatus

The initial studies by Dixon and Chambers were made with centrifugal absorbers based on the well-known Piazza stillhead principle. The principle of such an absorber is illustrated in Figure 6.1. A horizontal rotating plate carries vertical rings which intermesh with stationary vertical rings. The absorbent liquor is fed to the centre of the rotor plate and by centrifugal action flows outwards, up the inside wall of the innermost rotor ring, and is

---

*Raising the temperature of the liquid to reduce its viscosity would reduce the absorptive capacity of liquids regenerated by heat.

flung off the rim in the form of spray or film to strike the adjacent stator ring. At this point some of the liquor is reflected from the stator ring in the form of fine spray ('impact' spray) which mixes with the primary spray, whilst the remainder fall to rejoin the main liquor stream. This process is repeated in the outer rings and the liquor is finally discharged from the base of the absorber. The gaseous mixture may pass through the absorber in parallel flow (as shown in Figure 6.1) or in contra-flow, passing in each case through the spray curtains between rotor and stator rings.

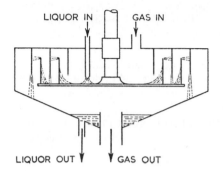

Figure 6.1 Principle of the centrifugal absorber

Details of a 510 mm diameter pilot unit used in the main investigations by Chambers are shown in Figure 6.2. In this design the liquor is thrown on to static vanes. Power consumption can be nearly halved by using a form of construction in which all the rings of vanes are rotated since the spinning liquid is not thereby alternately retarded and accelerated. An improved design of a 50 mm double rotor with fifteen plates with their height reduced to a minimum is shown in Figure 6.3; this arrangement can be built with at least six rotors on the shafts. This design also allows a greater liquor rate without flooding.

All the above apparatus has only been designed and tested at atmospheric pressure. The apparatus developed by the Bureau of Mines and illustrated in Figure 6.4 has been designed for operation at 24 bar(g) and is of far simpler construction. Absorbent is forced into the lift tube by the turbine, baffles in the lift tube being fitted to eliminate swirling action. The rising solution is broken into spray by the absorber impellor. Three distinct spray patterns are formed: (i) initial spray from the impellor consisting of small droplets moving at high velocities; (ii) impact spray formed when initial spray strikes the vessel walls; (iii) conjunctive spray formed when initial and impact spray droplets collide. No difficulty was experienced in removing entrained absorbent with a commercially available demister.

6.3 Absorption by Droplets

Dixon found that secondary impact spray is finer than primary spray. The droplet size of the latter was found to diminish substantially with increase in speed of the rotor. With a simple disc diameter of 100 mm rotating at 2000 rev/min the range of droplet diameter with glycol (which is similar in density, viscosity and surface tension to monoethanolamine) was 100–400 μm. In the centrifugal absorber of the type shown in Figure 6.1 the flight of drops from the rotating disc is interrupted by the stator with an appreciable reduction in the size. This is important as a factor which has a great bearing on the efficiency of these types of absorber in the frequency of forming, breaking and reforming the spray. The evidence is quite clear that better results are obtained in a given space with a large number of narrow spray curtains than with a smaller number of wider curtains. It is known that the absorption rate of a liquid droplet is greatest during the early stages of its life while some degree of turbulence persists in the surface layers. Continued rapid forming and breaking of the droplets continually exposes fresh surfaces to the gas stream. It is evident, therefore, that the absorber functions by virtue of its ability to expose continually renewed surfaces of very fine impact spray to the gas stream. Thus in designing a centrifugal absorber it is necessary to ensure that the frequency of forming and breaking the spray is as high as possible.

The rotor speed should be high because it determines the drop-size of the spray. Up to 3000 rev/min the performance continues to improve with

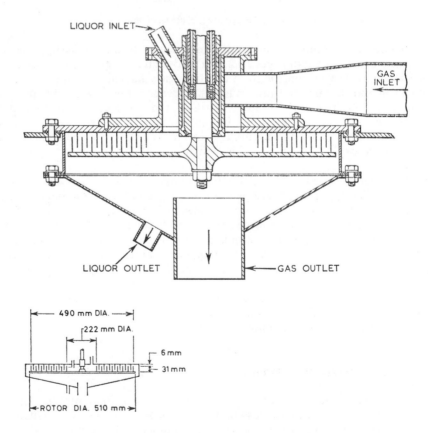

Figure 6.2 Details of 510 mm diameter centrifugal absorber

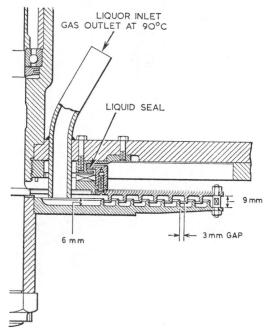

Figure 6.3 A fifteen-plate double-rotor centrifugal absorber

increase in rotor speed: it is probable that the limit will be fixed by considerations of bearing design and power consumption rather than by
absorption performance. At very high speeds and very small spacings there
is a danger that the time of flight of the droplets may be short compared with
the rate of absorption: should this happen, the performance will suffer.

6.4 Power Consumption

The power consumption of the 510 mm diameter pilot unit, Figure 6.2,
was 2·3 kW (by wattmeter on motor) for 400 m^3/h gas and 680 litres/h
100 per cent MEA liquor; the temperature rise was from 33° to 88°C. The
power consumption with the unit running free was 0·9 kW.

The power consumption was reduced by 30 per cent without reduction
of absorption capacity by drilling sufficient 3 mm diameter holes in the base
of the rotor rings to by-pass 70–50 per cent of the liquor as it flowed outwards. This modification arose from the consideration that the amount of
liquor required to produce a spray curtain of given density between the outer
pair of rings is about four times that required for the inner rings.

The Bureau of Mines turbine was driven by a 1 h.p. motor through a
pulley system giving speed of 500–800 rev/min: the actual power consumption
was not stated.

The power consumption of the unperforated double rotor design, Figure
6.3, is substantially less than that of the equivalent rotor–stator absorber,
Figure 6.2.

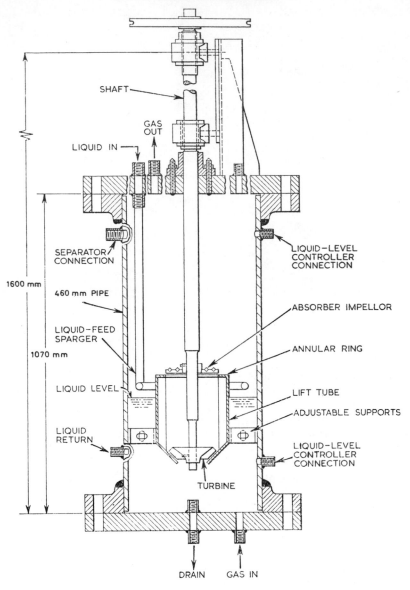

Figure 6.4 Bureau of Mines agitated gas–liquid contactor

6.5 Pressure Drop

The pressure drop through the 51 mm diameter single unit, Figure 6.2, was 58 mb (g) for a gas flow of 400 m³/h atmospheric pressure, liquor flow of 680 litres/h at 40°C, rotor speed 3000 rev/min. It was reduced by 50 per cent when the stator rings were perforated as described in Section 6.4. The pressure drop of the 15 plate, 50 mm diameter double rotor, Figure 6.3, was 62 mb for a gas flow of 68 m^3/h liqour rate 1130 litres/h at 60°C in contra-flow rotor speed 2300 rev/min; it was found to be approximately proportional to gas flow and independent of liquor flow.

6.6 Flooding

The maximum liquor rate for the 51 mm diameter unit, Figure 6.2, using 100 per cent MEA was 1000 litres/h using parallel flow of gas and liquor. With contra flow, flooding occurred very readily and the power consumption increases. With the 50 mm diameter double rotor unit, Figure 6.3, there is no sudden rise in resistance to rotation as the liquor rate is increased and the flooding point was greater than 2500 litres/h.

6.7 Carry-over of Liquor and Mist in Gas Stream

Although the simple centrifugal absorber has a high volumetric absorptive capacity, it is not a practicable proposition for absorption of CO_2 by MEA because of mist formation. The relatively coarse air-borne mechanical spray is readily removed by passing the gas through a series of baffles, but the residual mist with a gas flow of 200 m^3/h was found to be 0·34 per cent of the liquor rate.

The formation of mist is due to the high heat of absorption in MEA. The increase in temperature of the total liquor may be over 50°C and there will be much higher local temperature rises on the surface of the drops of spray while absorption is taking place. The result will be that amine vapour is flashed off but quickly cooled, thereby forming fine mist.

It was found that the mist was easily removed by electrostatic precipitation, and could probably be sufficiently extracted by passing the gases through a second centrifugal absorber running dry. For some purposes it would, however, be most undesirable to contaminate the scrubbed gas with an organic vapour—hence the advantage of the non-volatile alkazid solutions compared with MEA (Section 17C23), always provided that all mechanical carry-over of spray of this expensive absorbent can be collected.

Tests of the double rotor absorber, Figure 6.3, showed that mechanical carry-over was substantially reduced by shielding the liquor from the gas flow until it had attained the full rotational speed of the first ring; this arrangement did, however, reduce the amount of absorption slightly.

6.8 Temperature of Absorption of Carbon Dioxide by MEA

With the centrifugal absorbers it was found that the reduced viscosity and increased molecular activity of the absorbent at elevated temperature more than compensated the reduced driving force to effect absorption. Chambers stated that if the mist could be removed efficiently, the absorption capacity of a unit could be increased by over 50 per cent by raising the operating temperature from 40°C to 60–70°C; an additional advantage would be that small coolers would be required between the regenerator and absorber.

The effect of solution temperature in the absorptive capacity of the Bureau of Mines contactor, was, however, insignificant.

6.9 Performance of Absorbers

The absorption coefficient for centrifugal absorbers cannot be expressed in the usual units given in Chapter 5, e.g. in terms of mass absorbed per hour per unit of absorber surface. The most convenient expression is the overall absorption coefficient $K_g a$ per unit volume of absorber. The following simple formula may be used for the absorption of CO_2 in ethanolamine because the equilibrium pressure of the absorbed CO_2 over the solutions is very low

$$K_g a = \frac{Q}{V} \log_e \frac{p_1}{p_2}$$

where $K_g a$ = absorption coefficient in m^3 n.t.p./ second per atmosphere per m^3 absorber, i.e. absorber in volumes/hour per atmosphere

Q = gross flow in m^3/s, n.t.p.

V = absorber volume in cubic metres, arbitrarily taken as the block volume of the rotor

p_1 = partial pressure of CO_2 in inlet gas

p_2 = partial pressure of CO_2 in outlet gas

In the case of the double rotor centrifugal absorber it was found that values of $K_g a$ were substantially unaffected by variations in gas flow but increased with liquor flow. Using the units expressed above, values of $K_g a$ of 50000–100000 are readily obtainable for the absorption of 16 per cent CO_2 (in air) in 84 per cent of MEA aqueous solution (by weight) at 60°C. Scaling-up to units taking many times the maximum gas flow of 560 m^3/h in these small absorbers would, however, be difficult.

The Bureau of Mines workers compare the performance of their absorber by calculating the size of equivalent packed tower. The volume of their agitated absorber is taken as volume of solution in the vessel Figure 6.4. For the absorption of 20 per cent CO_2 (in air) in 40 per cent of DEA aqueous solution (by weight) under a total pressure of 20 bar gauge, a tower of 0·0465 m^2 cross-section packed to a height of 1·52 m with 19 mm Raschig rings would be required to give the same performance as the agitated absorber containing 0·305 m of solution in a vessel of 0·46 m diameter, i.e. the relative volumes are 1:4:1. The improvement in absorption performance per unit volume compared with a packed tower is negligible when account is taken of the space occupied by spray above the solution.

Some data on the absorption of SO_2 from a coal-fired power plant flue gas in a limestone-ash slurry on a 15 cm diameter flooded disc are given in a paper by R. J. Cleeson et al. to the 69th National Meeting of the American Institution of Chemical Engineers, 1971.

7

Regenerative Processes for Gas Absorption

L. BARBOUTEAU AND R. GALAUD

7.1 Introduction

This chapter relates to the purification of a gaseous mixture by the absorption, with the aid of a liquid, of one or more of its components. By heating or reduction of pressure, the gas is desorbed from the liquid, which can afterwards be re-used; this process is illustrated by the removal of hydrogen sulphide from natural gas[1]. The gas at Lacq leaves the wells at 150°C and 600 bar(g), containing 15 per cent H_2S, 10 per cent CO_2 and some condensable hydrocarbons.

The operation of absorption has already been discussed in Chapter 5. The process of liquor regeneration takes place in a column, which is usually one fitted with plates. The rich solution from the bottom of the absorber is subjected to reduced pressure in a degassing vessel in order to liberate the hydrocarbons absorbed before it enters the regeneration column.

In Sections 7.3.3 and 7.3.4 special consideration is given to two types of washing: (i) *washing with water*, that is partial desulphurization with water, and (ii) *washing with an amine*; the total desulphurization by chemical action. We shall first examine what are the criteria which must guide the user's selection.

7.2 Criteria for the Selection of the Process

The selection of the process is based on (i) the nature of the absorber, which is sometimes linked to the possibilities of supply; (ii) the nature of the gas to be treated and, in particular, its content of impurities; (iii) the purity of the commercial gas to be obtained; and (iv) the cost of the energy available at the treating works.

7.2.1 Nature of the Absorbent

It must have the following essential characteristics: (i) high solvent power for the gas and the capacity for undergoing a reversible solvent–gas reaction on reduction of the pressure or on heating; (ii) low price; (iii) low volatility; (iv) zero corrosivity and high stability; and (v) low viscosity and, if possible, non-foaming properties. The problem of amines and of water will be discussed in detail.

The use of amines is now an old-established practice; on the other hand, water washing of large quantities of natural gas is new and has been put into effect on an industrial scale, principally in the south-west of France at the gas-treating works at Lacq (Société Nationale des Pétroles d'Aquitaine).

The chemical formulae of the three amines used are as follows:

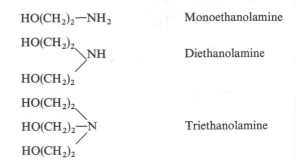

$HO(CH_2)_2—NH_2$	Monoethanolamine
$HO(CH_2)_2$⟩NH $HO(CH_2)_2$	Diethanolamine
$HO(CH_2)_2$⟩N—$HO(CH_2)_2$⟨$HO(CH_2)_2$	Triethanolamine

(i) *Monoethanolamine.* (a) *Properties.* The properties of monoethanolamine are given in Figures 7.1–7.5.

(b) *General reactions of MEA with* H_2S *and* CO_2. H_2S and CO_2 react with MEA in the following manner:

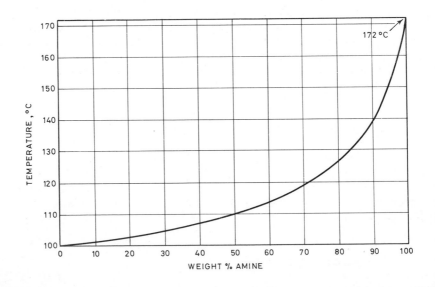

Figure 7.1 Boiling point of monoethanolamine solutions at 1 atm absolute

$$HO-CH_2-CH_2-NH_2+H_2S \rightleftharpoons HO-CH_2-CH_2-NH_3/HS$$
MEA hydrogen sulphide

$$HO-CH_2-CH_2-NH_2+CO_2+H_2O \rightleftharpoons HO-CH_2-CH_2-NH_3/HCO_3$$
MEA hydrogen carbonate

and

$$2(HO-CH_2-CH_2-NH_2)+CO_2+H_2O \rightleftharpoons (HO-CH_2-CH_2-NH_3)_2/CO_3$$
di-MEA carbonate

Thus the action of MEA on H_2S requires only one molecule of H_2S, while that on CO_2 requires 1 or 2 molecules.

(c) *Reaction with* COS. When the gas to be treated contains COS, the MEA reacts to form

<table>
<tr><td>Hydroxyethylthiocarbamic
acid</td><td>$HO-CH_2-CH_2-NH-C{\overset{SH}{\underset{\parallel}{}}}\\\qquad\qquad\qquad\qquad O$</td></tr>
</table>

The hydroxyethylthiocarbamic acid exists in two forms:

thiolo form $HO-CH_2-CH_2-NH-C\diagup^{SH}_{\substack{\parallel\\O}}$

and

thiono form $HO-CH_2-CH_2-NH-C{=}S$
OH

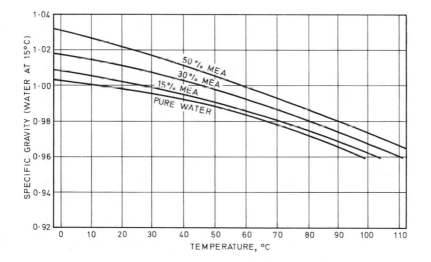

Figure 7.2 *Specific gravity of monothanolamine solutions. (Reproduced by permission from 'Gas Purification', by Kohl & Riesenfeld, Copyright 1960, McGraw-Hill Book Company, Inc)*

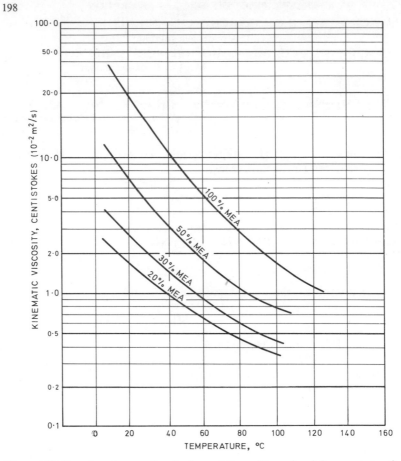

Figure 7.3 Viscosity of monoethanolamine solutions. (Reproduced by permission from 'Gas Purification', by Kohl & Riesenfeld, Copyright 1960, McGraw-Hill Book Company, Inc)

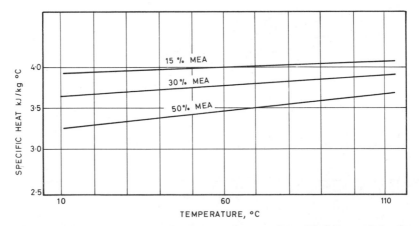

Figure 7.4 Specific heat of monoethanolamine solutions. Reproduced by permission from 'Gas Purification', by Kohl & Riesenfeld, Copyright 1960, McGraw-Hill Book Company, Inc)

The hydroxyethylthiocarbamic acid has not been found capable of being isolated. It decomposes thus:

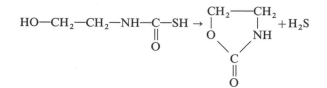

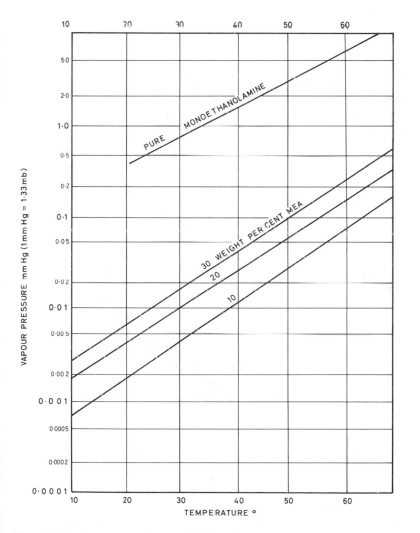

Figure 7.5 Vapour pressure of monoethanolamine over aqueous solutions. (Reproduced by permission from 'Gas Purification', by Kohl & Riesenfeld, Copyright 1960, McGraw-Hill Book Company, Inc)

The oxazolid-2-one reacts with the excess of MEA.

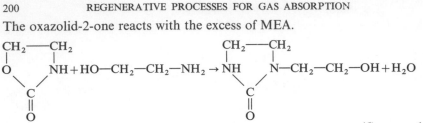

(Compound 1)

The N-(β-hydroxylethyl)-iminazolid-2-one hydrolyses:

HO—CH$_2$—CH$_2$—N $\begin{array}{c} \text{CH}_2\text{---CH}_2 \\ | \qquad | \\ \end{array}$ NH + H$_2$O → HO—CH$_2$—CH$_2$—NH—CH$_2$—CH$_2$—
NH$_2$ + CO$_2$

(Compound 2)

to give N-(β-hydroxyethyl)-ethylenediamine.

Unfortunately it is not possible to regenerate the compounds (1) and (2), and the recirculated amine solution becomes enriched in these residues, which have, therefore, to be eliminated; moreover, they also contribute to the corrosion of the unit[2].

(ii) Diethanolamine. (a) Properties. The properties of diethanolamine are given in the following graphs: distillation temperatures (Figure 7.6), specific gravity of solutions at various concentrations and temperatures (Figure 7.7), viscosity curve (Figure 7.8), specific heat as a function of the temperature (Figure 7.9) and vapour pressure curve (Figure 7.10).

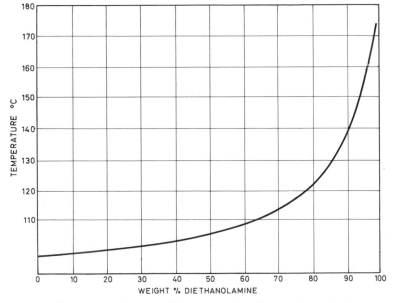

Figure 7.6 Boiling point of diethanolamine solutions at 1 atm absolute

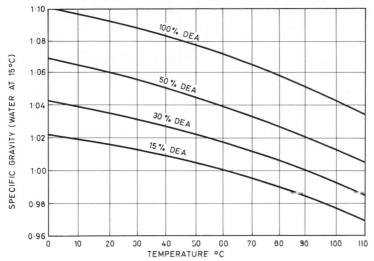

Figure 7.7 *Specific gravity of diethanolamine solutions. (Reproduced by permission from 'Gas Purification', by Kohl & Riesenfeld, Copyright 1960, McGraw-Hill Book Company, Inc)*

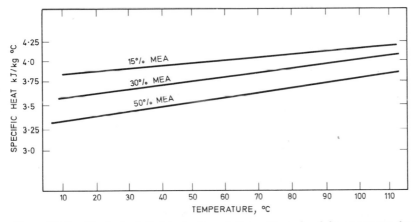

Figure 7.8 *Specific heat of diethanolamine solutions. (Reproduced by permission from 'Gas Purification', by Kohl & Riesenfeld, Copyright 1960, McGraw-Hill Book Company, Inc)*

(b) *General reactions of* DEA *with* H_2S *and* CO_2. H_2S and CO_2 react with DEA in the following manner:

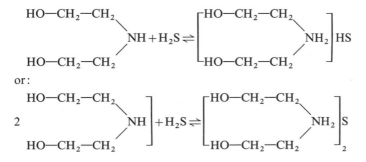

or:

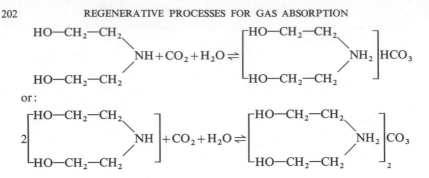

or:

Polderman of Union Carbide recognizes that DEA combines with CO_2 to give 3-(2-hydroxyethyl)-oxazolid-2-one.

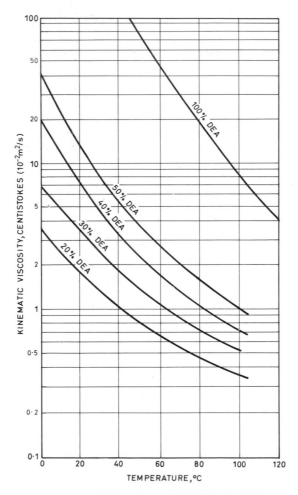

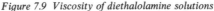

Figure 7.9 Viscosity of diethalolamine solutions

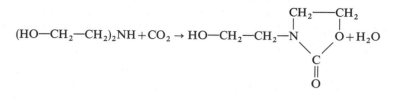

At elevated temperatures in the presence of a base, N,N'-di-(2-hydroxyethyl)-piperazine is formed.

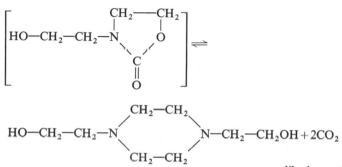

dihydroxyethylpiperazine

No trace of this compound in the generated DEA has been found in the plant for the treatment of crude gas at the Société Nationale des Pétroles d'Aquitaine in France[2].

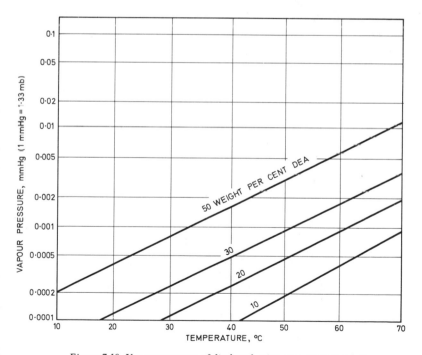

Figure 7.10 Vapour pressure of diethanolamine over aqueous solutions

(iii) Triethanolamine. The tertiary amine is used to a much smaller extent because it is relatively more expensive. However, increasing the concentration can make it more selective[3].

(iv) Hot Potassium Carbonate Solution. This process was developed by the U.S. Bureau of Mines, at Bruceton, Pennsylvania[3,4,5]. The specific heat and the specific gravity of the potassium carbonate solution are given in Figure 7.11. The hot carbonate process permits only a partial purification of the gas, and it is necessary to complete the washing with an amine solution.

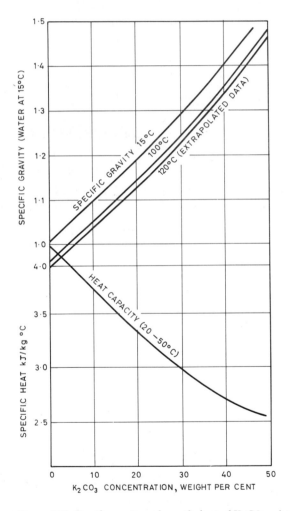

Figure 7.11 Specific gravity and specific heat of K_2CO_3 solutions

The carbonate reacts in the following manner:

$$H_2S + K_2CO_3 \rightleftharpoons KHS + KHCO_3$$
$$CO_2 + H_2O + K_2CO_3 \rightleftharpoons 2KHCO_3$$

However, the solution becomes progressively more concentrated in KHS up to an equilibrium which is a function of the pH of the solution.

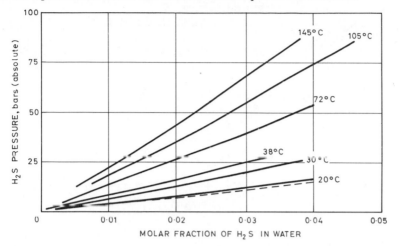

Figure 7.12 Determination of the coefficient $K = Y/X$ in the system H_2S/H_2O

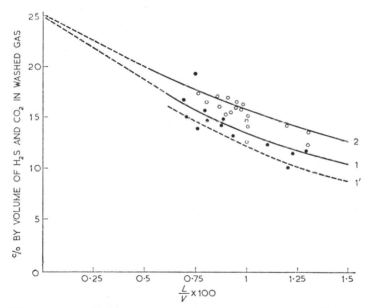

Figure 7.13 Content of acid gases in the washed gas as a function of $L/V \times 100$. L, expressed as m^3/h of water; V, expressed as m^3/h of washed gas; ●, $28 < \theta < 34°C$; ○, $38 < \theta < 50°C$ curve 2; curve 1' = curve 1 as calculated

(v) Other absorbents. The following processes are also in use: Removal of H_2S and CO_2 by ammoniacal solutions and by alkaline solutions; the Seaboard vacuum process; carbonate process; tripotassium phosphate process; sodium phenolate process; alkacid process; Giammarco and Vétrocoke process[6].

(vi) Water. Since the absorption by water is a physical absorption, in order to purify a gas completely and economically it is necessary to follow the washing with water by chemical absorption[7].

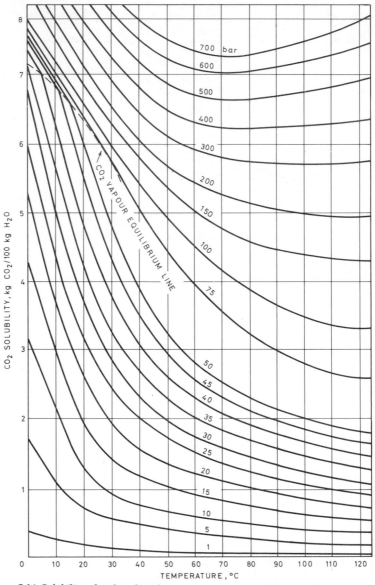

Figure 7.14 Solubility of carbon dioxide in water at pressure of 1 atm and greater. (Courtesy of Industrial & Engineering Chemistry, Chemical and Engineering Data Series)

(vii) Equilibrium curve of binary mixtures. Although the solubility in water of H_2S and CO_2 at elevated pressures approximately follows Henry's law, the evaluation of the partial pressures of the crude gas is not classical as Figure 7.12 shows. It has been shown, in fact, that for a given temperature, the law of

perfect gases is far from holding good. It has been successfully verified by calculation, taking as reference each of the binary mixtures H_2O–H_2S, H_2O–CO_2 and H_2O–CH_4, that the activity coefficients thus calculated are in acceptable agreement with the results obtained. The results found on a pilot plant and those observed on an industrial installation are given in Figure 7.13, which represents the variations in the content of acidic gases in the water-washed gas as a function of the ratio $(L/V) \times 100$. L represents the throughput of water in the main wash in cubic metres per hour, and V represents the throughput of crude gas in cubic metres per hour (760 mm, 30°C).

Examination of these curves shows that the variations in the H_2S–CO_2 content of the washed gas may be approximated to a very flattened hyperbola and, in the working region, to a straight line.

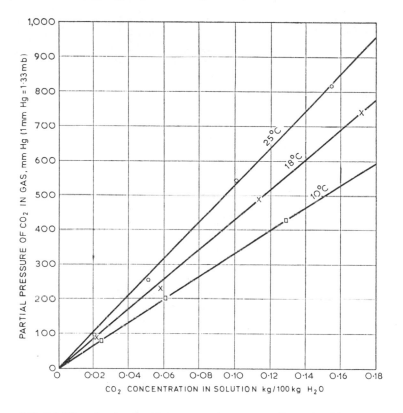

Figure 7.15 Solubility of carbon dioxide in water at low pressure. (Reproduced by permission from 'Gas Purification', by Kohl & Riesenfeld. Copyright 1960, McGraw-Hill Book Company, Inc)

(viii) Data for solubility in water of H_2S and CO_2 individually. There is considerable literature on the solubility in water of the individual gases H_2S and CO_2. Figure 7.14 gives the solubility of CO_2 in water at above 1 atm as a function of the temperature[8].

Figure 7.15 gives the solubility of CO_2 in water at low pressures. Table 7.1 shows the solubility of H_2S in water.

Table 7.1 SOLUBILITY OF HYDROGEN SULPHIDE IN WATER

H at various temperatures

Pressure	5°C	10°C	20°C	30°C	40°C	50°C	60°C
1	3.12×10^2	3.64×10^2	4.78×10^2	6.04×10^2	7.35×10^2	8.65×10^2	9.81×10^2
2	3.19×10^2	3.69×10^2	4.80×10^2	6.06×10^2	7.39×10^2	8.77×10^2	10.02×10^2
3.	3.26×10^2	3.72×10^2	4.83×10^2	6.09×10^2	7.42×10^2	8.83×10^2	10.11×10^2

Values given are for H, in equation $P = Hx$, where x = mole fraction of solute in the liquid phase and P = partial pressure of solute in the gas phase in atmosphere.

7.2.2 Nature of the Gas to be Treated

We shall consider the content of H_2S, CO_2 and other impurities. Since the solubility of H_2S in water is very different from that of CO_2, it will be advantageous to treat with water a gas rich in H_2S. Further, the content of impurities has a very great influence on the amine treatment which follows the water wash. The latter acts as a filter and the difficulties which may arise in the amine wash will be solely due either to a malfunctioning of the water unit or to a condensation of hydrocarbons in the amine absorber. Every amine treatment gives rise to losses of amine which are of two types: (1) losses due to entrainment and vapour pressure, proportional therefore to the throughput of gas to be treated, the temperature of the treatment, and the gas velocity at the top of the regenerator, and (2) losses by the formation of non-regenerable addition compounds with the amine (COS, HCN, CS_2).

The first of these losses will be especially appreciable with the acid gases. In fact, the water treatment only allows an increase in the total throughput of the works as a function of the content of H_2S in the crude gas. The amine wash will be limited by the dimensions of the absorber and, in the limit, the output of purified gas will scarcely be any greater, the amine itself absorbing CO_2 with more difficulty than H_2S. The second loss will be decreased if the non-regenerable impurities are soluble in water, which is not the case for COS. The efficiency of a water wash can be increased by the addition of adjuvants. The characteristics of the gas, that is, its pressure at the outlet from the deposit and its content of heavy hydrocarbons, are also important factors.

Two washes in series (water and amines) lead to an extra loss of pressure, which is prejudicial to the overall energy balance. It is therefore necessary that the pressure of the treatment of natural gas is sufficient to avoid a final recompression of the purified gas. A water wash causes a pressure loss of about 2 bar.

If the content of heavy hydrocarbons is considerable, two washes in series are not advisable. We shall see later on that the losses of hydrocarbons in the water wash may be great. The purity of the purified gas must be very high if it is intended to domestic use; its transport by pipe-line necessitates an almost complete desulphurization, all the more extreme since some customers may use the gas for chemical purposes. The absorption processes used take account of the content of impurities in the gas.

(i) Crude gas with a low content of sulphur compounds. A chemical agent is advisable (amines).

(ii) Crude gas with a high content of sulphur compounds. The amine wash may be preceded by a water wash if the throughput of gas to be treated is greater than $500\,000$ m³/day.

It is possible to speak of the economics of such a system only if it is compared with a desulphurization by an amine alone. If the specifications for the purified gas are not too demanding from the point of view of the H_2S content (case of the production of fuel gases from acidic gases), it is obvious that desulphurization could be achieved by several successive water washes, but the usage of water would be very large and the selling price prohibitive.

7.2.3 Cost of Energy[7]

The steam for heating in the regeneration of the amine is the most important factor.

Let us suppose that the water wash removes 40 per cent of the acid gas content of the natural gas. For a water wash followed by an amine wash, the total electrical energy consumed is greater than the electrical energy that would be needed for a single amine wash. This excess is between 20 and 40 per cent. In a system with a water wash followed by an amine wash, the amount of cooling water is considerably reduced, namely by about 40 per cent. The most important factor is the steam consumption in the amine wash which is directly proportional to the amount of amine in circulation, the amount of acidic gas to be removed from the gas and the reflux rate of the amine regeneration tower. Taking these into account, it can be said that the economy in steam realized in comparison with the amine wash alone and for the same throughput of natural gas is about 25 per cent.

7.3 Types of Liquid Phase Desulphurization

We shall take as examples only three truly typical cases. The plants have been used to treat a natural gas containing 25 per cent of acidic gases consisting of H_2S and CO_2.

7.3.1 Preparation of the Feed

Before entering the absorber, the crude gas must be freed from all heavy hydrocarbons. As shown in Figure 7.16, separators fitted with baffles are placed in series to collect particles of water and hydrocarbons. The yield of the absorber is much affected by the efficiency of the separators because the hydrocarbons cause foaming which leads to the instability of the wash and an increased cost of treatment, and consequently heavy losses of absorbing solution.

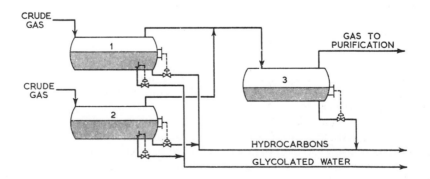

Figure 7.16 Preparation of the feed

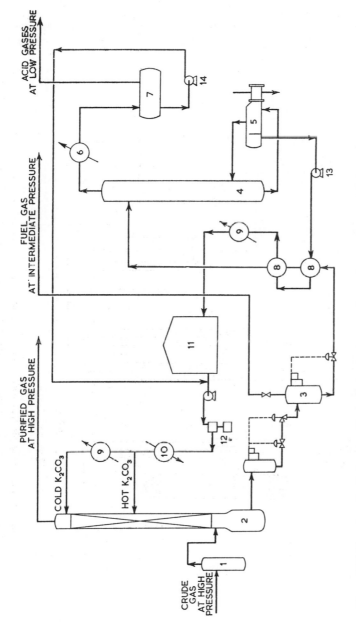

Figure 7.17 Flow-sheet for H_2S removal by potassium carbonate solution. 1, separator; 2, absorber; 3, degassing vessel; 4, regenerator; 5, reflux vessel; 6, condenser; 7, reflux vessel; 8, exchanger; 9, cooler; 10, preheater; 11, carbonate tank; 12, feed pump; 13, draw-off pump; 14, reflux pump

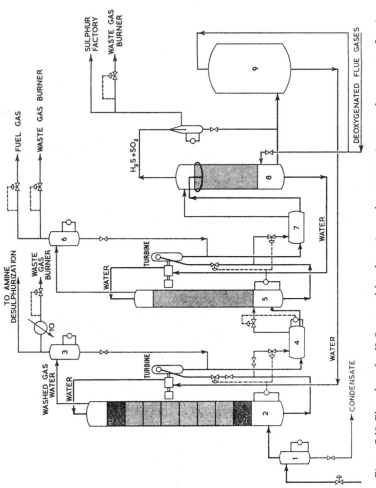

Figure 7.18 Flow-sheet for H_2S removal by absorption under pressure in water. 1, separator; 2, primary washing column; 3, primary washing separator; 4, primary degassing vessel; 5, secondary washing column; 6, separator; 7, secondary degassing vessel; 8, regenerating column; 9, water tank; 10, reheater

7.3.2 Washing with Carbonate

(i) *Principle.* This process is very simple. Since the rate of absorption of CO_2 by potassium carbonate increases with the temperature, it has proved best to work near the temperature of reversibility of the reaction

$$K_2CO_3 + CO_2 + H_2O \rightleftharpoons 2KHCO_3$$

Because of this, it is necessary to provide a minimum amount of steam to regenerate the solution. If a high pressure is used in the absorber, the release of pressure alone suffices for the regeneration, the action of H_2S and CO_2 on the carbonate being almost non-exothermic. A few plates are necessary at the head of the absorber to complete the washing with relatively cold carbonate.

(ii) *Description of the flow-sheet* (Figure 7.17). The feed gas passes through a separator and then enters the base of the absorber, while the purified gas leaves the head of the column. A separator for the purified gas enables entrained absorbent solution to be recovered. The regenerated carbonate is returned to the head of the absorber; the rich carbonate passing into conditions of reduced pressure in a degasser through a level-regulating valve and then, after passage through heat exchangers, goes to the top of the regenerator.

The acid gases and the water vapour pass through a cooler and a reflux vessel, where the water separates out from them; the acid gases are led to the sulphur recovery unit and the water is refluxed to the head of the regenerator. A reboiler completes the regeneration of the carbonate and makes up the heat losses of the plant.

(iii) *Operating data.* The process has been investigated experimentally on a semi-industrial scale. The temperature in the absorber was 120°C and 95°–105°C at the top of the regenerating column and 110°–120°C at the bottom. As the unit operated, the content in the solution of KHS and $KHCO_3$ continuously increased up to an equilibrium valve depending on the pH.

The H_2S content of the Lacq gas is too high for single-stage removal by carbonate and consequently it was decided to use the amine process despite the disadvantage of the volatility of the amine (Section 7.3.4).

7.3.3 Washing with Water (Figure 7.18)

(i) *Principle.* Washing with water is analogous to washing with carbonate, it being possible to carry out the desorption by reduction of pressure. The absorption is purely physical and there is also a relatively high absorption of hydrocarbons, which are liberated at the same time as the acid gases.

(ii) *Description of the unit.* The crude gas, at the ambient temperature (but above 20°C in order to avoid the formation of hydrates which takes place with gas containing 15 per cent of H_2S and 10 per cent of CO_2) enters at the bottom of the main washing column and comes into direct contact with the water fed to the top of the tower. The washing takes place in counter-current on plates, which may be either stepped plates or plates of the conventional type; Raschig rings may be used with an almost equal efficiency.

The washing takes place at a pressure of about 75 bar; a slight evolution of heat due to the absorption of the acid gases raises the temperature of the water leaving the column charged with H_2S and CO_2 by a few degrees.

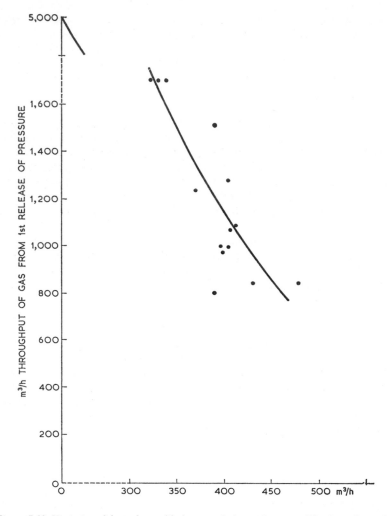

Figure 7.19 Variation of throughput of fuel gas washed, as a function of the throughput of wash water

The gas so washed deposits the entrained water in a main washing separator from where it is re-introduced into the main circulation. The charged water from the bottom of the absorber undergoes a first reduction of pressure to 15 bar, the energy of which is recovered in a turbine. This, coupled with a balancing motor, provides the energy for a pump to feed the water to the top of the absorber.

In the course of this release of pressure, a large quantity of fuel gas very rich in H_2S and CO_2 is produced. The mixture of these gases is washed in a secondary washing column supplied with water in counter-current to absorb the maximum amount of acid gases. The residual gas from the top of the secondary washer is passed, like all the acidic fuel gases of the works, into an amine washing unit, the role of which is to refine these gases as combustible gases while recovering the H_2S.

The water leaving the secondary washing column and that brought to a pressure of 12 bar are degassed in a third column where the dissolved gases are recovered by reducing the pressure to an effective value of 1 bar. This desorption is facilitated by the injection at the base of this column of inert gases consisting of flue gases from the central heating plant which have been deoxygenated before use. The release of the pressure on the water from 12 bar to 1 bar produces a certain amount of energy, which is recovered in a turbine.

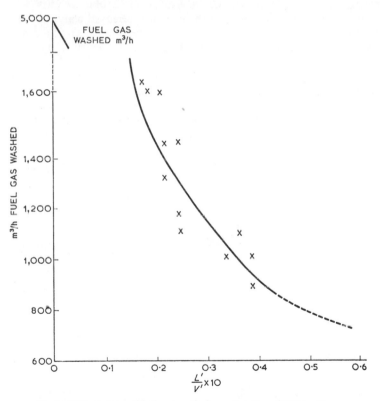

Figure 7.20 Volume of fuel gas washed as a function of $L/V' \times 10$

The regenerated water from the bottom of the degasser is discharged into a reservoir whence it is taken to feed both main and secondary washing columns. The acid gases at the head of the degasser, containing less than 1 per cent of hydrocarbons, are passed to a sulphur-making unit.

(iii) General considerations. The water washing unit is characterized mainly by the recovery of the energy of the release of pressure on a liquid containing gases in solution, and a working temperature in the region of the ambient temperature.

The role of the turbines is essential, not only from the energy point of view, but as a regulator of the temperature of the absorption water. In fact, the release of pressure takes place with a rise in the temperature of the water which is not negligible, and if this energy is not converted into mechanical energy· the plant would have to be provided with coolers the dimensions of which prove to be prohibitive. The temperature of the water has a marked influence on the efficiency of the washing of the gas. Another important factor for the washing process is the ratio L/V, where L is the amount of water of the primary washing, and V is the amount of crude gas.

If it is desired to double the efficiency, then, for a given volume V, twice as much water is required. Unfortunately, as the solubility of the hydrocarbons is not negligible, increasing the throughput of water involves losses of hydrocarbons which increase with increasing molecular weights.

The content of hydrocarbons in the pressure-released water in the secondary washing implies a reduction in the yield of purified gas and a duty to treat the residual gas in order to free it from H_2S and CO_2, permitting its utilization as fuel gas within the works.

The second requirement leads to the desulphurization being carried out in two steps: a first washing with water at 12 bar followed by a second wash, with amines. Figures 7.19–7.22 illustrate quantitatively the water washing of the gas from the first pressure release. It follows from an examination of

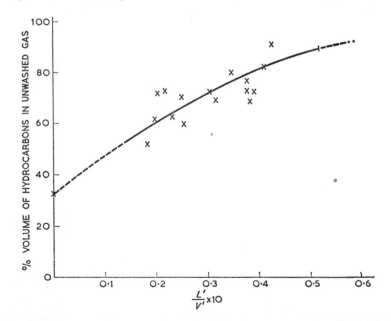

Figure 7.21 Percentage volume of hydrocarbons in the fuel gas washes as a function of $L/V' \times 10$
L, throughput of water m^3/h;
V', throughput of fuel gas washed m^3/h $(L/V) \times 10$

these figures that for a throughput of 70000 m^3/h of crude gas, the volume of gas from the pressure-releasing stage is 5000 m^3/h, and that this gas contains 30 per cent of hydrocarbons before washing. An increase in the throughput of water permits a higher recovery of acid gases but involves a higher re-absorption of hydrocarbons. The working optimum between the ratio L/V', the output of washed fuel gas obtained and the percentage of hydrocarbons contained in the latter, has the co-ordinates: $(L/V') \times 20 \sim 1.2$.

$$\text{Fuel gas washed} \sim 600 \ m^3/h$$

It must also be mentioned that the content of hydrocarbons in the final acid gases is a dead loss and a source of trouble for the sulphur-making unit, particularly the CH_4 which, combining with the sulphur, gives CS_2, thus diminishing the yield.

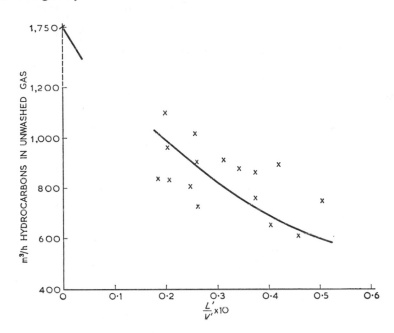

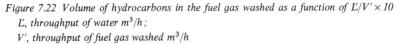

Figure 7.22 Volume of hydrocarbons in the fuel gas washed as a function of $L/V' \times 10$
L, throughput of water m^3/h;
V', throughput of fuel gas washed m^3/h

(iv) Corrosion. One of the principal characteristics of such a unit is the particularly severe working conditions; the high percentage of H_2S and CO_2 in the gas, and the higher pressure, giving high concentrations of H_2S and CO_2 in the water.

The CO_2–H_2S mixture, dissolved in water, is more corrosive than the binary systems H_2O–H_2S and H_2O–CO_2. In order to fight against possible severe corrosion, two solutions can be envisaged: (*a*) to increase the extra thickness to compensate for corrosion (about 8–10 mm) or (*b*) to slow down the rate of corrosion in order to increase the life of the apparatus. A 'corrosion inhibitor' is used which, added in an amount of a few parts per million, offers an easy solution, provided it is well chosen.

The rate of corrosion without an inhibitor has been determined by measuring the loss in weight of samples of metals. These consisted of iron wires rolled up into a spiral, each representing a surface of 20 cm^2; they could easily be withdrawn while leaving the plant under its operating conditions.

The eight tests with different times of exposure are represented in Figures 7.23, 7.24 and 7.25. At pressures of 70 and 12 bar after some hours the

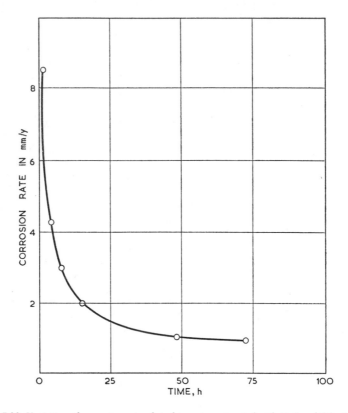

Figure 7.23 Variation of corrosion rate of steel in water saturated with H$_2$S and CO$_2$ (no agitation, pressure 70 bar, 40°C)

corrosion is approximately 1 mm/year; at atmospheric pressure it is smaller by a factor of 2. After several days' operation, the corrosion becomes stabilized at from 0·3 to 0·15 mm/year. The effect of temperature on the rate of corrosion is illustrated in Figure 7.26. It is desirable to operate at the lowest possible temperature in order to have the minimum corrosion. The data are inadequate to examine the influence of the H$_2$S/CO$_2$ ratio; however, the rate of corrosion is multiplied by 10 when the H$_2$S/CO$_2$ ratio is multiplied by 6. This influence is very marked on the ethanolamine units following the water washing units. When the gas to be treated has been washed with water a corrosion of only 0·0125 mm/year is obtained.

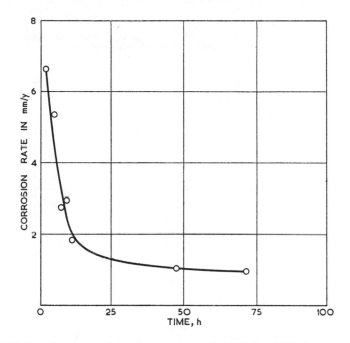

Figure 7.24 Rate of corrosion of steel in water saturated with H_2S and CO_2 (no agitation, pressure 12 kg/cm², 40°C)

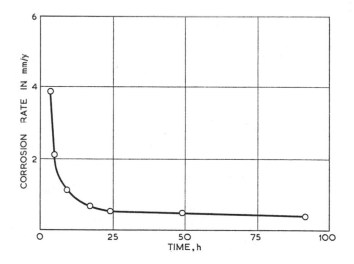

Figure 7.25 Variation of corrosion rate of steel in water saturated with H_2S and CO_2 (no agitation, atmospheric pressure, 40°C)

The experimental study of the influence of inhibitors is in progress. Figure 7.27 shows the comparative efficiency of Nornst AC 10 and the inhibitor of the Institut Francais du Pétrole designated 'Multix' in tests carried out in the

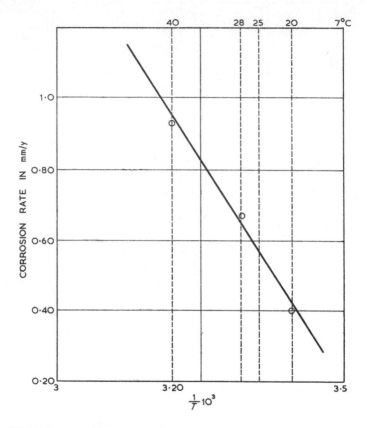

Figure 7.26 Influence of temperature on the rate of corrosion in water saturated with H_2S and CO_2 at atmospheric pressure

laboratory. The shapes of the three curves are identical during the first few hours, then, as the inhibitor is adsorbed on to the surface of the metal, the corrosion decreases more rapidly. It has been found that the addition of a soluble inhibitor allows the rate of corrosion to be reduced by a factor of 4. Summarizing, the data given show that the employment of an inhibitor can be avolded while at the same time building the water-washing plants in ordinary steel.

7.3.4 Washing with Amines

(i) Principle. The washing of a gas with amines is identical, from the point of view of the principle involved, with washing it with potassium carbonate.

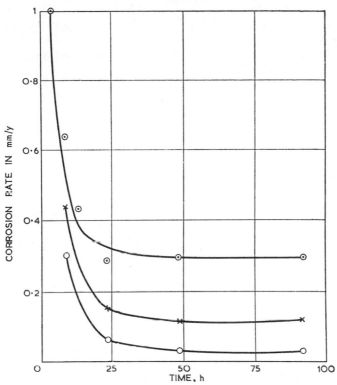

Figure 7.27 Influence of inhibitors on the rate of corrosion of steel by water saturated with H_2S and CO_2 (no agitation, atmospheric pressure, 40°C). ○ *without inhibitor;* × *with 20 p.p.m. of A* ⊙ *with 20 p.p.m. of A, +p.p.m. of B*

The amine reacts chemically with the acid gases with the liberation of quite an appreciable amount of heat. It will therefore be necessary to compensate for the absorption of heat at the moment of regeneration by supplying the balance of calories. There is consequently quite an appreciable consumption of steam. On the other hand, the purified gas is directly marketable and the precise object of the washing process is thus attained.

(ii) Description of the plant (Figure 7.28). After passing through the separator, the gas reaches the bottom of the absorber. It is washed in counter-current with an amine solution. The purified gas leaves the head of the column and then passes into a separator which enables any entrained amine to be recovered. The regenerated amine is drawn into a tank and fed with the aid of a pump to the top of the absorber. The charged amine leaves the base of the column and, via a level-regulating valve, passes into a degassing vessel. The gaseous phase ($H_2S + CO_2$ + hydrocarbons) is subjected to a diminution of pressure in the fuel gas collector via a pressure-regulating valve. The amine, now at reduced pressure, is reheated by a battery of heat exchangers, and

forms the feed of the regeneration column. The feed takes place two plates below the top. The acid gases ($H_2S + CO_2$ and a small percentage of hydrocarbons) pass into the head of the column and are cooled in two coolers which condense the water. The latter separates out and is fed back as reflux; the acid gases are directed to the sulphur recovery unit.

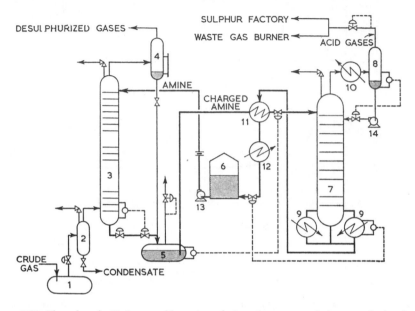

Figure 7.28 Flow-sheet for H_2S removal by amine solutions. 1, separator; 2, decanter; 3, absorber; 4, decanter; 5, degassing vessel; 6, amine storage; 7, regenerator; 8, reflux vessel; 9, reboiler; 10, condenser; 11, exchanger; 12, cooler; 13, feed pump; 14, reflux pump

The heating at the bottom of the regeneration tower is effected by means of two steam reboilers. The amine leaving the reboilers gives up some of its heat to the charged amine and is then cooled in a cooler before being sent to the amine storage tank, whence it is withdrawn by a pump and fed to the head of the absorber.

(iii) General considerations on operation. (a) Mode of working of the regeneration column. In order to obtain complete regeneration of the amine, there is a tendency to heat to the maximum, which involves an exaggerated consumption of steam. This excessive reboiling leads to an unduly high production of steam at the head of the column and, consequently, an unduly low partial pressure of the acid gas.

(b) Degasser. This intermediate vessel between the absorption and regeneration stages allows the dissolved hydrocarbons, undesirable in the acid gases, to be released. A variation in the ratio

$$\frac{\text{moles of water (80 per cent of the solution)}}{\text{moles of acid gases}}$$

is revealed by a large variation of the output of the degasser from both the quantitative and qualitative points of view.

The hydrocarbons consist mainly of methane. The volume of hydrocarbons stays the same if, with a fixed throughput of amine, the amount of crude gas is progressively increased and the pressure of the degassing vessel remains constant. If this pressure is reduced, the volume of hydrocarbons increases in the fuel gas but decreases in the acid gases at the head of the regeneration column, the total output of desorbed hydrocarbons remaining substantially the same.

When the throughput of amine is too large, there is little acid gas in the fuel gas liberated under reduced pressure, chemical combination being preponderant there at this moment. On the other hand, if the throughput of amine is too low the desorption due to the reduction in pressure is large, and the content of acid gases in the fuel gas, as well as the output of the latter, increases considerably. If the volume of hydrocarbons in the acidic fuel gas is very low, the gas can be passed to the sulphur recovery units, thus eliminating the desulphurizing unit for this residual gas.

(c) *Foaming.* Heavy hydrocarbons are the principal cause of foaming. For this reason it appears necessary to check the correct operation of the separators placed at the inlets of the units. The yield of two absorbers of the same dimensions can be remarkably different if foaming takes place in one of them. Knowledge of the differential pressure of the column can be very useful if it is desired to follow the operation of the absorber.

Foaming can be reduced by addition of anti-foaming products (for example silicones) which modify the surface tension, or, if the foaming persists, by reduction of a feed and increase in the temperature of the feed amine. It is, moreover, advantageous slightly to reduce the absorption by raising the temperature, rather than by condensing the hydrocarbons in the absorber, because there is a very considerable increase of the partial pressures of the hydrocarbons when the crude gas contains a high proportion of constituents to be absorbed.

The diminution in the absorption may be compensated for by a slight increase in the concentration of the amine. The two effects; namely, diminution of the percentage of water in the solution, and rise in the temperature, tend to diminish the absorption of the hydrocarbons and, consequently, the importance of the degassing step in the intermediate vessel.

(d) *Filtration* (Figure 7.29). The amine must be freed from solid particles in suspension which activate the foaming. At the same time the filtration medium will, if possible, be an adsorbent for hydrocarbons (carbon or activated earth). The sealing of the filter is carried out with the help of an adjuvant. The duration of a filtration is established experimentally. A good filtration of the amine and a perfect separation of the condensates from the crude gas will ensure the stability of the gas-washing process.

(e) *Assembly of the Unit.* The assembly of the unit presents no difficulties. When operating at a relatively high pressure, problems of vibration may arise but can easily be resolved. If the throughput of gas is high, necessitating large throughputs of absorbing solution, it will be necessary to anchor the degassing vessel, together with the automatic pressure-releasing valve, at the bottom of the absorber.

(f) *Materials of Construction.* The most exposed parts are the base of the absorber, the pressure-releasing valve leading to the degasser and the re-boilers for the regeneration column, especially in the case of MEA. The base of a mild steel absorber is doubled by using 18/8Mo steel up to the first plate. The automatic level control valve at the base of the column is of 18/8/3 Cb steel. Corrosion being very severe with MEA, it is advisable to use automatic valves in parallel, one being in use and the other in reserve: this

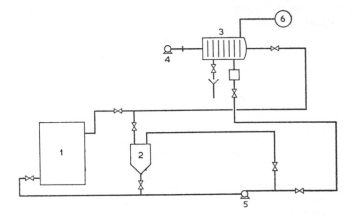

Figure 7.29 Filtration of circulating amine. 1, amine storage tank; 2, tank for pre-mixing the filtering aid; 3, disc filter; 4, pump for cleaning the discs; 5, feed pump; 6, cleaning water

enables a stoppage of the unit to be avoided on deterioration of the valve in use. The degassing vessel, in the case of the treatment of gas at high pressure, will have the same specifications as the absorber. The last heat exchanger between charged and discharged amine before the entry of the amine into the regeneration column will be of 18/8/Mo steel. It was assumed that corrosion took place when there was an over-charging of the absorbing solution with acid gases, namely over 0.8 m^3 of gas per cubic foot of solution. This value was generally considered to be the upper safe limit from the point of view of corrosion[9]. In fact, these concentrations are widely exceeded and only MEA proves to be corrosive. It is known that aqueous MEA solutions saturated with CO_2 dissolve iron, which is precipitated in the form of insoluble iron salts when the solution is freed from CO_2. Regions of corrosion in the regeneration column of carbon steel seem to confirm this.

The steel 'Inox 316' appears to stand up to the corrosive medium, even at high temperatures. Carbon steel gives satisfaction in the condensers at the head of the regeneration column, even though working under very severe conditions (50 per cent water, 50 per cent H_2S and CO_2).

(*g*) *Instrumentation.* The operation of the unit is a function of the reliability of the instruments. These must be inspected very frequently. The regulation of the bottom of the absorber in the case of a crude gas at high pressure is the most sensitive part of the plant. When a considerable degree of foaming takes place, the absorbing liquid is retained in the column and the time of response of the automatic valve to the impulse arriving from the automatic level controller must be a minimum. It is necessary that the differential pressures of the absorber and the regenerator should be indicated and recorded in the control room. The operator can thus survey the working of the column and carry out the operations necessary in case of malfunctioning.

(iv) Characteristics of washing with amines. The losses of absorbing solution may be of three types:

(*a*) *Losses by entrainment.* These losses take place when foaming occurs in the absorber or the regenerator. They are reduced by an effective separation of the heavy hydrocarbons from the crude gas or by the addition of an anti-foaming agent.

(*b*) *Losses through the vapour pressure of the gases.* These losses can be reduced by washing the purified gas with water or glycol on a number of plates at the head of the absorber. Use may also be made of adsorbents (for example, bauxite) capable of being regenerated. Theoretically, it would be necessary to use amines with a very low vapour pressure, but the use of such amines (triethanolamine, methyldiethanolamine) is expensive.

(*c*) *Losses by degradation of the amines.* The amines are quite stable at the regeneration temperatures but, on the other hand, they are subject to chemical degradation. The presence of oxygen reacting with the H_2S, for example, can give free sulphur which, in the hot, reacts with the amine forming dithio-carbonates or other non-regenerable products. It is therefore necessary to avoid the presence of oxygen in the plant, particularly in the amine storage tank.

The gas to be treated may also contain some acidic compounds (traces of formic or acetic acid, carbon disulphide, carbon oxysulphide) which react with amines and give non-regenerable salts. These must be eliminated from the absorbing solution since they adversely affect the absorption, increase the viscosity and may possibly activate foaming.

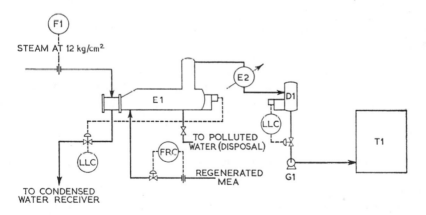

Figure 7.30 Purification of purge from circulating amine system. E1, purifier; D1, purified MEA vessel; E2, condenser; G1, MEA discharge pump; T1, MEA tank; LLC, level regulator; FRC, flow regulator

In order to avoid an increase in the concentration of these residues non-regenerable in the hot, it is necessary to remove a small quantity of regenerated solution from the bottom of the regenerator and to feed it to a small associated plant (Figure 7.30). The amine passes through an automatic feed valve into a reboiler. The supply of re-heating steam is regulated by the level of the amine. The amine vaporized is condensed in E2, passes into the vessel D1, is withdrawn by the pump G1 and sent into tank T1. The starting temperature is a function of the concentration of the amine. As the concentration of the residue increases, the temperature rises and then becomes stabilized. Before discharging the apparatus, since some MEA is left, a supplementary addition of demineralized water is made in order to recover the maximum amount of amine; the apparatus is then discharged.

7.3.5 Analyses

(i) Crude gas. Since the feed gas has a practically constant composition, the analysis is only carried out from time to time.

(ii) Purified gas
    (a) *Determination of sulphur compounds by hydrogenation (total sulphur*
    Principle: The sulphur compounds are converted into H_2S by catalytic hydrogenation in an oven at 1000°C. The H_2S is fixed in the form of zinc sulphide by bubbling the gas through a solution of zinc acetate. The reaction of the hydrosulphide with *N,N*-dimethyl-*p*-phenylenediamine gives methylene blue quantitatively, which is estimated colorimetrically.
    Sampling: The purified gas is retained in a burette after it has been well swept out.

    (b) *Determination of* H_2S
    Principle: By bubbling the gas to be analysed through a solution of zinc acetate the H_2S is retained in the form of zinc sulphide. By the reaction of the zinc sulphide with *N,N*-dimethyl-*p*-phenylenediamine in sulphuric acid and the subsequent addition of a hydrochloric acid solution of ferric chloride, methylene blue is obtained and can be estimated calorimetrically.
    Method: Set up the bubbler, containing 30 ml of zinc acetate, in the circuit of the gas to be analysed. Circulate the gas at a maximum rate of 30 litres/h. The volume of gas to be passed through depends on its H_2S content. It must not be less than 60 litres.

    (c) *Determination of mercaptans*
    Object: The gas to be analysed is first freed from its H_2S by washing with a solution of cadmium sulphate. Mercaptans are analysed by reaction with silver nitrate in solution, the excess being determined by titration with ammonium thiocyanate.
    Sampling: Set in position the two bubblers containing 50 ml of cadmium solution and then two others containing 25 ml of silver nitrate solution. Circulate the gas at 15 litres/h, checking that all the H_2S is retained in the first absorber; if not, reduce the flow of gas. Pass through between 50 and 150 litres of gas.

    (d) *Determination of sulphur by combustion*
    Principle: The gas under examination is burnt. The combustion products, entrained by a current of purified air, bubble through a solution of hydrogen

peroxide, which converts the sulphur dioxide formed in the combustion into sulphuric acid. The sulphuric acid is then determined.

Method: Gas flow: 85–90 litres/h, air; 500 litres/h, bubbling tube with 100 ml of hydrogen peroxide solution.

(e) Acid gases

H_2S and CO_2 are to be determined.

Principle: Absorption of the H_2S and CO_2 by a known amount of KOH, followed by titration of the KOH solution for H_2S.

Method: Pass the gas through a separator and then through a 250 ml flask. Produce a slight overpressure by first closing the outlet tap after sweeping out the apparatus.

(f) Various analyses

Charged amine (amine charged with acid gases). The combined H_2S in the amines is determined by iodometry.

Discharged amine (regenerated amine). The same procedure as for the charged amine, except that the volumes of amine solution and iodine solution are different. (Charged amine: 1 ml of amine for 25 ml of iodine; regenerated amine: 10 ml of amine for 10 ml of iodine.)

Determination of mono- and di-ethanolamine in the amine solutions

These amines are oxidized by periodic acid according to the reactions:

$$HO-CH_2-CH_2-NH_2 + HIO_4 \rightleftharpoons 2HCHO + NH_3 + HIO_3$$
$$(HOC_2H_4)_2NH + 2HIO_4 \rightleftharpoons 4HCHO + NH_3 + 2HIO_3$$

The periodic acid HIO_4 and the iodic acid HIO_3 are reduced by arsenious acid, and the excess of arsenious acid is determined by an iodine solution.

Determination of monoethanolamine in regenerated amine solutions and in the recovery purges

This is done by distillation under partial vacuum of the water and the monoethanolamine contained in the samples and acidimetric determination of the MEA in the distillate.

(iii) Analysis by means of physical apparatus. The installation of continuous analysers, with recording of the results, allows the purity of the gas to be followed, and hence the absorption to be checked without a break. These instruments must be very sensitive, since the gas frequently contains only a few parts per million of H_2S. Some of them are based on the degree of coloration of a paper sensitive to H_2S (monocolour).

7.4 Technological Calculations

7.4.1 Absorption Towers

The size of the absorption towers may be calculated by the methods given in Chapter 5, Part A. The gas phase is the controlling factor and, because of the speed of the chemical reaction, the liquid-phase coefficient may be neglected.

7.4.2 Regenerators

The number of plates in the regenerators is usually established from experimental measurements rather than by theoretical calculations. Data for the design of stripping columns have been given by Muhlbauer and Monogbran[10].

Table 7.2 HEAT TRANSFER COEFFICIENTS

Apparatus	Heat transfer coefficient $(W/m^2\,°C)$
Amine–amine exchangers	600
Condensers (for acid gases at the top of the regeneration columns)	450
Coolers (for regenerated amine)	800
Re-boilers	1400

7.4.3 Heat Exchangers

Table 7.2 shows the practical heat transfer coefficients used in design.

7.5 Safety

7.5.1 General

Safety is a most important consideration since, working with a toxic gas at high pressure, any mistake in operation or breakage may lead to an accident with grave consequences. The toxicity of hydrogen sulphide and the symptoms of poisoning are well known and have been described in numerous publications on safety in chemical factories. In addition to automatic valves which, while ensuring the regulation of the plant, also ensure safety of operation, the plant is provided with pneumatic safety devices, safety valves and alarms.

7.5.2 Pneumatic Safety Devices

(i) In the path of the crude gas at the absorber inlet. A cut-off is provided at a distance from the crude gas inlet. The rise in pressure caused by the closure of the valve permits the immediate evacuation of the gas to a waste gas burner.

(ii) In the path of the charged solution leaving the base of the absorber. In the case of an irregularity of the level or of the automatic valve at the base of the absorber, or of a rise in the level in the degasser, the flow of charged amine to the degassing vessel can be shut off.

7.5.3 Safety Valves

To make good any failure of the safety devices and control valves, each absorber possesses a safety valve at the base of the tower. In order to break the vortex in the case of a high rate of flow of absorbing solution, the valve is guided by flat plates. During the starting-up of the unit, or during decompression, it is necessary to carry out these operations slowly in order not to damage the float of the valve; it is necessary, also, to choose appropriate dimensions of the spindle for the float assembly.

7.5.4 Alarms

High-level alarms, in particular, are placed on almost all the units of apparatus, namely at the separator, at the crude gas inlet, at the base of the absorber and at the separators at the head of the absorber, degassing vessel, reflux vessel and regeneration column.

Similar safety devices are installed on the pre-washing plant for the crude gas, often to an amplified degree, because of the more serious danger in the handling of water rich in acid gases.

7.5.5 Particular Case of Washing with Water

Any escape of water from the plant is shown by the immediate desorption of acid gases, which makes this unit more dangerous than chemical washing units.

In addition to the safety devices mentioned above, the arrangements provided on this unit consist in automatically placing the plant in the shutdown condition, that is with the motors stopped, the high pressure circuits isolated from the medium pressure water circuit, and the medium pressure circuits isolated from the low pressure water circuit.

This operation is brought into play by the various incidents which may occur, such as loss of pressure, overheating of a motor, low level in the high pressure column, lack of pressure in the control of the automatic valves, or high level in the separator at the crude gas inlet.

All these safety devices are connected to a diagram which allows an operator on the unit to assure himself of the correct running of the plant and to determine the origin of a derangement of the unit.

8

Solid Chemical Absorbents for Gases

E. R. WARD

8.1 General

The use of solid chemical absorbents for gases on the large industrial scale is not looked upon favourably by chemical engineers for the obvious reasons that:

(i) Unless the solid is highly porous the rate of chemical reaction rapidly falls off as the surface of the solid absorbent is covered by a layer of reactants. Consequently, only a small proportion of the weight of the absorbent is usefully employed unless regeneration can be carried out *in situ*.

(ii) The labour cost of replacing exhausted solid absorbents is high except when the solid can be handled by the 'moving burden' or 'fluidized solids' techniques.

Thus the industrial equivalent of the laboratory soda-lime tube normally is favoured only when traces of an impurity in a gas have to be removed. Several examples of this are given in Part B.

In spite of these disadvantages, however, and of the many attempts to replace it by means of a 'wet' process, the 'dry' purification process, in which high concentrations of hydrogen sulphide are removed from fuel gases by oxide of iron, with continuous regeneration of the resultant iron sulphide by oxygen in air added to the gas, remains the most reliable and most commonly used process for this purpose when dealing with low pressure gases made from solid fuels or 'residual oil'. Although in practice it is known that the sulphiding and re-oxidation reactions take place independently and at different speeds, these reactions may be summarized as follows:

$$H_2S + \tfrac{1}{2}O_2 \rightarrow H_2O + S \tag{8.1}$$

Expressed in this way the process may be regarded loosely as catalytic.

The iron oxide also removes residual suspended material, a most important function since town gas is distributed over miles of piping and the bulk of it is finally discharged through the fine jets of domestic burners.

With minor exceptions the iron oxide process, as described in Section A, is used for the purification of coal gas made by the town gas and coking industries throughout the world.

Town gas based on coal is, however, being replaced at a revolutionary speed by gas made from hydrocarbon oils or by natural gas. The former is manufactured mainly from hydrocarbon oils and gases which in most processes demand the desulphurization of the feedstock. This latter process involves the use of either zinc oxide or a special form of iron oxide as solid absorbents as described in Part B.

The H_2S content of gas from coal carbonization plants in the U.K. is usually within the range 0·8 to 1·2 per cent by volume, dry basis, equal to 11·8 to 17·6 g/m^3.* In addition, the gas contains 0·5 to 0·7 g/m^3 of sulphur in the form of organic sulphur compounds (COS, CS_2, C_4H_4S, etc.) after benzol recovery. These last are not removed by iron oxide but by the methods described in Part B.

Under powers given by the Gas Act of 1948, Statutory Instrument No. 792, Gas (Quality) Regulations 1949 was issued prescribing that town gas must be free from hydrogen sulphide. Under the same powers 'Gas Examiners General Directions' have been given, the last of which is dated 1956. This direction prescribes a test which can be interpreted as demanding a concentration of H_2S in town gas of less than 1–2 p.p.m. by volume.

PART A REMOVAL OF HYDROGEN SULPHIDE FROM COAL GAS

8.2 Reactions Involved in Absorption of H_2S

8.2.1 Basic Reactions

Hopton and Griffith[1] and Morcom[2] examined seven known forms of ferric axide as set out in Table 8.1, and found that with the exception of the β form—which appears only to exist in acid conditions—they all react completely with H_2S to give ferric sulphide, usually in the hydrated form as represented by the following equations:

$$2Fe_2O_3.H_2O + 6H_2S \rightarrow 2Fe_2S_3.H_2O + 6H_2O \qquad (8.2)$$

$$2Fe_2O_3 + 6H_2S \rightarrow 2Fe_2S_3.H_2O + 4H_2O \qquad (8.3)$$

They found that the best results for the removal of H_2S from fuel gases were achieved by using $\alpha Fe_2O_3.H_2O$, the hydrated γ form giving only slightly poorer results.

The inferior results obtained from the anhydrous forms were attributed to the difficulty of preparing them in a sufficiently porous state; to their tendency to produce the anhydrous sulphide which is slower to reoxidize than the hydrate; and to the induction period of their reaction with H_2S which renders them unsuitable for complete H_2S removal. The amorphous oxide is very unreactive owing to the great volume change on sulphiding which chokes the pore structure.

The sulphide hydrate $Fe_2S_3.H_2O$ which may be formed from all forms of iron oxide, is readily oxidized, and if the temperature is below 50°C and

---

* It should be noted that from 1971 the U.K. gas industry will use the standard cubic metre at 15°C, 1013·25 mb dry, in place of the cu. ft at 60°F, 30 in Hg pressure, sat. for the expression of gas volumes, and grams in place of grains for the weight of impurities.

the pH is above 7·0, the product is either $\alpha Fe_2O_3.H_2O$ (favoured by dry conditions) or $\gamma Fe_2O_3.H_2O$ (under moist conditions). The conversion by this means of the less active forms of ferric oxide to the more active forms, after a cycle of sulphiding and oxidation, is put forward as a possible reason for the improvement noted in the activity of some purifying materials in use under favourable conditions.

Table 8.1 FORMS OF FERRIC OXIDE[1]

αFe_2O_3	Bright red, with low magnetic susceptibility; very stable on heating
$\alpha Fe_2O_3.H_2O$	Yellow brown, with low susceptibility. Changes to αFe_2O_3 on heating at 250°–300°C
$\beta Fe_2O_3.H_2O$	Bright yellow with low susceptibility. Changes to αFe_2O_3 on heating above 100°C
γFe_2O_3	Chocolate brown; intensely magnetic. On heating at 300°C changes to αFe_2O_3 with loss of magnetic properties, the conversion being complete in about 24 h
$\gamma Fe_2O_3.H_2O$	Orange with low susceptibility. On heating at 300°C changes to γFe_2O_3 with great increase in magnetic properties, but on prolonged heating at this temperature slowly converted to αFe_2O_3 with a fall of susceptibility as for γFe_2O_3
$\delta Fe_2O_3.H_2O$	Dark red-brown, intensely magnetic. On heating at 150°C is converted completely to αFe_2O_3 with a great fall in susceptibility
Amorphous Fe_2O_3	Red-brown, low susceptibility hardly changed on heating; at 100°C becomes αFe_2O_3 even under boiling water, when colour becomes bright red

At temperatures above 40°–50°C, dehydration of $Fe_2S_3.H_2O$ takes place and the resulting anhydrous sulphide is slower to oxidize than the hydrate. This effect is enhanced in the case of $Fe_2S_3.H_2O$ formed from an anhydrous oxide. The rehydration of Fe_2S_3 also is a slow process.

A further change which takes place at temperatures above 40°C under neutral conditions, or at a lower temperature under acid conditions, is the decomposition of the ferric sulphide into FeS_2 and Fe_8S_9, forms which oxidize slowly, producing the sulphate in the case of the former, and the completely inactive oxide in the case of the latter.

Hopton[3] states that whereas at 40°C the neutral $Fe_2S_3.H_2O$ was converted to 42 per cent FeS and 58 per cent Fe_8S_9 (iron basis) in three to four hours, this conversion does not occur below 99°C when the pH is 8·0. The ill-effects of elevated temperatures on the dehydration of $Fe_2S_3.H_2O$ is, however, not affected by alkalinity.

Apart from the molecular structure, the related porosity and type of pore structure of ferric-oxide-based purifying materials is shown to be the most important factor controlling the interaction with hydrogen sulphide, and it was found that these properties were not improved by the reduction in the bulk density of poor purifying materials, achieved by the addition of light fibrous material, although the addition of such materials may be advantageous in other respects; see, however, Section 8.12.

From the known molecular volumes of $Fe_2S_3.H_2O$ and $\alpha Fe_2O_3.H_2O$ it can be calculated, that a tablet of the oxide with a volume porosity of

50 per cent would be converted into a mass almost devoid of porosity, on complete change to the hydrated sulphide. It is therefore the volume porosity above 50 per cent which is critical in determining the value of any particular material.

At temperatures in the range 250°–400°C, the hydrogen sulphide and organic sulphur compounds in coal gas, such as carbon disulphide and carbon oxysulphide, react with Fe_2O_3 and FeO to give FeS, which on roasting in air returns mainly to Fe_2O_3.

8.2.2 Identification of Iron Oxide

The identification of the physical form of iron oxide can be carried out by determining the rate of change of magnetic properties on heating, and the rate of solution in acid under standard conditions[20].

8.2.3 Summary of Controlling Factors in the Interaction of Hydrogen Sulphide and Ferric Oxide

(i) Molecular form of the oxide. $\alpha Fe_2O_3.H_2O$ is the most active form, closely followed by $\gamma Fe_2O_3.H_2O$. In the case of the less active anhydrous oxide, the induction period shown in the reaction with H_2S not only slows down sulphiding but could impede complete H_2S removal.

(ii) Porosity of iron oxide. The rate of reaction of H_2S with a given ferric oxide depends chiefly upon the penetration of the gas into the mass, i.e. the rate of diffusion through the surface layer as stated by Bramslev[4], and is therefore related to porosity and pore structure. These are the most important physical properties involved. These properties in a poor material are not improved by the reduction in bulk density brought about by the addition of fibrous material.

(iii) pH of iron oxide. Acid conditions are harmful and can result in permanent loss of activity, but excessive alkalinity could produce the risk of the evolution of traces of H_2S from the re-oxidized material. In use, a satisfactory pH is 7·0, but it may be necessary to charge the material initially at a higher pH in order to achieve this.

(iv) Temperature at which sulphiding and reoxidation takes place. Only the hydrated sulphide oxidizes rapidly and produces $Fe_2O_3.H_2O$. Dehydration of this sulphide which takes place readily at temperatures above 40°–50°C is therefore harmful; still higher temperatures can result in decomposition of the ferric sulphide with more permanent loss of activity.

8.3 Types of Main Plant Used, Including Ancillaries

8.3.1 Types of Purifiers

(i) Static box purifiers. Static box purifiers are usually constructed in cast iron, but occasionally in steel or concrete, and range up to 21 m wide on the major axis. The covers are of steel. A comparison made in 1952[5] showed steel and concrete boxes to be similar in cost, with cast iron appreciably dearer. The latter may, however, be more lasting.

The total depth of the purifying material used is normally from 1 to $2\frac{1}{2}$ m. If it exceeds approximately 1·5 m, the boxes are sometimes referred to as 'deep purifiers'. Even with shallow boxes, the material is commonly arranged in two, or even three, layers, but in some instances single layers up to 1·5 m in depth have been employed. The disadvantage of multiple layers lies in the greater cost of supporting grids and possibly in a slight increase in the cost of handling the oxide in and out of the box. The advantages are: better gas distribution, less packing of the material, and improved control over the composition of the material in the top and bottom of the box.

The gas flow in purifiers is generally upwards through the material, but latterly downward flow is favoured on the grounds of reduced oxide consolidation immediately above the purifier grid slots, and reduced condensation on the purifier covers. In some cases, the gas enters between the layers, i.e. the flow is both upward and downward. The use of two layers each of approximately 0·5 m in depth with either upward or downward flow is common.

Valves and connections permitting the reversal of the gas flow are in some cases provided, with a view to increasing the period in use of the oxide charge. The economic advantage of this is doubtful, as is also the case where provision is made to operate with upward, downward and reverse flow.

With deep box purifiers, multiple layers with divided flow are normal. This system shows some advantage in capital costs, but in operation suffers from the disadvantage of less uniform contacting of the gas with the oxide than is the case with simple flow. It is arguable whether on balance the deep box with divided flow is more economical than the shallower purifier with two layers and simple downward flow, except when dealing with low concentration of hydrogen sulphide.

The majority of box purifiers have been constructed on ground level, but some are overhead. Similarly, the new and part-spent material floor space is in some cases at ground level, and in others overhead. Operational costs have been put forward indicating that the elevating of box purifiers could not be justified on economic grounds.

In a small number of instances, the oxide charge of box purifiers is held in removable containers similar to those used for tower purifiers, but normally the oxide is charged from a heap using barrows or the mechanical plant described later.

Arrangement of static box purifiers. Purifier boxes are usually arranged in series of from 4 to 6 or, more rarely, from 7 to 8 units may be employed. The valves used may be water seals, standard types of gas valves, or, more rarely, an elaborate 'centre valve'—now out of date—may serve a whole series.

The valves and connections are arranged so that the order of the boxes can be changed, bringing the last box in the series into the first position. Recently the valves concerned in this operation have been mechanized in certain instances in order to facilitate a more rapid rotation than has been used in the past.

When only three or four purifiers are used in series, it has been a practice in the past to provide one or two catch purifiers for the final position which are not rotated with the primary purifiers. This arrangement is generally considered less economical than the use of four to six purifiers without catch purifiers.

(ii) Static tower purifiers. Static tower purifiers are constructed of steel, and are mainly circular, but sometimes rectangular in section.

Typical measurements for low pressure towers of the Thyssen-Lenze type are 6×18 m high, and for the Klonne type, which is similar, 9×12 m high. The Thyssen-Lenze towers are described in detail in Section 8.11.1. High pressure versions of these towers are cylindrical, smaller and operate up to 30 bar.

The oxide charge is contained in a number of superimposed shallow steel trays, each containing a layer of purifying material approximately 0·5 to 1·0 m in depth. These trays or containers may hold a single layer of purifying material, in which case the gas flow is normally from the annulus surrounding the trays, downward through all the layers in a tower in parallel, and into the centre offtake, or each container may hold two layers, in which case the gas enters from the centre inlet between each pair of layers flowing upward through one and downward through the other to the annulus.

Sets of rectangular towers with single layer trays and common vertical division plates are sometimes referred to as tower boxes.

Arrangement of static tower purifiers. Tower purifiers are normally arranged in series, with valves and connections for the 'rotation' or 'swinging' of the order of the towers, in the same way as is described for static box purifiers.

In a 1959 installation[6], ten towers were arranged as five 'takers' consisting of two towers in parallel; hand-operated valves being provided to allow either tower to be taken out of service and leaving the other tower to take 100 per cent overload.

Tower purifiers operating under high pressure, say, from 20 to 30 bar, present a problem with regard to the possibility of valve leakage. This may be dealt with by installation of pairs of valves, with vents between, in place of single valves. Another method used to overcome this difficulty, as with the Bischof towers[7], is to dispense with all valves other than the main inlet, main outlet, and the bypass to the standby stream. This latter may be an operational stream subjected to overload, or a single box used only when the main stream is off. With this arrangement, the whole stream is purged and taken off the line, when the first taker is discharged. Following this, the trays are removed from each of the other takers in turn and placed in the next purifier upstream; the last taker is then charged with fresh trays. In effect this is a forward rotation system, in which the material alone, instead of the charged purifier, is rotated.

(iii) Gastechnik dynamic purification plant. The 'Gastechnik' process—sometimes termed the Rafflor process—has been developed to use pelleted oxide over the pressure range atmospheric to 30 atm. The first full-scale plant of this type to be installed in Britain[9] operates at atmospheric pressure approximately, and is described as follows:

(a) General. This installation which operates at approximately atmospheric

pressure, uses 12 mm pellets made by extruding a paste made from 90 per cent of a commercial 'prepared' oxide and 10 per cent of plaster. These pellets are worked up to 30 per cent by weight of sulphur before sulphur extraction and re-use.

(b) *Towers.* The cylindrical steel towers, each 3 m dia. × 12 m high with conical bases, are mounted 6 m off the ground on steel supports, and are arranged in series of three towers. Gas flow is concurrent with the intermittent downward flow of the oxide pellets in the first two 'takers' and countercurrent to the pellet flow in the third 'taker'. Each tower is provided with top, and bottom gas locks, each holding the equivalent of one charge of pellets for the $1\frac{1}{2}$ m^3 capacity charging skip.

(c) *Pellet-handling plant.* The towers are replenished intermittently, for example daily, using mechanically operated skips, the displaced pellet batch being removed by electric truck to the pellet screening plant. The screenings are transferred for use in conventional purifiers and the pellets are carried to the sulphur extraction plant.

(d) *Sulphur extraction process.* The sulphur in the spent pellets is usually extracted using tetrachlorethylene at 121°C and at slightly above atmospheric pressure, but on one installation, carbon disulphide at a lower temperature and at atmospheric pressure, was used. The extracted pellets which contain from 3 to 5 per cent of sulphur are then screened and re-used. The sulphur recovered by the evaporation of the solvent is steamed and run off into moulds at 90 per cent purity approximately.

It is estimated that a 100 000 m^3/day installation is the minimum economic scale required to justify the capital cost of the sulphur extraction unit, without which the process is uneconomical except for the removal of a very small concentration of hydrogen sulphide. By 1969 four Gastechnik plants were installed in the U.K., one of which has become redundant.

(iv) Fluidized beds of iron oxide

(a) *Fluidized desulphurization at 400°C using iron ore (Appleby Frodingham Process).* This multi-stage fluidized bed process operates at 400°C using 0·1–1·0 mm iron ore particles. Designed to deal with coal gas it reduces hydrogen sulphide to 1 p.p.m. w/w and removes 80 per cent of the organic sulphur compounds present. Full-scale plants have operated at the Appleby Frodingham steel works and at gas works at Nottingham and Exeter.

The sulphur produced from the cyclic reoxidation of the sulphided iron ore is in the form of dioxide and must therefore be used to manufacture sulphuric acid. Large-scale operation and appropriate acid prices are required to render the process economical. The rapid rate of change from solid fuel based gases to those based on low sulphur content hydrocarbons or sulphur-free natural gas in town gas systems greatly diminished the prospects of the process and no plants were in operation in 1969.

(b) *Fluidized operation at near atmospheric temperature with hydrated iron oxide.* On a laboratory scale, fluidized particles of hydrated iron oxide in the range 8–250 μm have been used successfully in a continuous process for the removal of 1 per cent of H$_2$S from nitrogen containing 0·8 per cent of oxygen.

Plant design and operational data were given [11] for a plant to treat 28 000 m^3 of coal gas per day.

It was found desirable to use a highly active form of iron oxide and multi-stage countercurrent operation in order to achieve a satisfactory degree of hydrogen sulphide removal, and an economical concentration of sulphur in spent oxide.

8.3.2 Types of Ancillary Plant

(i) Oxide handling plant. Purifying material is charged into purifiers, or purifier trays, by means of hand barrows, belt conveyors, skips, grabs and mechanical shovels. After being loosened by means of hand forks or pneumatic tools, it may be discharged by hand shovel on to barrows, skips or conveyor belts. None of these tools needs to be designed specifically to handle purifying material except that non-sparking, non-ferrous metals are sometimes specified for tools such as pneumatic chisels which dig into the material being discharged *in situ*.

Where the purifying material is removed in a container or tray, this is usually lifted out using a specially designed crane traversing on a pair of rails, either overhead or at ground level, one on either side of the set of towers. A typical crane is shown in Figure 8.1. Following this, the material may be loosened up by means of hand forks or pneumatic tools, and the tray emptied either by hand or by rotation through 180° by means of a mechanical tippler. In another type of discharger, the tray is clamped to a turntable which is

Figure 8.1 Low-pressure tower purifiers at the Isle of Grain works of the South-Eastern Gas Board

mechanically rotated against a number of ploughs fixed to a beam which is slowly lowered through the oxide layer.

The subsequent treatment of purifying material after discharge usually involves the addition of moisture, of an alkali for pH control, and possibly admixture with unused material. Formerly, the material after these additions would be mixed by hand turning, but mechanical means are now available such as the paddle conveyor. The paddles of this conveyor pass part of the material forward to allow the remainder to fall back on to the material of the paddle behind. Ribbon conveyors also are used for this purpose.

Part-spent purifying material is usually lumpy and needs to be reduced in particle size prior to re-use. The required breaking or 'disintegration' can be achieved either by means of a Crone and Taylor type thrower/breaker, in which two cages rotating in opposite direction break the material, and the bars of the outer case throw the material clear of the apparatus in order to minimize trimming, or by means of an adapted jaw crusher, for example, of the British Jeffrey Diamond type.

Air blowers. Blowers used to supply air into the gas stream for *in situ* revivification have no special features.

Control of gas temperature and humidity. In the past, connections were commonly provided for the addition of live steam into the unpurified gas stream for the purpose of raising the gas temperature and humidity, but more recently, simple closed surface gas heaters are preferred.

Purging apparatus. Spent, or part-spent, purifying material at the time of its removal from a purifier can be pyrophoric, and although in some cases the gas contained in purifiers when taken off is displaced using air blown into the bottom of the purifier by means of a steam ejector, the modern trend is to use an inert gas such as carbon dioxide from a battery of cylinders, or gas from purge gas machines which may be fixed or mobile.

8.3.3 Plant for Extraction of Sulphur from Spent Oxide

Plant for the solvent extraction of the sulphur content of spent purifying material pellets so that they may be re-used, is regarded as a normal ancillary for large Gastechnik purifier systems. Tetrachlorethylene is used as a solvent; alternatives are toluene and carbon disulphide.

Static box and tower purifiers, however, are rarely used in conjunction with the solvent extraction process, but spent oxide from such purifiers may in some cases be solvent extracted by the purchaser of the material for sulphur or cyanide recovery, or both.

8.4 Choice of Dry Purification Plant

8.4.1 Summary of Systems Available

The dry purification systems available for hydrogen sulphide removal from fuel gases are summarized as follows:

Systems operating at 350°–450°C
   removal of H_2S as FeS in static bed
   removal of H_2S as FeS in fluidized bed

Systems operating at 10°–50°C
   shallow box purifiers
   deep box purifiers
   'dynamic' tower purifiers
   static tower purifiers

The removal of hydrogen sulphide in static beds of zinc oxide or iron oxide at elevated temperatures finds economic application in cases, such as those put forward in Section B, where, for example, low sulphur content natural gas or refinery gas or vapourized hydrocarbons have to be preheated and desulphurized prior to being reformed with steam.

8.4.2 Factors Affecting Costs

The principal factors influencing to varying extents the costs relating to the normal temperature purification systems are summarized as follows:
   (i) scale of operation;
   (ii) concentration of hydrogen sulphide in the foul gas and the desired efficiency of removal;
   (iii) space available;
   (iv) cost and availability of labour;
   (v) cost and availability of natural and 'synthetic' purifying material;
   (vi) value of recovered elemental sulphur or spent oxide.

8.4.3 Choice of Systems

(i) Scale of operation. For small-scale operation, e.g. for processing less than 25000 m^3 of gas per day containing 1 per cent vol./vol. of H$_2$S, shallow static box purifiers, installed at ground level and with the simplest possible mechanical aids for purifying material handling, normally yields the lowest full cost. In view of the resulting sporadic labour demand for manhandling material and the unsatisfactory working conditions involved, some degree of mechanization of material handling may, however, be practised whether economical or otherwise.

With increasing scale of operation, short of that justifying the cost of the material handling equipment associated with tower purifiers, deep static boxes and 'dynamic' towers of the Gastechnik type are competitive. For installations dealing with, say, 350000 m^3 per day of foul gas, the tower purifier system begins to compete for overall cost, and most of the large-scale installations of dry purifiers installed in recent years have been towers.

(ii) Concentration of hydrogen sulphide in foul gas and desired efficiency of removal. The lower the concentration of hydrogen sulphide to be dealt with, the less is the influence of purifying material and of the value of spent oxide and sulphur, i.e. capital cost is the dominant factor dealing with small quantities or concentrations of hydrogen sulphide. This principle could lead to the use in appropriate cases of small quantities of relatively expensive solid reactants, which may be discarded in the sulphided state, e.g. the use of

zinc oxide pellets costing £1500 per ton of sulphur removed is economical, in hydro-desulphurizing practice, for removal of sulphur from gaseous hydrocarbons up to concentrations of 300 p.p.m. w/w of sulphur in feedstock.

High removal efficiency, such as that demanded by statute in the case of town gas in Britain, increases capital cost in static systems by increasing the number of takers required.

(iii) Space available. The space required for 'dynamic' and static tower purifiers is considerably less than that required for box purifiers, and this could be the determining factor in appropriate circumstances.

(iv) Cost and availability of labour. In view of the nature of the work involved in manhandling purifying material, labour shortage and high rates of pay are likely to arise and must be taken into account when the degree of mechanization and capitalization is decided upon in general.

(v) Cost and availability of natural and 'synthetic' purifying material. A substantial increase in the relative cost of natural purifying materials, arising for example from shortage of supply, could stimulate still further the production of 'synthetic' materials generally, and in particular possibly that of pelleted materials and processes, such as 'Gastechnik', which uses and regenerates them.

(vi) Value of recovered elemental sulphur or spent oxide. The general and relative level of spent oxide and recovered sulphur prices have a substantial but somewhat complicated influence on the choice of dry purification process, further complicated by the sliding price scales relative to sulphur concentration normally operated in spent oxide transactions.

The form in which the sulphur is to be disposed of and the concentration of sulphur in spent oxide to be aimed at, if it is produced in this form, are therefore factors which are taken into account in new projects.

Some flexibility in this matter is provided by the fact that if conditions change, spent oxide normally disposed of in that form could be extracted for sulphur and re-used, and control of the concentration of sulphur in spent oxide can be exercised by varying process conditions in given installations.

Consideration should also be given to the possibility of the disposal of spent oxide on the basis of its Prussian blue content.

8.5 Basic Data and Plant Design

8.5.1 General

Having made a choice of process, or processes, it is necessary to detail the basic data required by the design engineer. This comprises the gas loading, chemical and physical characteristics of the untreated gas, the desired standard of purity of the treated gas, information with regard to the purifying material to be used, and the area and permissible loading of the site.

An example of the information required is set out below:

Basic Information for a Projected Scheme for the Erection of Tower Purifiers

Gas throughput
Peak winter load   20000   m³/h
Normal summer load   7000   m³/h

Characteristics of untreated gas
Hydrogen sulphide content (0·8–1·0 per cent vol./vol.)   11·7 g/m³
Tar, after electrostatic detarring   0·02 g/m³ max.
Ammonia   0·12 g/m³ max.
Naphthalene (after preliminary washing)   0·23 g/m³ max.
Hydrocyanic acid   1·40 g/m³ max.
Maximum pressure available   100   mb (gauge)
Temperature (summer maximum)   24°C
Temperature (winter minimum)   40°C
Specific gravity (air = 1·0)   0·45 to 0·55

Treated gas
Hydrogen sulphide content max. 0·1 p.p.m. by volume
Gas pressure outlet purifier max. 30 mb (gauge)

Purifying materials to be handled
Natural bog ore moisture content   38–45 per cent w/w
                        bulk density   670 kg/m³ natural bases
Prepared oxide (peat base) moisture   35–40 per cent w/w
                        bulk density   670 kg/m³ natural bases

Spent oxide
Moisture content   5–10 per cent w/w
                        bulk density   960 kg/m³ natural bases
Any information available with regard to the source and the activity of the purifying material.

Site
Plan of site. (This would be appended.)
Permissible loading   16·4 t/m²

With the foregoing basic data in mind, the design engineer then proceeds to make a number of decisions, based on experience, which determine all the main features of the design of the installation. These features are set out below, and to some extent reiterate points made in Section 8.3.

There are a number of reasons why after more than half a century the basis of the design of dry purification plant is almost entirely empirical. One important reason is the difficulty of expressing in relevant scientific terms the activity of the material used, and of controlling this activity in use—because it derives from such factors as the limited control of the reaction temperature which it is economical to achieve, and the effect of impurities other than hydrogen sulphide on the complex of chemical reactions and physical changes which occur.

Hopton[3], for example, states that in laboratory experiments under conditions in which heat losses were relatively high, it was found that the slip (S) was independent of the H_2S concentration in the gas, and that it increased with increasing gas velocity (V) according to the following equations:

$$\frac{\log S}{\log S_1} = \frac{V}{V_1}^{-0\cdot6} \tag{8.4}$$

In practice, however, he states that reverse effects could result from increased loading arising from the effect of this on the reaction temperature.

8.5.2 Main Features of the Design and Arrangement of Static Purifiers

(i) Maximum stream capacity. Normally, box purifier streams are built for maximum capacities of 2–300000 m³/day, and tower purifier streams to a maximum of from 300000 to 600000 m³/day.

(ii) Number of purifiers per stream. Under full load, the efficiency of the first taker of a series of box purifiers, with daily rotation, is normally allowed to fall before discharging and re-charging to the point where from 70 to 80 per cent removal of H_2S is achieved. The efficiencies of the 'takers' in series with the first purifier are much higher, rising sharply to 98 per cent approximately at the last 'taker'.

At these efficiencies, a minimum of three purifiers in series would be required in order to purify gas containing 0·1 per cent by volume of H_2S to within the prescribed limit, which is equivalent to 1 p.p.m., and minima of four or five purifiers would be needed to deal with gas containing 1·0 and 2·0 per cent by volume, of hydrogen sulphide respectively. With series purifiers installed to these minima, it would be important to ensure that during periods of peak loading, purifiers are discharged and recharged on the same day in order to minimize the period during which the series operates below the normal margin of safety.

In the past, partly because of the inadequate margin of safety provided by three purifiers during recharging operations, and partly because of the possibility of the 'throwing off' of H_2S from the last 'taker' (although this might occur regardless of the number of purifiers in series), one or two non-rotating catch purifiers were commonly provided in series with primary streams comprising three or four 'takers' only. Where this was not done, relatively low loadings were commonly employed.

Where concentrations of hydrogen sulphide in excess of $1\frac{1}{2}$ per cent by volume have to be removed, the danger arises of the overheating of the purifying material with resulting permanent loss of activity. This danger can be reduced to some extent by making provision for the rapid 'swinging' or rotation of the purifiers, but when the concentration reaches 2 per cent or over, a more effective method of controlling peak temperature in the purifying material is to recirculate part of the gas.

The number of takers employed per stream of static tower purifiers, as shown in Table 8.2, is usually greater than that for box purifiers. The main reason for this is that the material layer thickness varies from roughly 0·5 to 1·0 m in the case of towers, compared with from 1·0 to 1·5 m for static purifiers, and this reduced thickness of layer is at most only partially offset

Table 8.2 COMPARISON OF NUMBER OF TAKERS EMPLOYED PER STREAM WITH VARIOUS PURIFIER TYPES FOR REDUCTION OF H_2S CONTENT TO 1 P.P.M.

H_2S content of foul gas percentage by volume	Box purifiers		Tower purifiers		'Dynamic' towers
	Min.	Normal	Min.	Normal	Normal
0·1	3	3	3	3	—
1·0	4	4–6	5	5–6*	3
2·0	5	5–6	6	6*	—

*Seven or eight 'takers' are sometimes installed but this is difficult to justify on economic grounds except in special circumstances.

by the specific layer area, so that the overall effect is one of increased loading of the purifier.

In a 'dynamic' system of purifiers, e.g. a Gastechnik installation, three 'takers' only may be used in series for the removal of 1 per cent by volume of hydrogen sulphide. The more frequent movement, the more active state of the purifying material in this system, and the greater the depth of material through which the gas passes, results in a higher gas loading relative to the purifying material content of a stream as a whole, and this allows greater control over the reaction temperature than in static systems. This factor, together with the more uniform, more controllable and more predictable chemical and physical characteristics of the pelleted purifying material used, should render this type of process more amenable to design based on fundamental scientific principles than are static systems.

(iii) Arrangement of purifier valves and connections. The usual arrangement of static purifiers in a series is for them to be provided with connections allowing the untreated gas to enter, and the treated gas to leave, any purifier. Interconnections are provided allowing the gas to pass from one purifier to the other in a predetermined sequence.

Usually only one 'long' connector is provided and this means that the regular periodic 'swinging' of the boxes is interrupted while any of the purifiers are off line for recharging. With this arrangement, if a purifier is taken off line for a period, for example for repairs, a temporary connector can be installed to permit rotation.

The arrangement described above is demonstrated in Figure 8.2 in which diagram (*a*) shows a series of six purifiers operating in the sequence 2 3 4 5 6 1; diagram (*b*) shows the position after 'backward' rotation, or 'swinging', to 1 2 3 4 5 6; and diagram (*c*) shows the position after rotation to 1 2 3 4 5 in order to release No. 6 purifier for recharging. Diagrams (*d*) and (*e*) show how by the modification of the long series connector the stream can be operated as one stream of six rotating purifiers or as two streams of three rotating purifiers.

The introduction of 'rapid' rotation of purifiers, i.e. the rotation of the purifiers in a series at, say, two-hourly intervals compared with the more normal daily rotation, creates a problem in that it is difficult to exploit fully any advantage gained if the series has to be maintained in an efficient state unrotated for a substantially longer period than two hours while a purifier is being recharged. One way of dealing with this is to provide a multiplicity of connections so that any five purifiers of the series of six can be rotated.

An alternative method which has been used to permit the rotation of a series whilst a purifier is being recharged, involved the construction of five pairs of twin towers operated as a single series. An automatically operated valve, to facilitate rapid rotation, was provided on the inlet, outlet and

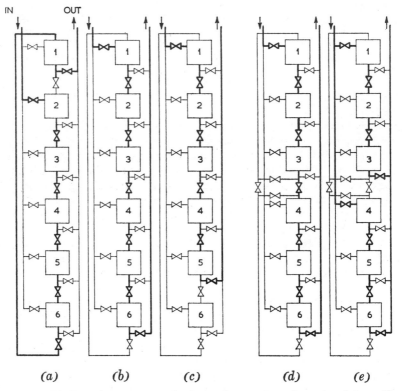

Figure 8.2 Typical arrangement of valves and connections of a series of six purifiers
——— *connections in use and open valves*
——— *connections not in use and closed valves*

connector common to each pair of boxes, and a hand-operated isolating valve was installed on the inlet, outlet and connector of each box. By this means, though at the cost of overloading one of a pair of towers by 100 per cent, a tower could be recharged without interrupting the rotation of the series.

(iv) Material layer depth in purifiers. The use of shallow layers of purifying material involves additional costs for grids and supports, and in the case of tower and removable tray box purifiers, for trays. On the other hand, there is less risk of lack of uniformity and of compacting the material in the charging of shallow layers of material than of deep layers. Layer depths in practice vary from 0·4 to 1·5 m and in most modern installations from 0·5 to 1·0 m.

(v) *Direction of gas flow through purifiers.* The flow of gas may be upwards or downwards through the purifying material layers, or it may enter between layers passing upwards through half of the material and downwards through the remainder, and provision may be made for the reversal of the direction of flow. Downward flow is now favoured on the grounds of reduced oxide consolidation immediately above the purifier grid slots and reduced condensation on the purifier covers.

When dealing with low concentrations of hydrogen sulphide, or when operating under conditions where pressure absorption must be minimized, the use of divided flow, or of reversible flow, or both, may be justified.

(vi) *Purifying material content of purifier streams.* An index of loading commonly used is the '*R*' ratio which is derived by dividing the maximum quantity of gas to be treated per hour by the purifier stream by the space occupied by purifying material in a single 'taker'.

If gas is not effectively de-tarred before its entry into the dry purifiers, this could determine the loading and result in operation at an *R* ratio of 20 or less for the removal of 1 per cent by volume of hydrogen sulphide.

Normally, however, the foul gas is effectively de-tarred and in some cases also subjected to partial or complete naphthalene removal. In these conditions the permissible loading is determined by the capacity of the system for hydrogen sulphide removal which depends upon the following prime factors:

(*a*) the activity of the purifying material in use, which is dependent upon the initial activity and also upon the number of exposures which it is given in the process of being worked up to the desired concentration of sulphur;

(*b*) the method of presentation of the material to the gas, i.e. the relativity of the depth to the area of the material through which the gas passes;

(*c*) the number of takers used in series; and

(*d*) the temperature of the reacting gas and material particularly in the first and second takers. This may be partly controllable.

In spite of the crucial influence which variations in the abovementioned factors have on the efficiency of hydrogen sulphide removal, it is not unusual to find standards for *R* ratios quoted without reference to any of them. One reason for this is that in some cases the *R* ratio quoted relates to conditions which are standard and understood, although not defined. A reason for variations in standards with regard to *R* ratios is that capital spent to permit low ratios can, over a certain range, be recovered in the form of reduced process costs, since fewer exposures of the purifying material would be needed to produce the desired concentration of sulphur in the spent oxide than when operating with high *R* ratios. This practice is, however, pressed too far if, as the result of operating with very low loading, either the purifiers operate with low efficiency because of the resulting low-reaction temperature, or, alternatively, if and when they do operate satisfactorily, the savings resulting from the less frequent exposure of purifying material is offset by the greater unit basis cost of handling the material subjected to lengthy exposures compared with the softer spent oxide resulting from shorter periods of exposure.

Static purifier systems are designed for *R* ratios over the range 20–80.

The risk when operating at the lower limit of this range is of the waste of capital, and at the higher limit there is the risk of failure unless a high standard of process control is constantly maintained. Most of the installations built in recent years have been designed for R ratios in the range 30–50 approximately, with four taker streams designed nearer the lower limit, and five and six taker streams nearer the upper limit.

The optimum R ratio for the first installation of Gastechnik towers installed in Great Britain[9] was found to be 50 when treating gas containing 0·6 per cent by volume of hydrogen sulphide and using a particular pelleted oxide described; only three 'takers' were employed.

8.5.3 Basic Features of Ancillary Equipment

(i) Equipment for control of gas temperature and humidity. The most economical means of controlling the temperature and humidity of the foul gas is by the admission of low pressure exhaust steam. The quantity of steam and the pipes and fittings sizes involved can readily be determined from the maximum gas loading and the temperature increase required, which is usually in the order of 5–10°C.

From the point of view of the moisture control of spent oxide, it is not always desirable to maintain the water vapour saturation of the foul gas when it is preheated, and in such cases indirect heaters are employed using either steam or gas. Such heaters are most economically sited on the common inlet to the stream, but where low concentrations of hydrogen sulphide are dealt with, and/or abnormal heat loss from the purifiers is anticipated, they may be sited on the inlet to each taker. In such circumstances, if economical, the lagging of the purifiers could be used as an alternative or supplementary method of maintaining the gas temperature. No special features are involved in the heater design, although it is prudent to provide a bypass for the gas.

A typical specification for an indirect heater would provide for the raising of the foul gas from its minimum temperature of, say, from 4° to 38°C. The heat input in this case would approximate to that required to raise the temperature of the gas from 4° to 13°C under saturated conditions.

(ii) Revivification air blowers. It is usual to provide duplicate blowers, each capable of delivering from 2 to 3 times the oxygen equivalent of the H_2S content of the gas against the maximum possible gas pressure, i.e. with an H_2S concentration of 1·0 per cent by volume to be dealt with, each blower would be capable of adding from 5 to 7·5 per cent of air to the gas stream.

A connection, with non-return valve and measuring device, is made to the common inlet when low concentrations of H_2S are to be dealt with, but where more than from 0·75 to 1·0 per cent by volume of H_2S is present in the foul gas it is desirable for the purpose of gas-temperature control to provide connections to all purifiers.

Means may be provided either for automatic proportioning of the air supply to the gas or for the closing of the air supply in certain emergencies, such as the loss of gas flow or pressure.

(iii) Purging facilities. All types of purifiers are provided with vents, normally at the top, which are used to release gas in order to reduce the gas pressure to atmospheric pressure in purifiers being prepared for discharge. In the case of high-pressure purifiers, the gas released may be discharged into a low-pressure gas stream, if available, but with low-pressure purifiers it is normally discharged into the atmosphere.

Connections of from 10 to 15 cm dia. are also provided on each taker for the upward displacement of the gas by the injection of air, purge gas, or in rare cases in which they may be available economically, carbon dioxide or nitrogen.

The air blast is produced by means of a steam ejector; this method might be considered slightly hazardous and is now obsolescent. Carbon dioxide and nitrogen, if available, are normally already endowed with sufficient pressure for the purpose. Purge gas made by the combustion of either gas or oil in a mobile or stationary purge apparatus is the normal means used in modern systems.

The purge apparatus comprises an air blower, a combustion chamber into which gas or oil is fed under pressure, and a quenching chamber. The capacity of the unit is determined by the gas content of the purifier to be purged, and the desired purging rate. Typical purging time would range from $\frac{1}{2}$ to 2 h, and in calculating the rate of 'displacement' an allowance of approximately 100 per cent should be made for the effect of mixing on the efficiency of the displacement of the gas.

A vent is provided which may also be the purge point, for the discharge of purge gas by downward displacement with gas prior to putting the purifier back in stream. This process is normally carried out in 10–20 minutes.

(iv) Condensate drains and tank. Each purifier base should slope a minimum of 5 cm to a 5–8 cm I.D. drain, normally provided with a valve, connected to a cast-iron sealpot with a seal exceeding by six to twelve inches the maximum working gas pressure. Gas mains should be similarly drained, 4–5 cm connections are normally adequate, and the sealpot overflows are led to an appropriate buffer tank for disposal.

(v) Oxide handling equipment. A considerable number of standard tools and items of equipment are used for the handling of the new part-spent and spent purifying material used in static purifiers; forks, shovels, pneumatic tools, mechanical shovels and dozers, and ribbon, paddle and bucket conveyors, and certain crushers, come into this category. In the case of these items, the main considerations affecting specification are that they should be sufficiently robust and of adequate capacity.

The frequency with which the contents of purifiers or trays have to be dealt with can be determined from the maximum sulphur loading and the estimated number of exposures to which the material is subjected before disposal. From this can be calculated the maximum rate at which the various material handling operations must proceed. It is usually assumed that the operations will be confined to daytime, excluding the week-end and allowing an ample margin for contingencies.

Items of equipment which may have to be specially designed or at least specially adapted for oxide handling are as follows:

Cranes. Although for certain operations standard cranes can be used, the travelling crane used for tray or tower purifiers would be specially designed to lift the maximum weight of the filled tray and traverse with it over the appropriate area of the installation.

Mechanical oxide dischargers. The discharger also would be specially designed. The choice would be made between the tippler type which rotates the tray through 180°, the use of which involves a prior or subsequent breaking up of the material mass, or the type in which the tray is rotated on a turntable against ploughs which break up the material and lead it to the centre opening of the tray through which it falls. The plough type of discharger is more readily adaptable to a continuous mechanical handling system than the tippler.

Buffer hoppers. Dischargers and the various types of conveyors used in series in a continuous oxide handling system would be designed as far as possible for an appropriate matched handling rate, and if necessary buffer hoppers would be designed of adequate capacity to smooth out any remaining disparity.

Enclosed chutes and conveyors. In designing the enclosures of chutes and conveyors used for handling unrevivified discharged material, consideration should be given to the possibility of dust explosions. This risk can be minimized by spraying any desired addition of water to the material upstream of such conveyors.

Filling turntables. These are used to facilitate the charging of the trays from a chute which may be traversed by hand across the radius of the tray, and have no special feature other than a rotation speed to match the charging rate.

Material stocking place. Adequate stocking space, preferably covered, should be provided for part-spent, spent, and for a working stock of new purifying material. The main stock of new material can be stored in the open. The actual space required for the main stock of new material and revivified spent material is determined by the scale of operation, the timing and size of deliveries to and from the works, and the height to which the material is stocked. There is no special restriction of the height to which new material may be stocked, nor spent material, provided it has been fully oxidized.

The floor space required for partially spent material for static boxes is determined by the scale of operation, the number of exposures to which each charge is subjected, the case with which material discharged from one purifier can be charged into another, and the stocking height. Freshly discharged material is best stored in a layer not more than 0·5 m high, at least until revivified, but the need to conserve space or to reduce handling costs may increase this to 1·0 m or more, in which case care should be taken to deal quickly with any spontaneous overheating which could lead to a fire.

In the case of tower purifier and tower box streams, the main stock of untreated spent and prepared new and part-spent material is normally contained in either of two 'stocking towers', which, except with regard to gas connections, are similar to the working towers. One of these towers would be used to store the trays from a discharged purifier and the other would hold a complete set of freshly charged trays. The use of these stocking towers enables the charging and discharging of a purifier to be carried out in one day, the discharged material then being handled at the desired rate in the interval elapsing before a further purifier has to be discharged.

It is possible for one pair of stocking towers to serve for two streams of purifiers, particularly where the sulphur loading is low, and the distribution of gas between the streams can be manipulated in order to avoid the clashing of the recharging operation of two towers. Where, however, this clashing can occur, stocking towers should be provided for each stream.

A covered stocking frame is used in some installations for the recharged set of trays. This is cheaper than the enclosed tower but exposes the material to the effects of weather.

(vi) Access and guarding. Platforms and stairways should be provided, giving access for operation and maintenance.

Platform brackets fabricated from tee or channel are preferable to spaced angles. As a precaution against corrosion, platform brackets should be continuously welded to the casing and not stagger welded. All cheaper plate platforming should be amply supported to avoid deflection giving rise to pools of water. Stairways should be no steeper than 45° and if of the open type should have a broad visible nose. There should be an additional means of exit from the tower platform at the opposite end to the stairway; a steel ladder may suffice at this point. The crane and any other item of machinery used should be adequately guarded, but this presents no special features.

8.6 Instrumentation

8.6.1 Gas Pressure

It is standard practice to measure the pressure at the inlet and outlet of each purifier tower or box. Water-filled U-gauges are commonly employed, although bellows or aneroid types of gauges are also used, especially where the pressure reading exceeds 125 mbar (gauge). The aneroids are usually of stainless steel.

In some instances the pressure from the inlet and outlet of the individual boxes, or a stream of boxes, are brought to a common differential gauge to facilitate the reading of pressure absorption. Remote indication can be provided either by direct or pneumatic transmission.

8.6.2 Gas Temperature

Thermometers are normally provided on the inlet and outlet of the purifier stream and on each purifier outlet.

Mercury-in-glass thermometers in direct contact with the gas with a range of from 0° to 100°C are commonly used, but where indication at a short distance is required, the mercury-in-steel type of instrument is provided. For longer distances pneumatic transmission may be necessary. An alternative system for transmission to a central control panel is to use electrical resistance thermometers.

8.6.3 Flow Measurement

Orifice plate devices, using either floating bell or ring balance indicators and recorders are used for the approximate measurement of gas and revivification air.

If it is considered adequate, the comparatively crude hot wire anemometers are sometimes used. In one particular application, two hot wire anemometers of the modified Simmons pattern were used, and their outputs were 'backed off', the resultant signal being applied to a centre zero galvanometer. If, for example, the task of the operator is to run his streams so that approximately equal volumes of gas pass along each path, this condition arises when the indicator reads zero. A deflection indicates that too much gas is passing down one or the other of the streams.

8.6.4 Gas Analysis

(i) Oxygen determination. The testing of period gas samples for oxygen is normally carried out by chemical absorption, latterly, however, oxygen indicators and recorders based on difference in the magnetic properties of oxygen and other gases have been introduced. This type of instrument is described in Chapter 3 and can be usefully employed on the inlet and outlet of purifier streams.

(ii) Hydrogen sulphide determination. Chemical tests are normally used for the determination of the hydrogen sulphide content of unpurified and partially purified gas. Purified gas is commonly tested using either the official test prescribed under the 1948 Gas Act in *Gas Examiners General Directions 1956*, or some other standardized test also involving contacting the gas with lead acetate papers, the significance of which in relation to the prescribed test is understood.

A summary of the officially prescribed test referred to above is given below in metric units. This is generally interpreted as permitting the presence of an amount of hydrogen sulphide not exceeding 1–2 p.p.m.

The test consists in exposing to the gas slips of white absorbent paper which have been dipped in a solution containing 65 g of lead acetate per litre of water and then dried. One of these slips, which are $5 \times \frac{1}{2}$ cm is hung suspended at about $\frac{1}{2}$ cm from its upper end on each of the six wire hooks provided in a container. This container may be either a mercury-sealed glass bell- or a Kilner jar, provided with a gas inlet connection above the papers, and an outlet connection below.

Gas is passed at the rate of 140 litres/h for a period of 3 min, and is to be taken as containing hydrogen sulphide if all the slips at the end of the test are unmistakably darker in any part than an unexposed comparison slip.

The continuous determination and recording of low concentrations of hydrogen sulphide can be carried out if desired by such instruments as the 'Liverpool hydrogen sulphide detection unit', which is based on the increase in the absorption of transmitted light of lead acetate paper on sulphiding.

(A commercial form of this instrument can be obtained from Thermocontrol Installation Co., Ltd.)

8.6.5 Automatic Controller for Rapid Rotation of Purifiers

The current trend is towards power-operated valves on large purifier installations, and this is linked with the trend towards the more rapid rotation of the purifiers than was previously practised.

The power operation of gas and air valves renders possible the automatic rotation of purifiers at predetermined intervals of time. One such system used an electrically driven controller comprising a cam shaft which revolves every 10 h, and initiates purifier rotation every 2 h.

At each change, a cam closes a switch to operate a solenoid hydraulic valve which sends a pilot signal to initiate the operation of the hydraulically operated control valve of the first gas valve in the sequence. A hydraulic cylinder is mounted above this valve, which initiates the second gas movement and so on until the train of movement of the six gas valves and two air valves which comprise a sequence change have all completed their movement. Arranging the tappets to operate at the end of stroke ensures that each valve completes its movement before the next valve starts. The hydraulic system includes a series of valves which, as a sequence goes through, sets up the circuit ready for the next sequence.

When the last valve is fully closed, an hydraulic signal reports back the successful completion of the sequence, but if the report-back signal is not received within 3 min, an alarm is sounded and the timer is stopped. A dial shows the position of the camshaft and the sequence of gas flow at any moment, and a lamp indicates that a sequence change is taking place. The camshaft can be rotated manually for testing and setting purposes. A descriptive diagram enables the operator to appreciate the exact condition of the installation at any time.

8.7 Purifier Erection and Maintenance

8.7.1 Erection

It is necessary during erection of tower purifiers to see that the vessels are plumb and completely circular and the base stools are true and level, that all welded joints are sealed on the inside, all drains in the base of the tower have a free flow, and that the drain neck is placed with the invert at base plate level and does not protude inside the casing. Jointing rings should be of the correct size and the joint groove should be so cut that the joint ring can spread and not be pinched. Top cover clamping bolts should be accurately placed to permit inter-changing of the lids.

8.7.2 Maintenance

Planned and preventive maintenance are of particular importance in relation to dry purification, especially in the town gas industry, since the almost complete removal of hydrogen sulphide is prescribed by law, and the process must therefore operate continuously.

During off-peak periods in multi-stream systems, a series of purifiers may be taken off-stream for repairs. If a purifier of a single stream has to be taken off it normally prevents the rotation of the remaining purifiers, and it is sometimes necessary to provide a temporary connection between this purifier and those up-stream and down-stream in order to restore this facility.

Apart from the fact that maintenance must be so planned as to render the equipment available with certainty when it is required, and that in doing this allowance must be made where appropriate for the corrosive and dust-producing properties of the purifying material, the remaining aspects of maintenance of all the ancillary equipment, such as the air blowers, purging machine, and mobile and static oxide handling equipment, offer no special features.

With regard to the purifiers themselves, adequate spares, based on experience, for the replacement of trays and tray grids, valves and valve parts, purifier cover jointing, and so on, should be available for emergencies as well as for any replacements which are planned, normally during the annual off-peak period.

Some examples, which are not comprehensive, of the periodicity of the repair or replacement of plant items used as the basis of the planned maintenance of a particular set of tower purifiers, and the associated oxide handling equipment, are as follows:

Trays replaced after	13 yr
Turntable rollers repaired	2 yr
Turntable centre pin ball-bearing renewed after	5 yr
Turntable drive pinion and spur wheel renewed after	$7\frac{1}{2}$ yr
Belt conveyor idlers renewed after	$1\frac{1}{2}$ yr
Belt conveyor head and tail drums renewed after	2 yr
Oxide crushers rebuilt after	2 yr
Paddle conveyor blades renewed after	$\frac{1}{2}$ yr
Dry valves refitted after	5 yr (daily rotation)
(rapid rotation might involve a shorter period)	

The conditions to which the interior of steel purifier shells or cover are subjected are not rigorous, but their protection by coating with grease paint or other appropriate media is practised in some gas works.

With static box purifiers, care should be taken to clean out any material which remains below the grids on the purifier after discharging, in order to facilitate the drainage of the purifier base. This is also a good precaution from the process aspect.

The systematic testing of purifiers for leakage to atmosphere should be carried out whenever a purifier is taken out of or put into service by checking the capacity of the purifiers for the retention of gas pressure with the connecting valves and vent closed, and the checking of the tightness of the connecting valves by observing the build-up of pressure from the ambient level under the same conditions after venting.

8.8 Process Control

8.8.1 Control of Purifying Material for Static Purifiers

An excellent account of process control has been given by Moignard[13].

In static purifiers, light and porous bog ores with a moisture content, usually from 35 to 45 per cent, to produce maximum voidage and therefore free gas flow[14] are preferable to those of greater density and inert mineral content. Unsuitable material can be improved physically by admixture, if economical, with lighter artificial material or with peat.

Artificial materials can be made up, preferably on a peat base, with a controlled activity and porosity. Sawdust and wood chips, although used as a base, are less satisfactory than peat, and in one case at least the 'throwing off' of hydrogen sulphide into clean gas was traced to mouldy or putrifying wood sawdust and chippings used for this purpose. By-product hydrated oxides of iron, such as lux derived from bauxite, are used as activating materials.

The blending of new with part-spent material is likely to be uneconomical unless carried out to counteract excessive moisture content of the new material, or less commonly, to counteract the excessive activity of new material, such as the lux referred to above. Part-spent material, like new, should be charged with a moisture content to produce maximum voidage. This is likely to be from 10 to 15 per cent by weight of moisture. For the final exposure of a charge, especially if carried out at off-peak loading, slightly lower moisture contents as charged may be tolerated, bearing in mind that the activity of the material falls off greatly if the moisture content in use falls below 4 per cent by weight.

Adequate stocks should be maintained of new material of known quality in order that its behaviour may be predicted; unknown material is best tried out under conditions which would allow of safeguards against a degree of failure, although this risk can be minimized by the laboratory testing of such material beforehand.

The pH value of oxide as charged should be from 7·0 to 8·0. This can be controlled, if necessary, by the addition of sodium carbonate or lime; such treatment is normally required for part-spent material, which in addition should be adequately revivified and reduced to the optimum particle size so that the maximum activity is exerted short of causing the purifier to be discharged through giving excessive back pressure before it is fouled.

The activity of the material purchased for use within the permissible practical limits can be controlled by consideration of overall operating costs for existing systems, but for projected systems, considerations of capital costs are also involved.

8.8.2 Charging of Static Purifiers

The method used for charging purifiers should aim at minimizing packing and segregation. The optimum layer depth is from 0·5 to 1 m.

The normal order of charging should be such as to distribute the activity of the material throughout the stream, e.g. in a six-box stream, the charging order could be 1, 6, 2, 4, 3, 5 or 1, 4, 3, 6, 2, 5. Where multiple layers are employed, part-spent material should be placed in the first taker position.

8.8.3 Control of Hydrogen Sulphide Content of the Gas to be treated

When the hydrogen sulphide content of gas to be treated exceeds 1·25 per cent by volume there is a risk of excessive heating of the purifying material with consequent permanent loss of activity. Although the more rapid systematic rotation or swinging of the purifiers can reduce this possibility, a more effective method is to reduce the sulphur content of the foul gas either by admixture with gases of lower sulphur content, such as carburetted water gas, or by the recirculation of part of the treated gas.

8.8.4 Pre-treatment of Gas

Electrostatic de-tarring followed by naphthalene washing is desirable prior to the removal of hydrogen sulphide in order to avoid loss of activity and increase in back pressure of the charge through the deposition of tar or naphthalene (see Chapter 4).

In order to retard the rate at which the purifying material becomes acid in use, it is usual to leave a small quantity of ammonia, e.g. 120 mg/m^3 in the gas entering the purifiers.

A normal optimum temperature range for the gas entering the purifiers is from 18° to 24°C saturated, and in order to achieve this, the addition of live steam will be required under certain conditions. Alternatively, closed surface steam heaters can be used to preheat the gas where excessive loss of moisture from the purifying material does not take place.

Temperature control should aim at a maximum of 50°C at the hottest point within the charge. If gas temperature on the purifier outlet is used as the criterion, a maximum temperature of 43°C should be used.

8.8.5 Rotation Schedule

The sequence of a series of purifiers is normally changed periodically by 'backward rotation', i.e. the process of placing the last 'taker' in the first position. This process normally continues until a purifier has to be discharged for loss of activity. When this happens the purifier to be discharged is taken off in the last position in the series, and no rotation is possible until it is back in service from 8 to possibly 32 h later.

There is a slight advantage, especially when dealing with high concentrations of hydrogen sulphide, in reducing the periodicuty of rotation to, say, 2 h, because of reduced temperature gradient and moisture transfer between one part and another of the charge. With normal concentrations of hydrogen sulphide, however, and with systems which are immobilized for a substantial proportion of a day when purifiers are being discharged, there is little to be gained by rotating at shorter intervals than one day except in emergency. This is because the increased margin of capacity arising from rapid rotation cannot be fully exploited since sufficient margin of capacity must be maintained to withstand the longer period arising from the discharging and recharging operation.

Whether the period of backward rotation is 2 or 24 h, there is little doubt that it should be systematically maintained except in an emergency.

Where low concentrations of hydrogen sulphide, say, up to 0·04 per cent by volume, are to be removed, the principles of periodic backward rotation and the discharging of purifiers after use in the final taker position has less relevance. Forward working with rotation only occurring following the discharge of a purifier can be more economical, mainly with regard to capital since fewer purifiers in service are required for this method of operation.

8.8.6 Control of Air for Revivification in situ

Satisfactory limits for the oxygen content of the gas leaving dry purifiers are 0·3–0·5 per cent oxygen by volume. The effect of operating at the upper or lower limit of this range on the cost of operation of existing purifiers, or on the sizing of projected purifiers is not great. Operation with substantially higher oxygen concentrations in the outlet gas could lead to excessively long exposure of the charge with consequent hardening and little net reduction in operating costs. These limitations on the oxygen content of the treated gas are governed to some extent by considerations not concerned with purification.

Control of air admission as between the first and second taker affords a measure of control of the temperature distribution between these two takers. The oxygen content of the gas on the inlet to purifiers as a result of uncontrolled air admission should be taken into account in this context.

With a hydrogen sulphide content of the foul gas up to 0·7 per cent by volume, there is normally little risk of excessive heating the charge resulting from first taker admission of the air. With hydrogen sulphide contents exceeding 1·0 per cent by volume, except in circumstances where there is little or no oxygen present in the foul gas, the air is normally best admitted to the second taker. Second 'taker' admission has a slight advantage in that it improves the efficiency of hydrocyanic acid removal by the first taker.

8.8.7 Avoidance of Excessive Exposure of Charges to the Gas

With static purifiers it is generally uneconomical to instal a plant of such capacity as to allow for the working up of the spent oxide to a saleable sulphur concentration in a single fouling. The reason for this is that a large amount of capital, plant and equipment is employed in purification for the movement of a relatively small quantity of material. The service on this capital expenditure, even at the level which provides for two to three exposures (foulings) of the purifying material before disposal, is such that operating costs have to be reduced to zero in order to justify doubling it.

Even when the possibility of long periods of exposure of a charge is rendered possible, for example, by operation on a low load factor, it is advisable to set a limit of, say, six months to this in order to avoid the excessive hardening of the charge (which could result in heavy handling costs). An economical way to set this limit would be to charge used material of high sulphur content, and therefore of reduced activity, during periods of low loading.

8.8.8 Control Analyses

(i) Purifying material. The minimum requirement under this head is for the sulphur content, moisture content and pH value of each charge or part charge where more than one material is used. In the case of bulk deliveries of new material any laboratory test which gives an indication of its activity even in relative terms is of value, together with the bulk density.

(ii) Gas. Quantitative chemical tests for hydrogen sulphide should be carried out as a daily routine on all purifiers allowing more than a trace to slip, and standardized tests using lead acetate papers on the remainder. These tests should be carried out at a fixed time in relation to the rotation schedule, although some form of paper test should be continued at, say, hourly intervals.

It is desirable that a test for traces of hydrogen sulphide such as that prescribed by law, or an apparatus such as that described in Section 8.6.4 for the continuous determination and recording of low concentrations, should be maintained on the treated gas, and should be subjected to frequent observation.

Untreated and treated gas should be tested for oxygen either by gas analysis on daily samples or, if the scale of the installation justifies it, continuous oxygen recorders could be used for the purpose.

8.8.9 Common Faults in Operation

Purifying material. New material is sometimes charged with excessive moisture content and part-spent charges may not be sufficiently homogenous.

Prior treatment of gas. The gas to be treated is commonly below the optimum temperature, and occasionally insufficient care is taken with regard to ammonia, naphthalene and tar fog removal prior to the dry purification.

Purifier operation and testing. Irregular rotation is not uncommon, and the effect of this is sometimes exacerbated by irregular measurements for hydrogen sulphide, gas temperature and pressure absorption.

Revivification air. Use is sometimes made of excessive quantities of revivification air.

Spent material. Purifying material is not uncommonly disposed of with a sulphur content above or below the optimum economical level. This may arise either as a result of the failure to use off-peak periods in which to increase the sulphur content, or the failure to make the necessary calculation regarding new and spent material values and oxide handling costs.

In making the foregoing calculations, it is important that allowance should be made for the gain in dry basis (d.b.) weight of part-spent oxide due to the absorption of tar, naphthalene, ammonia, oxygen and added alkali. These substances may represent from 12 to 15 per cent by weight of the elemental sulphur. Using the latter value and allowing for the relatively higher bulk density and lower moisture content of part-spent oxide, but ignoring any sulphur in combination, it is interesting to note that a given volume of part-spent oxide removes as much sulphur in being raised from a sulphur concentration of from 45 to 50 per cent d.b. as the same volume of new material removes in acquiring a sulphur concentration of 25 per cent d.b.

8.8.10 Control of Timing of Recharging of Purifiers

After consideration of the above factors affecting the operation of the purifiers of the daily test data available, and of any 'rapid' swinging, i.e. swinging or rotation ahead of the normal schedule, of the sequence of purifiers which may have taken place during the previous twenty-four hours, tentative decisions can be made with regard to the timing of the replacement of the purifying material in the least efficient purifiers. These decisions may be revised but become firmer as the time for recharging approaches.

The operation is usually timed to occur either when a purifier allows a predetermined proportion, for example, 80 per cent of the hydrogen sulphide content of the gas to slip by the end of its normal period as first taker; or when in order to maintain a given lower slip at some point further on in the stream, it has to be rotated out of the first taker position a given time ahead of the normal rotation period. These control factors are determined by experience.

8.8.11 Control of Dynamic Tower Purifiers

Many of the points made with regard to the control of static purifiers such as those relating to the hydrogen sulphide content and pre-treatment of the foul gas, and the control of air for revivification, and relating to testing, have some relevance to dynamic purifier towers systems such as the Gastechnik, whilst the points made with regard to charging, rotation schedules, and the avoidance of excessive exposure of the charges are irrelevant.

Other matters deserving of special reference are as follows.

Purifying materials. The moisture content of purifying pellets, as charged, should be at the minimum, usually 10 per cent by weight consistent with satisfactory operation. They should also be screened and be strong enough to stand the burden of the charge, and care must be taken in filling towers to minimize breakage of the pellets.

Control of air for revivification. The pellet temperature is normally controlled at a level approximating to the maximum possible, i.e. 50°C, without causing any permanent loss of pellet activity. The control of air addition in total, and its distribution between the first and second 'taker', is therefore more critical and should be more stringent than in the case of static towers, since a period of air deficiency followed by the use of excess air would be more likely to produce permanent ill effects on the purifying material.

8.9 Commissioning of New Plant

Box purifier systems normally involve the use of very little mechanical plant. Once the purifiers, purifier covers, and valves have been checked as gas-tight, few difficulties should be experienced with regard to commissioning except those arising from starting off with all purifiers in a cold state and containing freshly charged material.

The low temperature of the purifiers has a more marked effect in winter than in summer, but can be offset sufficiently to get the purifiers working by preheat of the gas, under these conditions indirect heating is the most appropriate.

The hazards represented by the purifiers all being freshly charged at the same time can be reduced by using a substantial proportion of partly spent material, and so placing it as to produce differences in capacity for sulphur removal in the various purifiers. If subsequently the first one or two purifiers are discharged before they are fouled to the normal extent, the possibility of an excessive number becoming due for discharge at the same time should be eliminated.

The points made above with regard to the commissioning of box purifiers apply to tower purifiers also, except that in this case more mechanical plant is involved. The crane and the equipment used for discharging and re-charging the oxide trays are all capable, if they break down, of becoming the limiting factor in the operation of the plant. Apart from the obvious impor-tance of quickly remedying defects, any fouled trays should be emptied, recharged and placed in the stocking tower as quickly as possible whether or not an immediate need for them can be foreseen.

As a further precaution, a part of the abnormal margin of capacity of the purifiers arising from their all being freshly charged should be retained until all plant is operating reliably.

8.10 Safety Precautions

Dry purifiers demand special consideration with regard to safety for the following reasons. They are normally the largest of gas purification vessels, they are taken out of use more frequently than other vessels. In the case of box purifiers, they are entered for the process of material replacement by a relatively large number of men compared with those involved in other items of plant, and most important of all, the part-spent material in the purifier to be discharged is liable to spontaneous ignition.

Recommended codes of practice[15] have been issued by the Institution of Gas Engineers after consultation with the Factory Department, for the guidance of those responsible for the operation of box and tower purifiers. These detailed recommendations mainly bear on the following aspects:

(i) The manner of authorization of the person in charge of operations and the way in which he, in turn, authorizes operation.

(ii) The means used to ensure adequate purging of purifiers when taken off, and to reduce the possibility of the subsequent firing of the gas or purifying material content.

(iii) The precautions taken against the leakage of gas from the system in normal operation as well as when purifiers are being discharged, and against the possibility of injury to personnel by gassing, or of injury to personnel and plant by explosion.

(iv) Precautions to be taken against abnormal conditions, such as excessive gas temperature, which may arise during the operation of purifiers and lead to incidents covered by (ii) and (iii) above.

8.11 A Modern Installation. The Low Pressure Dry Purification Plant at the Isle of Grain Works of the S.E.G.B.

8.11.1 General Description

The low pressure installation of Newton Chambers static purifiers (Thyssen-Lenze type) at the Isle of Grain Works of the S.E. Gas Board (Figure 8.1), comprises twelve working towers and four stocking towers, each 13 m high and $6\frac{1}{2}$ m in diameter. The working towers are fitted with eleven trays, each of which holds a single 0·7 m layer of material. The total oxide content of the eleven trays is 270 m^3, equivalent of 180 tonnes of spent oxide.

As shown in Figure 8.3, the gas flows from the annulus surrounding the trays, downward through the single layer of oxide in each of the eleven trays in parallel, and out through the main formed by the central aperture of the

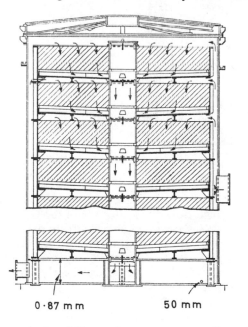

0·87 mm   50 mm

Figure 8.3 Vertical cross-section of Thyssen-Lenze type tower purifier with Newton Chambers type trays

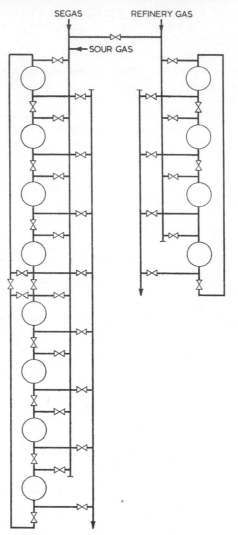

Figure 8.4 Low-pressure static purifier tower system at the Isle of Grain works of the South Eastern Gas Board

trays. In order to facilitate replacement, the top sealing rings are fitted to the top of the towers instead of to the underside of the covers.

The towers are normally operated as one stream of eight, and one stream of four, although the eight-tower stream can be operated as two four-tower streams (Figure 8.4). Systematic backward rotation, manually operated, is practised at daily intervals, or longer when the H_2S concentration is low. The function of the eight-tower stream is to purify the output of the Segas plants, which may vary from 450000 m^3/day of gas, containing 0·5 per cent by volume of H_2S, to 500000 m^3/day of gas containing from 0·05 to 1·20 g/m^3 of H_2S. The 'sour gas' derived from the 'Alkazid' process of the adjacent Shell Co.'s gasification unit, consisting of 4200 m^3/day of H_2S

with a similar quantity of carbon dioxide, is also treated by this stream. The addition of the sour gas, particularly in circumstances of reduced output from the Segas plant, could produce an excessive concentration of H_2S in the mixed foul gas, and in order to counteract this, a booster has been installed which can recirculate up to $380\,000$ m^3 of gas per day from the outlet of the fourth taker to the foul gas inlet. Using this device, the H_2S content of the gas entering the stream can be limited to slightly more than 1 per cent by volume.

The series of four towers can deal with up to $420\,000$ m^3 of refinery gas per day, containing from 0·7 to 1·9 g/m^3 of H_2S. This gas is used mainly for the enrichment of the hydrogen made by the Shell plant.

Gas heater. Each purifier is provided with a closed surface steam heater, capable of raising the temperature of the gas by 33°C. Maximum steam consumption 700 kg/h at 1 bar gauge.

Gas connections and valves. Gas connections are 812 mm bore, welded, using 6 mm body plates and 19 mm flanges. Double-faced Holmes 'Western' type valves are used.

Revivification air. An electrically driven Keith Blackman air blower, with standby, is provided, capable of delivering 1200 m^3 of air per hour. This air is delivered to the main foul gas inlets to streams.

Purging machine. A stationary gas-fired purging machine, with a capacity of 420 m^3/h of inert gas is connected to all working and stocking towers.

8.11.2 Oxide Handling Equipment

A 50 tonne Carruthers electric travelling 'Goliath' crane is employed to lift the oxide trays in and out of the towers, and on and off the oxide discharger and charging turn-tables.

The control gear is of the contact type, on hoist and long travel, with drum control on cross-traverse. Electro-mechanical braking is fitted to the former motions, and an electro-hydraulic brake on each motor on the long travel gear.

The tray charged with spent oxide is placed by the crane on to the discharger turn-table and is clamped in position. The centre tube of the tray, previously treated with grease-paint, is then removed. A movable cutter beam is placed in position above the tray, which is then rotated against the ploughs fixed to the beam. The beam lowers the ploughs slowly, and the oxide is broken up and discharged through the centre opening on to a two-way chute feeding either the oxide crusher or a conveyor belt leading to a loading hopper for the disposal by road vehicle of the spent oxide. The oxide ploughs have so far proved adequate for the disintegration of the oxide mass, and a Jeffrey–Diamond rigid hammer oxide crusher is normally bypassed.

From the crusher or crusher bypass outlet, the material falls on to a short ribbon conveyor, the purpose of which is to mix in any water or alkali added at this point. (Where mixing is unnecessary this could be replaced by a belt conveyor.) The ribbon conveyor feeds a 40 cm wide troughed belt radial conveyor which can be used either to feed a road vehicle for the transfer of part-spent material to stock, or it can be manipulated by hand in order to recharge a rotating tray on the filling turn-table. The recharged tray is then placed in the stocking tower by the crane. All of the equipment, from the discharger ploughs to the final radial conveyor, can handle an oxide discharge rate of up to 46 tonnes/h.

8.12 The Honolulu Low Iron Process

A form of oxide of iron purifying material first made by the Honolulu Gas Company and since used in Australia[16] and Singapore, is claimed to reduce greatly the capital and process material costs of dry purification.

This consists of wood shavings saturated with sodium carbonate solution of pH 9–10, mixed with $1\frac{1}{2}$ kg to 4 kg of powdered iron or swarf per 100 kg of dry shavings. This material is mixed and exposed to the atmosphere for 2 weeks to 6 months according to the sizing of the iron particles. The optimum size of the iron particles is stated to be 150–500 μm. The product is a low density purifying material of low resistance to gas flow, consisting of an active iron oxide coating diffused almost uniformly over the surface of the shavings.

Using the rapid rotation technique already described (see Section 8.6.5), it has been found possible with material made in this way to achieve R ratios (see Section 8.5.2*(vi)*), i.e. plant loadings expressed in that form, of approximately twice that obtainable with other synthetic materials and bog ore. This is equivalent to a saving of 50 per cent of capital cost.

Furthermore, the material remains effective until it reaches a substantially higher sulphur concentration involving a manifold saving in new material, varying according to the cost of the material which it displaces.

PART B. ORGANIC SULPHUR REMOVAL

8.13 Catalytic Removal of Organic Sulphur Compounds from Fuel Gases

8.13.1 Catalysts

The sulphides of cobalt and nickel are highly active at 400°C for the hydrogenation of all the organic sulphur compounds normally contained in fuel gases, other than thiophene. They are active also for a large number of other reactions including the oxidation of many organic sulphur compounds, not including thiophene, and for the oxidation also of hydrogen sulphide and hydrogen[17].

Molybdenum disulphide and certain compound sulphides with other metals, e.g. cobalt, described as thiomolybdates, are more active than nickel subsulphide and catalyse all the reactions referred to above and others including the hydrogenation of thiophene and of unsaturated hydrocarbons. This comparatively greater activity on the part of molybdenum is attributed to a particularly favourable arrangement of the molybdenum atoms in the disulphide mass structure[18].

There are normally present in coal gas a number of unsaturated hydrocarbons which are polymerized on the nickel and molybdenum catalysts. These polymers which assume a gummy form at 250°C and a carbonaceous form at 350°–400°C, retard the catalyst activity and render periodic regeneration by oxidation essential. In this respect also the molybdenum catalyst is the more active, in regard to certain hydrocarbons and the more readily poisoned and this quickly prevents it from exercising its power to decompose thiophene in coal gas at low pressures[17]. Molybdenum based catalysts such as 'Comox' and 'Nimox' are successfully used, however, for the reduction of organic sulphur compounds, including thiophene, and for the hydrogenation of unsaturated hydrocarbons, in natural gas and refinery gas which do not normally contain unsaturated hydrocarbons such as cyclopentadiene (which polymerize on molybdenum disulphide in the manner described). Light hydrocarbon distillates vaporized in hydrogen also can be treated in the same way if free from those unsaturated hydrocarbons likely to affect the catalyst in this way. At hydrogen partial pressures of 10 bars or more, the molybdenum-based catalysts acquire the power to hydrogenate the acetylene, and olefins and other substances which poison it at lower pressures, and therefore become effective even in the presence of these substances.

Zinc oxide is used extensively for the removal of sulphur compounds from hydrocarbon gases prior to their passage with steam over nickel-based 'steam reforming' catalysts for the production of the lean gas element of town gas and synthesis gas. An active form of zinc oxide containing 95 per cent ZnO is employed[19] in the form of granules at from 350° to 420°C. The chemical reactions involved in the removal of sulphur compounds by zinc oxide are varied by the presence of hydrogen which renders the process more effective since zinc oxide can operate also as a hydrogenation catalyst.

Zinc oxide is effective in removing the H_2S, COS, CS_2 and mercaptans. It is only partially effective for organic sulphides, and in particular thiophene, but when these are present they may be dealt with, as already stated using a molybdenum-based catalyst in the presence of hydrogen. In this case zinc oxide may be used to absorb the hydrogen sulphide produced.

Natural gas or methane ethane mixtures are treated at an operating temperature of about 420°C. Gases containing butane or higher hydrocarbons must be desulphurized at slightly lower temperatures to avoid thermal cracking of the butane and deposition of soot on the zinc oxide.

For the extremely rigorous desulphurization of synthesis gas, e.g. to less than 1 p.p.m., such as is required in order to guard a methanation catalyst, a metallic copper/zinc oxide catalyst is used at high pressure and 250°C which will hydrogenate and remove the more refractory sulphur compounds, i.e. organic sulphides, disulphides and thiophene. This mild hydrogenation catalyst is made by reduction in hydrogen of a dehydrogenation catalyst consisting of the oxides of copper and zinc.

Metallic nickel on Sepiolite can be used as a catalyst/absorbent for the removal of small traces of organic sulphur in any form, but must be replaced when sulphided.

Table 8.3 CATALYSTS USED FOR REDUCTION OR OXIDATION OF ORGANIC SULPHUR COMPOUNDS IN COMBUSTIBLE GASES

	Nickel subsulphide*	Nickel subsulphide†	Copper or Nickel thiomolybdate	Nickel/Molybdenum (Nimox) Cobalt/Molybdenum (Comox)	Zinc oxide	Zinc oxide and copper
Support	Fireclay	China clay	Alumina	Alumina	No support	—
Gas treated	Coal gas	Coal gas	Coal gas	Refinery gas and vaporized light distillate with hydrogen		Hydrogen with low CO content
Reaction temperature	420°C	300°/380°C	300°/360°C	380°C	400°C	250°/350°C
Example of reaction pressure bars	1	1	1	1–35	10–35	100
Approximate period before regeneration or replacement, days	30	100	25	800	(Varies with sulphur content of treated gas)	
Typical space velocity, approximately, h^{-1}	500	1000	800	1000	200/300 ‡	> 1000
Results achieved	Approx. 90% removal of organic sulphur compounds other than thiophene			Approx. 100% reduction of organic sulphur compounds including thiophene. Hydrogenation of unsaturated hydrocarbons	Hydrogenation of COS, CS_2 and mercaptans and absorption of resulting H_2S	Reduction to p.p.m. of sulphur compounds including thiophene and organic sulphides
Final form of sulphur	H_2S	SO_2 mainly H_2S trace	H_2S	H_2S	ZnS	Sulphided catalyst

* Used as reduction catalyst.　† Used as oxidation catalyst.

‡ This space velocity is not controlled by reaction rate but arbitrarily according to the desired reserve capacity of ZnO for use as solid absorbant for H_2S.

8.13.2 Heat Requirements of the Process

The reaction heat of the catalytic hydrogenation or oxidation of the sulphur compounds in fuel gases is usually negligible because of the low concentrations of these compounds dealt with. The heat requirement of the process is, therefore, related to heat losses from the plant, and the heat content of the outgoing gas, which in turn is related to the efficiency of heat exchange with the ingoing gas.

Using nickel subsulphide as an oxidation catalyst with sufficient oxygen present in the gas to provide the net heat requirements of the process by catalytic oxidation of hydrogen, the heat required after heat exchange may be as little as 1 per cent of the potential heat of the coal gas treated. Using nickel subsulphide, or a thiomolybdate, as a reduction catalyst, the net heat requirement will be increased above this level in proportion to the losses involved in the indirect preheating stage.

Using molybdenum-based catalysts for the hydrogenation of organic sulphur compounds and unsaturated hydrocarbons, for example, in refinery gas for reforming with steam, the thermal balance of the process will be dominated by the exothermic hydrogenation of the latter which, if present in sufficient quantity, could provide for all the heat losses of the process; if present in excess, overheating of the catalyst could result.

A summary of the catalysts referred to above, and of typical conditions under which they operate is given in Table 8.3.

8.13.3 Removal of Hydrogen Sulphide from Hydrogenated Gas

It is normally economical to pretreat process materials containing more than 800 p.p.m. w/w of sulphur before subjecting them to hydro-desulphurization. If this is done luxmasse pellets can be used, in series with the hydrogenation stage, as a solid absorbant for the hydrogen sulphide produced, and discarded after use. The 1969 cost is in the order of £1000 per tonne of sulphur removed, and commonly a zinc oxide catch is used in series with the luxmasse in order to ensure a suitably low sulphur concentration in the treated gas.

Using process materials containing less than 300 p.p.m. w/w of sulphur, zinc oxide alone at a cost of £1500 per tonne of sulphur removed is commonly used.

In processes which can tolerate economically the liquefaction by cooling of vaporized feedstock after hydrogenation, there is no economic limit to the initial sulphur content, but solid materials would not be used as absorbants for the resulting hydrogen sulphide. Normally this would be converted to sulphur either in a Claus Kiln or by means of a wet treatment such as the Stretford Process[21,22].

9

Adsorption

R. D. FULKER

9.1 Introduction

Adsorption gas purification processes are based upon the physical properties of specially prepared granular solids, known as adsorbents, by which they attract selectively and retain gases on their surfaces. The most widely used adsorbents are activated alumina, activated carbon, silica gel and molecular sieves. Examples of industrial applications include the dehydration of gases, the deodorization of air, the recovery of volatile solvents, the extraction of benzole from town gas and the separation of hydrocarbon gases one from another.

In all these processes the adsorbent is worked on a cyclic basis. The gas and adsorbent are contacted until the desired point of saturation is reached; the adsorbent is then removed from the gas stream and desorbed. Collection of the stripped component may be carried out at this stage if recovery is required. Heat is evolved during adsorption and a means of removing this heat is often provided when the heat of adsorption produces a marked rise in the temperature of the adsorbent.

The main function of the adsorption equipment is to bring the gas and solid adsorbent into direct contact to facilitate adsorption. This is normally achieved in adsorbers, in which the granular adsorbent is contained. Fluidized bed and moving bed equipment may be used for large-scale continuous operation.

The regeneration, desorption or stripping of adsorbents may be accomplished in a number of ways; the most common methods used for industrial applications are by heating with hot gas or direct steaming of the adsorbent. Examples of these methods are the use of hot air to regenerate silica gel, and the use of steam for stripping out solvent vapours from activated carbon.

9.2 Description of a Gas Drying Plant

A typical plant for the dehydration of gases by adsorption is shown diagrammatically in Figure 9.1. The figure shows two adsorbers, each containing a bed of adsorbent such as silica gel or activated alumina.

The gas or air stream drawn by the fan A is passed through filter B and pre-cooler C before being blown through the bed of adsorbent in the adsorbers D or E. The dried gas is passed through an after-cooler H to remove any excess heating up caused by the heat of adsorption. A second fan F and gas heater G are used for drying out the adsorbent after it has

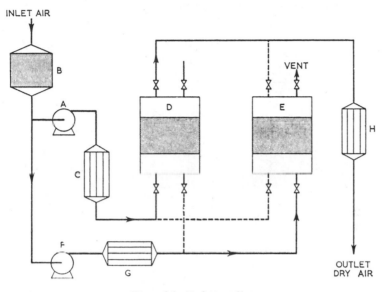

Figure 9.1 Air drying plant

become saturated. The adsorbers are of sufficient size to allow one vessel to be on stream whilst the second vessel is being regenerated, thus permitting continual operation.

9.3 The Carbon Adsorption Process of Solvent Recovery

The carbon adsorption process will be best understood by reference to Figure 9.2, which shows, in diagrammatic form, an installation with two adsorbers A_1 and A_2 charged with activated carbon. The solvent-laden air is drawn from a solvent evaporating process by means of the axial fan and blown upwards through the carbon bed of adsorber A_1. The adsorber A_2 has become fully saturated with the solvent and is undergoind regeneration. The air inlet and outlet valves are closed and live steam is passed downwards through the carbon; the mixture of steam and solvent passes through the distillate pipe into the condenser. The condensed mixture of steam and solvent is, in the case of non-miscible solvents, automatically separated into two layers in the separator: the recovered solvent, after being metered, is collected in the tank from which it may be pumped for re-use. When solvents miscible or partially miscible with water are used, such as acetone, ethyl acetate, etc., the condensate or water layer from the separator is distilled so that the water-soluble constituents can be recovered in a dry state for further use.

The steamed out adsorber is then dried by means of fresh air blown

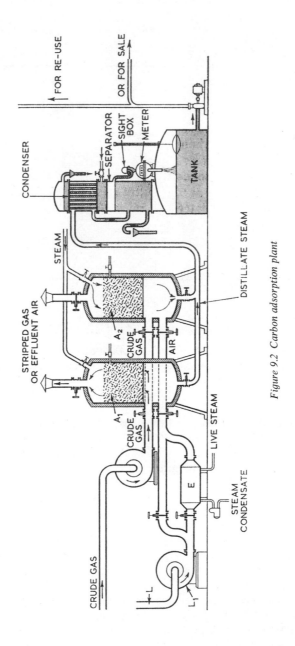

Figure 9.2 Carbon adsorption plant

upwards through the carbon bed by the blower L_1 and heater E. After the carbon has been dried the air heater is bypassed and the carbon cooled by means of cold air. After cooling, the adsorber is again put on stream and each adsorber in turn is successively steamed out, dried and cooled. In this way the carbon can be used almost indefinitely. When non-miscible solvents are used the recovery plant may be simplified by drying and cooling with solvent-laden air.

Solvents may be recovered at the cost of a few £ per m^3 with this system from low solvent air concentrations (less than 1 per cent, vol per cent) and recoveries of over 90 per cent of the solvent contained in the solvent-laden air stream are often obtained in commercial plants.

9.4 Theory of Adsorption

A gas or vapour when brought into contact with a solid substance has the tendency to collect on the surface of the solid. This phenomenon is known as *adsorption.*

The amount of adsorption on the surface of most solids is exceedingly small but certain materials, e.g. activated alumina, silica gel, activated carbon, have been developed to adsorb substantial quantities of gases and vapours on their surfaces. These materials are porous solids and have an unusually high surface development in the form of an ultra-microporous structure, thus possessing a very large internal surface. A fluid is able to penetrate through the pore structure of these materials and be in contact with the large surface area available for adsorption.

The mechanism by which this surface adsorption takes place is very complex. Many theories have been formulated to explain adsorption, details of which may be found in the literature. The most important types of adsorption are physical adsorption, in which case the gas is attracted to the surface of the adsorbent, and chemical adsorption in which the gas shows a strong interaction with the adsorbent in the manner of a chemical reaction.

The surface attraction is due to van der Waals' forces: the intermolecular forces that produce normal condensation to the liquid state. On a smooth surface the van der Waals' adsorption is restricted to a layer of not more than a very few molecules thickness, but in a porous solid possessing a capillary structure, the surface adsorption is supplemented by capillary condensation which is also brought about by the van der Waals' forces of attraction.

All adsorptive processes are exothermic. The heat of adsorption due to surface attraction is rather greater than the heat of condensation of the gases being adsorbed. The heat of chemical adsorption is of similar magnitude to the heat of chemical reaction.

Adsorption increases progressively with increase in partial pressure of gas. At low partial pressure adsorption is by surface attraction, and at higher partial pressures the smallest wetted capillaries become effective and condensation begins. At the higher pressure the larger capillaries become effective.

Figure 9.3 shows the relationship[1] between maximum effective pore size and vapour pressure (or vapour concentration) for benzene at 20°C. These sizes are computed on the basis of the capillary condensation theory.

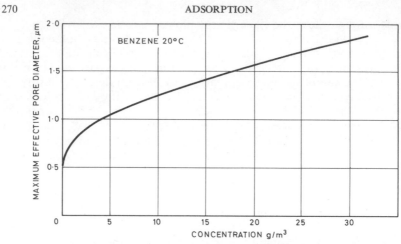

Figure 9.3 Relationship between pore size and vapour concentration

The relationship between pressure and amount adsorbed is, therefore, dependent upon the size distribution of the capillary pores as well as the area of the exposed surface and the nature of both adsorbent and gas.

These relationships can be expressed graphically in the form of adsorption isotherms. These are determined experimentally and are expressions of the amount of gas adsorbed under true static equilibrium conditions.

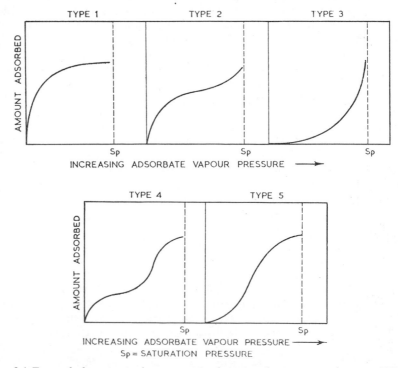

Figure 9.4 Types of adsorption isotherms: type 1, adsorption of oxygen on carbon at −183°C; type 2, nitrogen on iron catalyst at −195°C; type 3, bromine on silica gel; type 4, benzene on ferric oxide gel at 50°C; type 5, water vapour on carbon at 100°C

9.5 Adsorption Isotherms

Various types of isotherms are observed and the shapes of the graphs vary according to the adsorbate–adsorbent system investigated. According to Brunauer *et al.*[2] five types of adsorption isotherms exist in the literature on the adsorption of gases, and these are shown in Figure 9.4. It will be noted from these curves and Figure 9.5 that adsorption is a specific property depending upon the nature of the system. *Preferential adsorption* is of great industrial importance for the selective removal of a gas from a gaseous mixture. Very little quantitative data is available on the adsorption of a mixture of gases and vapours, but it is apparent that when mixtures of gases are adsorbed, the presence of each affects the equilibrium of the others. In general, a gas of high molecular weight, high critical temperature and low volatility is adsorbed in preference to a gas of low molecular weight, low critical temperature and high volatility. A preferentially adsorbed gas will displace other gases which have already been adsorbed.

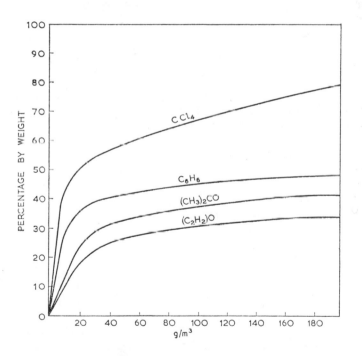

Figure 9.5a Adsorption isotherms for solvents on activated carbon[1]

Use of this preferntial adsorptive property is made in the selective adsorption, by activated carbon of a single hydrocarbon gas from a mixture. In this application the activated carbon filter may be regarded as a rectification

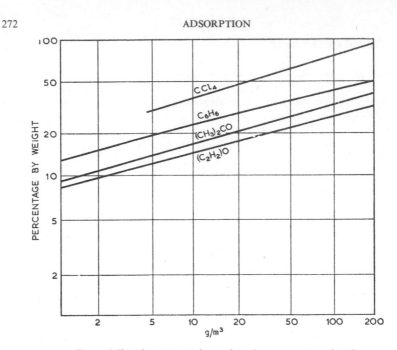

Figure 9.5b Adsorption isotherms for solvents on activated carbon

plant. By adjustment of the adsorption period any particular cut can be produced from the fractions contained in the gas. For example: in a hydrocarbon mixture, methane which is adsorbed first, will be displaced by ethane which in turn will be displaced by the propane, and this process of displacement will continue throughout the series of hydrocarbons.

9.6 Regeneration or Desorption

The regeneration, desorption, or stripping of the adsorbed gases from an adsorbent may be accomplished in a number of ways:

1. The temperature of the adsorbent may be raised until the vapour pressure of the adsorbed gas exceeds atmospheric pressure. The adsorbed gas will then be evolved and may be collected at atmospheric pressure.

2. The adsorbed gas may be withdrawn by applying a vacuum, lowering the total pressure below the vapour pressure of the adsorbed gas.

3. The adsorbed gas may be withdrawn in a stream of inert gas passing through the adsorbent, keeping the partial pressure of the stripped gas in the gas stream below the equilibrium pressure of the adsorbed gas.

4. The adsorbed gas may be withdrawn in a stream of an easily condensable gas such as steam. The stripped gas is recovered by condensing the stripped gas and steam mixture.

5. The adsorbed gas may be displaced by the adsorption of a gas which is preferntially adsorbed.

9.7 Activated Carbon

9.7.1 Raw Materials and Manufacture

Activated carbon may be manufactured from a wide range of carbonaceous substances including bones, coals, wood dust, peat, nutshells and wood charcoal.

The fine capillary structure is formed during the activation process. According to Lamb, Wilson and Chaney[3], the raw material is a compound of amorphous carbon and hydrocarbons not in itself active but becoming active when the hydrocarbons held in the carbon are removed by oxidation. During this process a form of etching takes place on the residual carbon, the combined effect producing an ultra-fine capillary structure throughout the carbon.

Over the past 40 years many processes have been patented for the manufacture of activated carbon, but the principal commercial methods used today are chemical activation and steam activation.

The chemical method of activation consists of mixing a pulverized form of carbonaceous material with a liquid dehydrating agent, drying the mixture and heating in a retort to complete the activation. The most widely used chemicals are zinc chloride and phosphoric acid.

The raw material for steam activation is usually a carbonized material derived from wood, peat, brown coal, etc. The charcoal is heated in a retort to a high temperature. Steam, the activating agent, is passed through the bed of heated charcoal to produce the desired porous structure, and the resulting water gas produced is often used for heating the retorts.

The quality and characteristics of activated carbon are dependent upon the physical properties of the raw materials and methods of activation used. The manufacturers have at their disposal a wide choice of raw materials and control of the activation process, and are thus able to produce activated carbons having widely varying physical and adsorptive properties.

Two differing forms of activated carbon used in gas phase applications are represented by the use of carbon for solvent recovery, and for use in gas masks. The carbon used for solvent recovery must be capable of adsorbing the maximum amount of solvent at a relatively high concentration. A gasmask carbon, on the other hand, has to be more efficient for adsorbing toxic gases which may only be present in low concentrations in order to give complete protection to the user.

Table 9.1 TYPICAL PROPERTIES OF ACTIVATED CARBON FOR GAS PURIFICATION

Type	1	2	3	4
Form	granules	granules	pellets	pellets
Mesh sizes, mm: through/on	5/2, 3/1, 2/1	5/2, 3/1, 2/1	5/2	5/2
Carbon content weight, per cent	97	98	93	93
Ash weight, per cent	3	2	7	7
Bulk density, kg/m^3	500	450	650	450
Surface area, m^2/g	1100	1400	950	1100

The differing physical properties of the many types and grades of activated carbon commercially available make selection difficult. For this reason it is advisable to discuss the application with the carbon manufacturer in order to obtain the grade of carbon best suited for the gas purification or solvent recovery problem. Most manufacturers are willing to co-operate and offer useful information regarding the application of their materials. Table 9.1 gives typical physical properties of some grades.

Activated carbons are available in the form of irregular granules and several pelleted forms. The use of the regular shaped granules such as cylindrical pellets is recommended for use in filters where an even packing of low resistance to gas or air flow is required.

9.7.2 Activated Carbon, Properties and Applications

Activated carbons have strongly selective powers for the adsorption of organic vapours from gases, even in the presence of water vapour, and are widely used for gas purification and solvent recovery applications. The great advantage that activated carbon has over other solvent recovery systems (including recovery by refrigeration, condensation, absorption, etc.) is the outstanding ability to recover solvents from low concentrations and inexpensively. This is very desirable in processes using inflammable or toxic solvents, where it is necessary, for safety reasons, to ensure adequate ventilation to prevent solvent concentrations reaching dangerous proportions inside machinery and workrooms from which the solvent is evaporated.

Gas purification applications, involving the removal of small quantities of impurities, include the deodorization of air, the removal of traces of organic impurities from gas streams to prevent catalyst poisoning, the removal of traces of oil vapours from compressed gases, the purification of carbon dioxide before liquefaction, the filtration of gases for special heat treatment furnaces to remove sulphur compounds, and the removal of similar substances from gas streams.

Important gas separations utilizing activated carbon include the extraction of benzole from town gas, the extraction of gasoline from natural gas, the separation of hydrogen from ethane, and heavier hydrocarbons, the extraction of ethylene from cracked gas streams. Others are, the removal of odours in ventilation systems of buildings, cold storage rooms, etc., and the removal of dangerous toxic vapours from air streams. The carbon is normally regenerated by direct steam to facilitate the collection of the stripped solvents by simply condensing the steam-solvent vapours produced.

9.7.3 Silica Gel

Silica gel is a granular adsorbent having a translucent appearance. Manufacture consists essentially of adding a solution of sodium silicate to sulphuric acid, washing the gel with alcohol, drying, roasting and grading.

Silica gel shows a specific selective adsorption for water vapour which is higher than either activated carbon or activated alumina and hence its principal application is for the dehydration of gases. It is capable of adsorbing up to 40 per cent of its weight of water vapour and may be simply reactivated by passing heated gas or air through the adsorbent and cooling.

9.7.4 Activated Bauxite and Activated Alumina

Aluminium oxide base adsorbents are prepared by heat treatment of bauxite or alumina hydrate, producing a porous solid adsorbent.

Activated alumina has the higher adsorbent capacity but because of its lower cost, activated bauxite has found wide dessicant application in competition with silica gel and activated alumina. Both activated alumina and activated bauxite are also widely used for the dehydration of gases. Reactivation is carried out by passing heated gas or air through the spent adsorbent and cooling.

9.8 Selection of Adsorbent

The preferential adsorption characteristics and physical properties of the industrial adsorbents determine the main applications for each type. All the adsorbents are capable of adsorbing organic solvents, impurities and water vapour from gas streams, but each has a particular affinity for water vapour or organic vapours.

Activated alumina, silica gel and molecular sieves will preferntially adsorb water from a gas mixture containing water vapour and organic solvent. This is a serious disadvantage in solvent recovery work where the water content of the air or gas stream is often greater than the solvent content.

Silica gel and activated alumina disintegrate under the influence of liquid water. This renders their use for the desorption of organic solvents much more difficult from the point of view of plant design, since direct steam may not be used. These adsorbents, therefore, are normally used only for the drying of air and gases and are regenerated by blowing a stream of hot air or gas through the adsorbent bed. The carbon is normally regenerated by direct steam to facilitate the collection of the stripped solvents by simply condensing the steam-solvent vapours produced.

9.9 Carbon Adsorption Process of Solvent Recovery

9.9.1 Design Considerations

The plant designer has four basic stages to consider when designing a carbon adsorption solvent recovery plant. They involve the operational conditions of the apparatus from which the solvent is evaporated, and the operations through which each adsorber passes during the recovery cycle and are considered under the following headings:

  (i) The efficient collection of solvents evaporated in the process.
 (ii) The adsorption process during which the carbon is charged with solvent.
(iii) The steaming or stripping process, and collection of stripped solvents.
(iv) The drying and cooling of the carbon in preparation for the next adsorption charge.

9.9.2 Collection of Solvents

The primary factor in any recovery system is to ensure that the maximum amount of solvent is collected efficiently and safely from all sources where evaporation may occur. With the carbon adsorption process recoveries of over 99 per cent of the solvent in the air stream passing to the carbon adsorption plant are readily achieved in present-day equipment. Experience shows that the greater loss of solvent occurs in the handling and manufacturing process, rather than in the recovery plant. In most cases slight losses of solvent are unavoidable no matter how many precautions are taken to prevent incidental losses.

From the theoretical point of view the problem of solvent recovery is simple. If the manufacturing process could be carried out continuously in a gas-tight apparatus it would be possible to recover the solvents efficiently and cheaply by direct condensation at normal temperatures. The principle of direct condensation is employed in many processes including distillation, extraction and similar plants, but in a large number of processes it is impossible to work in a completely closed system, and in a continuous manner. Even in the case of a simple tank every filling operation is attended by the expulsion of air saturated with vapour at the temperature of its contents.

Some industrial processes are of such a nature that it is impracticable to work with an entirely closed apparatus, and continuity can only be secured over short periods. Processes such as coating, impregnating, film casting, and photogravure printing are such that a considerable ingress of air is almost unavoidable, and, indeed, is often necessary to ensure that the rate of evaporation or drying can be controlled.

For reasons of safety, when using inflammable or toxic solvents such as acetone, benzene, carbon disulphide, carbon tetrachloride, toluene, etc., adequate ventilation must be used to prevent solvent concentrations reaching dangerous proportions inside machinery and workrooms where the solvent is evaporated.

The approximate lower and upper explosion limits in air[4] for some commonly used solvents are given in Table 9.2.

The quantity of air used to entrain the solvents being evaporated from any particular source of equipment will depend upon the manufacturing process, but as a general rule the volume of air must be sufficient to ensure that the solvent concentration will be below the lower explosive limit. Concentrations in the order of 25–50 per cent of the lower explosive limit are used in commercial practice.

The size and cost of a carbon adsorption plant is directly dependent upon the volume of air to be handled, and it is, therefore, important to build up the solvent concentration to as high a level as can safely be tolerated.

The solvent concentration may be increased in the equipment of many processes by the use of air recirculation. This is often advantageous for increasing the rate of evaporation, since air may be blown directly on to the surface of the products from which the solvent is evaporating, thus increasing the rate of evaporation and permitting a higher production rate for a given size machine.

The use of a high air recirculation rate is advantageous in many processes, including photogravure printing and the proofing of textiles, but, in many industries the use of highly turbulent air for drying would spoil the product. This is especially true in the film casting industry where rapid evaporation would cause the formation of bubbles and rippling of the film surface. Also with some processes the higher rate will cause more solvent to be evaporated unnecessarily, and care must be taken to avoid this happening. This can happen in processes where liquid solvent is present inside the machinery, in such processes as dipping, spin drying and impregnating.

Table 9.2 EXPLOSION LIMITS OF INFLAMMABLE LIQUIDS IN AIR

	Lower explosive limit (per cent by volume in air)	Upper explosive limit (per cent by volume in air)
Benzene	1·4	7·1
Toluene	1·4	6·7
Xylene commercial ortho	1	6
meta para	1·1	7
n-pentane	1·4	8
n-hexane	1·2	6·9
n-heptane	1·2	6·7
Petrol	1·3*	6*
White spirit	1·1*	6*
Carbon disulphide	1·25	44
Ether	1·85	48
Methyl ethyl ketone	1·8	10
Acetone	3·0	11
Methanol	7·3	36
Ethyl alcohol	4·3	19

*Depends on composition.

The range of processes from which solvents are evaporated is very extensive, and each process presents a specific problem for the designer of the recovery system.

As long as the air volume employed for suction is sufficient to ensure that the lower explosive limit is not reached, flame propagation or explosion need not be feared. It must be realized, however, that the evaporation of solvents from industrial plants, rubber spreading machines, mixers, dry-cleaning plants, photogravure printing, etc., is by no means regular. Machines are started and stopped throughout the day, and in consequence it is important not only to provide a sufficiently large air volume, but to take into account the fluctuations and provide additional safety precautions. The fluctuations which take place in the rate of solvent evporation may be as much as eight or nine times the average evaporation. In these circumstances it would be uneconomical to build a plant of nine times the average size and capacity to meet this condition, and in any case, a slight increase or fluctuation would still show that the increased air volume was inadequate.

A safe method of ensuring controlled suction in the right place is to provide a hood over every machine where solvent is evaporated, a valve to shut off the suction when the machine is not in use, and a flowmeter and valve to regulate the volume of air drawn off to suit the rate of evaporation. In this way a proper distribution of the air volume over many machines in operation can be maintained.

Additional safeguards can be made by dividing up the suction system between machines by employing flame arrestors, and pressure release membranes on each hood, flame arrestors at the junction of main suction lines, and, in certain cases, bursting discs facing into the open air so that any pressure in the trunking may be released safely.

The flame arrestor is based on the rapid removal of the heat of combustion during the passage of the burning gases, so that they are extinguished. This principle is employed in the mine safety lamps, the Davy mine screen, etc. Suitable designs are marketed constructed of sheet metal curved to produce a large number of air passages. A water-cooled heat exchanger of the extended or finned tube variety is a first class flame arrestor, and is often installed on recovery systems to cool the solvent-laden air prior to the carbon adsorption plant.

The design of a simple pebble-filled flame arrestor and correct method of installation of breaking flanges, in inflammable vapour pipelines is given by Radier[5].

Reducing the volume of hoods over solvent evaporating apparatus will also increase the safety factor. The smaller hood will give a higher air velocity for a given air rate, and prevent the building up of pockets of solvent as well as reducing the solvent capacity of the hood. It will be seen that if for any reason an explosive mixture was built up in a small hood, the total quantity of vapour which could be ignited would be only of a small order, and would not be a source of danger, especially if the machine were isolated from the rest of the plant by means of a flame arrestor and explosion membrane.

The design and distribution of suction lines for solvent-laden air is a most important part of the recovery process, and as much care and thought must be given to this part of the installation as to the production equipment and carbon adsorption recovery plant. The installation of a well-designed trunking system provides a major contribution to the efficiency of solvent recovery as well as ensuring that the production plant will be run under the safest controlled operating conditions.

9.10 The Adsorption Process

9.10.1 Dynamic Adsorption

The use of an adsorbent for gas purification comes under the category of dynamic adsorption. In cases where a high extraction efficiency is required the adsorption would be stopped when the break-through point is reached. The relationship between adsorbate concentration in the gas stream and solid may be determined experimentally and plotted in the form of isotherms. These are usually determined under static equilibrium conditions but the dynamic adsorption conditions operating in gas purification problems bear little relationship to these results. The isotherm indicates the affinity of the adsorbent for the adsorbate, but cannot relate the contact time or amount of adsorbent required to reduce the adsorbate from one concentration to another.

Factors which have a considerable influence on the service time of a bed of adsorbent include the following:

 (i) The grain size of the adsorbent.
 (ii) The depth of adsorbent bed.
 (iii) The gas velocity.
 (iv) The temperature of gas and adsorbent.
 (v) The pressure of the gas stream.
 (vi) The concentration of the adsorbates.
 (vii) The concentration of other gas constituents which may be adsorbed at the same time.
 (viii) The moisture content of the gas and adsorbent.
 (ix) The concentration of substances which may polymerize or react with the adsorbent.
 (x) The adsorptive capacity of the adsorbent for the adsorbate over the concentration range applicable over the filter.
 (ix) The degree of efficiency of adsorbate removal required.

The effect of these factors may be appreciated by considering the progress of adsorption of hydrocarbon gases through a bed of activated carbon, shown diagrammatically in Figure 9.6 and described by Edeleanu[6]. Curve A shows the theoretical saturation under equilibrium conditions, say 35 per cent

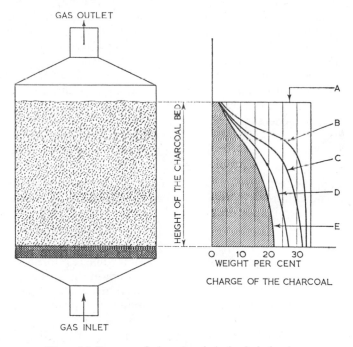

Figure 9.6 Progress of adsorption through a bed of carbon

by weight, which would correspond to a petrol content in a gas of 50 g/m^3 approximately 1 per cent by volume and to an activated carbon temperature of 25°C. Such a saturation would be obtained by slowly passing the gas until the limiting uniform charge has been attained on the whole height of the activated carbon bed. In practice, the gas is passed at a high rate through the carbon bed, and, theoretically, the charge of the carbon decreases from 100 per cent of the saturation pressure at the inlet of the bed to zero at the outlet surface of the carbon. The height of the carbon bed in which the adsorption is taking place is termed the adsorption zone. An allowance must be made in the capacity of the carbon for the length of the zone as indicated by curve B.

As the adsorption progresses the carbon is heated by the exothermic heat of adsorption, and this heat is carried ahead of the adsorption zone by the gas. The effect of increase in temperature lowers the capacity of the carbon as shown by curve C. Two other factors contribute to further lowering the charge; these are, the moisture in the gas, and residual moisture in the carbon; curves D and E represent the capacity taking these factors into account. The last curve E is a function of the above-mentioned factors, and the area which is encloses divided by the height gives the mean capacity of the carbon at the end of the adsorption period. In practice, this charge may only be between 10 and 16 per cent against a corresponding saturation capacity of 35–40 per cent by weight at the inlet concentration conditions.

It will be appreciated from the foregoing description that the normal dynamic adsorption conditions present in industrial plants have far more complex factors entering into the process. For instance, the carbon is very rarely completely stripped of the adsorbed solvents during the regeneration period as this would require a very large quantity of steam to remove the last traces of solvent from the carbon. Also in many instances several solvents may be received simultaneously, each upsetting the equilibrium of the others. All these factors will tend to reduce the capacity of the carbon and so lengthen the adsorption zone, and in order to maintain a high recovery efficiency deep bed filters are generally used.

There are no general formulae or relationships existing for calculating the capacity of an adsorber operating under dynamic conditions from a knowledge of the physical or chemical characteristics of the adsorbate or adsorbent.

A method has been developed by Hougen and Marshall[7] for calculating the time, temperature, and concentration conditions in both gas and solid during the adsorption of dilute gas flowing through granular adsorbent beds. The method deals with the following adsorption problems.

(i) Isothermal adsorption with linear equilibrium relationships between concentration in the gas phase and concentration in the adsorbed phase.

(ii) Isothermal adsorption with complex equilibrium relationships.

(iii) Non-isothermal adsorption with complex equilibrium relationships.

The last two cases are those primarily applicable to adsorption on activated carbon as equilibrium here is seldom linear; double step-wise integration of equations by graphical means is required to obtain results in the number of transfer units required. Height of transfer unit in the case of activated carbon must be determined experimentally. Knowing the height and number of transfer units, the required depth is defined (cf. Chapter 5).

In actual practice, the adsorptive capacity, height of bed and stripping conditions for a given adsorption problem are obtained experimentally in laboratory units when the designer has not the applicable experience available. Although methods have been proposed for arriving at the quantities of dessicants required for the drying of gases under isothermal or adiabatic conditions, the use of laboratory tests to determine adsorption capacity is often preferred.

The type of apparatus which may be used to determine adsorptive capacity under dynamic conditions is shown diagrammatically in Figure 9.7. Dynamic adsorption tests should be conducted with gases related as closely as possible to the conditions under which the adsorption plant will operate. Whenever possible the test filter should be used on the gas stream to be treated.

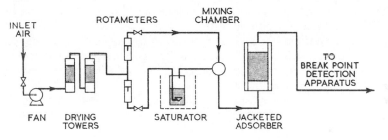

Figure 9.7 Pilot plant for carbon adsorption

Details of an experimental adsorber used by Hollings, Pexton and Chaplin[8], for investigation of the causes of fouling of activated carbon used in the extraction of benzole from town gas, give an indication of the important work which can be carried out in a small pilot adsorber. Similar small adsorbers may be used for establishing contact times and mass flow rates for the selective removal of constituents from gas streams.

9.10.2 Steaming Process and Regeneration

The rapid growth and development of the carbon adsorption recovery process has been attributed to the discovery of the comparative ease with which adsorbed solvents may be stripped from activated carbon by means of direct steam. The importance of this discovery can be seen by the following comparative methods of regeneration[1].

Table 9.3 ACTIVATED CARBON CHARGED WITH 20 PER CENT ETHER

Heating	Percentage of charge expelled
At 100°C	5
66 mb absolute at 20°C	10
Gas circulation at 130°C	20
Direct steam at 100°C	100

The stripping process is a dynamic process and the quantity of steam required to desorb a given amount of carbon is more dependent on the physical design of the adsorption plant, than on the theoretical amount of heat required to distil the solvent from the carbon.

Much care must be taken with the design of the steam manifold, carbon bed, distillate piping and condensing system to achieve an economical steam consumption. A well-designed plant will have a steam consumption in the region of 1·0–4·0 kg steam per kg of recovered solvent.

The following factors must be considered when designing the stripping process.

1. The length of time required for steaming or regeneration should be as short as possible, as this represents time off from adsorption. If continuous recovery is to be maintained a stand-by vessel must be used to recover solvent whilst one vessel is undergoing regeneration. Generally two or more adsorbers are used to permit continuous recovery.

2. The shorter the time of regeneration, the higher will be the steaming rate, and greater will be the heat duty of the condensing system. In order to keep the size of the condenser practical and economic, the regeneration times are usually chosen between 30 and 60 min.

3. The steaming direction should be in the opposite direction to the adsorption. This will prevent the accumulation of polymerizable substances, if present, from being driven deeper into the carbon bed and permit the stripped solvents from the upper layers to wash out the lower layers of the carbon, thus assisting the removal of adsorbed substances.

4. In order to secure the rapid stripping and high heat transfer it is essential that the inert gas or air is swept out of the adsorber and condensing system as quickly as possible. The design of adsorber vessel, steam-manifold and condenser can greatly assist the removal of unwanted air.

5. Further steam economy may be obtained by placing the distillate piping and condenser below the adsorber to enable the liquid condensed in the adsorber to drain directly into the condenser and separator. This will prevent accumulation of liquid in the distillate piping, which would obstruct the free path of air and steam to be swept through the system.

6. The quality of the steam. A high proportion of the heat content of the stripping stream is used to heat up the adsorber vessel, and its carbon contents, and in order to achieve rapid heat transfer it is essential that the steam condenses quickly. The steam should, therefore, contain only a slight superheat to allow condensation to take place.

7. The quantity of steam will depend on the physical properties of the adsorber and its carbon contents. As an example, the heat requirements of the stripping process are given in Table 9.4 for the removal of benzole from an activated carbon adsorber in the Beckton benzole plant[9]. The adsorber contains approximately 7 tonnes of activated carbon and has a capacity of 1070 kg of benzole per cycle. It will be seen that only 6 per cent of the total heat requirements is accounted for by the heat of adsorption of benzole being stripped. The heat leaving the adsorber with the scavenging steam is about 70 per cent of the heat input and the balance is used for heating up the adsorber and its contents.

8. The carbon should have a low retentivity to enable the solvent to be easily stripped out.

Table 9.4 HEAT BALANCE OF STEAMING CYCLE

(Adsorption capacity of carbon, 14 per cent by weight = 1070 kg of benzole per adsorber. Basis for calculations, 20°C. One adsorber steaming.)

Item	Heat input	MJ	%
1	Indirect steam: 455 kg steam at 14 bar gauge and 260°C —2·89 MJ/kg	1310	8
2	Direct steam to steam regenerators: 2720 kg as in 1	7850	48
3	Heat of adsorption of water adsorbed by carbon: 540 kg at 3 MJ/kg	1620	10
4	Heat in steam from steam regenerators: 2040 kg at 635 mb abs.—2·6 MJ/kg (heat in steam minus heat in feed water (item 5))	5300	33
5	Heat in feed water to steam regenerators: 2040 kg at 45°C (heat introduced through condensed indirect steam partly covering feed water requirements)	200	1
6	Turbine steam	—	—
	Total	16000	100

(Adsorption capacity of carbon, 14 per cent by weight = 1070 kg of benzole per adsorber. Basis for calculations, 20°C. One adsorber steaming.)

Item	Heat output and loss	MJ	%
1	Heat content of adsorber shell, coils, grids, and carbon	2650	16
2	Heat of adsorption and sensible heat of benzole leaving adsorber: 1070 kg at (790 + 140) MJ/kg	1010	6
3	Latent and sensible heat of water vapour accompanying benzole: 420 kg at 260 MJ/kg	11000	69
4	Heat in condensed indirect steam	260	2
5	Heat unaccounted for (radiation, etc.) by difference	1070	7
	Total	16000	100

9. The stripped solvents are recovered by condensing and cooling the steam–solvent mixture removed from the carbon bed. Tubular heat exchangers are normally used for the condensers and after-coolers.

9.10.3 Drying and Cooling the Carbon Bed

During the steaming period a certain amount of condensation will take place in the carbon bed, increasing the moisture content of the carbon.

The amount of moisture may be controlled, to a certain extent, by the dryness of the steam used, and the pressure and temperature conditions in the carbon bed during steaming.

In order to achieve the maximum adsorption capacity and adsorption efficiency, when recovering miscible solvents, it is desirable that the carbon bed should be dried and cooled before being returned to the solvent air stream The desired state of dryness will depend upon the physical properties of the solvent and concentration of solvent in the air or gas stream. It is desirable, when using high solvent concentrations, to leave some moisture in the carbon, so that the heat of adsorption may be used in evaporating the moisture from the carbon, thus preventing any undue rise in temperature of the carbon bed.

The humidity of the carbon bed at the end of steaming, drying and cooling periods, for a typical petrol recovery plant, is given[6] in Figure 9.8.

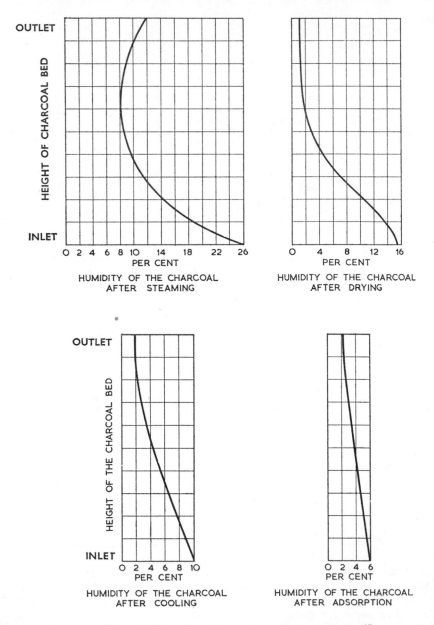

Figure 9.8 Humidity of charcoal in a petrol recovery plant[6]

The heat required for drying the carbon after steaming may be supplied by several methods, either singly or in a combination:

1. The sensible heat of carbon and adsorber in cooling from steam temperature down to adsorption temperature.
2. The sensible heat content of a heat generator placed below the carbon bed which becomes heated during the steaming period. Several commercial plants utilize a layer of pebbles beneath the carbon bed for this purpose.
3. The use of an external air heater.
4. The use of the heat of adsorption by recovering from a sufficiently high solvent concentration when drying with solvent-laden air or gas.

Caution. Air should not be used for drying when using solvents which may oxidize, polymerize, or decompose when in contact with hot moist activated carbon. The catalytic effect of activated carbon in this condition may cause such solvents to break down or hydrolyse causing the formation of acids. In these cases it is desirable to dry and cool the carbon with inert gas.

9.11 Choice of Process for Solvent Recovery

The recovery of solvent entrained in an air or gas stream may be accomplished by absorption, condensation or adsorption.

9.11.1 Absorption

The selective removal of a constituent of a gas mixture by absorption in a liquid in which only the constituent is soluble has found a wide application for the recovery of solvents. A well-known application is the removal of benzole from town gas by the intensive oil washing process. Although absorption equipment is used for a wide range of applications, the recovery of solvents from very dilute gas or air mixtures of less than 1 per cent, is not economically achieved by the absorption process.

9.11.2 Condensation

The recovery of solvents by direct condensation is normally used where pure solvent vapours, or solvent vapours at a high concentration, will be condensed by cooling. The method of cooling may be indirect as in the use of a heat exchanger or by bringing the solvent vapours into direct contact with the cooling medium, such as water in a jet condenser.

Examples of applications using condensation as a means of solvent recovery are dry-cleaning machines and many coating machines. In both cases air or inert gas recirculated within the hood or casing of the machine passes through three sections. The air passes over a heater in the first section, then through the solvent evaporating zone, where it takes up solvent and becomes saturated, and then passes through a cooling zone where the solvent is condensed out. If the machine is completely enclosed, practically 100 per cent of the solvent may be recovered.

The main disadvantage of this system is that any air or gas exhausted from the system is saturated with solvent, and this cannot be recovered economically by lowering the dew-point by refrigeration. A great disadvantage of this system is that, if the solvent is inflammable, the ingress of air may cause an explosive concentration to be reached within the external casing of the system.

9.11.3 Adsorption

The outstanding feature of the carbon adsorption process is that it enables solvents to be recovered with high efficiency from air or gas at very low concentrations. This is of vital importance for the recovery of solvents evaporated in processes in which large quantities of air may be present, or used to prevent the concentration of solvent reaching inflammable or toxic proportions, or to allow manipulation of the process. Processes such as rubber coating, artificial silk, acetate film, dry cleaning, photogravure printing, etc., evaporate organic solvents in large volumes of air which may be efficiently recovered by the carbon adsorption process.

The combination of recovery by condensation followed by adsorption recovery is occasionally utilized where a high concentration of solvent in the gas stream is present in the first instance. This combined method of recovery is used where solvent is evaporated in a batchwise process.

An example of this is the modern dry cleaning machine in which the bulk of the solvent may be recovered by condensation from a recirculating air stream. However, since the machine has to be periodically opened for re-charging, before the machine is opened, fresh air is drawn through the machine to sweep out the remaining solvent vapours, and these may be recovered in a carbon adsorption plant. A number of batchwise operated machines may be connected to a single adsorption plant, thus ensuring that the loss of solvent from the process will be reduced to a minimum.

9.11.4 Fluidized Bed Adsorption

A recent development in adsorption techniques has been the use of fluidized beds for drying gases[10] and for solvent recovery[11]. Capital cost is substantially lower as much less adsorbent is used though the cost of vessels is higher. A plant of this type using activated carbon is operating successfully at a viscose staple factory recovering 1·5 tonnes/h carbon disulphide from a ventilation air stream of 120 m^3/s.

As may be seen from Figure 9.9, a feature of the plant is the multi-tray adsorber. Thus, operating in a manner analogous to a liquid phase absorption column, several theoretical separation stages are achieved, and CS_2 in the air stream is reduced to about 50 p.p.m.

Because of the excellent mixing characteristics of a fluidized bed, the problem of slip associated with fixed bed plants does not occur and high, uniform solvent loading on the carbon are achieved. Consequently the stripping steam requirement is substantially below that for equivalent fixed bed plants.

Stripping is carried out in a vessel through which the carbon flows as a plug. Steam is injected at the mid-point, and the steam–CS_2 mixture is collected from the top of the vessel, condensed and separated. The carbon finally flows into a fluid bed, in which it is cooled and dried, before being returned by an elevator to the top tray of the adsorber. Carbon fouling is dealt with by continuously feeding a sidestream from the main circulation system to a regeneration plant. Attrition is not serious.

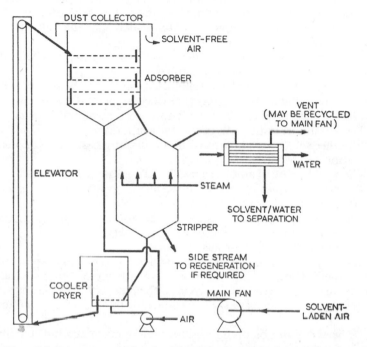

Figure 9.9 Solvent recovery by adsorption in fluidized beds of activated carbon

There seems little doubt that this type of adsorption plant is a significant advance over any existing fixed bed plant by virtue of its improved mass transfer behaviour. It is particularly suited to continuous applications. Thorough pilot plant work is necessary to obtain design information. While present work has been devoted specifically to solvent recovery, the technique may well be developed to give a more economical method of achieving quite difficult gas separations.

9.12 Preparation of Inquiries

The information that the designer of a carbon adsorption solvent recovery plant requires, is basically:
 (i) the nature of the solvent;
 (ii) the quantity of solvent to be recovered per hour;
 (iii) the air or gas rate accompanying the solvent.
These details should be elaborated to provide as much information as

possible concerning the process and manner of working, in order that the designer may provide the plant best suited to the process conditions. A suggested list of items to be included when preparing inquiries for solvent recovery plants is as follows:

1. The name and chemical formula of the solvents to be recovered. If a mixture of solvents is to be recovered, it is necessary to know the proportions either by weight or by volume.

2. The condition in which the solvent is to be recovered, i.e. if a mixture of solvents is to be recovered, whether these have to be separated to individual components. Also the amount of water which may be tolerated in the recovered solvent should be stated.

3. The known characteristics of the solvent (boiling point, specific gravity, solubility in water, azeotropes, special hazards, etc.).

4. The quantity of solvent normally used per hour, the number of hours worked per day, and number of days per week, or plant data on raw material, feeds and finished products from which the solvent rate may be calculated.

5. The variations in the rate of solvent evaporation.

6. Whether solvent is evaporated in an air- or gas-stream and if gas, the composition of gas used.

7. The volume rate of air or gas used to evaporate the solvent.

8. The concentration of solvent in the air- or gas-stream, and the desired limit of solvent concentration in the air.

9. The temperature and pressure of the solvent–air mixture, either at machine or where it is proposed to enter recovery plant.

10. The humidity of air- or gas-stream.

11. Description of material from which solvent is evaporated, and whether there is any possibility of any constituent of this material being entrained in the air stream and carried to the recovery plant, i.e. paper, dust, fluff, dirt, or any foreign matter which could clog the fine pores of the activated carbon.

12. A brief description of the process, type of machines and contributions to total of any individual sources of solvent vapour.

13. Whether the process is enclosed and complete with solvent air ducts, flame traps, and controls, etc., for collecting solvent vapours from every evaporation source.

14. Details of factory services including cost and quality of steam and water supplies.

15. Particulars of site available for plant: site area, headroom, enclosed or outside location, distance from solvent evaporation process, etc.

16. Future extensions: whether allowances are to be made for future extensions and whether there is any possibility of changing the solvents to be recovered at some future date.

17. Method of operation of plant—whether manually operated valves or automatic valve control is required.

9.13 Instruments for Process Control

An activated carbon plant may be controlled quite simply with the aid of flow meters and thermometers. The most important factors to control are:

(i) The solvent concentration. This must be kept to a safe concentration which may be calculated from a knowledge of the weight of solvent being evaporated per hour, and the quantity of air or gas being drawn through the adsorption plant. In the majority of cases the rate of solvent evaporation is known, and a simple orifice type flow meter is sufficient to enable the concentration to be calculated and maintained.

The low concentrations involved of less than 1 per cent by volume may be measured in a number of ways, depending upon the physical and chemical properties of the solvent. Methods used include the following:

(a) Adsorption of the solvent in a small test adsorber containing activated carbon. A measured volume of solvent-laden air is passed through the adsorber, the carbon is steamed and the solvent condensed, collected and weighed.

(b) Qualitative analysis. Chlorinated solvent vapours may be decomposed by passing through a quartz tube heated above 400°C. The chlorine is detected by a 2 per cent potassium iodide solution and starch.

(c) Quantitative analysis. The solvent vapour is adsorbed in a solution and titrated with selected indicator. Most solvents can be detected and the concentration ascertained by chemical analysis, but the procedure is often difficult and lengthy, and not very suitable for routine checks on the plant.

(d) Infra-red gas analyser; gas chromatography; atomic-adsorption spectroscopy. The development of these techniques has greatly assisted the analyst in detecting and measuring single components of a gas mixture, even from a complex mixture of gases. These methods are capable of detecting a few parts per million of a component in a gas mixture with comparative ease within a few seconds. Analysers may be used continuously to monitor selected components from one or several process streams such as measurement of solvent concentration at various points, in the plant and building, as well as the solvent concentration at the inlet and outlets of the adsorbers.

(ii) The temperature of adsorption. Thermometers should be placed at strategic points in the solvent air line and carbon bed. Any change in method of operation of the adsorption plant is generally reflected as a change in the operating temperature of the plant. Temperatures should be recorded in order that any change will be noticed at once by the operator.

The use of recording thermometers in the carbon bed at different levels will indicate the progress of adsorption, and provide a true record of the operation of the plant. They greatly assist in tracing the cause of any faults which may occur, so that they may be rectified with the minimum delay and loss of solvent.

9.14 Safety Considerations

The carbon adsorption process of solvent recovery may be applied to practically all of the solvent-using industries. In view of the nature of the process, in that it generally involves dealing with highly inflammable or toxic substances, it is essential, from a safety point of view, to ensure that the ventilation system and recovery plant is designed and installed by an experienced contractor specializing in this type of installation. Too little knowledge may lead unwittingly to the design of a hazardous plant, and great care must be taken to ensure that the final installation is as safe as possible.

The risk of fire, with its accompanying disastrous effects, cannot be too highly stressed when using inflammable solvents, and it is essential that the advice of an expert be sought at an early stage when a new solvent evaporating process is being considered.

All of the usual safety precautions necessary when handling toxic or inflammable solvents must be strictly observed. Recommended methods of handling solvents are given in safety codes of the various engineering societies, chemical and oil companies supplying the solvents, and there are legal regulations regarding the storage of toxic chemicals and solvents.

The collection of solvents from evaporating sources from the point of view of safety from fire risks, and possibility of flame propagation through the suction lines carrying the solvent-laden air have been dealt with in Section 9.9.2. The main basic points are:

1. Adequate ventilation to prevent solvent concentrations reaching dangerous proportions in workrooms or machinery.

2. Adequate hooding and ducting to prevent solvent vapour polluting the workrooms where people are employed.

3. Isolation of machinery and sources of solvent by the fitting of valves and flame traps in the ducting between solvent vapour collecting devices. This helps to localize and extinguish any mishaps which may occur.

All types of activated carbon if raised to a suitable temperature and exposed to oxidizing conditions will burn. This tendency, however, depends upon the quality of the carbon employed, and this may vary considerably. The majority of activated carbons are safe for operation in air temperatures below 150°C.

The temperatures which are obtained in normal operation of a solvent recovery plant are as follows.

During the adsorption period the temperature of the carbon may be anything from room temperature up to 50°C. During desorption, i.e. the period when saturated steam is passed through the adsorber, the highest temperatures are usually from 120° to 140°C. During the drying of the carbon the temperature is reduced owing to evaporation of moisture from the carbon, falling from 110° to 40°C. It will be seen that all of these temperatures are below the maximum operational temperature limit of the carbon. Activated carbon has, however, a strongly catalytic effect on certain solvents, which are readily oxidizable at the temperatures at which a carbon adsorption plant operates.

Where ordinary commercial solvents, such as benzene, toluene, xylene, alcohol, ether, acetone and common esters are being recovered, no difficulties of any kind are experienced providing the recovery plant is properly designed and operated.

There is no risk of oxidation during the adsorption period providing:

1. The temperature of the carbon is limited to between 20° and 50°C.

2. A low solvent concentration is used so that the thermal capacity of the air is very great in relation to the heat of adsorption.

3. The heat of adsorption is so small that even in the most favourable case the highest temperature rise during an adsorption period is limited to 10°C.

4. The carbon is dried and cooled after each steaming before being connected on to the solvent air stream.

Recommended points of plant design and operation with special relationship to safety are:

1. Use of a high quality activated carbon of the regular grain type. These are relatively expensive materials.

2. Use of high quality valves to ensure long life and freedom from leakages.

3. Progressive drying of the carbon after steaming at the lowest possible temperature.

4. Provision of sufficient instruments, e.g. thermometers in the carbon bed, flowmeters for measurement of solvent air rate, etc., to ensure that the plant operator is in full control of the adsorption plant and is readily informed of any change from normal operation.

5. Provision of proper instruction for plant operators. When a plant is started up it is essential for a specialist to train the operators and give detailed working instructions, not only to cover the essential precautions to secure recovery efficiency, but also to maintain absolute safety of working. This is necessary with any solvent recovery plant, no matter what system and is probably one of the most important obligations of a contractor supplying an installation in which inflammable materials have to be handled.

9.15 Methods of Operating the Plant with High Technical Efficiency

Activated carbon will last for many years in a well-maintained recovery plant.

Providing the activated carbon is maintained in a good condition, the only way of destroying the adsorption efficiency of the carbon is to load it with fouling substances other than the solvent to be recovered. The greatest cause of inefficiency is waterlogging of the carbon. If the carbon contains more than 30 per cent water it will be rendered temporarily inactive, and must be dried out before further use. This fault may happen if the carbon is not properly dried out after the steam regeneration cycle, or through a faulty valve, or wet steam.

Other substances which may foul the activated carbon, and are undesirable contaminants, are polymerizable organic materials and mists of oil or water.

Periodic removal of the carbon for screening to remove accumulated dust and fine particles of carbon will improve the porosity of the carbon bed and facilitate the uniform passage of gas or air.

10

Purification of Cryogenic Gases

D. E. WARD AND D. O. BRISCOE

REVISED BY D. T. LINNETT

10.1 Introduction

In this chapter the various methods of removing the minor impurities from cryogenic gases prior to their low temperature liquefaction or processing are described, together with some of the more important aspects of their practical operation. Cryogenic gases are defined generally as those with a boiling point below about 115 K at one bar[1]. The gases considered are air and its constituent gases, coke oven and converter gases, and hydrogen.

Gas purification, as applied to low temperature plant, can be classified under four main headings:

(i) Chemical purification. This depends on removal of the impurity by chemical reaction with another compound, with the formation of a waste product. Material is continuously consumed, and chemical purification methods are generally best suited to the removal of low concentrations of impurity; for example a solution of caustic soda in water can be used to remove carbon dioxide from air with the formation of sodium carbonate.

(ii) Absorption. This is fundamentally a process in which the impurity is removed by preferential entry into a liquid. The process can be reversed by heating the liquid or stripping it with an inert gas. No significant quantities of material are consumed. The absorption of carbon dioxide by mono-ethanolamine is a typical example.

(iii) Adsorption. This is a reversible process whereby certain components of a fluid are concentrated at the surface of a solid. It may be employed at ambient or low temperatures and is best suited to the removal of small quantities of impurity to a low residual concentration. The removal of carbon dioxide from air can, for example, be effected at about 140 K by passing the air through a vessel containing an adsorbent such as silica gel. Dual vessels are often used, one on-stream whilst the other is off-stream being reactivated.

(iv) Formation of another phase. As a gas mixture is cooled, one or more

components can become liquid and/or solid. By separating the liquid or allowing the solid to accumulate these components can be partially or completely separated from the main process gas. Use of this principle is made in blocking exchangers, in which carbon dioxide is removed from air by causing it to deposit in one of a pair of low temperature exchangers.

Low temperature plants are unique in that heat entering below ambient temperature must be pumped from the plant by the use of energy, usually in the form of mechanical power. The energy required for pumping out the heat for a thermodynamically reversible process is given by the well-known equation below, based on the Carnot cycle.

$$W = Q \left\{ \frac{T_2 - T_1}{T_1} \right\} \tag{10.1}$$

where W = minimum theoretical work
  Q = heat entering plant at temperature T_1
  T_1 = temperature level at which heat enters plant
  T_2 = temperature of heat sink to which heat Q is rejected.

Thus to pump heat from a temperature level T_1 of 100 K, rejecting it at a temperature level T_2 of 288 K, the minimum theoretical work required is $1.88Q$. If T_1 is 20 K the work required would rise to $13.4Q$. The actual work is usually about $7Q$ and $50Q$ respectively. Work is also about three times more expensive than heat, so the approximate cost of producing cold at 100 K and 20 K can be respectively 21 and 150 times more expensive than supplying heat at near ambient temperatures. Thus in devising a purification system which has to operate at low temperatures it is essential to bear in mind the heat which it will carry into the plant. For example, it is generally more economical to use a large adsorber since a small one requires more frequent reactivation and thus a greater refrigeration load. This approach to the purification method adopted becomes more important the lower the temperature at which purification takes place.

It is usual practice to expect a large plant to be on stream for at least one year before maintenance or other requirements cause it to be shut down. In low temperature plants, many of the minor impurities become solid as the temperature of the feed gas is lowered and if not efficiently removed would deposit on heat exchanger surfaces and eventually prevent gas flow, causing premature shutdown. In nearly all cases, but depending on plant volume characteristics, it is essential to remove impurities which deposit as a solid to a concentration level of the order of 1 v.p.m.* In a large oxygen plant (see Figure 10.1), the annual intake of CO_2 with the air is about 85 tonne for every 100 tonne per day of oxygen produced. If the CO_2 concentration is reduced to 1 v.p.m. the volume of CO_2 deposited over one year is about 0.17 m^3, which could be sufficient to block the plant if allowed to accumulate.

Where possible, it is generally preferable to employ a physical process to bring about purification, often using waste gases for subsequent regeneration. For instance on a 100 tonne/day oxygen plant, carbon dioxide is usually removed by a physical, reversible process, as described in Section 10.2.4 (iv) and (v). If this CO_2 were removed by chemical purification using caustic

---

*Volumes per million volumes.

Figure 10.1 Air separation plant for the production of 720 tons per day of 99·5 per cent oxygen
(Courtesy of The British Oxygen Co. Ltd)

1. Plant building
2. Main air separation unit
3. Direct contact air cooler
4. Waste nitrogen silencer
5. Control room
6. Reversing heat exchangers

soda, the annual cost of the cuastic soda alone would be about £10,000 at 1969 prices.

At low temperatures, as the critical temperature of the bulk gas is approached, marked deviations from the ideal gas behaviour are common. For example at 123 K and 25 bar the actual concentration of carbon dioxide in air in equilibrium with the solid will be about six times the ideal value based on the vapour pressure of carbon dioxide alone. At 150 bar and 123 K the concentration in equilibrium with the solid rises to about 1040 times the ideal value. These deviations are obviously considerable and cannot be ignored in preparing designs.

This chapter is divided according to the bulk gas from which impurities must be removed. The removal of each impurity is described and lines of approach under given conditions are indicated. The most common gas is air and a major part of the discussion is devoted to purification problems in air separation plants; the principles can be widely applied, however, to other gases.

10.2 Air

10.2.1 General

By far the most important application of cryogenic plants is the separation of air into its three main constituents: oxygen, nitrogen and argon. The minor impurities which must be removed are dust, oil, carbon dioxide, water vapour, hydrocarbons and noncondensable gases. The hydrocarbons, and in particular acetylene, although usually present in the air in concentrations less than 1 v.p.m., can accumulate and cause serious explosions in the low temperature section of the plant unless effectively removed.

10.2.2 Dust Removal

Efficient dust removal is essential to ensure the satisfactory operation over prolonged periods of a variety of items of equipment on air separation plants.

(i) Air compressors. A typical figure for the amount of dust in the air processed by a 100 tonne/day oxygen plant in one week is 4·5 kg, although this amount would clearly vary considerably from site to site. This would cause considerable wear on compressor moving parts, valves and cylinders. In addition, in oil-lubricated compressors, solids drawn in at the suction may adhere to carbonaceous deposits in discharge ports and piping, where they would increase the risk of fire or explosion. It is therefore essential that the air drawn into a compressor be efficiently filtered.

Various types of air suction filter are available, but for duty on large scale oxygen plants there are two essential requirements:

(a) Low pressure drop. An increase of only 5 mb pressure drop on the suction filter of a 100 tonne/day oxygen plant could cause the power consumption to rise by approximately 3 kW.

(b) Continuous operation. The filtration system will be required to operate continuously for the period between routine shut-downs, which will normally be at least one year.

On plant requiring only a low air pressure for operation, such as those employing the Linde–Fränkl cycle, the process air is compressed by a turbo-compressor and will not normally come into contact with oil. For such plants therefore, it is advisable to avoid the use of oil-washed filters in order to minimize the carry-over of hydrocarbons into the low temperature sections of the plant. On high pressure plants on which oil-lubricated compressors are used, oil carry-over is unavoidable and oil-washed filters may be used before the compressor.

A comprehensive survey of the types of air filter available and their characteristics is given by Perry[2] (see also Chapter 17AII).

(ii) Catalytic oxidation units for hydrocarbons (see Section 10.2.6). It is essential that the air entering these units should have an extremely low dust content to avoid contamination of the catalyst, and after initial removal of the larger particles the air should pass through an 'ultra-filter' to remove virtually all material with a particle size larger than $0.3 \ \mu m$.

(iii) Adsorbers. Due to the cyclic operation of adsorbers, a certain amount of attrition of the adsorbent will invariably take place. Dust formed in this way could cause considerable damage to expansion machines, valve seats, etc., and if allowed to enter the rectification column could act as a source of potential danger by contentrating hydrocarbon impurities. It is necessary therefore to ensure that the dust is not carried forward, by installing suitable filters downstream of all adsorbers.

The requirements for both gas phase and liquid phase filters on oxygen plants are similar:

(a) a high efficiency for fine dust removal;
(b) a low clogging rate;
(c) a low pressure drop;
(d) ease of cleaning;
(e) non-inflammable materials of construction.

In addition to dust removal, the liquid phase filters (which are generally in pairs) also serve to remove solid carbon dioxide and ice from the liquid stream. Since cleaning these filters will involve warming to ambient temperature or above and then cooling to liquid oxygen temperatures when bringing the filter back on stream, they represent a regularly occurring refrigeration load. Their construction should therefore be such that, while conforming to the requirements listed above, the refrigeration load is kept to a minimum.

10.2.3 Oil Carry-over from Compressors

At the present time, oil-lubricated compressors are in common use on certain types of air separation plants. It is inevitable that the air leaving such a compressor will contain a certain quantity of oil vapour and oil droplets. While this, in any case, is generally undesirable because of the risk of fire or explosion in the compressor and associated pipework and coolers due to the formation of carbonaceous deposits, it is particularly undesirable in air separation plants for the following reasons:

(i) Hydrocarbon accumulation is a particular hazard in air separation plants.

(ii) Catalytic oxidation (see Section 10.2.6) may be used for removing traces of hydrocarbons from the air before liquefaction, and excessive amounts of hydrocarbon in the form of oil can cause the catalyst bed temperature to rise to the point at which sintering occurs.[3].

(iii) Oil contamination may result in loss of efficiency and powdering of adsorbents in adsorptive dryers.

(iv) Oil contamination of heat exchange surfaces leads to inefficient operation and eventual blockage.

(v) Oil contminated air supply for instruments and valves can lead to their malfunction.

It would obviously be an advantage if compressors using some other means of lubrication could be employed, but at present they generally have disadvantages with regard to initial cost, maintenance cost and power consumption, and therefore oil-lubricated compressors are still widely used for air.

The risk of fire and explosion in oil-lubricated compressors can be minimized by correct maintenance and operation, and the following points are particularly important:

(a) Selection of the correct lubricating oil, e.g. an essential characteristic is high resistance to oxidation.

(b) Use of the minimum quantity of oil required to give good lubrication of those parts in contact with process air.

(c) Regular and correct blowing of compressor drains.

(d) Ensuring that correct stage pressures and temperatures are maintained.

(e) Regular inspection and cleaning of filters, valves, pipework and coolers (both air-side and water-side).

It has been found that the existence of conditions necessary for compressor fires is accompanied by the formation of carbon dioxide; by bubbling an air bleed from the compressor discharge through barium hydroxide an indication of these conditions can be obtained[3].

At normal air exit temperatures the vapour pressure of most lubricating oils is extremely low and the major source of contamination is oil entrained in the air in the form of a fine mist. Removal of this entrained oil is basically carried out in two stages: agglomeration followed by separation.

The particular method of oil removal used varies with the liquefaction cycle employed in the air separation plant. Cyclone and impact separators are frequently used to remove the larger drops which usually constitute the greater proportion of entrained oil. In the case of adsorptive dryers and heat exchangers an additional and convenient precaution against oil contamination is a vessel upstream packed with the same adsorbent as that in the dryers. The adsorbent in this prefilter will deteriorate more quickly than that in the dryers and will finally be discarded. When the adsorbent from the dryers is replaced, the old material can be used to provide the packing for the prefilter.

In some cases oil removal is associated with cooling, as, for example, in refrigeration dryers (see Section 10.2.5 (ii)), where oil and water vapour are removed while the air is cooled. The removal of oil mist from dry gas is facilitated by the injection of steam[3].

10.2.4 Carbon Dioxide Removal

(i) Caustic scrubbing. Until recently the most widely used chemical method of removing carbon dioxide prior to air separation was by scrubbing the air with a solution of sodium hydroxide. It is desirable to reduce the carbon dioxide concentration in the process air from approximately 350 v.p.m. to 0·5 v.p.m. or less in order to ensure that no significant deposition or precipitation will take place in the low temperature sections of the plant.

Mainly because of the handling and disposal problems associated with sodium hydroxide, this method of carbon dioxide removal is now rarely used on new plants. It has largely been replaced by such techniques as adsorption or low temperature filtration. There are, however, many caustic scrubbing units still in use on existing plants.

The theory of the caustic scrubbing of air is covered in some detail by Sherwood and Pigford[4]. It is normal practice to employ a 2 N sodium hydroxide solution, since it has been found by Tepe and Dodge[5] that the absorption coefficient has a maximum value at this concentration level. Two scrubbing towers in series have been used for this operation, the liquor in the first tower being run close to complete exhaustion. With a single scrubber it is usual to discard the caustic at about 75 per cent exhaustion. A close check should be kept on the operation of such a scrubbing system by frequent analyses of the circulating liquor.

Carbon dioxide removal by caustic scrubbing was generally employed on medium and high pressure air streams which could not be purified by deposition methods (as in regenerators, for example). The operating pressures of the scrubbers still in use are generally in the range 5–35 bar. The scrubber often operates at an inter-stage pressure of a high pressure air compressor, the air passing from the aftercooler of one stage, through the caustic scrubber, and back to the suction of the next stage. It is particularly important in this case to ensure that there is no carry-over of caustic from the scrubber, by fitting efficient anti-entrainment devices, because the caustic can attack the compressor lubricating oil. This has been known to lead to compressor fires and explosions. If aluminium heat exchangers are used immediately downstream of the caustic scrubber it is necessary to include a water wash tower to ensure complete elimination of caustic carry-over.

An example of a single scrubber purification unit is shown in Figure 10.2. It comprises:

(a) A storage tank for the highly concentrated caustic soda solution prior to dilution to give the required 2 N concentration.

(b) A mixing tank, in which dilution is carried out.

(c) Mixing and transfer pumps.

(d) A holding tank for the 2 N solution prior to injection into a scrubber.

(e) Adjustable metering pumps to feed the fresh caustic to the scrubber continuously, in order to replace the spent caustic as it is withdrawn, and to maintain the required concentration of sodium hydroxide in the scrubber.

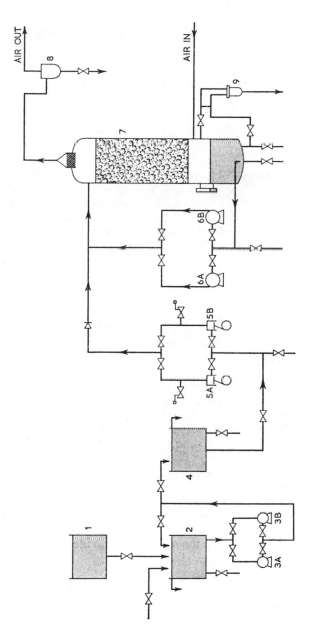

AIR OUT

AIR IN

Figure 10.2 Diagrammatic layout of single-stage counter-current caustic scrubber with auxiliary equipment. 1, concentrated caustic storage tank; 2, mixing tank; 3A and B, mixing and transfer pumps; 4, holding tank; 5A and B, metering pumps; 6A and B, circulating pumps; 7, scrubber; 8, separator; 9, level control

(f) Circulating pumps sized to give the required liquid loading in the scrubber.

(g) Disposal equipment: the spent caustic may merely be run off to waste after suitable treatment, or alternatively it may pay to instal equipment to recausticize the spent lye.

It is necessary to steam-trace all lines and valves where there is a possibility in cold weather of the sodium hydroxide crystallizing out and leading to a blockage.

(ii) Soda lime. An alternative method of carbon dioxide removal to the conventional caustic scrubbing described in Section 10.2.4 (i) involves the use of soda lime. It is, however, more expensive, and can only be used in batch-wise processes and therefore in air separation is used only on small plants.

Soda lime is a granular solid consisting essentially of a hydrated mixture of calcium hydroxide and sodium hydroxide, with a moisture content on the wet basis of about 16 per cent. It is manufactured by slaking quicklime with a solution of sodium hydroxide, followed by drying by heat.

When used for carbon dioxide removal, the basic reaction is the absorption of carbon dioxide on the small proportion of sodium hydroxide, followed by reaction of the resulting sodium carbonate with the calcium hydroxide, with the formation of calcium carbonate and sodium hydroxide. The overall reaction is:

$$Ca(OH)_2 + CO_2 \rightarrow CaCO_3 + H_2O.$$

When the soda lime becomes spent, a film of calcium carbonate is formed round the particles; it is not capable of regeneration.

As the presence of water is essential to the reactions, carbon dioxide removal by soda lime is only practicable from moist gas, otherwise the gas would dry out the soda lime. Soda lime purifiers would therefore precede the dryers in an air purification cycle, and would normally operate at the final discharge pressure of the compressor, unlike caustic scrubbers which usually operate at pressures between 5 and 35 bar.

As the air entering the soda lime vessel is saturated, the additional water formed as a result of the absorption of carbon dioxide will not be carried off as vapour by the air leaving the vessel, but must be allowed to drain off. In its passage down the bed it will tend to leach out the sodium and potassium hydroxides, and it has been shown that it is an advantage with respect to carbon dioxide removal for the air flow to be upwards through the bed because of the scrubbing effect of this solution as it passes countercurrent to the air[6]. However, general practice is for downward flow in order to minimize dust formation due to agitation of the soda lime bed. The absorptive capacity of soda lime for carbon dioxide is of the order of 35 per cent w/w. An appreciable variation in capacity with particle size occurs, which is accounted for by the calcium carbonate film which coats the particles preventing contact with the unreacted material inside. The capacity thus increases with smaller particle size. However, the possibility of blockage due to water formation increases with decreasing particle size. An optimum size has been found to be 1–2 mm for use on high pressure air separation plants. It has been shown[6] that the absorptive capacity varies considerably with linear velocity, and two expressions have been derived for high pressure air flow for the life of the soda lime:

For flows between 0 and 1.2 m^3/s per m^2 cross-sectional area of the bed,

$$\text{Life (seconds per metre length)} = \left(\frac{248\,000}{F}\right)^{1.07} \qquad (10.2)$$

For flows between 1.2 and 3.6 m^3/s per m^2 of cross-sectional area of the bed,

$$\text{Life (seconds per metre length)} = \left(\frac{2740}{F}\right)^{1.69} \qquad (10.3)$$

In each case F is the air flow in standard m^3/s per m^2 reduced to 273 K and one bar.

Certain precautions are necessary to ensure efficient use of the soda lime absorber. It is essential that oil be prevented from entering the bed, because it would tend to coat the first sections of the bed and render them ineffective. Filters are necessary downstream of the soda lime bed in order to prevent possible damage caused by dust in the remainder of the process. The soda lime is normally contained in a form of basket inside the pressure vessel, and as it cannot be regenerated it is necessary to recharge periodically. This operation can be carried out more quickly if a spare basket is available.

(iii) Low temperature adsorption. A particularly convenient method of carbon dioxide removal which has several attractive features is that of low temperature adsorption. This can be applied in both the gas and liquid phases. The capacity of adsorbents for carbon dioxide increases with decreasing temperature.

Karwat[7] has described a medium pressure air separation plant in which all the carbon dioxide is removed in silica gel adsorbers. This has the advantage that caustic scrubbing, with its use of consumable material and associated handling and disposal problems, is thereby completely eliminated. A further important property of silica gel at low temperature is its ability to adsorb acetylene and certain higher hydrocarbons, NO and NO$_2$ with high efficiency, thus leading to increased safety of plant operation.

Regeneration of the gel may be carried out either at elevated temperatures, which therefore results in an increased refrigeration load on the plant, or at low temperature, which while eliminating the extra refrigeration load results in a less effective reactivation and a rather lower efficiency of acetylene removal.

Another application of low temperature adsorptive carbon dioxide removal is in the method of balancing regenerators by withdrawing a bleed of air at a point part way down the regenerator (see Section 10.2.4 (iv))[8]. Subsequent purification of the bleed (which will still contain appreciable quantities of carbon dioxide) is carried out by passing it through a silica gel adsorber. In this application the temperature of the sidestream cannot be fixed at the deposition point of carbon dioxide since it is influenced by the flow and temperature conditions required in the regenerator and other parts of the process. However, the bleed temperature on a conventional low pressure plant is generally about 140 K.

In the liquid phase adsorbents may be used to remove both dissolved carbon dioxide and dissolved acetylene. Normal practice when using such adsorbers is to instal filters upstream in order to remove ice, solid carbon dioxide and other solid matter to enable the adsorbers to operate with maximum efficiency. These adsorbers should be regenerated at elevated temperatures, for example by a warm stream of waste nitrogen. As in the case of liquid filters, the construction of the adsorbers should be such as to minimize this additional refrigeration load.

(iv) Regenerators. Regenerators have been used extensively in low temperature plants to cool the feed gas usually to its dew-point by heat exchange with the outgoing product and waste gases. This type of heat exchanger was first suggested by Fränkl[10] in 1925. In recent years, most new air separation plants have incorporated reversing exchangers rather than regenerators but there are many regenerator plants still in operation and some new plants still have a requirement for this type of heat exchanger.

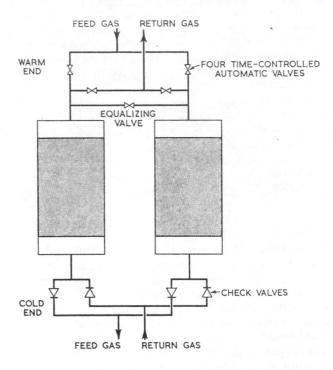

Figure 10.3 Operation of regenerators

It is fundamentally a heat storage device and usually consists of two cylindrical vessels packed with metal strip (Fränkl packing) or stones (see Figure 10.3). The warm feed gas and cold return gas are switched alternately between the vessels, so that the heat from the feed gas stored in the packing is used to heat the return gas and vice versa. At the warm end of the vessels the gas streams are switched automatically by externally operated valves through a timing mechanism and at the cold end by check valves which open or close according to the direction of the gas pressure exerted on them.

Regenerators are used on low temperature plants, particularly on air separation plants, because of three main factors:

(1) ability to handle very large gas flows;

(2) ability to remove impurities from the incoming feed gas by deposition on the packing;

(3) relatively low capital costs.

They are not however suitable for high pressure air due to the large air losses at change-over and to the prohibitive cost of the pressure vessels. The maximum volume of gas which can be handled by one pair of regenerators is only limited by the maximum economic diameter and thickness of the containing shell although maldistribution effects must be considered. At the present time the largest shells in use have diameters of about 3·7 m, which corresponds to the air/waste nitrogen regenerator of a 250 tonne/day oxygen plant. The impurities in the feed which are deposited on the packing are re-evaporated by the outgoing waste nitrogen and product oxygen provided that special conditions are adhered to with respect to temperature difference.

The low capital costs of this form of exchanger can be mainly attributed to the large surface area per unit volume of packing, which is usually between 1300–3300 m^2/m^3 compared with 165 m^2/m^3 for a normal type shell and tube exchanger as frequently used in the oil industry. The design of the regenerators is complicated and little literature is available. The basic theory the regenerators has been very extensively studied by Hausen[11,12,13] and more recently with the aid of an electronic computer Saunders and Smoleniec[14] have studied temperature distribution in regenerators, the effect of variation of heat transfer with temperature and the effect of different warm and cold gas-flow rates. As a first approach to understanding regenerator operation the reader is referred to a paper by Ward[15]. With regard to the purging of deposited carbon dioxide, the factors involved for correct operation are complex and only a rough guide can be given here to the operating conditions, etc., which must be employed.

The basis of the removal process is the effect of pressure on the equilibrium composition of a gas mixture. At a given temperature, a given mass of gas can hold more carbon dioxide at a lower pressure than at a higher pressure. If carbon dioxide is deposited from a gas stream under pressure, e.g. air, on to a surface at temperature T_s, there is, depending on the temperature difference between the bulk of the gas and the surface, and on the relative heat and mass transfer rates, a certain concentration of carbon dioxide in the bulk of the gas. In the converse process (i.e. the cleaning cycle) there is at the same point in the regenerator a corresponding concentration of carbon dioxide in the low pressure cleaning gas, e.g. waste nitrogen, again depending on the temperature difference between the bulk of the gas and the surface, and on the relative heat and mass transfer rates. For continuous operation, i.e. no accumulation of carbon dioxide, the product of flow and concentration in the cleaning gas must be greater than or equal to that in the depositing gas. This necessitates adjustment of the relative mass flows of air and nitrogen such that the temperature difference between the depositing and evaporating gas streams is kept below a limiting figure.

Denton et al.[16] have studied this problem with respect to reversing exchangers and derived an expression for the temperature difference between the bulk gas temperature of the feed and return streams which if exceeded results in the return stream being unable to remove all the impurity deposited.

The equation quoted below has been derived from the above work:

$$\Delta T_0 = \frac{(C_s^L - R.C_s^H)(1 + R^{1-a})}{E\left\{(R^{2-a}C_s^H)\dfrac{d \ln C_s^L}{d T_s} + C_s^L \dfrac{d \ln C_s^H}{d T_s}\right\}} \tag{10.4}$$

where ΔT_0 = overall bulk temperature difference between high and low pressure streams

E = ratio of heat to mass transfer

R = ratio of deposition gas flow to cleaning gas flow

a = exponent of Reynolds number in the heat transfer relationship for multi-entry plate fins,

$$St = A.Re^{-a}Pr^{-2/3}$$

T_s = surface temperature between streams

C_s^H = mol-fraction equilibrium concentration at surface temperature T_s in high pressure gas

C_s^L = mol-fraction equilibrium concentration at surface temperature T_s in low pressure gas.

Figure 10.4 gives typical values of this limiting temperature difference ΔT_0 for the case of equal flows of air and nitrogen when their respective pressures are 5·57 bar and 1·11 bar, which are typical values for a double column air separation unit. In general, on regenerators this limiting temperature difference may be exceeded and they may yet run for periods of up to perhaps one year without blocking with carbon dioxide. This is mainly due to the large volume of regenerators, the amount deposited at the very low temperature levels being so small that although complete re-evaporation is not achieved the amount left after each changeover is insufficient to cause blockage between routine plant shut-downs.

Unfortunately, if a pair of regenerators is operated with equal flows of air and waste nitrogen, with a temperature difference at the warm end of about 4 deg K, due to the increase of the specific heat of air as the pressure is raised and temperature is lowered, the temperature difference at the cold end of a regenerator would rise to about 10 deg K. This is shown in Figure 10.4 where the temperature difference curve is plotted as a function of the high pressure gas temperature for conditions of equal flow (curve (a)). It can be seen that the actual temperature difference in such a regenerator would exceed the limiting temperature difference over quite a large temperature range at the cold end and so it would block in a very short time. To overcome this problem of the cold end temperature difference, which is referred to as the balancing problem, many ingenious solutions have been proposed. The three basic approaches are depicted in Figure 10.5. The first method (Figure 10.5 (a)) depends on using a larger return gas stream than the feed stream along the entire length of the exchanger. Curve (b) of Figure 10.4 illustrates the temperature difference distribution if this technique is adopted. It is seen from curve (b) that a pinchpoint A occurs at about 160 deg K which limits the minimum practical warm end temperature approach to about 3·5 deg K when using this system. A further disadvantage is that some means of obtaining a greater flow returning through the regenerators than air entering the regenerators must be devised, and the usual method is to compress a small air stream to a high pressure and to pass it into the plant through a heat exchanger countercurrent to a waste nitrogen stream. This high pressure stream must be purified of carbon dioxide and water. Although this technique was employed in the earlier Linde–Frankl type gaseous oxygen plants, it is not at the present time a popular method of achieving the 'balancing' of regenerators.

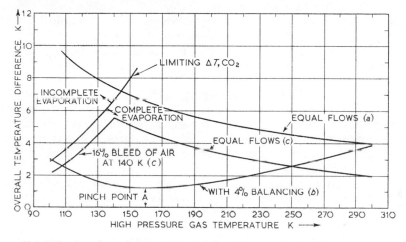

Figure 10.4 Balancing of regenerators. Air at 5·57 bar; WN$_2$ at 1·11 bar; A = null point = point of minimum temperature difference

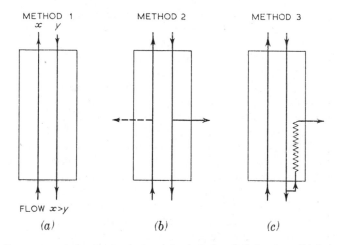

Figure 10.5 Regenerator balancing methods; (a) whole length balancing; (b) balancing by bleeding; (c) balancing by recirculation

A second system, shown in Figure 10.5 (b), uses a bleed of high or low pressure gas from a point approximately halfway down the regenerator, the temperature difference in these circumstances being shown in curve (c) of Figure 10.4. This method has the advantage that balancing is limited to the cold half of the regenerator, where it is needed, and it does not set any limit on the warm end temperature difference which can be achieved. If air is bled directly from a point near the middle of a regenerator in order to achieve these desired temperature distributions it will contain carbon dioxide. This is a distinct disadvantage and a number of methods have been devised to deal with this problem. One employs dual low temperature adsorbers (Section 10.2.4 (iii)) to remove the carbon dioxide from the side stream, the adsorbers being switched about once a week. Dual heat exchangers have also been used in which the carbon dioxide is frozen out, and which are periodically switched as they become blocked (Section 10.2.4 (vi)). In yet another system the side stream is warmed to room temperature, the carbon dioxide is removed chemically by caustic soda washing, and the carbon-dioxide-free air is then returned to the process against the side stream leaving the regenerators.

The third balancing method (shown in Figure 10.5 (c)) relies on recirculation of part of the feed or return gas, and is commonly known as the Trumpler pass method[17]. The overall effect is the same as that obtained by withdrawal of a side stream, but the bleed gas can be obtained uncontaminated by carbon dioxide. The disadvantage here is that expensive coils must be placed in the cold part of the regenerator.

An ingenious balancing scheme in which air and waste nitrogen are passed through a system of three regenerators is described by Baranov[18]. In principle, whilst two of the regenerators are receiving air or waste nitrogen the third replaces the duty of the Trumpler coil and receives air to a bleed point about half way up the regenerator and at the end of the cycle all the three streams, the air, the waste nitrogen and the Trumpler air are changed and passed through different vessels. A disadvantage of this system is, of course, that the three vessels are required instead of the usual two which also leads to extra valves and pipework.

It should be noted that a trace of carbon dioxide can escape from the cold end of a regenerator. This arises due to blowthrough of small quantities of solid carbon dioxide, and to a temperature rise of perhaps as much as 10 deg K of the air leaving the cold end as the air cycle proceeds. Account of this must be taken in design of the plant. One method of overcoming this difficulty is by using silica gel as the packing at or near the cold end of the regenerator, so that carbon dioxide is removed by adsorption rather than by deposition[9]. While, for the same operating conditions, this would lead to a larger regenerator, because the heat capacity per unit volume of gel is not as high as that of the conventional stone packing, the ability to remove acetylene from the process air is an important asset of this arrangement. It may, however, be difficult to ensure complete desorption of carbon dioxide and acetylene by the return stream. These disadvantages may be overcome by installing a pair of separate gel vessels downstream of the conventional regenerators, so that the gel can be reactivated at elevated temperatures, which is not possible with the arrangement described above.

(v) Reversing exchangers. A reversing exchanger is shown diagrammatically in Figure 10.6. It consists of two identical heat exchange channels which are thermally in contact. Automatically operated change-over valves at the warm end switch the air and return stream alternately between the two channels about every 15 min. At the cold end, check valves operate according to the gas pressure and direction of the force upon them. Further reversing or non-

reversing heat transfer channels in thermal contact can be added if these are needed.

So far only two types of heat exchangers have been devised which are suitable for large scale application as reversing exchangers: the plate fin type of heat exchanger[19,30] and the concentric tube type with internal finning as devised by Professor Collins during the Second World War[20].

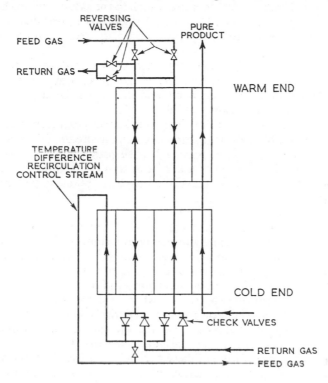

Figure 10.6 Reversing exchanger operation

The application of reversing exchangers to oxygen plants is described by Lobo and Skaperdas[21] and many of the practical points which arise in the operation are discussed.

As mentioned in Section 10.2.4 (iv), the operation of reversing heat exchangers for the removal of impurities from gas streams has been studied by Denton et al.[16]. The balancing system which is usually adopted in reversing exchangers is the recirculating Trumpler pass. The side-bleed method of balancing is used less frequently.

It should be pointed out that in calculating the limiting temperature differences account should be taken of the fact that the vapour pressure of carbon dioxide in the presence of an inert gas increases above the ideal value[23].

From the experiments carried out by Denton it becomes apparent that one of the main essentials of the reversing exchanger is the ability of the extended surface, which is used to reduce the exchanger size, to have a trapping action on the solid. This prevents carbon dioxide from depositing in lower temperature regions than that determined by the vapour pressure and from which complete evaporation cannot take place. This condition is particularly likely to occur when the mass transfer rate is less than the heat transfer rate, since under these circumstances super-saturation occurs in the condensing gas stream, and sub-saturation in the evaporating stream. Under the super-saturation conditions it is possible for solid to form in the bulk of the gas stream which does not attach to the sides of the exchangers at the correct temperature level. However this depends a great deal on whether nucleation particles are already present in the air stream, and the degree of turbulence which exists.

When blow-through does occur it often causes solid carbon dioxide to accumulate at the cold end valves, and it may be advisable to fit fine filters between the exit from the exchangers and the valves. Dual units should be fitted to ensure continuous operation.

The decision as to whether reversing exchangers or regenerators should be used to remove the carbon dioxide from an air stream will depend on the economics of any particular application; the problem has been dealt with generally by Ward[22]. Whereas a few years ago regenerators were in more common use, the major proportion of more recent plants have incorporated reversing exchangers.

(vi) Blocking exchangers. These are used to remove carbon dioxide and perform heat exchange primarily in two circumstances: firstly for balancing of regenerators, and secondly in cases where the reversing exchanger or regenerator technique, which is based on the pressure effects mentioned in Section 10.2.4 (iv), is no longer valid. To expand on this last point, in some circumstances a situation can arise[23] where instead of the saturation concentration being reduced according to Dalton's law as the pressure is raised, the exact opposite occurs, i.e. the saturation concentration of the impurity is increased as the total pressure is increased.

The warm end temperature of these exchangers is usually arranged to be a few degrees above the temperature at which carbon dioxide deposition commences. There are two methods of cleaning the blocking exchanger. The first method depends on warming the exchanger a few degrees along its entire length[24] which is usually sufficient to remove the solid carbon dioxide. The advantage of this method is that the refrigeration load is very small, since the cold required to return the exchanger to its operating condition is very small. In the second method, the exchanger is heated to a uniform temperature perhaps as much as 13–14 deg K above its warm end temperature, which imposes a much larger refrigeration load. The choice of method depends on the individual circumstances, particularly on the size of plant.

(vii) Low temperature filtration. This technique, which is the subject of a patent by the Union Carbide Corporation[60], is frequently adopted in medium and high pressure processes where deposition methods such as regenerators or reversing heat exchangers are unsuitable.

The principle of the method is to cool air at super-critical pressure to as low a temperature as possible without deposition of carbon dioxide on the exchanger surfaces. The air is then expanded to a lower pressure resulting in the formation of a two-phase mixture. The vapour part of this mixture is scrubbed by the liquid part, thus concentrating the carbon dioxide and any other high boiling impurities in the liquid phase. These impurities are removed from the liquid by filtration and/or adsorption.

A practical application of this method must take into account the following factors:

(a) In order to prevent deposition of carbon dioxide from the high pressure air, the temperature of the air and the exchanger surfaces must not fall below 118 K.

(b) Carbon dioxide must also be removed from low pressure air which has been passed through an expansion machine to provide refrigeration.

(c) The cycle must have sufficient flexibility to enable the heat exchange requirements to be met whilst still allowing the optimum percentage of the total air to be passed through the expansion machine(s). Of course, it is possible to operate a cycle without satisfying this condition, e.g. by controlling the air flow to the main exchanger to maintain the minimum exchanger surface temperature above 118 K[64]. In these cases there may be some loss in overall cycle efficiency.

One practical version catering from these factors is as follows. Air at super-critical pressure is cooled against low pressure nitrogen to a temperature between 188 K and 133 K prior to expansion to an intermediate pressure of about 20 bar. After expansion, the vapour part of the two-phase mixture is scrubbed by the liquid and is then condensed against low pressure nitrogen from the rectification system. The intermediate pressure is determined such that, in condensing the air, the temperature of the nitrogen is raised to an appropriate level to effect the required degree of cooling of the high pressure air whilst ensuring that deposition of carbon dioxide does not occur. The total liquid at the intermediate pressure passes through a filter and is then expanded to a lower pressure of about 6 bar, this being the normal operating pressure of the lower column in a double column air rectification system. A two-phase mixture is formed after expansion and the vapour part, together with low pressure air from the expansion machine(s) is scrubbed by the liquid before passing to the rectification system. The liquid, which now contains all the carbon dioxide and any other high boiling impurities from the total process air, passes through a second filter and an adsorber to remove the final traces of impurity before also passing to the rectification system.

10.2.5 Water Vapour Removal

(i) Adsorptive drying.

(a) General. As described in detail in the preceding sections, the removal of condensable impurities from air prior to liquefaction and distillation may be carried out in regenerators or reversing exchangers, both of which also fulfil the function of heat exchange. However, while this method of purification is suitable for comparatively low pressure streams, as, for example, in the Linde–Fränkl cycle, it becomes uneconomical for high pressure air. Air (and therefore power) losses would be large on switching from one regenerator to another. The proportions of the regenerator are fixed by the low-pressure return stream which could, therefore, lead to an extremely expensive pressure vessel. In the case of reversing exchangers, fabrication difficulties for high pressure duty have not yet been overcome. It is therefore necessary to purify the high-pressure air streams in some other way.

The two major condensable impurities to be removed are carbon dioxide and water vapour. The former may be removed by chemical means, such as caustic scrubbing, or by low temperature filtration and/or adsorption as described earlier while an efficient method of removing water vapour is by means of adsorption at ambient or near ambient temperatures.

Carbon dioxide and water vapour can be removed simultaneously in a single ambient temperature adsorption unit, molecular sieves being a particularly suitable adsorbent for this combined duty. Such units are in general use in such applications as natural gas purification prior to lique-faction and are sometimes employed on small air separation plants. On large high pressure air separation plants, however, it is more economical to remove carbon dioxide and water vapour separately.

Adsorption consists of the concentration of gas of vapour molecules at the surface of a solid as a result of the forces existing at the surface. The amount of material adsorbed (known as the adsorbate) is related to the nature and area of the surface available for adsorption, to the physical conditions—pressure, temperature, etc.—and to the characteristics of the adsorbate, particularly the boiling point and molecular volume.

Porous solids, with their high surface area per unit volume, are particu-larly useful as commercial adsorbents. The shape of the pores, as well as the porosity of the material, has an important bearing on adsorption.

The nature of the forces active at the solid surface is not fully understood. The type of adsorption undergone by the water molecules on the materials commonly used in adsorptive dryers is akin to condensation, in which the surface forces acting are relatively weak physical forces ('van der Waals' adsorption'), as opposed to 'chemisorption', in which the forces involved are greater and similar to those in chemical reactions. Adsorption decreases with increasing temperature and, as Le Chatelier's principle indicates, it takes place with the evolution of heat. The amount of heat evolved in van der Waals' adsorption is of the order of the heat of condensation of the adsorbate. Several theories have been suggested to account for adsorption phenomena and these are considered in some detail by Mantell[25].

It is desirable for the removal of moisture from the process air to be as complete as possible in air separation plants, since the presence of ice (or any solid impurity) reduces the efficiency of the low temperature equipment and ultimately leads to blockages. Tonnage oxygen plants are normally required to operate continuously for at least a year before being shut down for routine maintenance, and generally it has been found that a moisture content of 0·002 mg of water per litre of air entering the low temperature sections of the plant (i.e. a dew-point of 203 K at 1 bar pressure) is acceptable.

With regard to the condition of the air entering the dryer, the saturated vapour pressure of water increases rapidly with temperature and at the same time the adsorptive capacity of the more conventional adsorbents decreases significantly with temperature. This gives an incentive to consider other systems, for example the use of molecular sieves, which are more expensive than conventional adsorbents, but whose adsorption characteristics are less affected by temperature; alternatively some means of reducing the load on the adsorptive dryers may be installed upstream, for example a cooler using external refrigeration. The various systems will require close investigation and comparison before detailed design of the adsorptive dryer is carried out.

(b) *Adsorbents.* Several adsorbents are capable of removing water vapour to the required degree, the four adsorbents finding widest application in the oxygen industry being silica gel, 'Sorbeads' (Product of Mobil Oil Co. Ltd.), activated alumina and molecular sieves. Whichever adsorbent is employed, it is good practice to reduce to a minimum the oil and water in the form of fine droplets in the air entering the dryer.

Comprehensive data and information on particular applications can be obtained from the manufacturers, but the following general discussion will serve as a guide.

Silica gel, which is generally used in granular form on oxygen plants, has a high adsorptive capacity (i.e. will adsorb a large amount of water per unit weight of dry adsorbent), but will not give such complete removal of moisture as either activated alumina or molecular sieves, the dew-point of the air leaving a silica gel dryer being generally appreciably higher than when either of these adsorbents is employed. A further disadvantage of silica gel in high pressure drying applications is its comparatively low mechanical strength which results in powdering under certain conditions, particularly in the presence of water droplets. The main applications of silica gel, therefore, are where a high adsorptive capacity is required, but where an exceptionally low dew-point is not necessary.

Sorbeads, which consist of siliceous material in the form of small beads, have very similar adsorptive properties to silica gel, but will give a significantly lower dew-point and also have the advantage that they are more resistant to attrition by agitation. While Sorbeads have the same tendency as silica gel to shatter when in contact with water droplets, the manufacturers have developed a grade with high shatter resistance suitable for use at the inlet to the dryer, where contact with water droplets is most likely.

Activated alumina has significantly lower adsorptive capacity than silica gel or Sorbeads, but will give a dew-point at least as low as that obtained using Sorbeads. As explained previously, it is essential to have as complete removal as possible of condensable impurities, and therefore alumina and Sorbeads are more generally used than granular silica gel in air separation plant dryers. Alumina is mechanically strong, particularly in pelleted form, and so does not give rise to dust formation to the same extent as granular silica gel.

Molecular sieves are different from conventional adsorbents in that their pore sizes are many times smaller and in fact are of molecular dimensions. This results in a capacity for selective adsorption, some molecules being adsorbed while others are excluded. They are finding increasingly wide application, and are used, for example, for drying refinery off-gases[26] the smaller water molecule (molecular diameter 2·76Å) being adsorbed while the larger hydrocarbon molecules are rejected. A comprehensive review of available information on molecular sieves has been made by Hersh[27]. More recently, Collins[61], Burnett and Turnbull[62] and Warrior and Wood[63] have described in detail some of the many industrial applications of molecular sieves. The molecular sieves commercially available are synthetic alkali metal aluminosilicates, typical examples suitable for gas drying being Linde molecular sieves 3A, 4A and 5A (these are manufactured by the Linde Company Division of Union Carbide Corporation), which have pore openings of 3, 4 and 5Å respectively. The particular advantage claimed for the appropriate molecular sieves for high pressure air drying applications are: (i) their ability to give extremely low dew-points; (ii) the slight effect of temperature on adsorptive capacity, as compared to conventional adsorbents; (iii) good resistance to attrition and ability to withstand fast pressurizing and depressurizing; (iv) good adsorptive capacity for moisture from air with a low relative humidity; and (v) the slight effect of oil contamination on performance.

At present, molecular sieves are considerably more expensive than conventional adsorbents, but an arrangement which has been used with success is to remove the bulk of the moisture with a conventional adsorbent backed up by the appropriate molecular sieve to give a low dew-point.

(c) *Dynamic adsorption.* The adsorption data generally presented by the manufacturers and in the literature give the equilibrium weight of water adsorbed per unit weight of adsorbent as a function of the partial pressure of water at a given temperature, i.e. the isotherm. Such data are based on measurements under static conditions; however in an actual dryer, account must be taken of the dynamic state which exists.

From the air-flow rate, water content of the air entering and leaving the dryer, adsorptive capacity of the bed and change-over time, a bed volume can be calculated. In carrying out this calculation it is assumed that the adsorptive capacity of the bed is that associated with the initial water content of the air, but the final water content of the air is usually a very small fraction of the initial content and a finite length of the bed is required to bring the air to this condition. This length in which mass transfer of water from the air to the bed occurs has been termed the mass transfer zone (M.T.Z.). The remainder of the bed is a water storage capacity and contains the equilibrium amount of water associated with the water in the inlet air.

The M.T.Z. concept in adsorber design has in recent years become increasingly used. The length of the M.T.Z. depends on several factors[27] including adsorbent, particle size, air velocity, fluid properties, the initial water content, temperature and pressure of the air, residual moisture content of the reactivated bed and the previous history of the system. The shape of the water distribution curve in the M.T.Z. is such that the amount of water it contains can be obtained approximately by halving the volume of the mass transfer zone and considering it to contain the equilibrium amount of water adsorbed associated with the inlet air conditions. Thus to determine the volume of bed required for a given duty, the volume of the bed required to give the necessary water storage capacity should be calculated and to that should be added a volume whose length is equal to approximately half the length of the mass transfer zone.

(d) *Reactivation.* As mentioned previously, the amount of adsorption decreases with increasing temperature, and accordingly by raising the temperature sufficiently all the adsorbed moisture will eventually be driven from the adsorbent, which is thus reactivated. Continuous running may be ensured by installing a pair of dryers so designed that one can be reactivated before the adsorptive capacity of the other is exceeded. Care must be taken not to allow the adsorbent to be overheated, otherwise its structure may be damaged. On the other hand, since maximum moisture removal is required in air separation plants, and since the adsorption efficiency (defined as adsorbate removed by dryer/adsorbate entering dryer) will clearly be improved by the complete absence of adsorbed moisture when commencing the drying period, it is essential to ensure thorough reactivation.

Reactivation may be carried out in several different ways, but on air separation plants there is generally a particularly convenient method. The waste gas from the rectification column consists of nitrogen containing a low percentage of oxygen, and is completely moisture-free. A bleed from this stream passes through a heater and then through the adsorbent bed to waste. Temperatures up to 300°C are normally used for alumina and molecular sieves, and appreciably lower temperatures for silica gel and Sorbeads. It may be necessary, depending on the air separation cycle employed, to boost the bleed steam pressure by means of a blower upstream of the reactivation heater. The reactivation has will inevitably cool to a certain extent on its passage through the dryer. That part of the adsorbent bed nearest the reactivation gas inlet will reach the highest temperature, and will receive completely dry gas. It will therefore be the most completely reactivated part of the bed and for this reason the reactivation gas flow is normally in the reverse direction to the wet gas flow, thus ensuring the minimum dew-point. The wet gas flow is generally downwards, and the flow of reactivation gas is upwards through the bed. There will be a tendency for the upward-flowing gas to cause the bed to lift, particularly near the top, which would lead to excessive attrition of the adsorbent. This was investigated by Ledoux[28], who found that there was a certain maximum mass velocity, G, of the gas for a given adsorbent, below which no granular movement would take place. For the air flowing upward at atmospheric pressure he derived the equation

$$\frac{G^2}{d_g.d_a.D.g} = 0.0167 \tag{10.5}$$

where d_g is the gas density, d_a the adsorbent bulk density, D the average particle diameter, g the acceleration of gravity, and all symbols are in SI units.

Since the screen analysis and arrangement in the dryer of two batches will never be identical, G will vary and a design figure should be taken conservatively lower. Thus the maximum reactivation gas flow is fixed. However, the amount of heat required for reactivation is also fixed, by the dimensions and form of the dryer. Therefore, if the reactivating gas stream passing through the bed were the only source of heat, the situation might arise that there was insufficient time to reactivate one dryer before it was necessary to start reactivating the other. Other methods of providing heat to the dryer are employed, among them electric jacket heating, passing hot fluid through an annular space around the dryer, or through coils inside it. More recently, internally insulated vessels have been finding wide application. The use of internal insulation results in a much smaller quantity of heat being necessary for reactivation of adsorbers since only the bed is heated, not the vessel itself. It is essential, though, to pass gas through the bed in order to remove the moisture.

(e) *Cooling.* When the bed has reached a sufficiently high average temperature to ensure that the required degree of reactivation is obtained, it is necessary to cool the bed down before permitting the wet gas to flow through it once more. There are three reasons for this: (i) if the wet gas were to cool the drier it would itself be heated before entering the heat exchange section of the air separation plant, and thereby lead to a temporary increase in the refrigeration load of the plant; (ii) the adsorptive efficiency of the bed is reduced at high temperatures, and the gas would therefore still have an appreciable moisture content on leaving; (iii) although the wet gas could be blown to waste after cooling the dryer, it is at high pressure, and this would represent a power loss in the cycle.

Cooling is carried out in the obvious way, by turning off the heat supply, and allowing the reactivating gas stream to blow through the bed until the temperature of the gas leaving the dryer is sufficiently low to enable efficient drying to be carried out once more. The vessel is then isolated until required, in order to prevent atmospheric moisture entering.

(*f*) *Pressurizing and depressurizing*. Although some attrition may be caused by lifting the bed as a result of excessive reactivation gas flow, a far more frequent cause is unnecessary haste when switching the wet gas stream from one dryer to the other.

When pressurizing, excessive agitation of the adsorbent particles may be caused by allowing the high pressure gas to enter too quickly; when depressurizing, high pressure gas in the pores of the adsorbent is not able to escape as quickly as gas in the spaces between two particles, and if the dryer is depressurized too quickly a differential pressure will build up between the gas inside the pores and that outside which may cause the adsorbent particles to break up. A common way of obtaining close control when switching dryers is to include small pressurizing and depressurizing valves in the circuit.

(*g*) *Pressure drop*. It is necessary to be able to calculate the pressure drop through the dryer battery of both the wet high pressure gas and the low pressure reactivation gas. The more important of these is that of the reactivation gas, since the absolute pressure is only slightly above atmospheric. The pressure of the waste gas stream has a significant effect on the overall power consumption of the plant, and therefore if no blower is used, the pressure drop of this stream should be kept to a minimum, i.e. the permissible pressure drop through the dryer battery is limited.

The pressure drop through the pipework and valves can be readily calculated, but the calculation of the pressure drop through the packed bed is rather more complex. Chilton and Colburn[29] derived the following expressions from which the pressure drop for flow through uniform granular solid particles may be calculated:

(i) viscous region:

$$\Delta p = \frac{0.0171 \eta L V_0 A_f}{D_p^2} \qquad (10.6)$$

(ii) turbulent region:

$$\Delta p = \frac{7.6 \times 10^{-4} \eta^{0.15} L \rho^{0.85} V_0^{1.85} A_f}{D_p^{1.15}} \qquad (10.7)$$

where Δp = pressure drop (bar);
η = viscosity of fluid (Ns/m^2);
L = bed length (m);

ρ = density of fluid (kg/m^3);
V_0 = superficial fluid velocity (m per sec.);
A_f = wall-effect factor (dimensionless);
D_p = nominal particle diameter (m).

The viscous region is defined as that region where

$$N_{Re} < 40.$$

N_{Re} is a modified Reynolds number, calculated from

$$N_{Re} = \frac{D_p V_0 \rho}{\eta} \qquad (10.8)$$

When calculating the reactivation gas pressure drop, for a given flow rate the highest value will be obtained when the gas is hottest and at its lowest pressure. In fact, the reactivation gas will be hottest when entering the dryer and at its lowest pressure when leaving, and it is therefore necessary to esimate an average gas condition in the bed for this calculation.

The wet gas pressure drop does not present this difficulty, since although heat is evolved by the adsorption of water vapour as the wet gas passes through the bed, the amount of water vapour in high pressure air is relatively small at approximately ambient temperature, and therefore the heat liberated has a negligible effect on the air stream temperature, which can be considered constant throughout the length of the bed.

(h) *Precautions.* Apart from the usual precautions necessary when using high pressure equipment, certain other protective measures are required in a dryer battery, particularly with respect to the adsorbent.

Some oil vapour or mist will be carried over from the high pressure compressor by the air (see Section 10.2.3). It is essential that this should be prevented from reaching the dryer because it would then deposit on the adsorbent, which would lose its efficiency with respect to water vapour removal. On reactivation some of the oil would be driven off, but some would decompose, leaving a carbon deposit on the adsorbent. The oil contamination would move further down the bed until finally the air leaving the dryer would still contain appreciable quantities of water vapour.

An efficient after-cooler and separator on the compressor, backed up by an efficient prefilter, e.g. an alumina bed, regularly inspected, should be adequate to prevent oil contamination of the adsorbent. These items also serve to prevent liquid droplets from entering the dryer and damaging the adsorbent, leading to dust formation. Another source of dust formation is mal-operation, for example excessively fast depressurization. Since it is not economically possible to prevent mal-operation, it is necessary to guard against dust, as this may lead to damaged valve seats, and may also serve as a nucleus for the accumulation of dangerous impurities in oxygen-rich sections of the cycle. Dust filters are discussed in Section 10.2.2 (iii). A typical lay-out of a dryer battery and associated equipment is shown in Figure 10.7. Certain protective measures are necessary when reactivating the adsorbent. The temperature of the reactivating gas must not be allowed to exceed the specified maximum reactivation temperature of the adsorbent in use, and therefore the heating device should be fitted with a conventional thermostatic control based on the temperature of the reactivation gas entering the dryer. In addition, the actual heating device must itself be fitted with a protective device to prevent it becoming overheated if, for any reason, the reactivation gas supply should be cut off.

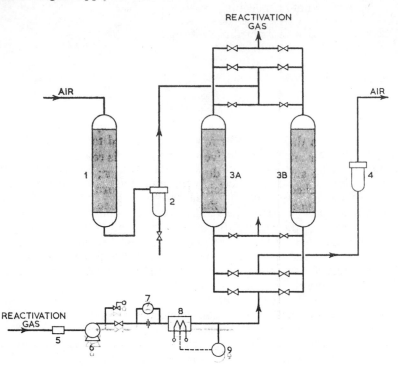

Figure 10.7 Diagrammatic layout of adsorptive dryer battery: 1, oil vapour trap; 2, moisture separator; 3A and B, dryer vessels; 4, dust filter; 5, filter; 6, reactivation blower; 7, flowmeter; 8, reactivation heater; 9, heater control

(*j*) *Design approach.* Several design methods are in use, but one approach is as follows:

(i) Fix the cycle time and hence the moisture to be removed in one dryer. Calculate the volume of adsorbent required, based on the static adsorptive capacity.

(ii) Select a length to diameter ratio slightly lower than that which would give the most economic vessel for the operating pressure involved, and calculate the bed dimensions.

(iii) Determine the length of the M.T.Z. in the above conditions, and make a suitable increase to the bed length in order to cover this and any design margin required.

(iv) Repeat steps (ii) and (iii) until the proportions finally obtained result in the cheapest vessel.

(v) Determine, bearing in mind any limitations on reactivation gas flow and pressure drop, whether it is possible to carry out heating, cooling, pressurizing and depressurizing in the time available.

(vi) If it is found that this is not possible due to limitations on the reactivation gas flow, it will then be necessary to repeat the calculation, assuming a lower length to diameter ratio for the adsorbent bed, and /or considering the economics of an additional means of supplying heat for reactivation. (It may be more economical to instal an additional source of heat for reactivation than to increase the vessel diameter to allow a greater reactivation gas flow.)

(vii) In order to obtain the optimum design of dryer battery, the above calculations must be repeated for a range of cycle times, and the capital costs balanced against the running costs (e.g. power required for reactivation, air losses, etc.).

(ii) Refrigeration drying. This refers to the removal of water vapour by condensation on a cold surface in the form of liquid or as ice. Two forms of this principle are employed. In the first, the gas is not cooled below 0°C, and only liquid water is formed which is drained continuously from the system through a separator. In the second form, ice is permitted to accumulate in the exchanger until an excessive pressure drop is reached and then the flows are switched to a duplicate exchanger; ice is removed from the blocked unit by raising the temperature above 0°C.

The main use of the first method is to reduce the load on an adsorptive drying battery. This arrangement has two advantages; firstly, the load on the adsorbent is reduced as a result of water vapour being removed by condensation in the cooler, and secondly, the capacity of the adsorbent is slightly increased because of the lower temperature. For example, by cooling the air from 20°C to 4°C, the same quantity of alumina will dry approximately three times the volume of air at 200 bar. Each case must be considered on its merits, but installation of the precooler may lead to appreciable overall economies.

In this form of refrigeration dryer, operating conditions should be such that no ice is formed since no duplicate exchanger is usually available. In order to prevent ice formation, the cold end temperature of the coolant must be close to 0°C, otherwise water vapour condensing on the heat transfer surface may freeze although the bulk temperature of the air is above 0°C. In addition condensate must be able to drain away quickly and freely.

Adsorptive dryers are not usually applied to the drying of low pressure gases because of their high moisture content and hence large dryer bed volume. The method of refrigeration drying in which ice is allowed to form in duplicate exchangers is often a cheaper alternative. Figure 10.8 shows diagrammatically the method of operation of a system of this type. It consists of two plate-fin type exchangers, A and B, in parallel, which are operated alternately. Exchanger A is, say, in circuit and B is out of circuit. A will continue in circuit until the pressure drop across the feed gas passage is excessive, exchanger B meanwhile is being warmed up by electric surface heaters so that all the ice deposit is melted and allowed to run to the water drain pot. After the ice deposit has been removed from exchanger B a small cold stream is permitted to flow through the coolant passages to re-cool the unit. When the pressure drop across the feed gas passage of exchanger A is excessive then the unit is taken out of circuit and B is brought into operation.

The water content of the process feed gas is such that the initial deposition is as liquid water, and in order to permit a reasonable length of switching time (usually about 12 hours), the exchangers must be designed so that the liquid water deposit can drain down the heat exchange channels into the water drain pots. To effect this the exchangers must be mounted vertically with the warm end nearest the ground and the feed gas velocity must be low enough to allow the water to drain down. The velocity parameter is governed by the kinetic energy function ρV^2 on which entrainment depends, which will be a maximum at the warm end of the unit.

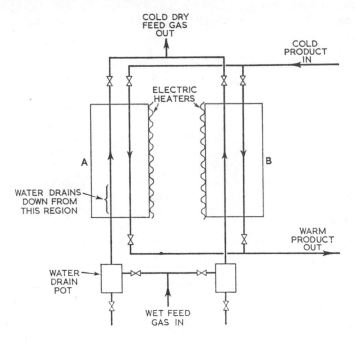

Figure 10.8 Operation of refrigeration dryer

Various forms of extended surface are manufactured for plate-fin exchangers but in order to allow drainage only plain fins should be used. If the design permits the liquid water to drain from the units, the blocking rate is governed by the rate of ice deposition at 0°C where the deposition is a maximum.

The rate of deposition of ice can be calculated from the equation below:[16]

$$m = \frac{M_{\text{water}}}{M_{\text{air}}} \cdot \frac{G(S_t)}{(T_s^2/\Delta t . 5300) - 1} \cdot \frac{P_s . Z}{P . E} \tag{10.9}$$

where m = deposition rate, kg/s.m³ of exchanger (including metal)

M_{water} = molecular weight of water

M_{air} = molecular weight of air

G = gas flow rate, kg/s.m² of free cross-section

P_s = vapour pressure of water at deposition temperature, bar

P = total pressure of feed air, bar

T_s = temperature of deposition surface, K

Δt = temperature difference between air and cold surface, °K

(St) = Stanton number, $h/\rho v C_p$, for heat transfer conditions at temperature of deposition

h = heat transfer coefficient, w/m²°K

ρ = density, kg/m^3
v = velocity, m/s
C_p = specific heat, J/kg°K
Z = surface area/unit volume, m^2/m^3 (including metal)
E = voidage of exchanger, i.e. free volume/(free volume + metal volume)

The system will probably be followed by a further heat exchanger and to ensure that ice does not block this unit it is advisable to maintain the temperature of the exit air at about 198 K and to fit an ice filter to remove any fine ice particles which may be entrained.

(iii) Glycol process. An interesting process combines water removal with cooling of the compressed gas from ambient temperature to about 233 K. This process[31] has found limited practical application in air separation. The compressed gas is scrubbed with a cold solution of ethylene glycol which both cools the air and reduces its water-vapour content. A 60/40 glycol/water mixture (by volume) has a freezing point of 224 K and since the glycol, being miscible with water, reduces the partial pressure of water vapour well below saturation, the cooled air is of less than 100 per cent relative humidity.

Referring to Figure 10.9 the compressed air flowing upwards in scrubber A is cooled and dried by the descending stream of glycol mixture. The glycol mixture then flows to scrubber B where it is re-cooled in countercurrent with

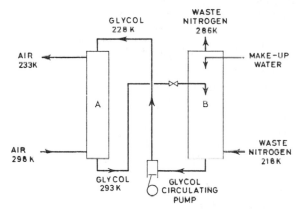

Figure 10.9 Glycol process

cold waste nitrogen from the air separation unit. The circuit is completed by a pump which returns the solution to scrubber A. Cooling of the glycol mixture may be augmented by a conventional refrigeration cooler (not shown). The nitrogen, being dry, vaporizes part of the water and this evaporation augments the cooling. The water removed as vapour by waste nitrogen considerably exceeds that precipitated from high pressure air in scrubber A. The make-up of distilled water can be used to scrub out the small quantity of glycol vapour present in the nitrogen and minimize glycol loss. This loss is, however, very small because of the low vapour pressure of the glycol.

For an air pressure of 20 bar, for example, the water vapour content of the cooled air corresponds to a dew-point of about 213 K at atmospheric pressure. If the air is further cooled by a heat exchanger system this dew-point is not sufficiently low to avoid blockage after continuous operation for an extended period and a single low temperature adsorber is advisable directly downstream of the scrubber A.

The overall action is thus drying of the compressed air and its heat exchange with cold waste nitrogen in a continuous process. As the glycol mixture is the heat exchange medium there are no heat exchange surfaces on which ice can deposit and the changeover fluctuations inherent in adsorptive dryers and refrigeration dryers are avoided. Owing to the capital cost of scrubber A and the power for pumping the glycol mixture, the economics of glycol scrubbing relative to refrigeration dryers show up rather better when pre-cooling medium or low pressure gases.

(iv) Regenerators. The mode of operation of regenerators and their use for the removal of carbon dioxide has been described in Section 10.2.4 (iv). The air feed to an air separation unit is usually saturated with water at about 293 K depending on cooling water temperature. As in the case of carbon dioxide, the complete removal by the cold return stream of water deposited on the packing from the feed gas depends on the pressure effect. In the case of water, however, the conditions of temperature difference which must be observed are very much less stringent and are given in Figure 10.10 for a reversing exchanger for air at 5·57 bar and waste nitrogen at 1·11 bar. These conditions apply approximately for a regenerator and are such that with the pressures and temperature differences normally employed no special precautions are required to ensure removal of the water from regenerators in air separation plants.

In arranging the piping to the warm end of the regenerator care has to be taken to avoid any cyclone effect due to the position of the air feed pipe. Often water droplets are entrained in the feed and will be thrown to the circumference of the vessel. This water can accumulate as ice in the regenerator and lead to blockage.

On large regenerators it is advisable to equalize the pressures before change-over to reduce air losses. In actual operation, directly after change-over, large quantities of water are physically blown off the packing as liquid drops which represents a loss of cold to the system since the latent heat of water was transferred to the packing during the air cycle.

The most important effect of water is on the regenerator volume required for a given duty. The deposition of water alters the behaviour of the regenerator and extra length must be added to allow for this. Approximate methods of calculating this extra length are given by Ward[15].

(v) Reversing exchangers. The principle of operation and the use of reversing exchangers to remove carbon dioxide are described in Section 10.2.4 (v). The removal of water vapour from air by reversing heat exchangers is readily achieved under the operating conditions normally encountered. The conditions of temperature difference which must not be exceeded are given in Figure 10.10 for equal air and cleaning gas flows. It should be noted that this limiting difference is reduced as the pressure ratio is reduced so that for very

low pressure processes, say below about 2 bar, careful consideration should be given to the process conditions. As in the regenerators, at change-over the air under pressure is released to atmosphere and considerable quantities of water are blown out of the exchanger as liquid, which represents a cold loss to the system equivalent to the latent heat of the water lost.

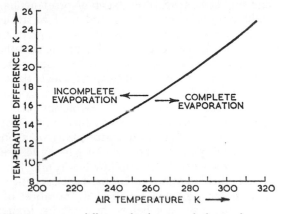

Figure 10.10 Limiting temperature difference for the removal of water from reversing exchangers. Air pressure 5·57 bar; waste nitrogen pressure 1·11 bar

It is essential to their successful operation that no oil is entrained with the air and an oil knock-out pot followed by an alumina bed may be necessary. Due to the periodic pressure changes, extra mechanical strength must be incorporated in the design to avoid fatigue failure. This is particularly important with materials such as aluminium. It is not usual to use reversing exchangers of the plane fin type over about 20 bar pressure.

10.2.6 Removal of Hydrocarbons, in particular, Acetylene

A résumé of the factors in the safe operation of air separation units has been given by Gardner[32]. Among the most important trace impurities in the atmosphere which are potential sources of danger are hydrocarbons, in particular acetylene. The hydrocarbons usually found are methane, ethylene, ethane, acetylene and propane. At the low temperatures of an oxygen plant these impurities tend to accumulate over a period of time where one or more of the main constituents are evaporated, in particular in the oxygen evaporator. The accumulation of hydrocarbons in such an oxygen-rich medium leads to a particularly hazardous situation. Several serious explosions in air separation plant have been at least in part attributable to accumulation of trace hydrocarbons, particularly acetylene[65,66,67,68].

Small concentrations of the simpler hydrocarbons such as methane, ethane, and ethylene (but excluding acetylene) which have relatively low boiling points, generally do not represent any significant hazard since they are appreciably soluble in liquid oxygen and their equilibrium constant at liquid oxygen temperature is high enough to prevent a dangerous concentration building up in the oxygen evaporator in a normal operating period between plant defrosting.

Generally a *homogeneous solution* containing less than 2 per cent hydrocarbons by weight in liquid oxygen cannot be detonated. However, if a heterogeneous system is formed, dangerous local concentration of hydrocarbons can be present although the overall concentration may be well below the danger limit.

Acetylenics and higher hydrocarbons, such as propane, have low vapour pressures at liquid oxygen temperatures and tend to accumulate. When combined with a low solubility, as in the case of acetylene, precipitation of the hydrocarbons as a solid can occur. It is for this reason that acetylene in particular is one of the most dangerous of hydrocarbon contaminants. The concentration of acetylene in the air varies quite widely depending on location and may vary from 0·2 to about 0·02 v.p.m. If it is assumed that the oxygen product from a conventional double-column plant is as gas only and the acetylene in the air feed is 0·1 v.p.m. then after a period of 6 h the concentration in the liquid oxygen evaporator of usualy proportions would be 8·3 v.p.m. The solubility limit is about 8·3 v.p.m. at 94 K and hence part of the acetylene would start to be precipitated as solid. (This also assumes that none of the acetylene is removed by the heat exchange system.) Solid acetylene can also be precipitated by local evaporation of oxygen, even though the overall concentration is below the solubility limit. Good circulation of liquid oxygen through the evaporator is essential to prevent this local concentration. In plants in which the oxygen is removed as liquid from the evaporator most of the impurities are continuously removed with this liquid and an inherently safer system is obtained, since build-up of impurities is much less likely.

Whether the plant is producing gas or liquid, very careful precautions must be taken to reduce acetylene to a very low concentration in the liquid oxygen in the evaporator. This may be carried out by adsorbing the acetylene and hydrocarbons on silica gel at low temperatures. Usually about 76–95 kg of gel are required per standard m^3/s of air when adsorbing from the liquid phase[33] using dual units reactivated about every four to seven days. It is sometimes advisable to circulate liquid oxygen from the evaporator continuously through a silica gel adsorber as an added safety precaution.

A method has been described[34] for the removal of acetylene and hydrocarbons by means of catalytic oxidation at about 200°C before the air enters the low temperature part of the plant. The application of this step when combined with low temperature adsorption would have the advantage that any sharp rises in hydrocarbons in the incoming air would be removed, giving the plant added protection. The capital cost and pressure drop of the catalyst units is not insignificant and should be carefully considered. Unless the catalyst units can be relied upon to remove hydrocarbons consistently over many years of operation to a very low level of concentration this method cannot be used without some other means of protection.

In industrial locations in which oxygen plants are installed, the hydrocarbon concentration in the air can vary over wide ranges and continuous monitoring of the hydrocarbons in the air feed is an added safety precaution. The instrument must be able to measure the concentrations of dangerous hydrocarbons, such as acetylene, down to a level of 0·01 v.p.m.; a chromatographic unit followed by a flame ionization detector is normally used. The use of this technique has been described by Parks and Hinkle[35].

10.2.7 Nitrogen Purification

Substantial quantities of oxygen-free nitrogen are required for many processes, e.g. ammonia synthesis, and as a blanketing gas. The nitrogen derived
from an air separation plant will usually contain at least 20 v.p.m. of oxygen
plus a substantially greater quantity of argon, depending on circumstances.
To purify the nitrogen further, the oxygen may be reacted with an excess of
hydrogen over a catalyst. Continuous analysis of the oxygen to the catalyst
bed is necessary and can be linked to the hydrogen flow to give an excess
of about $\frac{1}{2}$ per cent or less of hydrogen in the nitrogen product. This excess
hydrogen in the nitrogen is an advantage in some steel processes, since a
better surface finish to the product is obtained. The space velocity and
operating temperature of the unit will depend on such factors as oxygen
concentration of the feed, operating pressure and whether the feed is wet or
dry. At low oxygen concentrations the space velocity may be as high as
5000 reciprocal hours whereas, at high oxygen concentrations up to a
maximum of about 3 per cent, the space velocity will be smaller and the
operating temperature may rise to as much as 500°C. The catalyst is sensitive
to free water and the feed, if saturated, should be heated slightly to give an
unsaturated condition. The catalyst is also sensitive to sulphur compounds
and oil. If an oil-lubricated compressor is employed a knock-out pot filled
with alumina is advisable. The water vapour formed in the reaction can be
removed by a bed of alumina pellets or molecular sieve if a very low dew-point
is necessary.

If hydrogen-free nitrogen is required, the oxygen can be removed by
reaction with a bed substantially consisting of manganous oxide. A mixture
of higher oxides is obtained, and the bed can be regenerated by heating.

10.3 Ammonia Synthesis Gas Production

10.3.1 General

Up until about 1963 the feed gases for most plants producing ammonia
synthesis gas could be divided broadly into two categories: coke oven
gases containing 50–60 per cent hydrogen, and gases containing 85–95 per
cent hydrogen, obtained, for example, by partial oxidation of heavy fuel oils.

A typical average composition of the resulting coke oven gas after some
initial purification is given in Table 10.1. In addition, traces of carbonyl
sulphide, carbon disulphide, hydrogen cyanide and oxides of nitrogen are
usually present.

Gases containing 85–95 per cent hydrogen are obtained from such
sources as partial oxidation of heavy fuel oils, steam hydrocarbon reformers,
refinery gases and steam-iron processes, with subsequent reduction of high
carbon monoxide contents by shift conversion and bulk removal of carbon
dioxide by absorption in water or alkaline solutions. A typical composition
of the resulting purified converter gas is given in Table 10.1. In addition
traces of hydrogen sulphide, oxygen, unsaturated hydrocarbons, carbonyl
sulphide, carbon disulphide, hydrogen cyanide and oxides of nitrogen may be
present depending upon the source of gas.

Table 10.1 TYPICAL COMPOSITION OF COKE OVEN AND CONVERTER GASES

Gas	Crude coke oven gas (% by volume)	Purified converter gas (% by volume)
Hydrogen	54·0	91·8
Nitrogen	6·0	0·6
Carbon monoxide	7·0	6·0
Carbon dioxide	3·0	0·2
Methane	26·0	0·4
Argon	—	1·0
Ethane	2·5	—
Other hydrocarbons	1·2	—
Oxygen	0·3	—
Hydrogen sulphide	0·05–0·09 kg/m³	—

Both the above types of gas are generally subjected to low temperature nitrogen wash (see Section 10.3.4) in order to produce pure hydrogen–nitrogen mixtures for ammonia synthesis. Many such plants are currently in operation and new plants of this type are still being built. Since about 1963, however, there has been a general move away from the nitrogen wash approach, particularly for larger plants. The bulk of the ammonia now produced derives from steam reforming of a natural gas or light naphtha feedstock. A world survey of ammonia plants either in operation or under construction up to June, 1969, has been carried out by Cermak[36]. The sources of feed gas are listed and an analysis of plant capacities is presented.

A typical process for the production of ammonia synthesis gas from a natural gas or vaporized light naphtha feed incorporates the following main steps[69,70].

(a) Complete removal of sulphur compounds which will poison both the nickel-loaded reforming catalyst and the zinc-loaded low temperature shift catalyst used in subsequent stages of the process[71].

(b) Two-stage steam reforming in which hydrocarbons are reacted with steam over a catalyst to form carbon monoxide and hydrogen. Partial conversion of the carbon monoxide and steam into carbon dioxide and hydrogen also takes place.

(c) Two stages of shift conversion in which the reaction between carbon monoxide and steam to form carbon dioxide and hydrogen is taken further towards completion.

(d) Carbon dioxide removal, typically by a monoethanolamine unit or a steam regenerated Vetrocoke process.

(e) Methanation for final removal of small amounts of carbon oxides.

Some of the purification techniques which may be used in these and other processes are described below.

10.3.2 Carbon Dioxide and Hydrogen Sulphide Removal

Several processes for the removal of carbon dioxide and hydrogen sulphide from gas mixtures have a wide industrial application though not all of these are suitable for purification of ammonia synthesis gases. A comprehensive evaluation of these and many other gas purification processes has been presented[37].

Aqueous ammonia solutions are used to some extent for removal of carbon dioxide and hydrogen sulphide from ammonia synthesis gases. When gases containing hydrogen sulphide, ammonia and carbon dioxide are contacted with water, the ammonia and hydrogen sulphide are absorbed more rapidly than the carbon dioxide, the first two being controlled mainly by gas film resistance while the latter is more dependent upon the liquid film resistance. The operating conditions of the process can be so chosen that either hydrogen sulphide or carbon dioxide is preferentially absorbed. With respect to purification of ammonia synthesis gas, the process is most economical for treating partially desulphurized coke oven gases containing about 3 per cent carbon dioxide. Outlet concentrations of about 150 v.p.m. carbon dioxide are obtained and the process is usually followed by caustic scrubbing for final purification. The main disadvantages of this type of process are corrosion problems and incomplete recovery of hydrogen sulphide.

Alkali carbonate solutions may be used for hydrogen sulphide and carbon dioxide removal, sodium and potassium carbonate being both inexpensive and readily available. Sodium carbonate containing free hydroxyl ions is often used for final carbon dioxide removal from hydrogen following, for example, a water wash process. There are several variations of the alkali carbonate process, one incorporating vacuum regeneration[38,39] which enables recovery of hydrogen sulphide in a concentrated form.

The Ferrox process for removal of hydrogen sulphide, which employs a sodium carbonate solution containing suspended iron oxide, will give a final hydrogen sulphide content of about 20 v.p.m. and recovery of sulphur in the form of a slurry. The sodium carbonate required can be obtained from a caustic scrubbing system for final carbon dioxide removal. An added advantage of this process is simultaneous removal of hydrogen cyanide.

The Giammarco–Vetrocoke process for removal and recovery of carbon dioxide uses an alkali carbonate solution which is activated by organic or inorganic additives, e.g. arsenious oxide. It is possible to obtain low outlet concentrations of carbon dioxide with this process though normally it is followed by a caustic scrubbing system for final purification. Steam regeneration enables recovery of the carbon dioxide but air regeneration is usually employed where recovery is not required as this both reduces steam consumption and gives lower final carbon dioxide concentrations.

The hot potassium carbonate process may be used for bulk carbon dioxide removal where high purity is not required or where some other process can be used for final purification. The process is most economical, however, for higher carbon dioxide concentrations than are being considered here. A study of the economics of several schemes for removing carbon dioxide from an ammonia synthesis gas has been presented by Mullowney[40], including the hot potassium carbonate process combined with final purification.

Ethanolamines are frequently used for purification of gases containing hydrogen sulphide and carbon dioxide as the only impurities. Neither of the two amines of major commercial interest is suitable for coke oven and converter gases, as monoethanolamine reacts irreversibly with such compounds as carbonyl sulphide, and diethanolamine gives incomplete removal of hydrogen sulphide. Monoethanolamine units are sometimes used, however, for carbon dioxide removal after steam reforming.

Final carbon dioxide purification down to 1 v.p.m. or less can be effected by adsorption on molecular sieves.

The Rectisol process[72] is frequently used for the removal of relatively high concentrations of carbon dioxide and/or hydrogen sulphide from ammonia synthesis gases.

The first step of the process involves injecting methanol into the gas to prevent icing and cooling the gas to below the freezing point of water. The methanol–water mixture is separated from the feed gas and sent to a distillation unit for the recovery of the methanol. The remaining gas is subjected to various stages of methanol washing to remove the acid gases, the process being tailored to the level of impurities to be removed. The methanol solvent is recovered by stripping with an inert gas. Where high levels of hydrogen sulphide are involved, sulphur recovery can be incorporated.

The Rectisol process generally operates at temperatures in the range 210 K to 255 K.

10.3.3 Drying

Where subsequent purification of gases is to be effected by low temperature processing, removal of all moisture from the gas is essential to prevent blockage of the heat exchangers by ice. Drying down to 1 v.p.m. or less is effected by cooling the gas to about 277 K and passing it through vessels packed with suitable adsorbent, e.g. alumina pellets or molecular sieves (see Section 10.2.5 (i)).

10.3.4 Low Temperature Purification

Low temperature techniques may be employed for final purification of hydrogen to be used for ammonia synthesis. Where the feed gas to the low temperature plant is coke oven gas, most of the hydrocarbons and some of the carbon monoxide are removed by fractional condensation. The gas, having been subjected to pre-purification as described in the preceding paragraphs, is cooled to about 83 K in a series of heat exchangers against the returning products. Condensed methane, ethylene and propylene fractions are separated from the gas at various temperature levels and are evaporated and warmed against the incoming feed gas. Where methane and ethylene of a higher purity are required, these fractions are rectified before passing back through the heat exchanger system.

After cooling, the gas usually contains about 90–92 per cent hydrogen, the remaining impurities consisting mainly of carbon monoxide and nitrogen with small amounts of methane and oxygen. This gas enters a nitrogen wash column where it is scrubbed with liquid nitrogen to remove all the impurities. Where the feed gas to the plant has a higher concentration of hydrogen (85–95 per cent) little or no condensation occurs in the heat exchangers. The gas entering the nitrogen wash column is of a similar composition to that resulting from a coke oven gas feed.

The process in the nitrogen wash column is essentially one of stripping, the impurities in the hydrogen being replaced by nitrogen which is more volatile. The impurities concentrate at the bottom of the column as liquid and are subsequently expanded, evaporated and warmed to ambient temperature prior to being used as a fuel gas. This fraction usually contains about 20–30 per cent nitrogen. The purified gas leaving the top of the column contains about 8–13 per cent nitrogen and less than 15 v.p.m. of carbon monoxide and oxygen. This gas is warmed to ambient temperature against the incoming streams and is then made up with pure nitrogen to the stoichiometric ratio required for ammonia synthesis.

Pure nitrogen for washing and make-up is obtained from an associated air separation unit. Refrigeration requirements for the plant can either be supplied by the air separation unit or by nitrogen compression and expansion within the nitrogen wash plant itself. Where the source of feed gas is an oil gasification process the air separation unit also supplies oxygen for the gasification.

Various design modifications to nitrogen wash plants have been described by Guillaumeron[41], Ruhemann[42], Bardin and Beery[43], Baker[44] and Jester[45].

10.3.5 Nitric Oxide Removal

Nitric oxide contamination of the feed gas can be extremely hazardous in nitrogen wash plants. Even when present in these gases in amounts of the order of 1 v.p.m., it is particularly dangerous in the presence of small quantities of oxygen and higher unsaturated hydrocarbons (especially di-enes). The first stage is a reaction between nitric oxide and oxygen to produce nitrogen dioxide which reacts with the unsaturated hydrocarbons to give organic nitro-compounds. These polymerize to form nitro-resins which can build up in various parts of the plant and can cause serious explosions[46]. It is essential, therefore, to remove nitric oxide before these explosive resins can be formed.

When no unsaturated hydrocarbons are present in the feed gas, nitric oxide removal is still necessary in order to prevent blockage of the low temperature heat exchangers. Low temperature activated charcoal adsorbers are normally incorporated to remove unsaturated hydrocarbons and/or nitrogen oxides. The optimum temperature level at which the adsorbers should operate depends on the relative concentrations of nitric oxide, oxygen and unsaturated hydrocarbons in the feed gas and is governed by the following factors:

(a) Nitric oxide has a high saturation vapour pressure, is difficult to adsorb and does not itself deposit in the heat exchangers. If there is no oxygen in the feed, nitric acid should be adsorbed at as low a temperature as possible prior to entering the wash column where it would contact oxygen which enters with wash nitrogen.

(b) Nitrogen dioxide has a much lower saturation vapour pressure and must be removed at higher temperature before it can either react with hydrocarbons or deposit in the heat exchangers. The theoretical rate of conversion of nitric oxide to nitrogen dioxide is very small but increases with reducing temperature and higher oxygen concentrations and the reaction is catalysed by the surfaces of pipes, vessels and adsorbents.

(c) Unsaturated hydrocarbons can be effectively adsorbed at higher temperatures prior to the formation of nitrogen dioxide. Later removal of nitrogen oxides is then only necessary if the concentrations are sufficiently high to cause blockage.

As an additional safeguard parts of the plant may be periodically washed with lye or acetone to remove any accumulated resins.

10.3.6 Carbonyl Sulphide Removal

Carbonyl sulphide (COS) is often present in hydrogen feed gases to nitrogen wash plants and although it is not dangerous it will solidify in the cold parts of the plant and block the exchangers if not removed. Low temperature adsorbers are normally incorporated in the plant to remove the carbonyl sulphide together with any acetylene present in the feed gas which can also block the exchangers if present in sufficient quantity.

10.4 Hydrogen

In this age of space research, liquid hydrogen is an important rocket fuel, as a mixture of liquid hydrogen and liquid oxygen has one of the highest specific impulses of any chemical fuel system known at present. Liquid hydrogen is also used for various research purposes and, when subjected

Table 10.2 SOURCES OF HYDROGEN AND ASSOCIATED IMPURITIES

Hydrogen source	Typical analysis (% by volume)						
	H_2	CO_2	CO	N_2	O_2	CH_4	H_2S
Town gas	48	2	6	7	—	37*	trace
Electrolysis	99·8	—	—	0·1	0·1	—	—
Steam/hydrocarbon† Steam/hydrocarbon/oxygen }	99·4	0·1	0·2	—	—	0·3	—
Water gas/steam	97·2	0·1	1·2	1·2	—	0·3	—
Steam/iron	99·0	0·3	0·4	0·1	—	0·2	—

*Includes about 4 per cent hydrocarbons other than methane.
†Two stages of shift reaction.

to a distillation process, deuterium can be obtained from which, by oxidation, heavy water can be formed. This section considers the various sources of hydrogen and the purification required prior to its liquefaction.

Table 10.2 shows the main sources of hydrogen, together with some typical impurities which will be present.

With the carbon dioxide concentration at or below 1000 v.p.m. adsorption on molecular sieves can be used to remove all the carbon dioxide. If the concentration of the carbon dioxide is over 1000 v.p.m. a carbon dioxide prepurification system, e.g. monoethanolamine washing, may be designed to give a concentration below 1000 v.p.m. and preferably only about 10 v.p.m., and may be followed by a molecular sieve adsorber to remove the last traces of carbon dioxide.If the concentration is less than about 50 v.p.m. the use of low temperature silica gel adsorbers can be contemplated.

Oxygen is often present in very small quantities, i.e. about 10 v.p.m., which must be removed for the safety of the subsequent hydrogen liquefaction plant. It is possible to get crystals of solid oxygen in the liquefier which, due to static charges, can sometimes give rise to explosions. Oxygen can be reduced to less than 1 v p m by burning with hydrogen over a catalyst bed (e.g. De-Oxo type). This consists of a vessel containing finely divided platinum or palladium on alumina. A temperature rise of 10°C per 0·1 per cent of oxygen can be expected. It should also be remembered that the lower explosive limit of oxygen is about $4\frac{1}{2}$ per cent in hydrogen, so if concentrations above this are expected a recirculating dilution system or a burner must be used.

The removal of the remaining impurities, i.e. methane, carbon monoxide and nitrogen is the more difficult task in hydrogen liquefier design, and may be carried out by low temperature adsorption prior to liquefaction. It should be remembered that the liquefaction coefficient of a liquefier, i.e. the ratio of liquid product/gas processed, is usually about 25 per cent. Clean unliquefied gas is returned to the compressor suction so that impurities in the feed are diluted to one quarter of their original value.

On the small scale of liquefier, up to about 200 litres/h, hydrogen can be supplied most economically from electrolytic cells. In this case (Table 10.2) the only impurity to be removed at low temperatures is nitrogen. On this scale and concentration (1000 v.p.m.), low temperature adsorption at about 77 K (liquid nitrogen temperatures) is the best solution, using dual adsorbers for continuous running. Silica gel or charcoal are the most commonly used adsorbents. Data for their design are given by Hiza[47]. The temperature of the liquid nitrogen bath can be lowered, giving greater Joule–Thomson cooling and higher liquefaction coefficient, by reducing the pressure over the nitrogen. It should, however, be remembered that nitrogen solidifies at about 63 K, the triple point.

For liquefiers over the 200 litres/h scale, it is advantageous to use a process such as steam/hydrocarbon for the hydrogen supply, depending on local conditions. This supply source will contain carbon monoxide and methane as well as nitrogen (see Table 10.2). Here again low temperature adsorption may be employed, but it should be noted that the presence of methane will affect the adsorber design considerably.

An approximate design[48] can be calculated using the equation:

$$\frac{V_1}{V_1^*} + \frac{V_2}{V_2^*} + \frac{V_3}{V_3^*} = 1 \tag{10.10}$$

where subscripts 1, 2 and 3 refer to the components to be adsorbed,

V = adsorbent dynamic capacity for the individual component in the multi-component system

V^* = adsorbent dynamic capacity for the pure component at the total molar concentration of the multi-component adsorbate.

In order to evaluate the equation it is necessary first to obtain V_1^*, V_2^*, V_3^* and then assign values to the ratios V/V^* according to the order of displacement and concentration of the components such that the equation is satisfied.

The design pressure for hydrogen liquefiers depends on the scale. It usually varies from about 150 bar on the small scale to about 30–40 bar on the large units. At these pressures and the temperature of adsorption (about 77 K) the fugacity of the mixtures must be employed and not the ideal vapour pressures. Dokoupil[49,50] gives data for nitrogen, carbon monoxide and methane in the presence of hydrogen in the required temperature and pressure regions. Hiza[47] also considers this facet of the design problem.

The production of liquid hydrogen on a very large scale involves low pressure hydrogen cycles with expansion turbines to provide refrigeration at various temperature levels. At low pressures it can be more economical to use blocking heat exchangers which are periodically de-rimed, as opposed to adsorbers. Reversing exchangers cannot be used for liquefiers since hydrogen is recirculated to the compressor suction and does not leave the system. Thus a build-up of impurities would occur which would eventually block the system.

Hydrogen exists in two forms known as ortho- and para-hydrogen. At room temperature the equilibrium mixture of the two forms of hydrogen will contain 75 per cent ortho and 25 per cent para. At 20 K the equilibrium concentration will be 98 per cent para and 2 per cent ortho. Conversion from ortho- to para-hydrogen is accompanied by a release of energy comparable in magnitude with the latent heat of hydrogen. Thus if liquid hydrogen is to be stored for a considerable length of time, say about a week or more, conversion towards the equilibrium conditions at 20 K must be made in the plant. Catalytic conversion to 45 per cent para can be made at 77 K (liquid nitrogen temperature)[51]. Conversion to the 98 per cent para conditions can be made in the vapour or liquid phase at 20 K[52].

Plants in which heavy water is produced by the distillation of liquid hydrogen and subsequent oxidation of the deuterium obtained have similar purification problems. To produce 100 tonne/year of heavy water, the hydrogen flows of the plant will be equivalent to a liquefier producing about 350000 tonne/year of liquid hydrogen. On this scale the pressures of hydrogen may be less than 20 bar and adsorption of the impurities may not provide the answer since very large vessels indeed would be required. This problem of purification on the large scale for heavy water production has been studied by Denton et al.[16]. Their approach was to make use of a reversing exchanger and blocking exchanger system (see Sections 10.2.4 (v) and (vi)). The reversing exchanger technique can be applied down to about 40 K; below this level the phase equilibria[49] is such that only blocking exchangers may be used. Blocking exchangers must be periodically warmed to remove the deposit which will include nitrogen, carbon monoxide, oxygen and methane. This will impose a refrigeration load at 20 K level. Fortunately the specific heat of the aluminium making up the plate fin type of exchangers[16] used for this type of duty is very low, like all other materials at this low temperature, and the load does not impose any undue power penalty on the process.

10.5 Argon, Krypton and Xenon

Argon and the rare gases krypton and xenon can be recovered as a by-product from oxygen plants. Air contains 9320 v.p.m. argon, 1·139 v.p.m. krypton and 0·086 v.p.m. xenon.

Argon is usually separated in a side column in the air separation plant, which produces a crude argon product containing up to 2–10 per cent oxygen and a trace of nitrogen. This crude argon is then concentrated in a separate purification system. The oxygen can be removed by injecting hydrogen and burning over a suitable catalyst. The water formed is removed by adsorptive dryers or by refrigeration. The residual mixture of argon, nitrogen and excess hydrogen from the De-Oxo can be further purified by low temperature distillation. An alternative approach is to use the ability of some molecular sieves at low temperatures to adsorb oxygen and nitrogen preferentially[53].

Krypton and xenon, employed mainly in the lamp industry and for research purposes, concentrate in the liquid oxygen evaporator of the air separation unit together with methane, acetylene, propane and butane. By distillation of the liquid oxygen from the evaporator a primary concentrate can be obtained of composition approximately 0·4 per cent krypton, 0·03 per cent xenon, 0·5 per cent methane, 10 v.p.m. acetylene, traces of the other hydrocarbons and the remainder oxygen. Before further purification can proceed it is essential to remove the dangerous acetylene and other hydrocarbons, particularly methane, as methane is only slightly more volatile than kyrpton and xenon and will interfere with the subsequent distillation stages[54]. The hydrocarbons can be removed by oxidation at temperatures from 400°C to 700°C, depending on the catalyst[55,56]. Continuous hydrocarbon analysis of the oxidized products is desirable. After removal of the hydrocarbons, a secondary concentrate of 50–60 per cent krypton/xenon can be obtained by distillation. Further refinement to almost 100 per cent purity can be completed by a further distillation[57]. The residual oxygen and nitrogen can be removed by passing over heated calcium or lithium.

10.6 Helium

Helium can be obtained from an air separation plant; however, because of its low concentration in air (5·24 v.p.m.) it is not normally economical to recover this on any appreciable scale. Helium is often associated with natural gas deposits, particularly in North America. The concentration of helium may be as high as 8 per cent but a more typical composition of a natural gas helium source is given in Table 10.3.

Where helium recovery from natural gas is an economical proposition it is usually effected as an integral part of a general natural gas processing plant. A typical example of such a plant is the 'Sunflower Plant' in Kansas[74] which produces about 4·2 million cubic metres per annum of crude helium. This is piped to a helium purification facility where pure helium containing less than 20 p.p.m. of impurities is produced. The plant also produces annually about 150 million cubic metres of natural gas liquids (expressed as gas volume). More than 95 per cent of the helium and about 80 per cent of the propane contained in the feed are recovered, while rejecting about 80 per cent of the nitrogen.

Table 10.3 TYPICAL COMPOSITION OF A NATURAL GAS HELIUM SOURCE IN THE U.S.A.

	% by volume
Methane	64·1
Ethane	3·1
Propane	1·9
Butane	0·6
Isobutane	0·4
Pentane	0·2
Isopentane	0·2
Cyclopentane	0·05
Hexane	0·2
Nitrogen	26·2
Argon	0·1
Hydrogen	0·05
Hydrogen sulphide	—
Carbon dioxide	0·8
Helium	2·1

The natural gas feed is dried to a dew point of about 190 K in a molecular sieve adsorption unit and then cooled and partially condensed. The heavy hydrocarbons are removed by fractional condensation and the remaining gas is passed to a fractionation column to separate the bulk of the nitrogen. The helium leaves the column in the nitrogen overheads and most of the nitrogen is condensed from this stream by means of a nitrogen refrigeration circuit. The resulting crude helium leaves the plant and is separately processed to provide pure helium. This is normally achieved basically by cooling the helium to about 67 K by evaporating nitrogen under reduced pressure. The nitrogen and any residual hydrocarbons are condensed out to give 99·5 per cent pure helium. A final clean-up is achieved by low temperature charcoal adsorbers at about 77 K.

A general review of helium extraction and purification processes together with a history of the development of such processes has been presented by Wilson et al.[75].

Helium is very suitable as an inert gas for circulating through nuclear reactors to transfer the heat to the steam generators. The helium picks up radioactive krypton and xenon, by-products of the fission, together with small quantities of water vapour, carbon dioxide, argon, nitrogen, methane and hydrogen. Removal of these impurities to a very low level is essential to maintain a low level of radioactivity in the circulating gas and to prevent corrosion of the graphite moderator[59]. Hydrogen and methane can be removed by high temperature oxidation at about 400°C.

Removal of the water and carbon dioxide can be achieved by deposition in blocking exchangers (see Section 10.2.4 (vi)). The removal of radioactive krypton and xenon is a unique problem. The basic approach here is to delay the krypton and xenon in an adsorption bed for a sufficient time to allow sufficient decay of the radioactive level. The bed is in continuous operation and merely acts as a delay system, comparable to a very large bottle. The krypton and xenon leaving the delay trap are adsorbed in a further adsorber. This adsorber, which also removes the traces of argon and nitrogen, can be periodically reactivated by warm gas, the off-gas being passed to evacuated 'dirty' gas receivers.

The many other uses for helium have been reviewed by Firth[73]. These include the use as a pressurizing or ullage medium in liquid fuel rockets, metallurgical applications and at low temperatures for creating super-conductivity in certain metals.

11

Catalytic Destruction or Conversion of Impurities

PART A GASEOUS IMPURITIES

F. F. RIXON

11.1 Introduction

Where a gas contains an impurity in small concentration and either contains or can be mixed with a gaseous substance, in sufficient concentration, which can react with the impurity to yield a product which is either an inert diluent or can easily be removed from the gas, such a reaction can be brought about by passing the gas containing the impurity, with or without the addition of another gas, in contact with a suitable heated catalyst maintained within a desired temperature range. Where the product is water vapour, which may be condensed out, or water vapour, carbon dioxide, sulphur dioxide or nitrogen contained in a gas which is passed to waste, the gas treatment can be classed under catalytic destruction of impurities. Where the product is an inert diluent or a substance, other than water vapour, which can be removed from the gas, the gas treatment can be classed under catalytic conversion of impurities.

Catalytic purification processes utilize catalysts which increase the rate of a desired reaction, and since the catalysts are generally solids, involve heterogeneous catalysis. Chemical catalysis is very complex and not long ago was generally considered more of an art than a science. However, over recent years certain guiding principles and theoretical aspects of catalysis have been evolved and these are given in textbooks which have been written on the subject[1,2].

Various industrial processes have been separately developed for specific requirements dependent on the gas to be treated and the impurities to be removed. In the development of such processes the possibilities have been apparent from equilibrium constants, heats and free energies of reaction, but the types of practical catalyst and allowable space velocities have generally been developed as a result of experiments on the laboratory and pilot plant scales.

11.2 Types of Industrial Processes

Industrial processes for the catalytic purification of gases can be divided into two categories, typically as follows:

(i) Catalytic destruction of impurities

(a) Removal of oxygen (0·2–0·5 per cent by volume) from electrolytic hydrogen using a heated catalyst consisting of platinum or other precious metal supported on asbestos or alumina; similarly removal of hydrogen (0·4–1·0 per cent) from electrolytic oxygen[3,4].

(b) Destruction of oxides of nitrogen in tail gases from nitric acid plants or nitration plants by catalytic reduction (see Section 11.7.1).

(c) Destruction of organic impurities, and odours, in gases discharged to atmosphere by catalytic combustion (see Chapter 11, Part B).

(ii) Catalytic conversion of impurities

(a) Removal of small concentrations of carbon monoxide and carbon dioxide from industrial hydrogen and ammonia synthesis gas by catalytic hydrogenation into methane (see Sections 11.6.2 and 11.6.3).

(b) Removal of acetylene by selective catalytic hydrogenation from olefine—containing gases produced by the cracking of hydrocarbons (see Section 11.6.5).

(c) Removal of organic compounds from town gas by catalytic reduction or oxidation (see Section 11.6.6).

11.3 Specification for Purified Gas

Generally only a trace of the impurity in the purified gas is tolerable, either because of the obnoxious nature of the impurity when the gas is discharged into the atmosphere, or because the impurity constitutes a catalyst poison or hazard in the subsequent processing of the gas.

It is desirable to have a specification for the maximum allowable concentration of the impurity in the purified gas. For example, tail gases from nitric acid plants or nitration plants should contain less than 200 p.p.m. of oxides of nitrogen. Purified ammonia synthesis gas should contain less than 15 p.p.m. of carbon monoxide and less than 5 p.p.m. of carbon dioxide. Purified hydrogen for the hardening of oils should contain less than 10 p.p.m. of carbon monoxide. Ethylene streams derived from the cracking of hydrocarbons and gas separation processing should contain less than 20 p.p.m. of acetylene.

Where a gas is treated for the removal of odours before discharging the gas into the atmosphere, guidance on odour measurement and control should be sought, such as is given in a published manual[5].

11.4 Selection of Catalyst

Catalysts used in most gas purification processes are metals or metal compounds, usually supported on an inert carrier of large surface area. Typical carriers are alumina, magnesia, asbestos, china clay, activated carbon, porcelain rods and metal wire or ribbon.

The activity of any one catalytic material may be increased by the addition of one or more components, which additives are known as promoters.

Catalysts can be classified according to whether they promote oxidation or hydrogenation reactions. Examples of oxidation catalysts are platinum and platinum group metals, copper oxide and manganese dioxide. Examples of hydrogenation catalysts are nickel, iron, cobalt, and molybdenum oxide or sulphide. However, since the reactions concerned are generally reversible, a catalyst which promotes an oxidation reaction in one direction can also be active for promoting a hydrogenation reaction in the reverse direction, and vice versa. The equilibrium of the reaction will always be determined by the temperature and pressure at which the reaction takes place. While the catalyst increases the rate of the desired reaction involved in the gas purification, in practice the space-velocity of the gas passing through the reactor is generally such that equilibrium is not reached and the treated gas contains a concentration of impurity greater than the equilibrium concentration. At constant temperature and pressure the concentration of impurity in the treated gas increases with increasing space-velocity, and at constant temperature and space-velocity the concentration of impurity in the treated gas may vary with the pressure. The rate of reaction falls rapidly with decreasing temperature and generally there is a minimum temperature, known as the reaction initiation temperature, below which the catalyst becomes practically inactive for promoting the desired reaction. There may also be a maximum temperature above which the catalyst deteriorates and loses its activity.

Where, for a particular catalyst used for a specific reaction, data are available on concentrations of impurity in treated gas at various space-velocities, within a working range of temperatures and pressures, a suitable gas purification plant can be designed and its performance predicted. Where such data are lacking, it will generally be necessary first to carry out trials at least on the laboratory scale, and preferably on a pilot plant scale, to establish the performance of the catalyst within a desired range of temperatures and pressures.

In practice, most catalysts deteriorate or gradually lose their activity over a period of operation. This catalyst deterioration or gradual loss of activity may be due either to physical or chemical causes. Physical causes may be mechanical attrition resulting in excessive entrainment losses and high pressure drop through the catalyst bed, or overheating and sintering of the catalyst resulting in change of the catalyst surface and rapid loss of activity. Chemical causes may be due to the presence of other impurities in the gas which react to form stable reaction products which poison the catalyst, resulting in loss of activity, or the accumulation of deposits, either present in the gas stream or produced by side reactions on the surface of the catalyst, resulting in a gradual loss of activity.

Commercial catalysts must be generally uniform, have the required activity and the physical strength to stand up to the operating conditions.

In some cases the catalysts are made resistant to catalyst poisons. The catalyst may be in the form of pellets, spheres or contact rings or as elements built up from rods, wire, gauze or ribbon.

11.4.1 Activation of Catalyst

Some catalysts are supplied in an inactive form and have to be chemically treated, usually after the catalyst has been charged into the reactor, in order to render the catalyst active. Examples of such treatment are treatments of the catalyst by hydrogen or hydrogen sulphide to reduce metal oxides to metal or sulphide respectively. The catalyst treatment becomes part of the starting-up procedure. The treating gas is passed through the reactor at a required temperature until the catalyst becomes fully active, the gas leaving the reactor passing to waste.

11.5 Plant Design

In general, a plant for the catalytic destruction or conversion of impurities in gases comprises essentially an active catalyst contained in a reactor and preheating equipment for heating the gas to a temperature at which the catalytic reaction is initiated. The plant may include devices for the control of temperatures, rate of gas flow, etc., means for heat recovery and means for regeneration of fouled catalyst.

11.5.1 Reactor

The volume of catalyst contained in a reactor will be determined by the maximum allowable space-velocity and the operating pressure. The reactor may be designed so that when charged with new catalyst it will yield a gas which contains a concentration of impurity well below that acceptable, and an acceptable concentration of impurity is still achieved when the catalyst has been fouled to a certain extent. The design of the reactor will be influenced by the form of the catalyst element, and the depth of the catalyst bed is dependent on the maximum allowable pressure loss.

Where the catalyst is in the form of pellets, spheres or contact rings, the pellets, etc., are usually supported on a horizontal grid or perforated plate with upward or downward flow of gas through the bed. The bed of pellets, etc., can also be formed between vertical grids or perforated plates with cross-flow of the gas through the bed.

Catalyst elements, such as those formed from wire or ribbon, may be formed into mats which are built up into a bed supported on a horizontal grid in the reactor, or the element may be in the form of a hollow cylindrical cartridge suitably housed in the reactor with the flow of gas inward through woven catalyst and out through the centre[6].

Catalyst elements may also be formed from porcelain rods coated with the catalyst material and assembled into units which are laid horizontally on porcelain spacers supported inside the reactor.[7]

Where fouling of the catalyst is known or likely to occur during operation the following alternatives should be considered.

1. The provision of a single reactor designed so that a quantity of new or regenerated catalyst can be periodically fed to the top of a catalyst bed and an equal quantity of fouled catalyst removed from the bottom of the bed while the reactor is in continuous operation.

2. The provision of two reactors with piping and valves arranged so that the reactors can be connected in series or in parallel with respect to the gas flow. Normally the gas flows through the reactors in series and the first reactor in line with the incoming gas stream acts as a guard reactor, the catalyst in this reactor absorbing the fouling constituent or constituents in the gas. The first reactor is periodically isolated from the gas stream, which then passes through only the second reactor, and the fouled catalyst withdrawn from the reactor and replaced by new or regenerated catalyst. The first reactor is then connected in line with the gas stream, in series with the second reactor so that the incoming gas now passes first through the second reactor.

3. The provision of two or more reactors with piping and valves arranged so that the reactors can be connected in parallel with respect to the gas flow. Normally each reactor is connected to the gas stream in periodic rotation so that at any time one or more reactors are in line with the gas stream, having been in operation for different periods if more than one reactor is in line; one reactor, filled with active catalyst is on stand-by, isolated from the gas stream. When the catalyst in a reactor becomes fouled, this reactor is isolated from the gas stream and the stand-by reactor is connected to the gas stream. The fouled catalyst in the reactor which has been isolated may be regenerated *in situ* or may be withdrawn from the reactor and replaced by new or regenerated catalyst.

11.5.2 Preheating Equipment

Where the catalytically treated gas is required in a pure condition and is not passed to waste, the gas passing to the catalytic reactor must be heated to at least the reaction initiation temperature by indirect heat exchange. Where surplus heat from a process is not available for this purpose the incoming gas can be heated by indirect heat exchange with the hot gas leaving the reactor. Where a substantial amount of heat is given out by the reactions which take place in the catalyst bed and the reactor is suitably insulated against thermal losses, the temperature of the gas leaving the reactor may be high enough for preheating the incoming gas to at least the reaction initiation temperature. If the heat given out by the catalytic reaction is insufficient, the incoming gas must be further heated after the heat exchanger by indirect heat exchange with an additional source of heat, for example hot products of combustion from a burner, otherwise the reactor will cool down due to thermal losses and the incoming gas will enter the reactor at a temperature below the reaction initiation temperature.

Where the catalytically treated gas is passed to waste, the gas passing to the catalytic reactor may be heated to at least the reaction initiation temperature either by direct heating with burner gases or by indirect heat exchange, or both. Unless surplus heat from a process is available, direct heating with burner gases as a means for preheating the incoming gas is attractive on account of its simplicity and ease of control. Where feasible, heat economy can, of course, be achieved by heating the incoming gas by indirect heat exchange with the hot gas leaving the reactor, though on occasions it may be more convenient to recover the heat in the hot gas leaving the reactor by other means.

11.5.3 Heat Recovery

The hot gas leaving a catalytic reactor contains utilizable sensible heat. This heat may be recovered by indirect heat exchange with cold incoming gas, as described under preheating equipment, by recycling some of the hot reacted gas directly to the reactor, by raising steam in a waste heat boiler, or by raising power in a gas turbine.

Particularly in the case of the catalytic destruction of impurities where direct heating with burner gases is used for heating the incoming gas to at least the reaction initiation temperature, a plant can be operated so as to give a minimum concentration of impurity in the reacted gas without regard to heat recovery, or it can be operated so as to give an acceptable concentration of impurity in the reacted gas with stress on heat recovery.

11.5.4 Process Control

For maintaining satisfactory temperatures of the gas and catalyst in the reactor it is necessary to instal pyrometers for at least indicating the temperature of the incoming gas immediately before the catalyst bed, the temperature of the reacted gas leaving the catalyst bed and the temperature of the catalyst bed at one or more points.

In many cases it is desirable that instruments are incorporated for controlling one or more of these temperatures. For example, the temperature of the incoming gas immediately before the catalyst bed may be arranged to control an auxiliary gas burner so that the burner comes into operation, so heating the incoming gas, when the temperature falls below a set value. Where a substantial temperature rise in the catalyst bed is caused by reaction with oxygen in the gas, the temperature at a point in the catalyst bed, or of the gas leaving the catalyst bed, may be arranged to control regulating means for maintaining the desired oxygen content of the incoming gas.

The desirability of automatic control of temperature in the reactor will depend on the likelihood, in uncontrolled continuous operation, of the lower limiting reaction initiation temperature always being reached and the upper limiting temperature of the catalyst bed never being exceeded.

The rate of flow of the gas through the reactor generally should not exceed an upper prescribed limit and to ensure that, it is necessary to provide an indicating or recording flowmeter.

The gas leaving the reactor must be sampled at regular intervals and the impurity concentration in the samples determined. When it is found that the acceptable upper limit of the impurity concentration in the gas is being approached, it is an indication that the catalyst has become fouled to such an extent that it is time for the reactor to be isolated from the gas stream for either regeneration of the catalyst *in situ* or replacement of the fouled catalyst by new or regenerated catalyst.

11.5.5 Starting-up Procedure

The procedure for starting up a plant with new or regenerated catalyst may involve, firstly, activation of the catalyst by passing a treating gas, which may be different from the process gas, through the reactor at a required temperature until the catalyst becomes fully active, and secondly, passing the process gas through the reactor until the exit gas contains an impurity concentration below the acceptable value. Provision must be made for connecting the reactor to the respective gas streams and for passing the exit gas from the reactor to waste through a stack.

11.5.6 Catalyst Regeneration

By regeneration of the catalyst is meant the treatment of the catalyst in its pelleted or other shaped form to restore its activity, without breaking it up and re-forming it again into pellets or other shapes.

Quantities of fouled catalyst may be periodically withdrawn from a reactor, and, when a sufficient quantity has been collected, charged into a regenerator vessel where the fouling material may be burnt off by hot products of controlled combustion of a fuel, or driven off by passing through a stream of superheated steam with or without the addition of air. Such treatment causes oxidation of the catalyst and the catalyst may require activation, which can be carried out in the regenerator vessel by passing through a stream of a hydrogen-containing gas with or without the addition of hydrogen sulphide.

Alternatively, a reactor may be provided with means for regenerative treatment of the fouled catalyst and the fouled catalyst regenerated *in situ* after the reactor has been isolated from the process gas stream.

11.6 Examples of Catalytic Conversion Processes

11.6.1 Hydrogenation of Oxides of Carbon to Methane (Methanation)

Carbon monoxide and carbon dioxide can be catalytically converted to methane according to the reversible reactions:

$$CO + 3H_2 \rightleftharpoons CH_4 + H_2O \tag{11.1}$$

$$CO_2 + 4H_2 \rightleftharpoons CH_4 + 2H_2O \tag{11.2}$$

These reactions have been studied by many investigators. The generally accepted heats of reaction and equilibrium constants for the reactions have been determined by investigators of the U.S. National Bureau of Standards[8]. These are given, within the temperature range 127° to 827°C in Table 11.1.

The reactions are exothermic when passing from left to right (according to the above equations). The equilibrium constants K_p decrease rapidly with increase of temperature, indicating that lower temperatures are favourable for the conversion of carbon monoxide and carbon dioxide into methane while higher temperatures are favourable for the conversion of methane into carbon monoxide and carbon dioxide. For example at 327°C K_p is 1.977×10^6 for reaction (11.1) and 7.295×10^4 for reaction (11.2), and at 827°C K_p is 0.00318 for reaction (11.1) and 0.00338 for reaction (11.2). In an initial gas consisting mainly of hydrogen together with some water vapour and around 0·2 per cent by volume of CO and 0·05 per cent of CO_2, the equilibrium concentrations of CO and CO_2 are below 1 p.p.m. at 327°C whereas the CO and CO_2 will remain practically unconverted at 827°C.

Table 11.1 HEATS OF REACTION AND EQUILIBRIUM CONSTANTS FOR METHANATION OF CARBON MONOXIDE AND CARBON DIOXIDE

Temperature °C	Heat of reaction ΔH kJ/kg.mol		$K_p = \dfrac{P_{CH_4} \times P_{H_2O}}{P_{CO} \times P_{H_2}^3}$	$K_p = \dfrac{P_{CH_4} \times P_{H_2O}^2}{P_{CO_2} \times P_{H_2}^4}$
	equation (11.1)	equation (11.2)		
127	210818	170164	$4·087 \times 10^{15}$	$2·76 \times 10^{12}$
227	214692	174853	$1·145 \times 10^{10}$	$8·688 \times 10^7$
327	217969	179061	$1·977 \times 10^6$	$7·295 \times 10^4$
427	220657	182762	$3·722 \times 10^3$	$4·128 \times 10^2$
527	222795	185944	32·05	7·936
627	224494	188649	0·765	0·347
727	225681	190885	0·0376	0·0274
827	226597	192806	0·00318	0·00338

Increase of pressure is favourable for the conversion of carbon monoxide and carbon dioxide into methane because each reaction results in a decrease of gas volume at constant pressure.

A catalyst which is active for converting methane, or higher hydrocarbons such as propane, into CO and CO_2 at higher temperatures is generally also active for converting CO and CO_2 into CH_4 at lower temperatures. Sebastian and Riesz[9] found that nickel in practically all forms was the most active catalyst. Nickel sulphide, when prepared in about 1 to 2 molecular ratio on alumina was not only highly active but also resistant to sulphur poisoning. Nickel oxide catalysts were highly active but variable in sulphur resistance. Catalysts containing iron, cobalt, molybdenum or chromium compounds were generally less active in combination with nickel sulphide.

The performance of a nickel oxide catalyst when methanating carbon monoxide at a constant inlet concentration and constant temperature but at varying space-velocities and pressures[10] indicates that for a constant outlet concentration of CO, in p.p.m., the following relationship approximately holds:

$$\frac{V_P}{V_1} = P^{0·35}$$

where V_P = the space-velocity, as volume of inlet gas at 15·6°C and 1·013 bar per hour per volume of catalyst bed when methanating at P

and V_1 = the space-velocity when methanating at 1·013 bar.

11.6.2 The Methanation of Carbon Monoxide and Carbon Dioxide at approximately Atmospheric Pressure in the Production of High Purity Hydrogen

High purity hydrogen is produced industrially by first catalytically reforming a mixture of steam and hydrocarbon such as propane or butane into a synthesis gas consisting essentially of a mixture of hydrogen and carbon monoxide, converting the carbon monoxide in the gas by the water gas shift reaction into hydrogen and carbon dioxide and then removing the carbon dioxide by adsorbing it in a suitable solvent (see Chapter 7)—this step is carried out in two or three separate stages—and finally converting the residual carbon monoxide (and carbon dioxide) in the hydrogen gas into methane in a catalytic reactor. The gas which enters the methanation reactor usually contains from 0·02 to 0·2 per cent by volume of CO, from 0·02 to 0·05 per cent CO_2, and about 0·3 per cent CH_4, the balance being hydrogen (based on dry gas). The methanation reaction is carried out at slightly above atmospheric pressure.

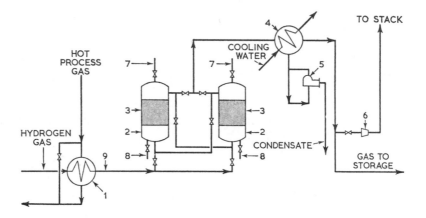

Figure 11.1 Flow diagram of process for catalytic methanation of carbon monoxide in the production of high purity hydrogen: 1, heat exchanger; 2, reactor; 3, catalyst bed; 4, cooler; 5, continuous drainer; 6, flame arrestor; 7, vent; 8, purge gas connection; 9, temperature recorder

Figure 11.1 is a flow diagram of a process for the catalytic methanation of carbon monoxide and carbon dioxide in the production of high purity hydrogen. Hydrogen gas leaving a second stage carbon dioxide absorber at 20°–30°C and about 1·15 bar (saturated with water vapour) passes through a heat exchanger where it is heated by means of the hot process gas leaving the second stage carbon dioxide converter (water gas shift reaction). The hot process gas enters the heat exchanger at 380°–390°C, and a by-pass pipe across the heat exchanger and a regulating valve are provided for the hot process gas so that the temperature of the preheated hydrogen gas can be controlled within the range 250°–270°C. The preheated hydrogen gas then passes through two catalytic reactors in series, each reactor containing a bed of catalyst pellets. The reactors are provided with connecting piping and valves so that they can be connected to the gas stream either in series or parallel and either reactor can be separately isolated from the gas stream. The gas enters each reactor at the bottom and leaves at the top, the flow through the catalyst bed being upwards. The catalytic reaction is exothermic and the reactors are insulated against thermal losses; nevertheless, due to the small concentration of CO in the hydrogen gas the thermal losses in the reactors are greater than the heat evolved in the reaction and the gas leaving the reactors shows a temperature drop of 20°–30°C. The hot gas leaving the reactors passes through a cooler where it is cooled with cooling water to within 5°C higher than the inlet cooling water temperature. Any water condensate which may occur in the cooler is continuously drained away through a sealed continuous drainer. The purified hydrogen gas is normally passed to a gasholder for storage. Piping, a valve and flame arrestor are provided for passing the hydrogen gas to waste through a stack, which is done when starting the plant up with new, unreduced catalyst and also in the event of the catalyst failing to achieve the required conversion of the CO. The concentration of carbon monoxide plus carbon dioxide in the purified hydrogen passing to the gasholder is always below 10 p.p.m. and usually below 5 p.p.m. with the gas entering the methanation reactor containing about 0·2 per cent of CO and 0·05 per cent of CO_2.

When using propane or butane feedstock containing not more than 0·02 per cent by weight of organic sulphur the operation of the plant is simple. The gas entering the first methanation reactor contains only a trace of sulphur compounds and no appreciable fouling of the catalyst in this reactor occurs over a period of continuous operation of upwards of one year; the catalyst in the second reactor is practically in its new condition. The operation is controlled by maintaining the preheated hydrogen gas at a temperature within the range 250° to 270°C and determining, at regular intervals, the concentration of CO plus CO_2 in the purified hydrogen leaving the second reactor.

The concentration of CO plus CO_2 in the purified hydrogen is determined by a method based on the oxidation by hot iodine pentoxide of the CO in the hydrogen, followed by the measurement of the resultant CO_2 by absorption in standard (N/25–N/100) barium hydroxide solution and back-titration with standard (N/25–N/100) hydrochloric acid solution using thymol blue as indicator. In the back-titration the rate of drop-wise acid addition should not exceed 1 ml per minute and the end-point is taken as the neutral colour between blue and yellow. If it is desired to determine the concentration of CO alone, the gas analysis apparatus is provided with an absorption vessel packed with soda asbestos in the train before the iodine pentoxide furnace for absorption of CO_2 prior to the oxidation of the CO. Provided that the determined concentration of CO plus CO_2 in the purified hydrogen is below the acceptable maximum for the concentration of CO alone, such a determination is a satisfactory guide on the performance of the plant.

Should the hydrocarbon feedstock contain a higher percentage of organic sulphur so that the gas entering the first methanation reactor contains an appreciable concentration of sulphur compounds, the catalyst in this reactor will gradually become fouled and its activity will decrease. In such a case the concentration of CO (or CO plus CO_2) in the partially purified hydrogen leaving the first reactor should be determined at regular intervals. When the determination of the concentration of CO in the hydrogen gas leaving the first reactor indicates a serious loss of activity of the catalyst in this reactor it becomes necessary to remove the catalyst in the first reactor (A) and replace it with new catalyst. The first reactor A is isolated from the gas stream by closing the appropriate valves, and the impure hydrogen gas is passed solely through the second reactor (B). The fouled catalyst in the isolated reactor A is removed through a lower handhole and replaced by new catalyst charged through an upper handhole. The gas inlet valve of the reactor A is cracked slightly open and a small stream of hydrogen gas is allowed to pass through the reactor and out through a vent connection at the top to purge the reactor. The vent is then closed and the valves adjusted so that the gas passes first through the reactor A and then the reactor B in series, as previously. This order of passing the gas is maintained for a period of not more than 24 hours in order to reduce the new catalyst in the reactor A to its required active state. Thereafter the valves are adjusted so that the order of passing the gas is reversed, the gas passing first through the reactor B and then through the reactor A. The catalyst in the reactor B will now be the first to become gradually fouled.

The catalyst is prepared by precipitating nickel hydroxide on a kieselguhr carrier and is in the form of pellets with convex ends, 6·4 mm cylindrical diameter by 11·2 mm overall length. The pellets are light green in colour, quite stable when exposed to air and are supplied in drums. The new catalyst is charged into a reactor from drums after sieving on a 6·4 mm mesh screen to remove any broken material.

The pellets as supplied in drums are not active until they have been treated with hydrogen to reduce the nickel oxide to metallic nickel. The procedure for replacing fouled catalyst in a reactor by new catalyst has been described above. When starting up a plant with new catalyst, both the reactors are charged with new catalyst and the valves are adjusted so that the reactors are connected to the gas stream in parallel. For a period, usually less than 24 hours, the hydrogen gas is passed through the reactors to reduce the catalyst to its active state and the gas leaving the reactors is passed to waste through a stack. The valves are then adjusted so that the gas passes through the reactors in series, the valve connecting to the stack is closed and the purified hydrogen gas is passed to storage.

Each reactor is a cylindrical vessel constructed of mild steel. The volume of the reactor is dependent on the accepted space velocity through the catalyst bed which may be from 1000 to 2000, as volume of inlet gas at 15·6°C and 1·013 bar per hour, per volume of catalyst bed. The diameter of the reactor is determined by the allowable gas velocity, which is dependent on the allowable pressure loss, usually less than 35 millibar. Each reactor is provided with a mild steel grating covered by a stainless steel wire mesh screen for supporting the catalyst pellets.

The heat exchanger for preheating the incoming hydrogen gas and the cooler for cooling the purified hydrogen gas are of conventional shell and tubes construction in mild steel.

When withdrawing fouled catalyst pellets from a reactor isolated from the gas stream the vent connection at the top of the reactor is opened and the purge connection near the bottom is connected to a supply of nitrogen. Nitrogen is passed through the catalyst bed to cool it. The lower handhole is unbolted, while the reactor is still under nitrogen, with the top bolt left loosely holding the cover plate. The cover plate is then swung sideways to release the catalyst pellets into a suitable bin or drum placed below the opening. It is recommended that several lumps of solid carbon dioxide be placed in the bottom of the bin or drum to provide an inert atmosphere for the fouled catalyst and to act as a coolant; in the reduced state the catalyst pellets are likely to be pyrophoric. It is also recommended that a water hose or light spray is available so that any tendency for the catalyst pellets to catch fire can be overcome by quenching with a water spray. The pellets should then be spread out in a thin layer in a place free from fire hazard and allowed to oxidize by exposure to air. The cold oxidized pellets are returned to the supplier of the catalyst.

The active area of the catalyst is the total outer surface area of the pellets. When the catalyst has become fouled with resultant loss of activity, this is due to fouled material on the outer surface of the pellets. By grinding up the fouled catalyst pellets into a powder and forming new pellets from the powder, a new exposed surface of the pellets largely free from fouled material is obtained and the activity of the catalyst may be largely restored. However, where a substantial amount of sulphur compounds has been adsorbed in the fouled catalyst pellets it is preferable to treat the ground pellets chemically for removal of sulphur as hydrogen sulphide and reprecipitation of nickel hydroxide prior to forming new pellets from recovered catalyst material for re-use.

11.6.3 The Methanation of Carbon Monoxide and Carbon Dioxide at High Pressures in the Production of Ammonia Synthesis Gas

In the production of ammonia synthesis gas, the gas after the conversion of CO by the water gas shift reaction and removal of CO_2 contains around 2 per cent of CO. As an alternative to removing this CO by scrubbing the gas with ammoniacal copper liquor under pressure, the CO can be converted to CH_4 by catalytic hydrogenation. This has been done in the case of several ammonia synthesis plants operating at high synthesis pressures of from 830 to 1033 bar[11]. The methanation step, treating gas containing from 1·5 to 2 per cent of CO, is generally carried out at synthesis pressure in a reactor which may be identical or similar in design to the ammonia converters. The reactor, or guard converter, is loaded with catalyst which may be the same as that used for ammonia synthesis (an active iron catalyst); spent synthesis catalyst is often employed. The treated gas contains less than 10 p.p.m. of CO plus CO_2. The reactor is designed with internal heat exchange and an arrangement for a by-pass around the heat exchanger such that the catalyst is maintained by the strong exothermic reaction within the range 400°–450°C.

The removal of CO and CO_2 in ammonia synthesis gas by catalytic conversion into methane has also been carried out by methanation at low pressure[12]. Gas from a first stage conversion of CO by the water-gas shift reaction and removal of CO_2 containing from 1·5 to 2 per cent of CO is passed to a second stage conversion of CO by the water-gas shift reaction and removal of CO_2, the exit gas from this second stage containing about 0·2 per cent of CO and less than 0·03 per cent of CO_2. This gas is then boosted to 2·05 bar and heated to about 316°C in a gas-fired heater, and the heated gas passed through a bed of a nickel base catalyst contained in a reactor. The gas leaving the reactor contains less than 10 p.p.m. of CO plus CO_2.

11.6.4 Hydrogenation of Acetylene to Ethylene and Ethane

Acetylene can be catalytically converted to ethylene and ethane according to the reversible reactions:

$$C_2H_2 + H_2 \rightleftharpoons C_2H_4 \tag{11.3}$$

$$C_2H_2 + 2H_2 \rightleftharpoons C_2H_6 \tag{11.4}$$

The generally accepted heats of reaction and equilibrium constants for the reactions have been determined by investigators of the U.S. National Bureau of Standards[13-15]. These are given, within the temperature range $127°$–$727°C$, in Table 11.2.

Table 11.2 HEATS OF REACTION AND EQUILIBRIUM CONSTANTS FOR HYDROGENATION OF ACETYLENE TO ETHYLENE AND ETHANE

Temperature °C	Heat of reaction ΔH kJ/kg.mol		$K_p = \dfrac{P_{C_2H_4}}{P_{C_2H_2} \times P_{H_2}}$	$K_p = \dfrac{P_{C_2H_6}}{P_{C_2H_2} \times P_{H_2}^2}$
	equation (11.3)	equation (11.4)		
·127	−177386	−316295	$7 \cdot 63 \times 10^{16}$	$2 \cdot 65 \times 10^{28}$
227	−179660	−320274	$1 \cdot 65 \times 10^{12}$	$1 \cdot 31 \times 10^{20}$
327	−181334	−323264	$1 \cdot 19 \times 10^{9}$	$3 \cdot 31 \times 10^{14}$
427	−182733	−325595	$6 \cdot 50 \times 10^{6}$	$3 \cdot 10 \times 10^{10}$
527	−182862	−327228	$1 \cdot 28 \times 10^{5}$	$2 \cdot 82 \times 10^{7}$
627	−184278	−328379	$5 \cdot 88 \times 10^{3}$	$1 \cdot 17 \times 10^{5}$
727	−184634	−329015	223	$1 \cdot 46 \times 10^{3}$

The reactions are exothermic when passing from left to right (according to the above equations). The equilibrium constants K_p decrease rapidly with increase of temperature, indicating that lower temperatures are favourable for the conversion of acetylene into ethylene and ethane while higher temperatures are favourable for the reverse reactions.

Increase of pressure is favourable for the conversion of acetylene into ethylene and ethane because each reaction results in a decrease of gas volume at constant pressure.

Various catalysts have been used for hydrogenating acetylene to ethylene and ethane, including palladium on silica gel, molybdenum sulphide on alumina, cobalt molybdate, a nickel base and a nickel–cobalt–chromium type.

11.6.5 Removal by Selective Hydrogenation of Acetylene from Ethylene Produced by Cracking of Hydrocarbons

Acetylene is present in ethylene streams in an ethylene plant comprising hydrocarbon cracking and gas separation equipment and various factors enter into the choice of the stage at which it is most desirable to remove the acetylene from the ethylene stream[16]. The acetylene may be removed by selective hydrogenation over a suitable catalyst as an alternative to removal by absorption in a selective solvent[17].

It is desirable that the catalyst be highly selective for hydrogenating acetylene without hydrogenating much of the ethylene in the stream; cobalt molybdate and nickel–cobalt–chromium catalysts are preferred on this account[16].

The acetylene content of the ethylene stream may vary from 0·01 to 0·1 per cent by volume for refinery gas, from 0·4 to 0·8 per cent for cracked ethane and cracked propane respectively, and up to 2 per cent for cracked heavy hydrocarbons. The hydrogen content of the ethylene stream may vary from 10 to 30 per cent.

The hydrogenation of acetylene in ethylene streams has been conducted commercially over fixed bed catalysts with the catalyst usually in the form of pellets contained in a relatively large bed with no provision for heat removal during the catalytic reaction. Catalyst bed depths are usually limited to about 3 m and the preferred flow of the process gas is downwards through the bed. The ethylene stream is fed at a pressure of from 6·2 to above 17·2 bar and is preheated so that the reactor is maintained at temperature within the range 177°–316°C. The space-velocity is generally from 500 to 1000, as volume of inlet gas at 15·6°C and 1·013 bar per hour per volume of catalyst bed. Steam may be added to the process gas, so that the steam content of the mixture is from 5 to 10 per cent, to improve the selectivity of the catalyst and retard the formation and deposition of polymers on the catalyst.

The concentration of acetylene in the purified ethylene stream is below 100 p.p.m. and usually below 20 p.p.m. A relatively small amount of ethylene is hydrogenated to ethane simultaneously and this amount increases as the concentration of acetylene in the purified gas is decreased.

During a period of operation, which may vary from two to four weeks, the temperature of the preheated process gas entering the catalytic reactor is gradually increased by about from 55° to 83°C to compensate for the loss in activity of the catalyst resulting from the deposition of polymers. At the end of the period of operation the catalyst is regenerated with superheated steam, or a mixture of superheated steam and air, then reduced with hydrogen at from 399° to 454°C, cooled to the operating temperature and placed on stream again. The catalyst regeneration and reduction procedure generally requires 24–72 h. A number of reactors operating in parallel are usually provided, the reactors being arranged so that any one reactor can be isolated from the process gas stream for regeneration of the catalyst.

11.6.6 Removal of Organic Sulphur Compounds from Town Gas by Reduction or Oxidation

Purified town gas which has been produced entirely or mainly from the carbonization of coal contains organic sulphur compounds (mercaptans, carbon disulphide, carbonyl sulphide and thiophene) to the extent of usually from 0·6 to 1·2 g/m^3 of organic sulphur per cubic metre at 15°C and 1·013 bar (gauge) of gas. Such gas is usually distributed but the desirability of removing the organic sulphur compounds from the gas, prior to its distribution, has long been recognized.

Two processes for the removal, by catalytic conversion, of organic sulphur compounds in town gas, which have been developed in England and are currently in operation on the industrial scale, have been fully described in the literature. The Holmes–Maxted process[18,19] employs a copper or nickel thiomolybdate catalyst maintained at a temperature within the range 310°–380°C and the organic sulphur compounds are hydrogenated, the sulphur being converted into H_2S. The gas is subsequently passed through an iron oxide purifier box for removal of the H_2S. The Gas, Light and Coke Company's process[20,21] employs a nickel subsulphide catalyst maintained at a temperature within the range 230°–380°C and the organic sulphur compounds are mainly oxidized, forming SO_2, but some H_2S is also formed by a side reaction. The gas is subsequently passed first through a scrubbing tower fed with a weak solution of sodium carbonate for removal of the SO_2, and then through an iron oxide purifier box for removal of H_2S. In both of the processes the thiophene in the gas is practically unconverted but about 80–90 per cent of the other sulphur compounds are converted and subsequently removed. The resultant gas contains organic sulphur in a concentration generally less than 0.23 g/m^3 (equivalent to 172 p.p.m. as COS or C_4H_4S) and sometimes less than 0.12 g/m^3.

In the Holmes–Maxted process the raw gas, which contains hydrogen and some oxygen, is heated first by heat exchange with the hot converted gas, then in a gas-fired preheater and finally by the exothermic reaction between the oxygen and some of the hydrogen in the gas promoted by the catalyst. If the oxygen content of the gas is 0.7 per cent by volume or above, sufficient heat is generated by the internal reaction and the gas-fired preheater is not necessary. The catalyst, which incorporates a carrier such as china clay or alumina, is in the form of spheres of about 6 mm diameter which have been shaped in a rotary drum and the catalyst bed is formed between vertical louvred walls in the reactor with cross-flow of the gas through the bed.

During operation the catalyst becomes coated with carbon largely formed from the carbonization of deposited polymer resulting from polymerization reactions promoted by the catalyst. This coating of carbon impairs the activity of the catalyst and for continuous efficient operation of the process some of the 'fouled' catalyst is periodically withdrawn from the reactor by way of a catalyst outlet hopper and replaced by the same volume of new or regenerated catalyst by way of a catalyst feed hopper.

The fouled catalyst, when a sufficient quantity has been collected, is placed in a regenerator vessel with an effluent chimney to atmosphere, through which the products of combustion from a gas-fired furnace are drawn and discharged to atmosphere from the stack. The inspirator type burner of this furnace is adjusted so that the oxygen content of the products of combustion is within the range 0.3–0.5 per cent by volume. This is done to prevent the catalyst, from which carbon is being burned, becoming too hot, the catalyst being maintained generally within the temperature range 250°–350°C. Permanent damage to the catalyst may be caused by temperatures exceeding 600°C.

In the Gas, Light and Coke Company's process a controlled amount of air is added to the raw gas to obtain a desired oxygen content and the mixture of gas and air is heated first by heat exchange with the hot converted gas and then by the exothermic reaction between the oxygen and some of the hydrogen in the gas promoted by the catalyst. New catalyst is produced by soaking china clay spheres or pellets in a solution of nickel sulphate, drying, and reducing to the active sulphide in a stream of town gas containing hydrogen sulphide. In one form of reactor several catalyst beds are formed between perforated plate or wire mesh vertical walls dividing the reactor into successive compartments with cross-flow of the gas through the beds.

During operation fouling of the catalyst takes place due to polymer deposition and subsequent carbonization of the polymer in a manner similar to that in the Holmes–Maxted process. The fouled catalyst is periodically withdrawn from the reactor and replaced by the same volume of new or regenerated catalyst.

The fouled catalyst is charged into a regenerator vessel and the carbonaceous fouling material is burnt off in a steam of air to allow controlled combustion to take place. During the regeneration process the temperature of the catalyst should not exceed 600°C. The oxidizing conditions in the regenerator convert the nickel subsulphide into a mixture of oxide and sulphate. When regenerated catalyst is charged into the reactor to replace a withdrawn quantity of fouled catalyst it is fed on the top of a bed of catalyst and as it slowly descends in this bed it is reduced to the active nickel subsulphide.

11.7 Examples of Catalytic Destruction Processes

11.7.1 Destruction of Oxides of Nitrogen in Tail Gases

In recent years catalytic reactors have been developed in the U.S.A. for the destruction of oxides of nitrogen in the tail gas from nitric acid plants and nitration processes, which is traditionally discharged into the atmosphere as a plume varying from yellow to reddish brown in colour. The presence of the oxides of nitrogen in the atmosphere is offensive in the locality of the plant, is a cause of corrosion and is also considered to promote formation of smog over a wider area than the immediate neighbourhood of the plant. Hence the desirability of destroying the oxides of nitrogen.

A typical analysis of a tail gas from a nitric acid plant is:

$NO = NO_2$	0·2 per cent (vol/vol)
O_2	2·5–3·0 per cent
H_2O	0·5–1·0 per cent
$N_2 + A$	Balance

It has been found that when such a tail gas is mixed with a fuel gas such as hydrogen, methane, refinery gas or vaporized naphtha, and the mixture passed over a suitable heated catalyst, the oxides of nitrogen are decomposed into nitrogen and products of combustion. Taking, for example, methane as the reactive constituent of the fuel gas the reactions which take place are as follows:

$$2O_2 + CH_4 = CO_2 + 2H_2O \qquad (11.5)$$

$$4NO_x + xCH_4 = 2N_2 + xCO_2 + 2xH_2O \qquad (11.6)$$

Each of the above reactions is strongly exothermic.

The order of reaction of oxides of nitrogen over the catalyst is such that the reddish-brown nitrogen dioxide, NO_2, is first reduced to colourless nitric oxide, NO, while excess fuel is reacted with oxygen; and then, when the oxygen is completely removed, the nitric oxide is reduced to nitrogen and water.

It can be seen that the extent of decolorization, heat production and /or purification is a direct function of the amount of fuel added. The process is limited, however, to catalytically combining only the amount of oxygen and oxides of nitrogen which will allow the reaction to proceed at less than the maximum allowable operating temperature of the catalyst (790° to 870°C). Thus, when high concentrations of oxygen must be removed, to effect substantially complete oxides of nitrogen reduction, it is necessary to perform the purification in two stages with intercooling, or to use a fuel with a relatively low ignition temperature.

The degree of purification of tail gas from oxides of nitrogen will depend on that demanded by the Alkali Inspector, the amount of capital investment available, the type and availability of fuels and the energy requirements of the nitric acid plant itself.

The visibility limit of nitrogen dioxide in air has been estimated at 200–300 p.p.m. and where the requirement of the Alkali Inspector is decolorization only, the nitrogen dioxide concentration must be reduced to below 200 p.p.m., although the total concentration of oxides of nitrogen may be around 500 p.p.m. The sole technical reason for installing a decolorization only process is because the fuel requirement and capital investment are the lowest.

Under normal weather conditions a decolorized tail gas will disperse in the atmosphere before re-oxidation to nitrogen dioxide can take place.

The temperature required for the initiation of the catalytic reduction of oxides of nitrogen depends to an extent on the catalyst used and ranges from 140° to 150°C for hydrogen and/or carbon monoxide to 400°–450°C for methane[22,27].

It is necessary to preheat the tail gas before adding the fuel gas, either by heat exchange with a hot process gas or by a direct fired fuel gas burner ahead of the catalyst bed.

The strongly exothermic reactions which take place cause a considerable temperature rise in the catalyst bed. For each 1 per cent free oxygen or equivalent oxygen in oxides of nitrogen consumed by the fuel there will be a temperature rise of 130°–135°C with methane as fuel and 150°–155°C with hydrogen or carbon monoxide[22,27].

The catalyst generally used consists of a platinum-type metal deposited on a suitable carrier material.

One form of catalyst consists of platinum or platinum-type metal deposited on spheres or pellets of ceramic material, such as alumina[6,22]. The maximum allowable catalyst bed temperature is given as 816°C and it is desirable to control both the reactor gas inlet temperature and the catalyst bed temperature by automatic control. Space-velocities, as volume of inlet gas at 15·6°C and 1·013 bar/h per volume of catalyst bed, of between 30000 and 60000 have been reported, with increase in pressure favouring the higher figure. The nitrogen oxides content of the stack gas can be reduced to below 50 p.p.m. with natural gas as fuel and to below 10 p.p.m. with hydrogen as fuel. The expected life of the catalyst is from 2 to 5 years.

Another form of catalyst consists of a crimped ribbon of a high nickel content alloy (80 per cent Ni, 20 per cent Cr) on which is deposited electrolytically a platinum alloy[6,22]. The ribbon may be woven into a hollow cylinderical cartridge, which is suitably housed in the reactor, or it may be formed into mats which are built up into a catalyst bed. The maximum allowable temperature for the ribbon catalyst is 870°C, which is somewhat higher than the corresponding temperature for a pellet catalyst. The ribbon catalyst is not subject to 'spalling' and on account of its high thermal conductivity and light weight it responds rapidly to temperature change, thus facilitating temperature indication and control. Space-velocities of up to 120000 have been reported.

Catalytic reduction of oxides of nitrogen can be accomplished at either atmospheric or elevated pressure. Where the oxides of nitrogen are generated at atmospheric pressure, for example in many nitration processes, the catalytic destruction of the oxides of nitrogen in the tail gas is also carried out at atmospheric pressure. Where the oxides of nitrogen are generated at an elevated pressure, for example, in modern processes for the production of nitric acid, economic advantages may be gained by carrying out the catalytic destruction of the oxides of nitrogen in the tail gas at an elevated pressure and subsequently expanding the treated tail gas with power recovery.

A typical installation for the destruction of nitrogen oxides at atmospheric presssure[23] is shown diagrammatically in Figure 11.2. The main components are the preheat burner, exhaust fan and catalyst bed. The process

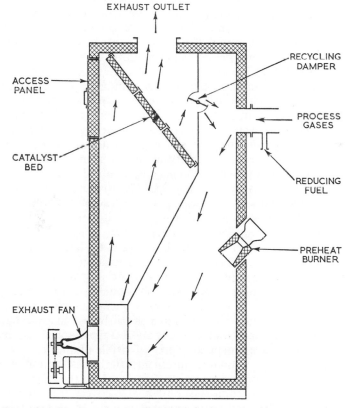

Figure 11.2 Diagram of an installation for the destruction of nitrogen oxides at atmospheric pressure

waste gas plus added fuel gas which enters the unit becomes mixed with and preheated by the recycled portion of the stream. The combined stream passes through the preheater zone, where it is heated by hot products of combustion from the preheat burner, and then enters the exhaust fan (where it is thoroughly mixed) which discharges it through the catalyst bed. Oxidation of the added fuel gas and reduction of the oxides of nitrogen takes place in the catalyst bed, with heat release in proportion to the fraction of added fuel gas. The temperature rise through the catalyst bed may exceed 260°C, depending on the concentration of nitrogen oxides in the process waste gas. A portion of the high-temperature gases leaving the catalyst bed is then recycled to accomplish the process waste gas preheating and dilution function. The remainder is released to the atmosphere substantially free of nitrogen oxides.

The unit is fabricated with heat- and corrosion-resisting steel inner liner and internal parts. High temperature insulation is applied to the liner and covered by a steel protecting jacket. The assembled unit is mounted on a structural steel base. Necessary access panels are included for serving the catalyst bed and inside parts. A fully integrated control system, incorporated in a cabinet, is included.

Figure 11.3 is a flow diagram of a process for the catalytic destruction of nitrogen oxides in the tail gas of a nitric acid plant in which the ammonia oxidation is carried out under pressure and in which the hot gas leaving the catalytic reactor is utilized for providing superheated steam for driving a steam turbine and then expanded in driving a gas turbine. These turbines provide all the power required for driving a process air compressor, no auxiliary drive for the compressor being required during normal operation (see also Chapter 5, Part B).

Tail gas containing about 0.5 per cent by volume of nitrogen oxides (NO plus NO_2) and 4 per cent free oxygen leaves the top of a nitric acid absorber at a temperature of about 35°C. The tail gas is preheated to about 400°C in a tubular heat exchanger by means of hot process gas from an ammonia oxidation burner entering the heat exchanger at about 500°C, after having been cooled in a waste heat boiler. Residual gas from an oil refinery, consisting of hydrogen and lower hydrocarbons, is mixed in sufficient quantity with the preheated tail gas in a mixing chamber upstream of the reactor; the gas mixture is then passed downwards into a reactor containing a bed of catalyst built up from mats formed from crimped metal ribbon. The gases leave the reactor at about 850°C and are cooled in the waste-heat boiler. Steam is raised in the boiler at about 42 bar (253°C), and is superheated to about 360°C. This superheated steam passes to a steam turbine, directly coupled to a rotary air compressor at one end, exhausting to a water-cooled condenser at sub-atmospheric pressure. The condensate from the condenser is returned by a pump to the waste-heat boiler. The gases from the waste-heat boiler at about 480°C and 5.6 bar pass to a gas turbine, and are exhausted to atmosphere at 175°C: they may contain 50–200 p.p.m. of nitrogen oxides. This discharge into the atmosphere is free of visible plume.

The plant has two operational requirements: (i) the destruction of nitrogen oxides in the tail gas to an acceptable value and (ii) the raising of power sufficient to drive the air compressor by heat recovery from the hot gases leaving the reactor. The first requirement is met by preheating the tail gas to a temperature at which initiation of the catalytic reaction takes place,

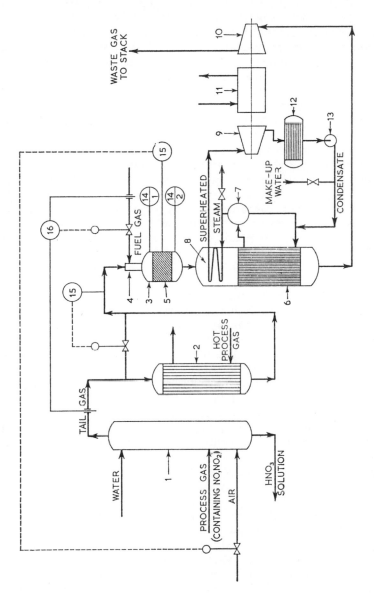

Figure 11.3 Flow diagram of process for catalytic destruction of nitrogen oxides in the tail gas from nitric acid production. 1, nitric acid absorber; 2, heat exchanger; 3, reactor; 4, mixing chamber; 5, catalyst bed; 6, waste heat boiler; 7, steam drum; 8, steam superheater; 9, steam turbine; 10, gas turbine; 11, air compressor; 12, steam condenser; 13, condensate pump; 14, temperature recorder; 15, temperature recorder controller; 16, flow ratio recorder controller

introducing into and mixing with the tail gas a quantity of fuel gas in slight excess of stoichiometric requirements, and maintaining the catalyst bed below a maximum allowable temperature above which the catalyst deteriorates. The second requirement is met by ensuring that the initial tail gas contains a sufficient concentration of free oxygen for liberating sufficient heat in the catalytic reaction, maintaining the catalyst bed, and consequently the hot gases leaving the reactor, at a high temperature not far below the maximum allowable temperature, and allowing all the hot gases leaving the waste-heat boiler to pass into the gas turbine while raising steam in the waste-heat boiler in slight excess of the quantity of steam required for driving the steam turbine.

A by-pass with a regulating valve is provided across the heat exchanger for preheating the tail gas, and by regulating this valve so that a small stream of the tail gas by-passes the heat exchanger, the temperature of the preheated tail gas passing to the mixing chamber is maintained at a desired value. Preferably the regulating valve is automatically controlled.

The composition of the fuel gas should be maintained fairly constant and the volumes of fuel gas required per volume of tail gas of different likely concentrations of nitrogen oxides and free oxygen should be calculated and tabulated. It is necessary to provide a flowmeter in the cold tail gas pipe between the nitric acid absorber and heat exchanger and another flowmeter and regulating valve in the fuel gas supply pipe to the mixing chamber. The flow of fuel gas for a particular composition of tail gas is adjusted in respect of the concentrations of free oxygen and nitrogen oxides in the gas. An automatic flow ratio control system is preferable.

Pyrometers are installed both in the catalyst bed and in the gas stream leaving the catalyst bed. The temperatures should be regularly observed to ensure that the catalyst does not reach the maximum allowable temperature and so become damaged. The temperature of the catalyst bed will rise with increased free oxygen content of the tail gas. The free oxygen content of the tail gas can be varied by regulating the quantity of secondary air passed in at the bottom of the nitric acid absorber. A regulating valve is provided in the secondary air supply pipe and the temperature of the catalyst bed can be varied by adjusting this valve. The pyrometer which indicates the highest temperature can be coupled to an automatic control system which adjusts the secondary air regulating valve to maintain a set temperature.

The secondary air-regulating valve is adjusted so that the tail gas contains a sufficient concentration of free oxygen for liberating, in the catalytic reaction, the heat required in the power recovery system. Usually this results in the catalyst bed and the hot gases leaving the reactor being not far below the maximum allowable temperature.

The catalyst consists of a crimped ribbon of a high nickel content alloy on which a platinum alloy is deposited electrolytically. The ribbon is formed into mats which are built up into a catalyst bed supported on spaced heat-resisting stainless steel bars. The maximum allowable temperature of the ribbon catalyst is about 870°C.

The reactor in which the catalyst is contained is a cylindrical vessel constructed of heat resisting stainless steel. The volume of the reactor is dependent on the accepted space-velocity through the catalyst bed, which may be from 50000 to 100000 as volume of inlet gas at 15·6°C and 1·013 bar/h per volume of catalyst bed. The diameter of the reactor is determined by the allowable gas velocity, which is dependent on the allowable pressure loss through the reactor, usually from 138 to 207 mb.

The mixing chamber is constructed of 18/8 stainless steel and can be in the form of a tube upstream of the reactor arranged to achieve thorough mixing of the tail gas and fuel gas streams and to avoid unmixed gas streams coming into contact with the catalyst and so cause localized hot spots which may damage the catalyst by overheating.

The shell of the steam superheater section of the waste heat boiler is constructed of 18/8 stainless steel and is lined with firebrick; the coil of the steam superheater is constructed of heat resisting stainless steel. The shell and tubes of the steam-raising section of the waste-heat boiler and the steam drum are constructed of mild steel. The gas outlet chambers of the waste-heat boiler, gas turbine and associated piping are constructed of 18/8 stainless steel.

As an indication of the gas volume involved in the process, a plant producing 2·35 kg/sec of HNO_3, as 60 per cent nitric acid, will yield about 8·4 m^3/sec (at 15°C and 1·013 bar) of tail gas, which requires the addition of 0·19 m^3/sec of fuel gas, consisting of a high hydrogen content refinery gas of a calorific value around 37 MW/m^3 for reaction in the catalytic reactor.

One company has developed a form of catalyst comprising metal-coated unitary ceramic cartridges. The ceramic cartridge, described by Warsh and Romeo[26] and Obaditch[27] consists of a block of ceramic material, such as alumina, through which a multitude of small parallel channels pass. These channels may have cross-sections of various shapes, such as triangular or hexagonal, the channel walls being coated with a platinum-type metal. The ceramic cartridge presents a honeycomb type structure. The ceramic cartridges are assembled into a suitable reaction vessel.

The advantages claimed for this form of catalyst are:
  (i) More surface area per catalyst volume thus giving a more active catalyst.
 (ii) Very low pressure drop thus affording more economical vessel designs, and flexibility in use in that the catalyst may be mounted vertically, horizontally or at an inclined angle without the possibility of channelling or bed shifting occurring.
(iii) High fuel efficiency using a wide variety of fuels.

The preferred metal for coating the channel walls of the honeycomb catalyst is, for most fuels, palladium; the maximum safe operating temperature is 790°C. Continued operation above this temperature may lead to a rapid sintering of the highly active palladium surface with a subsequent loss of efficiency of combustion.

The first tail gas treating unit comprising the honeycomb catalyst started up in the U.S.A. in April 1964. This operates on decolorization of tail gas and heat production duty, using natural gas as fuel. Since then several plants have been installed and gone on stream in the U.S.A. and Canada on similar duties. The space velocity has varied from 100000 to 140000 as volume of inlet gas at 15·6°C and 1·013 bar per hour per volume of catalyst bed. A recent installation in England has been guaranteed to remove oxides of nitrogen in tail gas from 0·16 per cent to less than 200 p.p.m. in a 18·3 kg/sec nitrogen stream, using naphtha as fuel. Performance reports had not been published by mid 1970.

PART B DESTRUCTION OF ODOURS

A. AIKENS AND F. F. RIXON

11.8 Introduction

Many objectionable gaseous industrial effluents can be rendered innocuous by catalytic oxidation. The offending materials in a large majority of industrial fume nuisance problems are of a combustible nature but in concentrations below the lower explosive limit, and it is possible to oxidize these materials satisfactorily at any concentrations in air between the lower explosive limit and zero, and at temperature considerably below the minimum ignition limit, by means of catalytic oxidation. Clearly, the process producing the effluent must be operated in such a manner that the discarded gases do not contain concentration of the explosive gases within the explosive range. Figures for explosive limits for many gases and vapours are given in a Bulletin issued by the U.S. Bureau of Mines[24].

An oxidation catalyst system, known as the Oxycat, is a development by Eugene J. Houdry who, in the mid-1930s, introduced to industry the catalytic cracking method of refining petroleum[25]. Oxycat equipment effects virtually complete elimination of the combustible constituents in industrial process exhausts, at temperatures and concentrations far below those necessary for ordinary combustion. It is particularly applicable for destruction of odours.

11.9 Description of the Oxycat System

The basic feature of the Oxycat system is an arrangement in a combustion chamber of standard-size units of platinum-coated rods of porcelain of special shape. The porcelain carrier presents the catalytic agent uniformly to the gas stream. An Oxycat element consists of seventy-one porcelain rods held in place by two porcelain end-plates. The catalytic agent is coated on the surface of the rods by a special process. The unit measures 143 mm long, 81 mm high and 76 mm wide and weighs 0·725 kg. The limiting temperature range through which the Oxycat functions is from 210° to 982°C.

Features which make the Oxycat system particularly suitable for oxidation of traces of combustible materials in gaseous effluents are:

(i) The development of a durable alumina-supported platinum catalyst. The catalytic film is abrasion-resistant and capable of withstanding high temperatures and thermal shock.

(ii) The use as main catalyst support of a high-grade spark-plug type porcelain. This has been selected because of its strength, chemical inertness, resistance to high temperatures, and because its coefficient of expansion is approximately the same as that of the catalyst coating.

(iii) The mechanical design of the Oxycat elements gives maximum efficiency and long life without maintenance. The porcelain rods are fitted loosely into end-plates to allow for thermal expansion. A cylindrical porcelain rod, placed in the centre of the Oxycat and cemented to the end-plates provides structural strength for the assembly. The rods have a symmetrical aerofoil cross-section in order to minimize back-pressure whilst presenting a maximum surface to the gas stream and to minimize impingement of suspended particles. The elements are assembled in stacks in the combustion chamber.

Because of the simplicity of the Oxycat combustion system and the ruggedness of the materials, installations have long life and require little maintenance. Under proper operation conditions and in the absence of catalyst poisons, no catalyst maintenance or replacement is necessary for over 20000 operating hours. When the catalyst activity declines significantly, the units can be re-processed by their manufacturers at only a fraction of the initial purchase price.

11.10 Application of the Oxycat System

The physical and chemical characteristics of the Oxycat have resulted in a versatile, durable and highly active catalyst, which has proved itself commercially practical for the following applications.

(i) Air pollution control. To eliminate odours and other objectionable characteristics of process waste gases by oxidizing the combustible materials at temperatures far below those required for direct flame incineration.

Although mostly employed for oxidation of hydrocarbons, the catalyst is effective with sulphur compounds such as H_2S and CS_2.

(ii) Condensate elimination. To obviate deposition of inflammable condensates in ducts, thus reducing fire and corrosion hazards as well as maintenance costs.

(iii) Waste heat recovery. To convert the chemical energy of process exhaust gas to useful heat. The release of heat in certain applications is sufficient to give an economic return on the plant for eliminating air pollution.

The first successful application of the Oxycat system was in the form of an exhaust purifier for petrol engines driving heavy lorries and was made in 1950 in the U.S.A. Table 11.3 gives a list of subsequent applications.

11.11 Operating Conditions

Whereas it is difficult to generalize, there are several basic factors which normally govern the designing and operating features of an installation. These are:

(i) Rate of gas flow. The phenomenon of catalytic oxidation being a surface reaction, it is logical that the completeness of the reaction be a function of the surface area of the catalyst. To determine the required surface area or the correct number of Oxycat elements to use for a given application, the main factor to consider is the rate of gas flow. Each element has a capacity range of from 0·00236 to 0·0118 m^3/s (16°C) depending upon the types of contaminant to be treated. For waste gases available under pressure, a greater

Table 11.3 INDUSTRIAL APPLICATION OF THE OXYCAT SYSTEM

Industrial process	Contaminating agents in waste gases	Approximate temperature required for catalytic oxidation (°C)
Synthetic ammonia manufacture	H_2S	175–345
Asphalt oxidizing	Aldehydes, anthracenes, oil vapours, hydrocarbons	315–370
Carbon black manufacture	H_2, CO, CH_4, fine carbon dust	425–540
Catalytic cracking units	CO, hydrocarbons	345–425
Coke ovens	Wax, oil vapours	315–370
Formaldehyde manufacture	H_2, CH_4, CO, HCHO	345
HNO_3*	NO, NO_2	260–650
Metal lithography ovens	Solvents, resins	260–370
Octyl-phenol manufacture	C_6H_5OH, etc.	315–425
Phthalic anhydride manufacture	Maleic acid, phthalic acid, naphthaquinones, carbon monoxide formaldehyde	315–345
Polyethylene manufacture	Hydrocarbons	260–400
Printing presses	Solvents	315
Varnish cooking	Hydrocarbon vapours	315–370
Wire coating and enamelling ovens	Solvents, resins	260–370

* Reducing atmosphere necessary and obtained by addition of hydrogen-rich hydrocarbon gases. Pilot tests only at time of writing.

weight of gas can be handled per element than under atmospheric conditions provided the maximum temperature limit given later is not exceeded.

(ii) Oxygen requirements. If the gas to be treated does not contain oxygen, it is necessary to add only sufficient air to give an oxygen content of 1 per cent greater than that required for complete combustion. On the other hand, gas streams with high oxygen content will usually permit the reaction to occur at lower temperatures and with less catalyst surface than required for gas streams with a low oxygen content.

(iii) Chemical composition of gases. Some chemical compounds are more difficult to oxidize catalytically than others and consequently the operating temperature of the catalyst, as well as the quantity of the catalyst, will vary, depending on the type of gas to be oxidized. The more stable compounds require a higher temperature and a greater catalyst surface. For example, hydrogen oxidizes readily at temperatures well below 260°C. On the other hand, methane, which is a very stable compound, requires temperatures around 540°C when the concentration is only about 0·7 per cent by volume, although a concentration of over 1 per cent only requires a temperature of 345°C. It has been found that for most industrial odour problems Oxycats will function effectively at approximately 260°C.

(iv) Concentration of combustibles. For a given gas, the correct operating temperature of the catalyst is achieved by adjusting the preheat of the gases. The efficiency of the catalyst remains constant regardless of the concentration of combustibles, once the catalyst reaches its operating temperature and provided it is not overheated.

11.12 Installation

The installation of an Oxycat battery is relatively simple. The normal components of catalytic installations are discussed as follows.

(i) Preheaters. Many installations can be operated without preheat; it is only when the exhaust gas to be treated is below 260°C that a preheater is required. In many cases where preheat is required for starting-up it may be reduced or shut off entirely when the combustible constituents exist in sufficient quantities to maintain an adequate outlet temperature after oxidation. In all cases, however, sufficient heat must be available from preheat and heat of combustion to ensure that the required outlet temperature is reached.

The usual forms of preheating equipment may be used. Thus electrical heating is simplest for starting up small installations whilst oil- or gas-fired preheaters may be necessary with larger installations. In some plants the cheapest method of obtaining the required preheat is to mix suitable hot gases with the gas to be treated; in such cases baffles or fans are employed to ensure thorough mixing (Figure 11.4). In large installations with insufficient heat release to maintain auto-thermal conditions, heat exchangers are an economic proposition (Figure 11.5).

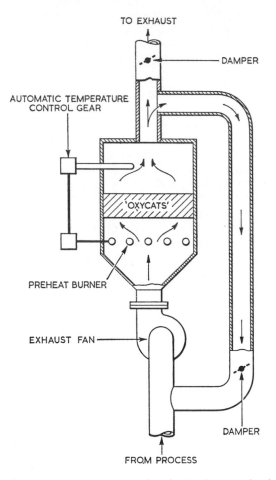

Figure 11.4 Basic Oxycat installation with preheating by recirculated purified gas

(ii) Catalyst chamber. The gas entering the catalyst chamber must be dispersed uniformly throughout the bed, for example by means of turning or splitter vanes, perforated plate baffles, or a combination of both. From this point, the design is dictated by the final temperature of the stream. For outlet temperatures not exceeding 400°C the catalyst bed is supported by a steel slatted grid and housed in a double skinned insulated mild-steel box. For final temperatures up to 540°C precautions must be exercised to protect metals which support and surround the catalyst and a heat-resisting alloy grate is employed.

A semi-refractory brick lining of suitable quality is built around the catalyst bed to protect the walls of the chamber and reduce heat losses; in

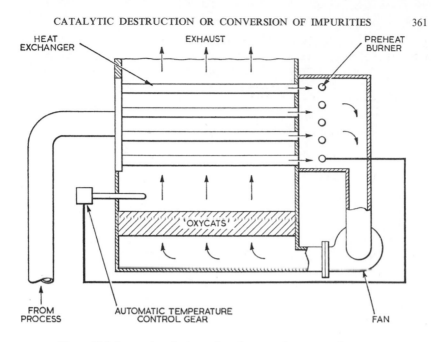

Figure 11.5 Oxycat installation with preheater and starting-up burner

addition, slag wool is inserted between the catalyst elements and the semi-refractory lining. This packing not only insulates, but provides for differential expansion and seals the bed, thus preventing the gases by-passing the catalytic elements.

For final temperatures of 650°C higher grades of alloys must be employed for catalyst support and chamber. Above 650°C the bed is supported by a suitable arrangement of refractory blocks and the chamber is lined with a suitable grade of refractory material backed by appropriate insulation.

(iii) Mounting of catalyst elements. The catalyst is stacked on top of the grate or refractory blocks, secured by ceramic spacers and is held in place by gravity. The bed may consist of three or more layers of Oxycat elements, the number being dictated by experience for the particular application. Pressure drop through the catalyst bed rarely exceeds 2 mb.

The maximum catalyst temperature is measured by means of a thermocouple situated at the outlet of the catalyst chamber. The temperature reading is used to control the amount of preheat so as to ensure that the catalyst and its supports are not damaged.

(iv) Disposal of effluent. The gases emerging from the catalyst bed are practically free from combustible contaminants and are, therefore, suitable to be discharged to atmosphere even in districts where air pollution control is stringent.

(v) Use of hot purified gases. The heat content of the purified gas should always be considered as a source of heat for the process from which it is drawn or for other processes which require heat in the form of clean hot

gases. There are many plants where recirculation of part of the hot exhaust gases is sufficient to supply the total heat load of the process from gaseous effluents which had previously been polluting the atmosphere (Figure 11.6).

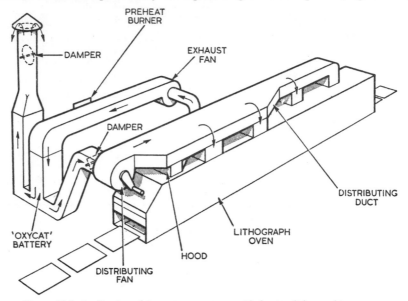

Figure 11.6 Application of Oxycat system to provide heat to lithographing oven

In some cases, especially in metal finishing where pretreatment such as phosphating, granodizing, etc., is applied to the metal work, and where a final wet rinse is given to the material immediately before applying the paint finish, catalytic oxidation is an economic proposition, showing good returns even when the exhaust temperature is comparatively low. In such a case, the exhaust from the paint-drying plant is passed through a preheat chamber (if the temperature is below catalyst activation temperature), then through the catalyst bed, oxidizing any solvent vapours present in the exhaust. The oxidation of these solvent vapours will give a temperature rise to the exhaust, in proportion to the calorific value of the solvent vapours per unit volume. The whole of this clean gas can then be passed into the dry-off oven, in some cases supplying the total heat requirements, in others a part of it which can be supplemented by conventional means. This method, when applicable, is particularly useful where solvent concentrations are weak, because the whole of the sensible heat, plus that from oxidized solvents and any preheat added prior to oxidation, can be recovered.

In other cases, the quantity of heat in the hot gas is sufficient to justify the installation of a waste heat boiler. In a large pressurized system, the hot gases can be used to drive a gas turbine for direct power generation.

11.13 Sample Calculations

(i) Volume of process gas   = 5 m³/s, n.t.p.
     Contaminant-toluene   = 65 g/s

Temperature of gas to Oxycat chamber $= 177°C$.

(ii) The exit temperature of the gas after complete destruction of the contaminant is calculated from the *net* heat of combustion of the toluene and is 410°C.

Hence the temperature of the gas leaving the catalyst elements is less than 600°C and is acceptable. The hot effluent gas is available for process heating.

(iii) From previous experience it is known that 100 Oxycat elements can treat $0.7 \text{ m}^3/\text{s}$ n.t.p. of this type of contaminated gas. Hence number of elements required is 720.

(iv) For this plant a catalyst bed three layers deep would be used, arranged thus:

$$
\begin{array}{lll}
\text{bottom row} = 21 \times 12 = & 252 \\
\text{middle row} = 20 \times 21 = & 240 \\
\text{top row} = 21 \times 12 = & 252 \\
\hline
\text{Total} & 744
\end{array}
$$

(v) Spacers are used in lengths of 254 mm and are available in two types, wide and narrow. The wide spacers secure the end-plates of two Oxycat units and are used in the interior of the bed. The narrow spacers secure the end-plates of single Oxycats and are used on the outside end plate of the Oxycat. In the above example, there would be required 36 narrow and 198 wide spacers.

(vi) Allowing for adequate flexible packing at the sides of the elements the internal dimensions of the catalyst chamber would be 1.65×1.75 m.

12

Removal of Dust from Gases

C. J. STAIRMAND

12.1 Introduction

In general, gas must be cleaned from dust for one or more of three purposes:
(i) The dust contained in the gas may be valuable as, for example, when it is the product from a process;
(ii) the gas itself may be required for use in a further process as, for example, blast-furnace gas used for firing stoves;
(iii) it may be an effluent which must be cleaned before discharge into the atmosphere to avoid nuisance or damage to amenities.

Gas cleaning can be a very expensive process, particularly if almost complete removal of all of the dust is required, and great care must be given to the selection of the most economic equipment for a particular purpose bearing in mind capital charges and running costs, and possible returns on the process. It is necessary, therefore, to have an adequate knowledge of the principal features and fields of application of the various types of gas cleaning equipment available.

It is clearly necessary to ensure that any dust arrestment plant is properly constructed and is, in fact, a satisfactory engineering design. What is equally important, however, is that the dust arrestment efficiency of the plant should conform to the design and it is here that the most costly errors are likely to be made if full data on the behaviour of the dusts involved are not available. For example, gross failures of electrostatic precipitator installations have occurred because the dusts had an electrical resistivity in the so-called 'critical range'. This, and other particular aspects of dust behaviour are dealt with in Section 12.5; Sections 12.2–12.4 deal with the more general problem of selecting a dust arrestor on the basis of its actual achieved efficiency.

12.2 Types of Gas Cleaning Equipment

Table 12.1 gives a list of the main types of gas cleaning equipment available, arranged in order of increasing dust-collection efficiency, with some indication of their fields of application. Detailed descriptions follow in Sections 12.2.1–12.2.5.

Table 12.2 gives the approximate efficiencies of the various types of dust collectors for particles of diameter 5 μm, 2 μm and 1 μm, of density 2700 kg/m³. These figures refer to average values for dust collectors of the types named and not to specific makes. Whenever claims are made differing widely from the values given in the Table it would be wise to enquire how far the claims have been established, since the figures given in Table 12.2 are the result of long-term plant and laboratory investigations and are unlikely

Table 12.1 SUMMARY OF DUST ARRESTOR PERFORMANCE

Type of equipment	Field of application	Pressure loss
Settling chambers	Removal of coarse particles, larger than about 100–150 μm	Below 0·5 mb
Scroll collectors, Shutter collectors, Low pressure-drop cyclones	Removal of fairly coarse dusts down to about 50–60 μm	Below 2·5 mb
High-efficiency cyclones	Removal of average dusts in the range 10–100 μm	2·5 to 10 mb
Wet washers (including spray towers, venturi scrubbers, etc.)	Removal of fine dusts down to about 5 μm (or down to sub-micron sizes for the high pressure-drop type)	2·5 to 60 mb, or more
Bag filters	Removal of fine dusts and fumes, down to about 1 μm or less	1 to 10 mb
Electrostatic precipitators	Removal of fine dusts and fumes down to 1 μm or less	0·5 to 2·5 mb

Table 12.2 EFFICIENCY OF DUST COLLECTORS* (STAIRMAND†)

Dust collector	Efficiency at 5 μm %	Efficiency at 2 μm %	Efficiency at 1 μm %
Medium-efficiency cyclone	27	14	8
High-efficiency cyclone	73	46	27
Low pressure-drop cellular cyclone	42	21	13
Tubular cyclone	89	77	40
Irrigated cyclone	87	60	42
Electrostatic precipitator	99	95	86
Irrigated electrostatic precipitator	98	97	92
Fabric filter	99·8	99·5	99
Spray tower	94	87	55
Wet impingement scrubber	97	95	80
Self-induced spray deduster	93	75	40
Disintegrator	98	95	91
Venturi scrubber	99·8	99	97

*For dust of density 2700 kg/m³.
†Figures from Reference 1, corrected to latest (1969) data.

to be seriously in error. The main reason for optimistic claims, made in good faith, is that accurate dust sampling, size analysis and testing are very difficult to carry out, and errors usually result in the dust being judged too coarse, and hence predicted efficiencies are too high. The techniques of sampling and size analysis are described in Chapter 14, and reference should be made to this section before attempts are made to assess performances of installed plant.

12.2.1 Inertial Collectors

Dust collectors in this class are mainly settling chambers with or without baffles or shutters to give some degree of inertial separation of the coarser particles. However, such dust arrestors are not always convenient except for very limited application, since they must be very large in order to reduce the gas velocity to a reasonably low value to allow the settling-out of the finer particles. (Dust particles of 20 μm diameter of density 2000 kg/m^3, fall at only 0·024 m/s in air and thus a settling chamber with a 'cut' of this size, dealing with 30000 m^3/h of gas, would have a volume of nearly 2800 m^3—a very large chamber for such a gas flow.) Application of this type of dust collector is therefore limited to the smaller plants or as a pre-separator to reduce the load on a more efficient secondary collector.

12.2.2 Cyclones

Cyclones are widely used for industrial dust collection, either alone or followed by secondary collectors. The principle of operation[2] is that the dust-laden gas is caused to 'swirl' in a cylindrical vessel, generally by admitting it tangentially at the periphery of the vessel and removing the cleaned gas at the axis. Particles are subjected to an outward centrifugal force and an inward viscous drag, the balance between the two determining whether the particle will move to the wall and hence into the dust-collecting hopper, or be carried inwards to the 'clean-gas' exit. Thus in theory the efficiency can approach 100 per cent for any size of particle if the centrifugal forces are great enough. Unfortunately there is a limit to the minimum size of particle which can be separated in practice, partly on the score of avoiding excessive pressure-drop, and partly because at high spinning speeds, bouncing and eddying cause the transference of particles, much larger than the theoretical cut size, to the 'clean-gas' exit. In practice, therefore, a sharp cut is not

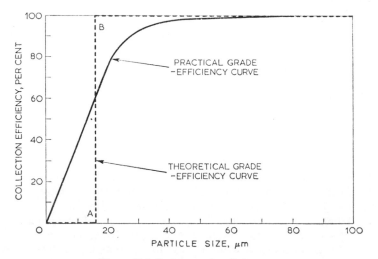

Figure 12.1 Cyclone grade–efficiency curves

obtained and a graded efficiency results, as shown in Figure 12.1 in which the efficiency of collection of a number of size-grades of particles is plotted against the mean size of the grade. If the ideal flow pattern obtained, the 'grade-efficiency' curve would take the form shown dotted where all particles larger than the 'cut' are collected at 100 per cent efficiency and all smaller escape completely. Zone 'A' represents particles which should have escaped collection, but are retained either because they are agglomerated or are swept from the gas stream by larger particles travelling to the walls, while the zone 'B' represents particles which should have been collected, but have escaped into the clean gas by bouncing or gas-eddying. The working grade–efficiency curve must usually be determined experimentally; the method of doing this has been described at some length by the author in a paper[2] which also enlarges on the preferred features of good cyclone design. Useful data on dust and gas flow-patterns have been given by ter Linden[3] which confirm the simple theory of 'Swiss-roll' flow.

Figures 12.19–22 give some typical grade–efficiency curves for a number of types of cyclone. These curves can be used to predict the actual collecting efficiency from a knowledge of the size distribution of the dust to be presented to the cyclone. The method of carrying out the calculations is summarized in a worked example in Section 12.3.1, and is given in more detail by Stairmand[2].

Theory suggests that small-diameter cyclones will have a performance superior to that of larger cyclones of similar proportions. This is borne out in practice to some extent, but nesting a large number of small units to deal with a large gas volume may result in some loss of efficiency owing to inability to maintain uniform gas and dust distribution throughout the system, and there is some risk that the performance will suffer still further due to adverse recirculation within the cyclone nest by preferential 'plugging' of the cyclone gas exit pipes[4]. However, the advantage of small diameter cyclones for duties where the dust is not particularly sticky or the gas not likely to deposit moisture, has been established and their use should be considered in suitable cases.

Medium-efficiency cellular cyclones have also been developed, which, operating at very low pressure-losses (often less than 3 mb) form a very useful addition to an electrostatic precipitation plant, particularly if the latter is a prior installation of obsolete or inadequate design[5].

Cyclones have also a useful role to play in separating grit particles from effluent gases from small furnaces such as those used in laundries and breweries and in small steam-raising plants. For this purpose they are cheap and efficient and can operate at low pressure losses. They are almost completely effective in avoiding grit and dust deposition adjacent to the stack, but do little to improve the appearance of a 'smoky' plume[6]. It should be noted that the effectiveness of cyclones in preventing dust deposition depends entirely on their ability to avoid the emission of coarse particles and any defect in design, construction, maintenance or operation which permits coarse particles to pass may nullify the advantage of fitting cyclones. It can be shown for example that 1 per cent of 90 μm particles in an emission otherwise all below 20 μm can double the deposition rate. On the other hand, as can be deduced from Table 12.2, there is little that can be done to increase the effectiveness of a cyclone in reducing the visibility of a plume, since the efficiency of even the best cyclone at 2–5 μm (the sizes most important in imparting colour to the plume) is very low[1].

The importance of avoiding air infiltration at the base of the cyclone (or internal circulation in a multi-cell arrangement) should also be appreciated. It has been shown, for example, that an air-leak at the dust-discharge point in a cyclone which allows only 10 per cent of air to infiltrate will reduce its efficiency from 90 to 65 per cent, i.e. it more than trebles the emission[4].

The efficiency of a cyclone can be increased by irrigating its walls, if the attendant disadvantages of a wet system can be tolerated. In Fig. 12.2 the broken line shows the grade–efficiency curve for a cyclone when dry, and the continuous line shows the grade–efficiency curve when the cyclone is irrigated with 1 m³ of water per hour per metre of shell periphery, introduced via a ring main located just below the cyclone top cover-plate. This simple means of water addition is adequate, though even better results would be obtained by designing the apparatus as a scrubber in the first place. The addition of water to a cyclone, however introduced, should therefore be regarded only as an expedient, e.g. to give a degree of improvement in the performance of an existing plant. The addition of water by the method indicated above, gives no increase in pressure-drop.

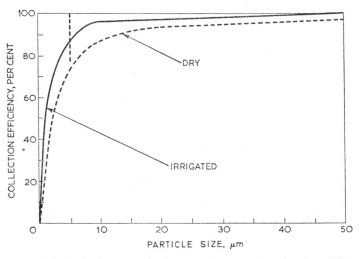

Figure 12.2 Grade–efficiency curve for large-diameter irrigated cyclone. Efficiency at 5 μm = 87 per cent

In certain cases two sets of cyclones can be used in series to enable a particular problem to be dealt with, apart from the use of primary cyclones as 'pre-collectors' to reduce the load on high-efficiency secondary dust arrestors referred to below. For example, the use of two sets of high-efficiency tubular cyclones in series on a small pulverized-fuel fired boiler would give an overall efficiency approaching 96 per cent. While this would not be good enough for a pulverized-fuel fired boiler burning, say, 10–20 tonnes per hour of coal it would probably be completely satisfactory for a small 'packaged' boiler.

Finally reference must be made to various special types of cyclones for particular duties. These include 'mechanical cyclones' in which a uniform vortex is assured by the use of a power-driven rotor. This undoubtedly contributes to a high efficiency, and a sharp cut-off of coarse particles is achieved, but it poses considerable mechanical problems, particularly for the larger sizes. Use of this type of equipment is therefore restricted to cases where a degree of classification is required, as opposed to more or less complete removal of dust particles of all sizes, and the equipment is usually relatively expensive in first cost and in maintenance, due to its mechanical complexity. Other special types are described by Johnson and Goodwin[7] with particular reference to grit arrestment.

Another special duty for which cyclones have been found satisfactory is for the removal of liquid mists either as carry-over from a wash tower (Chapter 16), or as the secondary stage in a venturi-scrubber gas cleaner (Section 12.2.3).

Cyclones are also widely used as primary collectors to reduce the load on more efficient secondary collectors such as electrostatic precipitators or bag filters. Use can be made of the grade–efficiency curve of the cyclone to predict the concentration and grading of the material which will reach the secondary collector, so that its performance can, in turn, be predicted (see worked example, Section 12.3.1). The grading of the material escaping collection in the primary collector is particularly important since it may influence profoundly the performance of the final collector, particularly if this is an electrostatic precipitator.

12.2.3 Scrubbers and Wet Washers

Wet washers can be grouped into two types, i.e. those in which dust collection takes place by impingement on a wetted surface and those in which the water (or other scrubbing liquid) is in the form of a spray providing a large number of obstacles on which the dust is collected. A particularly important feature of the latter method is that means can be devised whereby the relative velocity between spray droplet and dust particle is increased, so enhancing collection efficiency; for a theoretical treatment of the mechanism of dust collection by impingement the reader is referred to a paper by Stairmand[8]. The importance of increasing the impact speed can be seen from Table 12.3 in which the increase in efficiency with increase in relative gas velocity is clearly shown.

Table 12.3 COLLECTION EFFICIENCY FOR
1 μm DUST PARTICLES

Gas velocity m/s	Induced droplet diameter* μm	Target efficiency %
20	260	54
40	135	83
60	93	92
80	72	95
100	60	97
120	52	98

*Calculated according to Nukiyama and Tanasawa[9].

Packed-tower dedusters are generally large and expensive in relation to their gas-rate and are less widely used than formerly, having been superseded by the more modern venturi and cyclonic scrubbers (see below). Nevertheless, when the gas-rates are relatively small and pressure loss is a consideration, grid- or ring-packed towers are sometimes effective. Gas velocities are generally limited to about 1·5 to 3 m/s (calculated on the free-tower area) to avoid carry-over, and pressure drop is about 4 mb per metre of packing. Packing depths of about 3 to 5 m are usual. The dust collection efficiency of such a tower is not particularly high though most particles below 20 μm are effectively trapped. An exception is the Howden–ICI flue gas scrubber[10] which will remove dust particles down to at least 2 μm: this scrubber was initially designed for high-efficiency removal of SO_2 from flue gases and its water circulation rate is 10–20 times that normally used in wet dedusters. Gravity spray towers suffer from most of the disadvantages of packed towers, i.e. they are large, relatively expensive and not very efficient as dust collectors. They are, however, widely used as pre-coolers in the blast furnace gas industry[11] and in carbon-black plants[12]: in the former case they play a not inconsiderable part in reducing the load on the subsequent stages of gas cleaning.

The efficiency with which a droplet of a given size will collect dust particles can be calculated in terms of the known theories of impingement and diffusional contact. It has been deduced[8] that the efficiency per impact is related to the non-dimensional group Dg/Vf as shown in Figure 12.3 (D is the droplet diameter (m), g is the acceleration due to gravity (m/s^2), V is the relative velocity of approach of droplet and dust particle (m/s) and f is the free-falling speed (m/s) of the dust particle it is desired to collect). The

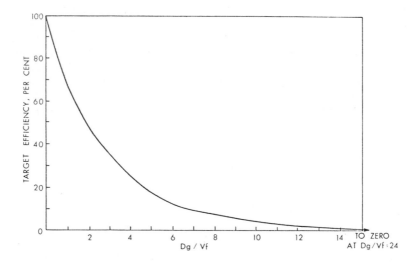

Figure 12.3 Target efficiency related to Dg/Vf

efficiency increases with a reduced value of Dg/Vf or, since f is constant for a given dust particle, with reduction in D or increase in V.

In a gravitational spray tower the effective value of V is the difference between the gravitational free-falling speeds of the dust particle and the water droplets; or since the dust particle is usually small compared with the droplet, V may be taken as equal to the free-falling speed of the droplet. Thus the two requirements for high collection efficiency of a given dust particle, namely a small obstacle and a high relative velocity between dust particle and obstacle, are mutually contradictory.

By calculating the target efficiency (i.e. the efficiency per impact) for various droplet and dust particle sizes it can be shown that there is an optimum droplet size for maximum collection efficiency. Figure 12.4, which refers to the collection of particles of density 2000 kg/m³ in a gravitational spray tower, illustrates this point. It will be seen that the curves show maxima, but the peaks of the curves are flat enough to enable a general conclusion to be drawn that droplets in the range 500–1000 μm are the most effective. This consideration of the mechanism of operation of a spray tower is to some extent an over-simplification since it takes no account of the actual volume of gas swept by the droplets. But even when this allowance is made the order of the optimum droplet size is unchanged, and the simplified treatment serves to illustrate the essential difference between a fibre filter and a spray deduster, where the 'obstacles' are mobile.

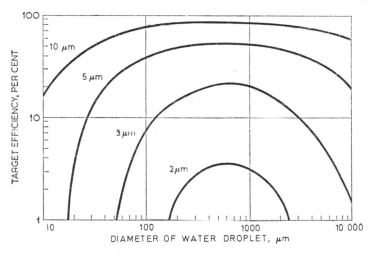

Figure 12.4 Relation between collection efficiency and droplet size

The calculations show, first, that the efficiency of a gravitational spray tower is very low for particles below 1 or 2 μm and, secondly, that there is little point in using very fine spray droplets, even if they could be produced economically. Realization of this fact will avoid much disappointment as well as directing attention to a more useful approach. The difficulty is obviously to retain the high relative velocity of impact without sacrificing small droplet size; this difficulty can be met in several ways, of which the following two are the most important: (i) by devising an arrangement in which the droplets are formed by the gas flow so that they will be initially at rest, and during the period of acceleration very high relative velocities between spray droplet and dust particle will obtain; or (ii) by shooting the water droplets at the dust particles so that high relative velocities will obtain even if only for short periods, and by arranging that this is done repeatedly so that a very large number of impacts is achieved.

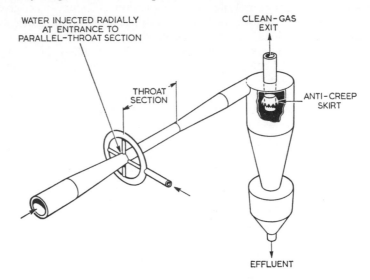

WATER INJECTED RADIALLY
AT ENTRANCE TO
PARALLEL-THROAT SECTION

CLEAN-GAS
EXIT

THROAT
SECTION

ANTI-CREEP
SKIRT

EFFLUENT

Figure 12.5   Arrangement of venturi scrubber

Both of these methods are used to advantage in commercial dust arrestors, the venturi scrubber and disintegrator scrubber being typical examples of the two techniques.

The general arrangement of a venturi scrubber is shown in Figure 12.5. In its simplest form it consists merely of a constriction in the duct carrying the dusty gas, the velocity being raised to 60 to 90 m/s or even higher. In the original design water was added at the throat, via radial jets[12], in quantities up to about 0·8 to 1·0 m³ per 1000 m³ of gas treated. The high gas velocity atomizes the water and the high relative velocity between the accelerating water drops and the dust particles in the gas leads to very high collection efficiencies for even the finest particles.

Figure 12.6 shows a typical grade–efficiency curve obtained in tests on a venturi scrubber with a 150 mm throat taking about 6000 m³/h of gas. The efficiency values for sizes above 2 μm were obtained on special silica test powders and those for the smaller sizes on dispersed non-pathogenic bacteria, or with a radioactive aerosol[13]. The curve suggests a very high efficiency indeed from a comparatively simple piece of equipment. In the author's opinion the design of the venturi section, the water-injection system or the spray collector is not critical, at least for the collection of industrial dusts down to, say 1 μm. It appears, however, that there is a very rapid fall-off in efficiency below about 1 μm and here attention to the design of the water-injection system may be of value both in increasing efficiency and in reducing pressure drop.

It has been claimed that equal efficiency can be obtained with rather lower water rates and hence lower pressure-drop, by substituting a fine pre-atomized spray for the radial injection shown in Figure 12.5; but when

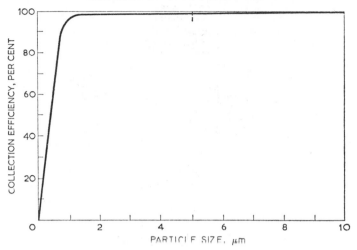

Figure 12.6 Grade–efficiency curve for venturi scrubber. Efficiency at
5 μm = 99·8 per cent

account is taken of the power required to produce the finer spray, little gain results—in fact, in certain cases the total energy usage is considerably greater. Boucher has also reported[14] that advantages are to be gained by the use of spray droplets whose sizes approach those of the dust to be collected, but the theoretical justification for these claims is not clear. By analogy with the reasoning in connection with the capture of dust particles in gravitational spray towers[8] it is possible to calculate the optimum droplet size for accelerated impact scrubbers also; this optimum size varies with the dust particle size, and with the gas velocity in the scrubber, and has been shown to lie between 28 μm and 500 μm for particles ranging from 0·4 μm to 2 μm (Figure 24 of Reference 21).

Boucher's claim[14] that maximum efficiency is achieved when the dust and droplet sizes are similar is clearly incorrect; indeed, this is reassuring since there is clearly little advantage in uniting, say a 1 μm dust particle with a 1 μm water droplet; for the resulting body would have an effective diameter of only $\sqrt[3]{2}(= 1·26)$μm and thus would be little easier to collect in the subsequent cyclone, or other spray collector, than the original dust particle. In practice the greatest advantage would appear to result from the optimum collection of dust particles on droplets of medium size, say 10 μm, and development should proceed along these lines pending the results of a fuller theoretical investigation of the mechanism of capture in an accelerated spray zone.

Recent developments in venturi scrubbers have generally taken the form of finding methods of injecting the water which avoid the use of fine nozzles, which tend to wear or choke. The original Pease–Anthony design[15] injects the water radially at the throat of the venturi through small diameter pipes rather than through jets, and other designs of venturi scrubber (Figure 12.7) are available in which the irrigating fluid flows over a weir on the walls of the ducting upstream to the venturi throat. This method of injection has the advantage that it allows the scrubbing fluid to be recirculated to a much

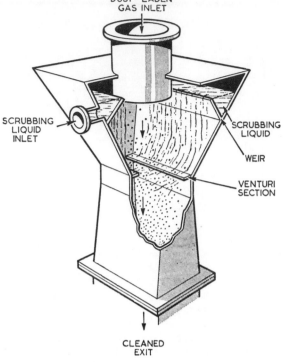

Figure 12.7 Venturi scrubber for recirculating scrubbing fluid

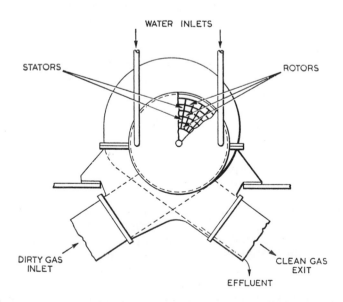

Figure 12.8 Diagram of disintegrator gas washer

greater extent than is possible with systems utilizing small-bore jets, thus effecting considerable savings in water make-up.

In disintegrator gas cleaners (Figure 12.8) the desired high relative velocity between the water droplets and the dust particles is achieved by the use of contra-rotating cages which break up the irrigating fluid into small droplets (probably below 80 μm), which bombard the dust particles. High collection efficiencies for particles down to 1 μm are possible and successful use has been made of this type of collector particularly in blast furnace gas cleaning[11]. They are, however, becoming less popular on account of the relatively high power consumption which may amount to over 500 kW for a unit to clean 100000 m^2/h of gas.

There are several other types of accelerated-spray deduster available and in each case the object is to secure the maximum relative velocity between the dust particles and the spray droplets. There is evidence, however, that this efficiency can only be raised at the expense of increased power usage[16], and any claims that high efficiencies have been achieved on sub-micron sizes at low pressure drop should be examined very critically. In many cases exaggerated claims arise because the size analysis quoted is that of the fully dispersed particles whereas the aerosol entering the scrubber is extensively aggregated and of quite a different size spectrum. If in practice the same degree of aggregation is not achieved, the collection efficiency of the scrubber will be much lower than that predicted; nevertheless, attempts to secure an effective increase in the particle size of the aerosol to be treated either by agglomeration or by condensation are often justified, though the cost of the pre-treatment, which may be considerable, must be taken into account. In one particular case, for example, attempts were made to enlarge fume particles, of average size 0·1 μm to about 10 μm by steam condensation, so that they could be collected with reasonable efficiency in a series of cyclones. It had not been appreciated that, even if condensation were completely efficient (i.e. if the particles grew equally so that all were about 10 μm in diameter) over 400 tonnes/h of steam would be required for treating about 100000 m^3/h of gas.

Figures 12.23, 24, 25, 26 and 27 (Section 12.3) show typical 'working' grade–efficiency curves for a spray-tower, a wet-impingement scrubber, a self-induced spray deduster, a disintegrator washer and a venturi scrubber respectively. These curves refer to average performances on a dust of density 2700 kg/m^3 and should be taken as comparative rather than absolute, as the actual performance in a particular case depends on a number of factors besides the actual size grading of the inlet dust. This is particularly true of wet washers treating hot gases, where the precise effects of condensation on the true grading of the dust entering the collector are difficult to predict; nevertheless, the curves will give a useful preliminary indication of the performance to be expected from the various pieces of equipment.

12.2.4 Electrostatic Precipitators

The electrostatic precipitator is generally regarded as one of the most efficient dust collectors, but there are many points to which attention must be directed if high efficiency is to be maintained. Though experimental work on electrostatic precipitation was reported late in the nineteenth century, the precise physics of operation of industrial installations are still imperfectly understood. The performance of new plant on untested duties is often unpredictable, large-scale plant failing to achieve its expected efficiency. It is clear that while a study of the fundamentals of electrostatic precipitation cannot fail to be of interest, it is unlikely to explain some of the very poor results obtained with 'difficult' dusts. There has recently been considerable study of these more practical problems and it is now believed that an important criterion is the electrical resistivity of the dust, as deposited on the electrodes. Sproull[17] and others have suggested that dusts with a resistivity below 2×10^8 Ω m will give little trouble, but higher resistivities are likely to lead to difficulties unless excessive deposition on the electrodes can be avoided. Modern research and development has therefore been directed towards producing more effective and reliable rapping gear so that dust deposits are not allowed to accumulate on the electrodes, or towards the development of electrodes which allow adequate current discharges in spite of dust build-up. Work is also being directed towards the production of collector electrodes which avoid re-entrainment of the collected dust into the gas stream, which can happen with the simpler types of collector electrodes if the resistivity of the dust is too low (100 Ω m has been quoted as a critical figure, below which creeping of particles can be serious). In the present state of development of commercial electrostatic precipitators it is clear that a knowledge of the properties, both electrical and physical, of the dust being treated is more important than a precise knowledge of the physics of charging and precipitation, important though this might be as regards the development of new and more reliable electrode systems and smaller and cheaper precipitators.

Theoretically it is possible to predict the efficiency of collection for any particular size of particle, by considering the electrical and viscous forces acting upon it, so that a grade–efficiency curve could be produced. The curve shown dotted in Figure 12.9 has been prepared in this way using a

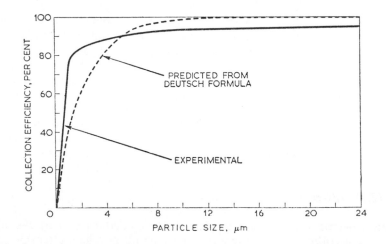

Figure 12.9 Grade–efficiency curves for electrostatic precipitator

modification of the Deutsch formula[18], the particle drift velocity being calculated from the field strength and the charge on the particles, the latter assumed proportional to the square of the radius, as predicted by theory[19]. In fact, neither the Deutsch formula nor the law of proportionality of charge to the square of the particle radius is exact, and practically determined grade–efficiency curves do not coincide with the theoretical, but take the form shown by the continuous line in Figure 12.9. It has, however, been shown that, over small ranges at least, the effect of changes in operating conditions of a precipitator can be related to the efficiency by the formula:

$$\eta = 1 - e^{-K/Q} \tag{12.1}$$

where K is a constant determined from prior tests, and Q is the gas flow rate.

When it is necessary to treat dust on which previous experience is lacking the only satisfactory approach is by experiment and much is to be said for the installation of a pilot plant to obtain prior design data. The pilot plant should, however, be a section of the full-scale unit and not a 'scaled-down' replica[20]. A number of such pilot plants are currently in use but so far few test results have been published. Even if such published data were available it is doubtful whether the information would be of very wide application, since in many cases the dust presents peculiar properties, e.g. of stickiness leading to excessive dust build-up, or abnormal electrical resistivity, which causes local spots of intense corona discharge leading to the effect known as 'back ionization'. This results in very high current requirements, often beyond the capacity of the electrical equipment; the voltage then drops and poor collection efficiency results. Attempts have been made to obviate these difficulties by 'conditioning' the gas and/or dust by the addition of various 'agents' such as steam or sulphur trioxide. Such agents are, however, generally specific and temperamental, and modern research, as stated earlier, is being directed towards improved mechanical design.

It is clear that, as in many dust arresting systems, theory lags behind practice, and fundamental studies can be regarded mainly, at least for the present, as aids to understanding the mechanism of operation of precipitators rather than likely to lead to precise design methods. The data presented in this Section are the results of practical tests on installed equipment and are to be regarded as indicative only. In particular cases it will be necessary to rely on manufacturers' experience or to carry out an adequate pilot-plant investigation. The warning against using scaled-down pilot equipment, given earlier, should be borne in mind.

The two main types of precipitator in normal use, namely the wire-in-tube type and the wire-and-plate type are shown diagrammatically in Figures 12.10 and 12.11 respectively. While the former is said to have superior electrical characteristics the author's experience has not shown that the performance is similarly improved. In fact, for many applications the plate type is superior since special trap-type electrodes can be used, which help to prevent creep of collected particles towards the cleaned-gas exit. It is probable that development of improved collector electrodes will play an increasingly important part in the future, as higher efficiencies are demanded. It is only recently that manufacturers have become alive to the fact that the initial test performance of the precipitator is not always maintained when the

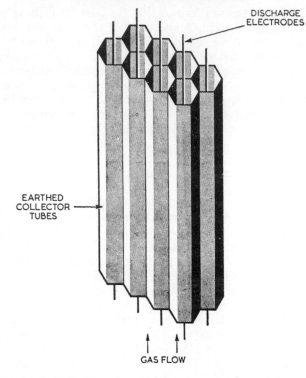

Figure 12.10 General arrangement of wire-in-tube precipitator

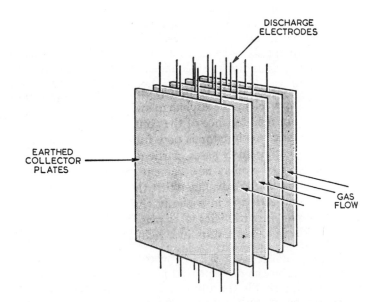

Figure 12.11 General arrangement of wire-and-plate precipitator

plant is in daily use, and more attention is being paid to improving the reliability of the mechanical parts.

The two-stage or pre-ionizing precipitator (Figure 12.12) provides a useful reduction in the cost of cleaning dusty gases, since its size and current requirements are considerably less than those of conventional designs. It is, however, generally unsuitable for dealing with heavy dust concentrations, and its main field of application is in air-conditioning plants for the removal of low concentrations of dust. There have been several successful installations

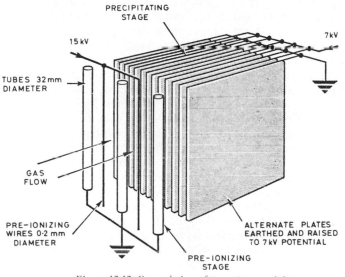

Figure 12.12 General view of two-stage precipitator

for this type of duty, including one in which cleaning the ventilation air to a telephone exchange switch-room resulted in a great reduction in maintenance of the contactors.

The electrostatic precipitator is now fully established as a reliable means of treating dusty gases, particularly effluent gases from pulverized-coal fired boilers and cement kilns. For the former duty it has the particular advantage that the small amount of dust which escapes collection is in a highly-charged state and further aggregation of the finer particles takes place in the stack and in the ducts leading to it. This results in a reduction in the 'blackness' or visibility of the plume, rendering it less conspicuous by a factor of at least 2. (It should be noted that the camouflaging of an emission in this way is not normally to be recommended, but where it can be shown that the emitted dust does not otherwise constitute a nuisance, any attempt to reduce the 'psychological factor' is praiseworthy.)

It is clear, however, that aggregation of the particles in an emission should not proceed too far, or enhanced dust-fall will be experienced. The general rule should be to encourage agglomeration of particles below 2 μm but to discourage the production of 'aggregates' larger than 20–30 μm. Electrostatic precipitators applied to boiler plant flue gases appear to achieve these desirable effects reasonably well, but in other cases, e.g. when used for cement kiln gases, much larger 'flakes' may be formed; their formation is probably more associated with the moisture content of the gases than with electrical phenomena, and the subject warrants further study, particularly since at the present time there is no reliable substitute for electrostatic precipitators for cleaning gases from cement kilns.

An interesting development is the use of a combination of cyclones and electrostatic precipitators for treating boiler flue-gases. The underlying reasoning is that the cyclones will effectively remove the coarser particles which tend to escape collection in the precipitators; also, in the event of temporary failure of the electrostatic precipitators (due for example to a broken discharge electrode) the maximum emission to atmosphere is limited to about 2 g/m^3. These are important advantages and are fully realized in well-engineered installations. Some difficulty was experienced in early installations of this type because the precipitators were unable to deal with the very fine dust escaping collection in the cyclones; this was largely due to attempts to use conventional precipitator designs, whose rapping gear was not able to cope with the stickier dusts which resulted from the use of pre-collectors. The first reaction was to limit the cyclone efficiencies to about 60 per cent, making up the loss by rather larger precipitators. However, in one large-scale installation, cyclone efficiencies around 80 per cent have been employed with success; in this case, however, the precipitator was designed with particularly effective rapping gear, and the gas flow to the particular section being rapped was isolated.

Where the dust is very fine or sticky, irrigated electrostatic precipitators can be used. In spite of claims to the contrary, there is considerable evidence that the irrigation has little effect on precipitation efficiency except indirectly by maintaining the electrodes in a clean condition. Irrigated electrostatic precipitators are well established for dealing with blast-furnace gases and, more recently, with fume from oxygen steelmaking processes[22]. However, fabric filters[23] and high efficiency wet washers can be considered as competitors for the latter duty (see Chapter 13, Part E).

12.2.5 Fabric Filters

Under the general heading of fabric filters are included all types of bag filters in which the filter medium is in the form of a woven or felted textile fabric, which may be arranged as a tube, or supported on a framework to conserve space. The former type includes the simple bag-house and the rather more complicated automatic filter in which the cleaning cycle is controlled either by a timing device or by the rise in pressure-drop as the fabric becomes loaded with dust.

In a normal fabric filter, particles considerably smaller than the apertures in the fabric will be trapped by impingement on the fine 'hairs' which span the apertures, as shown in Figure 12.13. In a typical filter cloth the main strands (the warp and weft) may be some 500 μm in diameter and spaced about 100 to 200 μm apart,* thus forming a 'sieve' with large apertures. The apertures are criss-crossed by fine 'hairs', i.e. the individual textile fibres,

*These dimensions are typical only, and differ in different fabrics; however, the deductions made are likely to apply to most fabrics in normal use.

which may be only some 5–10 μm in diameter; they form effective impinge-ment targets and will remove quite a high proportion of particles as small as from 1 to 2 μm. Thus a loose 'floc', whose voidage may be as high as 80–95 per cent, builds up on the surface of the cloth and provides an effective filter bed capable of removing particles down to sub-micron sizes. It is clear, however, that the filter will operate at reduced efficiency until the 'floc' has formed, and since the cloth must be cleaned from time to time to avoid excessive build-up of pressure-drop, these periods of reduced efficiency are

FINE HAIRS, 5 TO 10 μm DIA.

MAIN STRANDS, 500 μm DIA.

Figure 12.13 Diagram of filter fabric

recurrent. Table 12.4 shows the efficiency, on a fine radioactive aerosol containing 50 per cent by weight of particles below 0·3 μm of various types of filter cloth in the new condition, after build-up of a 'floc' and after clean-ing[13]. It will be seen that in service the efficiency of the light-weight cloth, after an initial very low figure of 2 per cent, oscillates between 13 and 65 per cent; with the heavier cloths the difference is not so marked, largely because the cloth itself has a reasonable intrinsic efficiency.

Table 12.4 EFFECT OF DEPOSITED DUST ON FILTRATION EFFICIENCY

Fabric	Aerosol efficiency		
	New clean cloth %	After dust deposition %	After cleaning by blowback %
Lightweight plain cloth (synthetic fibre)	2	65	13
Heavy raised-surface cloth (synthetic fibre)	24	75	66
Heavy raised-surface cloth (natural fibre)	39	82	69

Thus a normal bag filter cannot operate at 100 per cent efficiency, though if there are a large number of individual sections in the unit, and the cleaning periods are short, efficiencies approaching 100 per cent may be expected.

An important point in connection with normal fabric filters is that the velocity at which the gas passes through the fabric must be low, say, from 0·005 to 0·03 m/s. The main reason for this limitation is that higher velocities lead to compaction of the floc, which results in excessively high pressure-drop, or in local breakdown of the filter bed, allowing coarse particles to pass.

Thus in order to enable normal bag filters to operate at high efficiency it is necessary to provide large areas for filtration, and avoid frequent cleaning, which in turn limits the maximum dust concentrations with which the filter

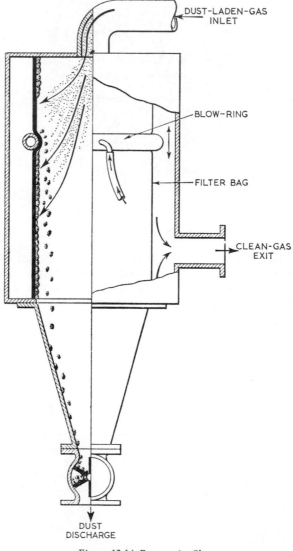

Figure 12.14 Reverse-jet filter

can deal. A possibility of overcoming these limitations lies in the 'reverse-jet' filter[23] which differs from the normal filter in the following important respects:

(i) The filter fabric used is a compressed felt which is of sufficiently close texture to act as an effective filter in its own right, i.e. without requiring a 'floc' of deposited material to aid its dust-retention properties.

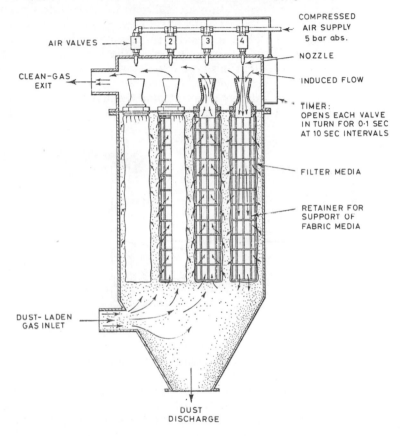

Figure 12.15 Pulse-jet filter

(ii) The deposited dust is removed by a reverse current of air from an external blow-ring which traverses the length of the bag, usually continuously (Figure 12.14). Thus the build-up of deposited material is avoided, which eases the limitation on operating velocity. Face velocities of 0·05 m/s are common and in favourable cases velocities up to 0·075 to 0·10 m/s have been employed. Efficiencies remain close to 100 per cent for particles down to about 1 μm and very high dust concentrations can be handled; since the maximum period between cleaning cycles is only a few seconds; in fact high concentrations are usually an advantage since the deposited dust then tends to be dislodged in 'slabs', rather than being redispersed in the gas to undergo redeposition, with consequent reduction in filter capacity. In early semi-technical tests on a filter of this type concentrations of 100 g/m³ were handled as easily as concentrations of 5 g/m³, with no additional pressure-drop or loss of efficiency.

Alternatively the bag can be cleaned by 'pulsing' a jet of air into it from the 'clean' side (Figure 12.15). This has the two-fold effect of stopping the forward flow of dust-laden air, and also of shaking the bag. In some designs of pulse-air filters the quantity and duration of application of the reverse-air is not enough to give a back-flow of clean air sufficient to remove dust from the interstices of the fabric. If the dust being filtered contains a proportion of fine fume this will lodge in the fabric and lead to progressive build-up of pressure-drop, with resulting fall-off in capacity, unless the bags are removed for cleaning. It is noteworthy that this type of unit was originally developed to deal with flake-like particles, which in a conventional bag-filter rapidly cause surface blinding but do not penetrate into the fabric. The surface layer is easily dislodged and for such duties the pulse-cleaner is very effective.

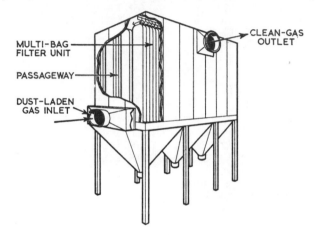

MULTI-BAG FILTER UNIT

CLEAN-GAS OUTLET

PASSAGEWAY

DUST-LADEN GAS INLET

Figure 12.16 General view of 'bag-house' (low face-velocity type)

Where a definite reverse flow is required in addition to the initial pulse this can, of course, be arranged by means of automatic valves, but in this case the convenience of the simple air-pulse is lost. Clearly the selection of the type of blow-back or shaking to be employed depends critically on the type of dust and the fabric used, and where possible a pilot test should be carried out. In cases where it can be done, much useful information can be obtained by depositing a cake of the dust on a small sample of the fabric and observing its behaviour on shaking and blow-back.

For convenience, bag filters can be regarded as falling into three main classes. The first class (Figure 12.16) is the 'bag-house' in which the con-struction, particularly of the bag-shaking gear, is relatively simple so that cheap units are a possibility. The main feature of this class of bag filter is that its operating face velocity is low, say about 0·01 m/s.*

While this type of filter is usually regarded as suitable only for the simpler duties (e.g. for removing sawdust from air extracted from rooms housing

*This operating face velocity is, of course, numerically equal to the gas flow rate in cubic metres per square metre of filtering area and is referred to by manufacturers as 'the air to cloth ratio' or merely the 'filtering ratio'.

wood-working machinery) there are cases where success has been achieved on dusts normally regarded as very difficult to trap, e.g. carbon-black. This is primarily because the low face velocity employed allows the dust to form a very loose, easily detached 'floc' which itself acts as an effective filter. Any attempt to use higher face velocities drives the sticky dust into the pores of the fabric, and the relatively simple cleaning mechanism is unable to restore the porosity of the cloth. Employed under suitable conditions, this type of filter is cheap and effective.

The second class of fabric filter is the conventional bag-filter in which some type of automatic bag-shaking is employed (Figure 12.17). This may be mechanical (cam-driven or pneumatic), vibratory or air-pulsed. Usually heavier fabrics are employed with this type of filter, and face velocities average about 0·02 m/s. The shaking mechanism can be adjusted either manually to a suitable cycle based on prior tests, or can be arranged to operate automatically when a pre-determined pressure-drop across the fabric is reached. In either case this type of filter will operate under more difficult conditions than the simpler 'bag-house' type, but it is considerably more expensive.

(iii) The third type of bag filter is the continuously-cleaned 'reverse-jet' filter (Figure 12.18) originally devised by Hersey[23]. This filter operates at face velocities around 0·04 m/s and can deal with very high dust concentra-

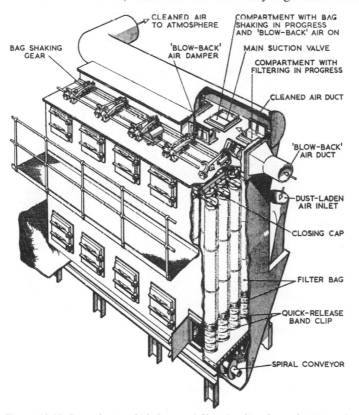

Figure 12.17 General view of 'shaker-type' filter (medium face-velocity type)

tions; the filter fabric is a compressed felt (either wool or synthetic fibre) and extremely high efficiencies are possible even on the finest dusts. While the smaller units (say those for gas quantities less than 2000 m³/h) are

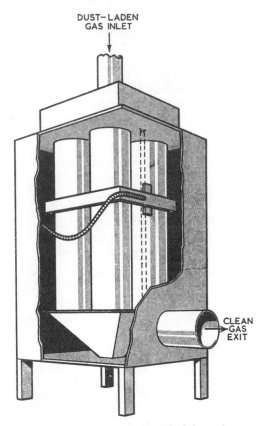

DUST–LADEN
GAS INLET

CLEAN
GAS
EXIT

Figure 12.18 General view of reverse-jet filter (high face-velocity type)

relatively expensive, due to the elaborate blow-ring operating gear and the additional blowers, in the very large units the equipment is usually cheaper than conventional bag filters, and may be more compact. However, reverse-jet filters are still relatively untried in this country on difficult effluent problems, particularly as regards reliability of the blow-ring operating mechanism under corrosive-erosive conditions, and further full-scale experience is necessary before their use can be widely extended in this field.

12.3 Performance of Dust Arrestors

12.3.1 Use of Grade–Efficiency Curves to Predict Performance

In this Section a selection of working grade–efficiency curves is given (Figures 12.19–28) from which it is possible to predict the actual performance of particular dust collectors, provided that the size analysis of the inlet dust is known. The method of carrying out such a calculation is given in the next Section; the following points should, however, be noted:

(i) For irregular particles the size analysis of the dust should be in terms of the free-falling speeds of equivalent spheres, i.e. the spherical particles having the same free-falling speed under similar conditions of fluid viscosity and density. This is particularly important when the aerosol under consideration contains particles which are loose flocculates, hollow spheres or porous materials with a high internal voidage. In most cases size analysis can be carried out by air elutriation (Chapter 14) which gives figures directly in terms of the equivalent sphere.

(ii) The grade–efficiency curves given are typical for the class of arrestor quoted, rather than particular for specific makes of equipment. They are, in most cases, the result of prolonged tests on full-scale plant under normal operating conditions and are more likely to give a true picture of the performance of an arrestor than loose claims, which should be discounted if they differ widely from results predicted from the curves given in this Section. On the other hand manufacturers' performance curves, if properly prepared, are likely to be reliable and can form the basis of an effective guarantee of performance.

(ii) The cyclone grade–efficiency curves given in Figures 12.19–22 may need modification if applied to conditions other than those for which they have been determined, i.e. operation on dry air at atmospheric temperature. The methods of transposing cyclone grade–efficiency curves for changes in the density of dust, the cyclone diameter and throughput and for the viscosity of the gas are as follows:

(a) The correction factor is calculated from the equation below:

$$\text{factor} = 1 \cdot 0 \times \frac{2700}{\sigma} \times \frac{\eta}{1 \cdot 83 \times 10^{-5}} \times \frac{D}{D'} \times \frac{15 \cdot 2}{V_I} \tag{12.2}$$

where σ = density of dust to be treated (kg/m^3)
   η = viscosity of gas (Ns/m^2)
   D = diameter of cyclone (mm)
   D' = diameter of cyclone for which original grade–efficiency curve was determined (mm)
   V_I = gas velocity at cyclone inlet (m/s).

(b) The grade–efficiency curve is replotted using abscissae multiplied by the correction factor calculated as in (a) above.

(c) This new grade–efficiency curve is used in exactly the same way as the standard grade–efficiency curve (see worked example, Section 12.3.2).

It should be noted that the correction factor may be greater or less than unity, depending whether the proposed cyclone will have a performance worse or better than that indicated by the standard grade–efficiency curve.

Transposition of grade–efficiency curves for arrestors other than cyclones is less easy and entails some knowledge of the mechanism of operation of the equipment in question. Electrostatic precipitator efficiencies are best corrected in terms of the 'effective drift velocities'[20], after the efficiency under standard conditions has been calculated from the appropriate grade–efficiency curve.

(d) Grade–efficiency curves for wet washers (including venturi scrubbers) can be corrected for the density of the dust (where this differs from the

388

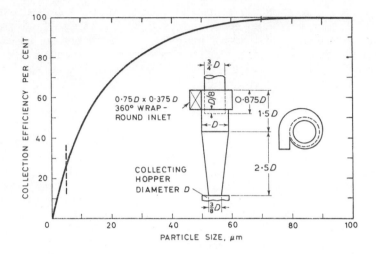

Figure 12.19 Medium efficiency, high-throughput cyclone. Efficiency at 5 μm = 27 per cent

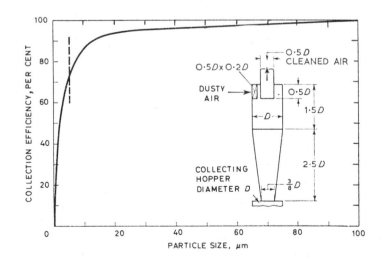

Figure 12.20 High efficiency (long cone) cyclone. Efficiency at 5 μm = 73 per cent

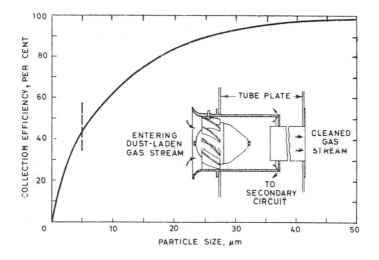

Figure 12.21 *Low pressure drop cellular cyclone. Efficiency at 5 μm = 42 per cent*

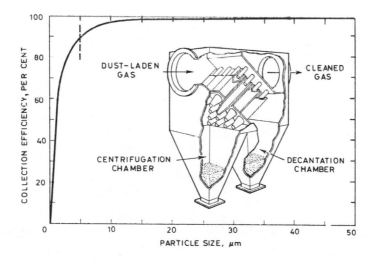

Figure 12.22 *Small diameter, tubular cyclone. Efficiency at 5 μm = 89 per cent*

390

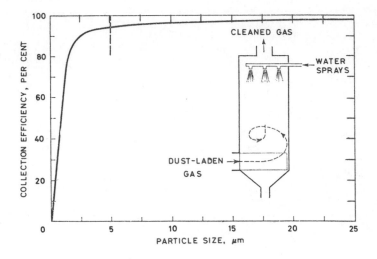

Figure 12.23 Spray tower. Efficiency at 5 μm = 94 per cent

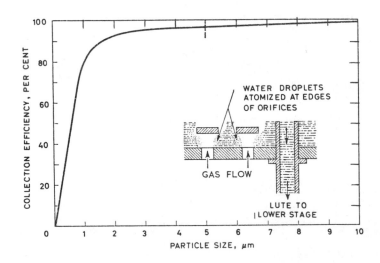

Figure 12.24 Wet impingement scrubber. Efficiency at 5 μm = 97 per cent

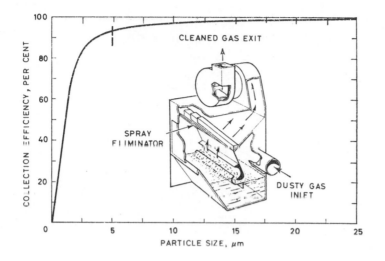

Figure 12.25 Self-induced spray collector. Efficiency at 5 μm = 93 per cent

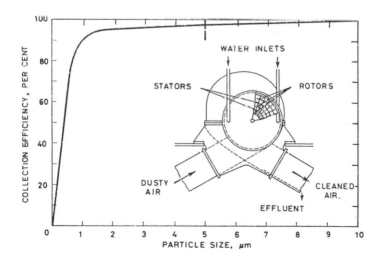

Figure 12.26 Disintegrator gas washer. Efficiency at 5 μm = 98 per cent

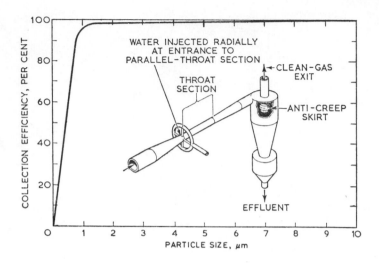

Figure 12.27 Venturi scrubber. Efficiency at 5 μm = 99·8 per cent

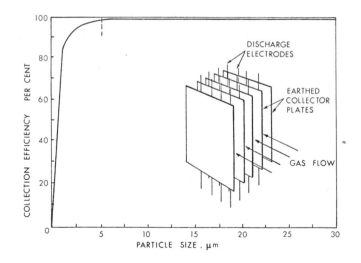

Figure 12.28 Dry electrostatic precipitator. Efficiency at 5 μm = 99 per cent

standard value of 2700 kg/m³ used in preparing the grade–efficiency curves in this Section), by multiplying the abscissae values by $2700/\sigma$ where σ is the density of the dust under consideration.

The actual method of using the grade efficiency curves is set out on p. 394.

12.3.2 Worked Example of Method of using Grade–Efficiency Curves

Problem. Calculation of the collection efficiency and exit burden from a combined cyclone and electrostatic-precipitator plant.

Suggested Plant. The plant under consideration consists of a nest of sixteen high-efficiency 1200 mm diameter cyclones, followed by an electrostatic precipitator giving a time of contact of 3 s.

Conditions at Inlet to Dust-collecting plant. These are given in Table 12.5.

Table 12.5 CONDITIONS AT INLET TO DUST-COLLECTING PLANT

Item	Detail
Gas rate	240000 m³/h at s.t.p.
Density of dust	2700 kg/m³
Dust concentration at inlet	10 g/m³ at s.t.p.
Grading of dust:	
Size of grade (µm)	Percentage in grade
104–150	3
75–104	7
60–75	10
40–60	15
30–40	10
20–30	10
15–20	7
10–15	8
$7\frac{1}{2}$–10	4
5–$7\frac{1}{2}$	6
$2\frac{1}{7}$–5	8
0–$2\frac{1}{2}$	12

Performance of cyclones. The grade–efficiency curve for the cyclones under consideration is that shown in Figure 12.20. The method of calculation of the collection efficiency is outlined in Table 12.6 which should be read in conjunction with the explanatory notes given below the table. The calculation consists of applying the appropriate fractional efficiencies to the percentages in each grade, and adding these amounts to give the overall collection as shown in Column 4. Column 6 gives the grading of the dust which escapes collection.

This calculation shows that the cyclone will collect 84·1 per cent of the dust presented to it, i.e. the emission will be

$$\frac{10 \times (100 - 84 \cdot 1)}{100} = 1 \cdot 59 \text{ g/m}^3$$

Table 12.6 PREDICTION OF OVERALL EFFICIENCY OF CYCLONES, AND GRADING OF THE EXIT DUST

1	2	3	4	5	6
Size of grade, μm	% in grade at inlet	Efficiency at mean size of grade, %*	Overall collection %	Grading of emitted dust	
				As % of inlet	Actual %
104–150	3	100·0	3·0	—	—
75–104	7	99·1	6·9	0·1	0·6
60–75	10	98·5	9·9	0·1	0·6
40–60	15	97·3	14·6	0·4	2·5
30–40	10	96·0	9·6	0·4	2·5
20–30	10	94·3	9·4	0·6	3·8
15–20	7	92·0	6·4	0·6	3·8
10–15	8	89·3	7·1	0·9	5·7
7½–10	4	84·2	3·4	0·6	3·8
5–7½	6	76·7	4·6	1·4	8·8
2½–5	8	64·5	5·2	2·8	17·6
0–2½	12	33·5	4·0	8·0	50·3
			84·1	15·9	100·0

* Read off from enlarged curve.
Notes: Column 2: from Table 12.5   Column 4: (column 3 × column 2)/100
        Column 3: from Figure 12.20   Column 5: column 2 − column 4
                            Column 6: column 5 × 100/Σ column 5

Performance of electrostatic precipitator. The efficiency of the electrostatic precipitator can then be calculated in a similar manner, using the appropriate grade–efficiency curve (Figure 12.28). The results of the calculation are set out in Table 12.7.

Table 12.7 PREDICTION OF OVERALL EFFICIENCY OF ELECTROSTATIC PRECIPITATOR

1	2	3	4	5	6
Size of grade, μm	% in grade at inlet	Efficiency at mean size of grade, %*	Overall collection %	Grading of emitted dust	
				As % of inlet	Actual %
104–150	—	—	—	—	—
75–104	0·6	99·2	0·6	—	Trace
60–75	0·6	98·7	0·6	—	Trace
40–60	2·5	97·7	2·4	0·1	0·7
30–40	2·5	96·8	2·4	0·1	0·7
20–30	3·8	96·5	3·7	0·1	0·7
15–20	3·8	96·0	3·7	0·1	0·7
10–15	5·7	95·5	5·4	0·3	2·1
7½–10	3·8	95·0	3·6	0·2	1·4
5–7½	8·8	94·0	8·3	0·5	3·4
2½–5	17·6	90·5	16·0	1·6	11·0
0–2½	50·3	77·0	38·7	11·6	79·3
			85·4	14·6	100·0

* Read off from enlarged curve.
Notes: Column 2: column from Table 12.6   Column 4: (column 3 × column 2)/100
        Column 3: from Figure 12.28   Column 5: column 2 − column 4
                                Column 6: column 5 × 100/Σ column 5

This calculation shows that the electrostatic precipitator will operate at an efficiency of 85·4 per cent, the exit dust loading being

$$\frac{1{\cdot}59 \times (100 - 85{\cdot}4)}{100} = 0{\cdot}23 \text{ g/m}^3$$

Performance of combined plant. The performance of the combined plant can thus be summarized as shown in Table 12.8.

Table 12.8 SUMMARY OF PERFORMANCE OF COMBINED
CYCLONE–ELECTROSTATIC PRECIPITATOR
DEDUSTING PLANT

Item	Detail
Inlet dust loading	10 g/m³ at s.t.p.
Exit dust loading	0·23 g/m³ at s.t.p.
Overall collection efficiency	97·7 %
Percentage of emitted dust coarser than 75 μm	trace
Percentage of emitted dust coarser than 20 μm	2·1%

12.4 Cost of Dust Collection

The preceding sections have provided data on various technical and design features of available gas-cleaning devices. The cost of the equipment clearly varies with the type selected and with the performance required. Also large variations in cost can be expected under different site conditions, particularly if special materials of construction are necessary. Further, the actual size of the plant may influence considerably the overall cost per unit volume of gas treated. Nevertheless, it is felt that some guidance will be helpful and Table 12.10 shows the approximate cost* for units of the various types to treat 100000 m³/h of gas, containing about 10 g/m³ of flue dust (of the grading shown in Table 12.9). The total cost of dedusting, expressed as new pence per 1000 m³ of gas cleaned, is plotted against efficiency in Figure 12.29.

It should be noted that the cost figures given are intended to be comparative only, as also are the performance figures, and individual practical cases will have to be considered on their merits, both technically and economically. Nevertheless the following broad conclusions can be drawn from the figures shown in Table 12.10 and plotted in Figure 12.29:

(i) Dust collectors fall naturally into groups, cyclones making up the lower-efficiency group, and bag filters the high-efficiency group, with wet washers and electrostatic precipitators falling in between.

(ii) The cost of dust-arresting plant (including installation) ranges from about £0·1 to over £1·0 per installed m³/h capacity, depending on the type of plant chosen.

*These cost figures are based on those first published in 1965[21]; they have, however, been modified in the following three ways.
1. The capital costs now include the full cost of the installation, i.e. erection, foundations, ducting, etc.
2. The costs have been corrected to 1969 values.
3. All values have been converted to S.I. metric units and costs expressed as New Pence (£1 = 100 p).

Table 12.9 GRADING OF STANDARD SILICA TEST DUST

Size of grade μm	Percentage by weight in grade	Percentage by weight smaller than top size of grade
104–150	3	100
75–104	7	97
60–75	10	90
40–60	15	80
30–40	10	65
20–30	10	55
15–20	7	45
10–15	8	38
$7\frac{1}{2}$–10	4	30
5–$7\frac{1}{2}$	6	26
$2\frac{1}{2}$–5	8	20
< $2\frac{1}{2}$	12	12

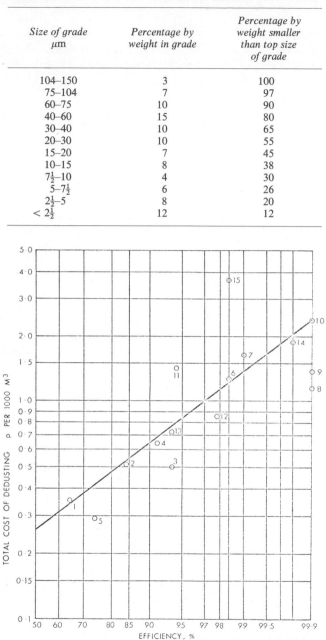

Figure 12.29 Graph of total cost of dedusting against per cent efficiency. 1, Medium efficiency cyclone; 2, high-efficiency cyclone; 3, tubular cyclone; 4, irrigated cyclone; 5, low pressure-drop cellular cyclone; 6, electrostatic precipitator; 7, irrigated electrostatic precipitator; 8, low velocity fabric filter (bags changed once per annum); 9, shaker type fabric filter (bags changed twice per annum); 10, reverse-jet fabric filter (bags changed twice per annum); 11, spray tower; 12, wet impingement scrubber; 13, self-induced spray deduster; 14, venturi scrubber; 15, disintegrator

(iii) The total capital, maintenance and running costs range from 0·29 to 3·6 p per 1000 m³ of gas cleaned, the cost rising rapidly for the higher efficiencies.

(iv) Electrostatic precipitators are no more expensive than would be expected from their performance; this is contrary to a popularly held belief.

(v) The cellular and tubular cyclones are attractive in terms of cost for a given performance.

(vi) Bag filters can be very attractive at the high-performance end of the scale.

Table 12.10 also shows, in columns 5 and 6 the relative sizes of the various plants (excluding dust storage capacity) for the 100000 m³/h units under consideration, and as a specific volume figure (m³ per m³/h). As expected fabric filters and electrostatic precipitators occupy most space and cyclones the least.

12.5 Factors Affecting the Choice of Gas Cleaning Plant

Preliminary selection of a particular type of gas cleaning equipment is usually made on the basis of the collection efficiency required from the plant. For example, if the gas contains a high proportion of fine fume particles (less than say 1–2 μm) many of the simpler collectors are ruled out and bag filters, high-efficiency wet washers or electrostatic precipitators are almost certain to be required. There are, however, a number of other factors such as gas temperature and humidity, the stickiness or otherwise of the dust, etc., which may exert an overriding influence on the final choice. In the following paragraphs the main features of the various groups of dust arrestors are reviewed from the point of view of general suitability for different operating conditions, and any design features to which particular attention should be given are enumerated. A more detailed treatment of the subject of selection is given in Reference 26.

12.5.1 Medium-efficiency Cyclones

Medium-efficiency cyclones (i.e. those with bodies greater than about 1 m in diameter, and fairly short in relation to their diameter) are not usually suitable when the dust to be collected contains much material below 10 μm. They may be used at almost any temperature, special heat-resisting alloys or refactory linings being used at the higher temperatures. However, care must be taken that the bodies of the cyclones are truly circular and internal projections or roughness due to welds or joins, must be avoided since they can cause serious loss of efficiency or increased erosion. The same remarks apply to abrasion-resisting coatings which must be smooth and should be free from uneven wear which would accentuate particle bouncing. With most types of cyclone the optimum inlet velocity is about 15 m/s, though in practice the actual value has a much smaller effect on performance than theory suggests, variations up to ±20 per cent having little effect on efficiency. On the other hand the pressure drop and the rate of wear are affected to a much greater extent and it is usual therefore to arrange for a fairly careful

Table 12.10 APPROXIMATE COSTS (1969) OF VARIOUS DUST-ARREST

(1)	(2)	(3)	(4)	(5)	(6)	(7)	(8)
Equipment	Efficiency on standard dust %[1]	Capital cost		Specific volume of plant		Pressure drop mbar	Pow cos £/annu
		£ Total[2]	£ per m³/h capacity	m³ for 100000 m³/h	m³ per m³/h		
Medium-efficiency cyclones	65·3	9400	0·094	170	0·0017	9·2	169
High-efficiency cyclones	84·2	18300	0·18	340	0·0034	12·2	226
Tubular cyclones	93·8	19700	0·20	119	0·0012	10·7	198
Irrigated cyclones	91·0	22300	0·22	255	0·0026	9·7	203
Low pressure-drop cellular cyclones	74·1	16100	0·16	102	0·0010	3·5	65
Electrostatic precipitators	98·5	88300	0·88	1420	0·014	2·2	100
Irrigated electrostatic precipitators	99·0	113400	1·13	1020	0·010	1·5	111
Low velocity fabric filter	99·9	48000	0·48	1190	0·012	5·0	169
Shaker-type fabric filter	99·9	62100	0·62	1700	0·017	6.2	187
Reverse-jet fabric filter	99·9	87100	0·87	2890	0·029	7·5	396
Spray tower	94·5	52500	0·53	425	0·0043	3·5	237
Wet impingement scrubber	97·9	31000	0·31	170	0·0017	15·2	290
Self-induced spray deduster	93·5	25100	0·25	255	0·0026	15·2	282
Venturi-scrubber	99·8	40600	0·41	567	0·0057	49·8	941
Disintegrator	98·5	51000	0·51	119	0·0012	—	2270

Numbered footnotes to Table 12.10 are on page 400.

EMS TREATING 100000 m³/h OF DUSTY GASES AT 20°C

(9)	(10)	(11)	(12)	(13)	(14)		(15)
			Total		Total cost including capital charges		Overall equivalent
Water usage 1000/m³	Water cost £/annum[5]	Mainten-ance, etc. £/annum[6]	running cost £/annum[7]	Capital charges £/annum[8]	£/annum	p/1000 m³ (100p = £1)	pressure drop mbar
—	—	60	1750	940	2690	0·34	14·5
—	—	60	2320	1830	4150	0·52	22·3
—	—	60	2040	1970	4010	0·50	21·6
0·64	660	150	2840	2230	5070	0·63	27·3
—	—	60	715	1610	2325	0·29	8·7
—	—	400	1400	8830	10230	1·28	55·0
0·40	440	420	1970	11340	13310	1·66	71·6
—	—	3000*	4690	4800	9490	1·19	51·0
—	—	3200†	5070	6210	11280	1·41	60·6
—	—	6000†	9960	8710	18670	2·33	100·4
2·9	3300	320	5995	5250	11245	1·41	60·5
0·48	550	320	3770	3100	6870	0·86	37·0
0·10	110	210	3140	2510	5650	0·71	30·4
1·1	1210	320	10940	4060	15000	1·87	80·6
0·80	850	200	23750	5100	28850	3·60	155·0

Includes complete change of bags once per annum.
Includes complete change of bags twice per annum.

control of the gas rate. It should be noted that when several cyclones discharge into a common dust hopper unequal gas loads may result in internal circulation in the dust hopper, leading to serious losses in cyclone efficiency[4].

The design of the equipment for removing the collected dust from the cyclone must be carefully considered since performance is drastically reduced if air is allowed to infiltrate into the base of the cyclone (see Section 12.3.1 and Reference 4). Re-entrainment may also occur if dust is allowed to accumulate in the hopper to more than half its depth.

12.5.2 High-efficiency Cyclones

Most of the remarks in Section 12.5.1 apply equally to the smaller high-efficiency cyclones and in this case attention to the circularity of the body and the absence of internal projections is most important. In the case of multi-tubular nested cyclones the avoidance of internal recirculation is even more critical (since the cells are usually too short to allow re-entrained dust to be re-separated). Certain manufacturers have endeavoured to avoid the worst effects by purging 5–10 per cent of the main flow from the dust hopper, treating it separately in a secondary dedusting system to remove the dust it contains. It is the author's view that this additional compensation is best avoided, and that recirculation should be reduced by careful design, particularly in ensuring that the total resistance to gas flow in the separate cells is the same. This, of course, requires uniform gas and dust flow, but this is in any case a pre-requisite for high efficiency. There are, however, occasions where for reasons beyond the control of the designer, it is difficult to achieve these and in such cases a base purge is an effective solution to the problem. A base purge is also useful where the dust has a tendency to cake in the dust discharge opening.

12.5.3 Electrostatic Precipitators

The design and performance of electrostatic precipitators has been substantially improved over the last twenty years and a number of publications have been issued dealing with various aspects of their design and operation. A good summary of modern practice has been given by Heinrich[24] and White[25]. The following remarks should also be noted by intending users of electrostatic precipitators.

Electrostatic precipitators are now firmly established for dealing with fly ash from large pulverized-coal fired boilers and for this application little more needs doing than to pay attention to the materials of construction, to

Footnotes to Table 12.10.
[1] See Table 12.9.
[2] Total cost including installation and auxiliaries (but not solids disposal equipment).
[3] Cost of electrical energy assumed 0·5p/kWh fan and motor efficiency taken as 60 per cent.
[4] Includes power consumed by auxiliaries (but not solids disposal equipment).
[5] Cost of water assumed 0·14p/m³.
[6] Estimated figure, including replacement bags for fabric filters.
[7] Assuming 8000 h operation per annum.
[8] Taken as 10 per cent of capital cost.
[9] Total annual cost expressed as power usage.

design and support of the electrode systems and to gas flow, including the avoidance of by-passing. In spite of the considerable amount of development work which has taken place in recent years it is quite surprising how non-uniform the gas flow distribution is on some modern plants. It is not really difficult to achieve ± 0.3 m/s for gas velocities in the range 1·2 to 1·5 m/s and calculation shows that such maldistribution will not have a very pronounced effect on overall efficiency. Nevertheless many modern plants do exhibit greater variations and this should not be tolerated. The choice of the rapping cycle is of considerable importance and depends, to a large extent, on the nature of the dust and the efficacy of the rapping gear. Very effective rapping, with de-energization and isolation of the gas flow from the section being rapped, is obviously the ideal but some types of rapping gear are insufficiently effective for this procedure to be adopted, since too long an off-time period for the section being rapped results in an overall loss of efficiency due to the overloading of the sections remaining on line. A good analysis of the effect of rapping cycles, with other data on precipitator operation, has been given by Little[20]. There seems to be little to choose between modern types of rectifier equipment, the mechanical type having been much improved, particularly as regards compactness and reliability. Automatic voltage controls, which maintain the applied voltage at its maximum stable value have also been developed to a high degree of reliability.

As stated in the main Section on electrostatic precipitators (Section 12.2.4) the electrical resistivity of the dust deposited on the electrodes plays a considerable part in determining whether a particular dust is likely to prove troublesome. It is, however, the author's view that much of the trouble experienced with 'difficult' dusts is enhanced by ineffective rapping gear and that serious attention to the production of well-engineered, thoroughly effective rapping gear will help to overcome many of the difficulties at present experienced. Unfortunately such equipment is likely to be expensive and where dusts are particularly sticky or have resistivities lying in the critical range (see Section 12.2.4) alternative forms of dust arrestor (such as bag filters or wet washers) may have to be considered. In certain cases the difficulties can be overcome by irrigating the precipitator electrodes, but this generally results in a much more expensive plant and it has proved acceptable only in a few special cases (e.g. blast-furnace gas cleaning).

12.5.4 Fabric Filters

Apart from the simple, relatively cheap 'bag-house' filters used in, for example, the wood-working and leather trades, modern industrial fabric filters are dependent for their successful operation on the efficiency of the arrangements provided for cleaning the fabric. It is very important that the filter be operated in the correct face velocity range taking account of the particular properties of the dust and gas being treated, the type of rapping gear provided, and the type of fabric employed. In many cases selection can be made from experience but in some cases a pilot trial may be required. If possible, it is, of course, helpful to consult with works where the types under consideration are already in use on similar duties. In considering proposals for a particular application attention should be paid to the effectiveness of the bag-cleaning mechanism, particularly its mechanical robustness, and freedom from leakage of valves and dampers, and the means provided for varying the cleaning cycle to suit the particular conditions likely to be encountered. The equipment proposed for removing the collected dust should also be examined critically bearing in mind that the dusts collected by bag filters are usually very fine, and, having poor flow properties, may give trouble in rotary discharge valves, conveyors or hoppers.

For design and performance of 'absolute' filters, reference should be made to White and Smith [27].

12.5.5 Wet Washers

While wet washers have many advantages and are often cheaper than other types of dust arrestor of comparable efficiency, they pose two particular technical problems, i.e. the disposal of the effluent slurry and the production of a visible falling plume. Where either of these aspects is likely to be a disadvantage it may be preferable to consider alternative types of arrestor.

Steamy plumes can sometimes be reduced by the use of 'abatement' scrubbers following the main recovery scrubbers, but these use considerable quantities of water and add appreciably to the cost of the installation.

Trouble is also sometimes experienced due to build-up of dust at wet–dry interfaces and special flushing systems may be required. Precoolers, and pre-separators to reduce the dust concentrations reaching the main collectors, may also be necessary.

If the washers are intended to deal with effluent gases before discharge to atmosphere as is often the case, care must be taken that suitable non-choking spray arrestors are fitted. Trouble is also possible owing to the formation of wet 'blobs' which considerably increase local deposition and corrosion of surrounding steelwork and buildings.

Where very high efficiencies are required it is likely that the dust arrestor will exert a considerable pressure drop on the system and the selection of suitable fans may present some difficulty; erosion of the blades may be a cause of high maintenance charges particularly if water droplets are carried over from the separator.

13

Dust Collection from Processes

General Introduction

The equipment available for removal of dust from gases has been described in some detail in Chapter 12. The present chapter contains accounts of the methods actually employed in removing dusts in certain industries, and includes discussion of procurement of plant, starting-up procedure, etc. Succeeding parts of this chapter deal with:

(A) *Sulphuric acid manufacture from pyrites.* An account is given of methods of removing the dust from the SO_2-laden flue gases before they are passed to the converters containing the catalysts for oxidation of the SO_2 to SO_3.

(B) *Power production from coal.* Methods employed to remove hundreds of tons of dust per day from the flue gases from the very large boilers employed in power stations are dealt with in this section. Individual boilers supplying 600 MW turbo-generators burn over 200 tonnes/h of coal containing 15–25 per cent of ash.

(C) *Cement production.* The volume of gas to be treated from a wet cement kiln is far smaller than that from a power station boiler, but the dust concentration is many times higher and the gases contain 30–40 per cent of water vapour, consequently corrosion difficulties are severe. Another difficulty of the cement industry is that there are numerous works producing about 5 million tons per year of cement in an area of 21 sq. km in north Kent, with the result that deposits on the ground of the residual dust leaving one cement chimney are augmented by those from other plants when the wind direction changes.

(D) *Brass foundries.* Here the problem is the removal from foundry furnaces of fumes of zinc oxide, often contaminated with black smoke from partly burnt oil before discharge to atmosphere.

(E) *Oxygen-using steel works.* Refining of steel with oxygen open-hearth and electric furnaces, and Bessemer converters has been extensively introduced since 1960 in order to increase furnace output. The use of oxygen gives rise to greatly increased volumes of iron oxide fume which is dfficult to collect.

PART A **PURIFICATION OF GASES FROM PYRITES ROASTING**

A. JACKSON AND H. ACTON

13.1 Types of Gas Cleaning Plant

The possible variations in gas cleaning plant can be suitably demonstrated by consideration of two cases: (i) flash roasting and (ii) hearth roasting without waste heat recovery.

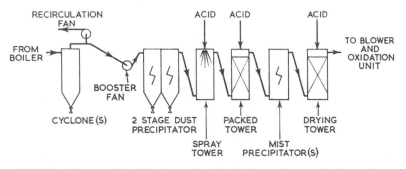

Figure 13.1 Flow diagram of purification train after flash roasting, employing cyclones and electrostatic precipitators

13.1.1 Gas Cleaning after Flash Roasting

A typical flow diagram of the gas purification trains is shown in Figures 13.1 and 13.2.

The distribution of pyrites cinders in the system above varies considerably with the degree of grinding of the feed, but the figures shown in Table 13.2 are typical. The dust burden of the gases leaving the flash roaster is in the range 70–90 g/m^3, n.t.p. A dust balance is given in Table 13.1.

An analysis of the arsenic distribution for a very high-arsenic-containing material is given in Table 13.2; it will be noted that the waste heat boilers themselves act as dust catchers for some of the arsenic fume.

Table 13.1 DUST BURDEN OF GAS LEAVING A
FLASH ROASTER

	% Dust and Grit
Total cinder produced	100
Cinder collected from roaster	50
Cinder collected from boiler	25
Cinder collected from cyclones	20
Cinder collected from dust precipitators	4·9
Cinder present in weak acid system (spray and packed towers)	0·1
Cinder drying acid	Nil

Table 13.2 ARSENIC CONTENT OF DUCTS FROM A
FLASH ROASTER

	% Arsenic
Pyrites as fed	2·0
Cinder from flash roaster	0·75
Cinder waste heat boiler	2·20
Dust precipitator cinders	3·30
Gas washing 5% weak acid	0·19
20% weak acid	0·20
Mist precipitator drips	0·20
Strong acid made	< 1 p.p.m.

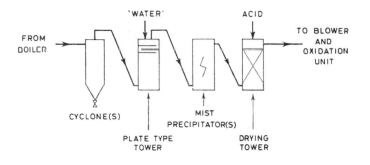

Figure 13.2 Flow diagram of purification train after flash roasting, employing cyclones and electrostatic precipitators

The ground pyrites as fed to the above-mentioned flash roaster had the size analysis given in Table 13.3.

Table 13.3 SIZE ANALYSIS OF GROUND
PYRITES TO A FLASH ROASTER

Size, μm	% by weight
> 152	4·0
102–152	9·5
76–102	8·5
53–76	18·0
40–53	7·0
30–40	16·0
20–30	16·0
15–20	8·0
10–15	6·5
5–10	5·5
5 and below	1·0

The dusts collected by the cyclone and electrostatic precipitators of Figure 13.1 had the size analyses given in Tables 13.4 and 13.5.

The spray tower is generally irrigated with 20 per cent sulphuric acid, especially if much arsenic is present in the dirty gas evolved. The packed tower is irrigated with acid of about 5 per cent concentration: this concentration is maintained by water addition and transferring the acid made to the 20 per cent sulphuric acid system. The precipitator liquor, which contains 15–20 per cent sulphuric acid is generally mixed in with the 'weak' acid for use elsewhere.

The dust collected by the plate type tower, Figure 13.2, had the size analysis given in Table 13.6.

The stripped liquor had a suspended solids concentration of about 1·5 kg/m^3.

The decision as to which of the alternative systems is chosen will depend not only on the designs based on the information given in Section 13.2, but also whether the weak sulphuric acid (produced as in Figure 13.1) could be used elsewhere, e.g. superphosphate manufacture; or whether the liquor

Table 13.4 SIZE ANALYSIS OF DUST COLLECTED BY CYCLONE AFTER FLASH ROASTER

Size, μm	% by weight
> 104	2·0
76–104	5·0
53–76	13·0
40–53	4·5
30–40	10·5
20–30	30·0
15–20	14·0
10–15	12·0
5–10	8·0
5 and below	1·0

Table 13.5 SIZE ANALYSIS OF DUST COLLECTED BY PRECIPITATION

Dust precipitator cinder, size, μm	% by weight
> 15	2·0
10–15	14·5
7½–10	52·5
5–7½	19·0
2½–5	9·5
2½ and below	2·5

produced in what is known as the *once-through* system of Figure 13.2 presents a disposal problem. When much SO_3 is formed during the roasting operation and a once-through system would remove it, the system shown in Figure 13.2 is ruled out on economic grounds.

Further consideration of the two diagrams will also show that although the system of Figure 13.1 has the greater possibility of recovering valuable dust in separate fractions in the dry state, it is a more costly and complex process.

If the dust carried forward from the flash roasting contains much fume, e.g. arsenic or selenium, and could both damage and slowly block the acid plant conversion system catalyst, it is usual to have two stage mist precipitation in order to ensure the production of optically clear gas.

Consideration of the suction conditions through both systems is important and the equipment must be so designed and arranged that the suction in the mist precipitator suction does not damage the lead of which the precipitator is constructed. This point is covered in the system shown in Figure 13.1 where a booster fan is interposed between the cyclones and the

Table 13.6 DUST COLLECTED BY
PLATE-TYPE TOWER

Size, μm	% by weight
> 20	6·0
15–20	8·5
10–15	39·5
5–10	38·0
5	8·0

dust precipitators so that they work under the slightest suction; consequently there is little chance of any air being drawn in at points such as dust valves, poke-holes, etc., to give corrosion and produce sticky dust. In the system shown in Figure 13.2 the total pressure drop of the cyclones and plate type scrubber will only be about 25 mb which is satisfactory for mist precipitators. With more recent designs of system a suction of 75 mb can be tolerated.

The SO_2 concentration and quantity of gas will not only determine the sizes of the various pieces of equipment in the main gas stream, but also the size of the fan necessary for the recirculation of gas which acts as the temperature control in the roaster. The cyclone between the roaster and the recirculation and the booster fans serves to remove the larger and more abrasive particles from the gas stream, and thus prolongs the life of their impellors and casings.

Because of the corrosive nature of the cooled gas and to a lesser extent of the dust, it is most important to ensure that the temperature gradients across the individual units are properly maintained by careful insulation.

Typical temperatures for system of Figure 13.1 are: inlet cyclones 380°–400°C; inlet dust precipitators, 360°–380°C; inlet spray tower, 300°–320°C; inlet cooling tower, 65°–70°C; and inlet mist precipitator, 35°–40°C. Typical pressure conditions in mb gauge corresponding to these temperatures with $9\frac{1}{2}$–10 per cent SO_2 are: inlet cyclone, $-1\cdot3$; outlet cyclone (inlet booster), -11; inlet dust precipitators, level gauge or $+0\cdot3$; inlet spray tower, $-2\cdot5$; inlet cooling tower, -8; inlet mist precipitator, -17. Similarly for the system of Figure 13.2, temperatures are: inlet cyclone, 320°–340°C; inlet plate type tower, 300°–320°C; inlet mist precipitator, 35°–40°C. Similarly pressures are: inlet cyclones, $-1\cdot3$; inlet tower, -11; inlet mist precipitator, -29.

As the dew-point of the SO_2–air mixture is about 275°C, it can be seen that mild steel suitably insulated can be used for all the items shown above this temperature, and lead–brick-lined construction can be used for the medium temperature region with lead itself in contact with the gas for the mist precipitators and gas mains.

The plate type tower in the system of Figure 13.2 is constructed with the humidifying section in mild steel lined with lead- and acid-resisting brick, whilst the scrubbing and the stripping sections shell and plates are of 316 columbium-stabilized stainless steel.

Because of the valuable gas concentration in the washing liquor a stripping section of suitable design is usually incorporated at the base of the plate type tower itself, the stripped liquor being bled away for neutralization and disposal; the method of disposal depends on local regulations for trade effluents.

13.1.2 Gas Cleaning after Hearth Roasting

The purification problem after hearth roasting is very much easier than after flash roasting as there is only about one-fifth as much dust in the gas. The gas strength used for design purposes is 8·5–0·9 per cent SO_2 and the dust carry-over is only about 5–10 per cent of the feed. One further difference which is of great importance from the purification angle is that with 'arsenic rich' pyrites, two stages of mist precipitation are necessary in order to produce arsenic-free concentrated acid, since upwards of 90 per cent of the arsenic in the feed is driven off during roasting by this method.

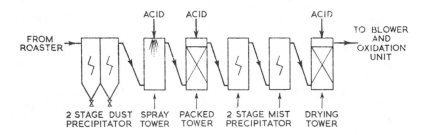

Figure 13.3 Purification system associated with hearth roasting

Figure 13.3 shows one arrangement of a purification system for SO_2 produced from 'arsenic rich' pyrites. A single stage of mist precipitation is satisfactory if the pyrites contain only a small percentage of arsenic. A typical analysis of pyrites feed to hearth roaster is given in Table 13.7 and the arsenic distribution for a hearth roasting system is given in Table 13.8.

Table 13.7 SIZE ANALYSIS OF PYRITES
TO A HEARTH ROASTER

Size	% by weight
8 mm	2·8
0·8–8 mm	75·7
Below 500 μm	22·5

Typical suction conditions in mb are: inlet dust precipitator, -203; outlet dust precipitator, -5; inlet packed tower, -9; inlet mist precipitator, -15.

Table 13.8 ARSENIC CONTENT OF DUSTS FROM A
HEARTH ROASTER

	% Arsenic
Pyrites feed	0·13
Roasted cinders	Nil
Dust precipitators	2·17
20% weak acid	0·21
5% weak acid	0·19
Mist precipitator drips	0·20
Drying tower acid (94%)	1·5 p.p.m.
	(single stage of mist precipitation)

The temperature range for this system, although rather different, since it has no boiler for control, still allows mild steel to be used as the material of construction for the dust precipitation unit, with the same materials for the rest of the unit. The conditions are: inlet dust precipitator, 500°–520°C; outlet dust precipitator, 420°–440°C; inlet spray tower, 320°–340°C; inlet packed tower, 65°–70°C; inlet mist precipitator, 35°–40°C.

13.2 Erection of Equipment

Because of the suction conditions on all the schemes shown, and of the danger of localized cooling with sulphate formation, extreme care is necessary in the erection of the gas cleaning equipment in order to reduce air in-leakage to a minimum in any of the units. Tightness of the pipe flanges should be checked thoroughly, e.g. by smoke tests, to reduce the possibility of sticky dust deposits at points of air in-leakage.

A most satisfactory but slow method of testing both new and reconditioned equipment is to use ammonia gas under slight pressure inside the vessel, e.g. a dust precipitator, and concentrated hydrochloric acid in a suitable container outside. A preliminary study of the drawings will show where leaks are to be expected, e.g. manholes, poke-holes, glands, insulator sleeves, etc., so that the hydrochloric acid should be applied to these parts first. Another method is to use ammonia with a suitable test paper.

If the hoppers of the dust precipitators are made of concrete and are tile lined, care must be taken to see that the surface and joints are as uniform as possible. Any flails fixed permanently inside the hoppers should be quite free to move under all operating conditions and safely earthed.

The electrical precipitation units should be checked in order to ensure that there are no sharp edges in the wrong places inside the precipitators which can cause spark-over. The spacing between the wire and plate electrodes must be as uniform as possible to ensure uniform precipitation and avoid inefficiency.

An air test should always be made on the electrical precipitators before heating up and the results obtained kept for reference so that the equipment can be rapidly re-checked after any repairs or maintenance. The method of air-testing is simply to allow air to circulate freely through the precipitators (both dust and mist precipitators) and run the electrical set from zero to maximum voltage. Any spark-over below maximum specified voltage should be investigated as this indicates a short-circuit which has to be investigated and corrected before full operation begins.

All rapping gear should be free to take up expansion when the 'hot' precipitator is heated to its equilibrium conditions so that it can work at its maximum efficiency when switched on.

Any dust valves fitted at the base of the cyclones or the dust precipitators should be checked carefully to ensure that they are gas-tight and counter-weighted to ensure the correct degree of 'float'.

One of the most important items of equipment on the electrical precipitation sections are the electrical interlocks which must be tested for correct operation before the current is ever switched on, their function being to ensure the system is earthed and admittance cannot be gained to any section for inspection when the section is still 'live'.

With both spray towers, packed or plate type, it is important to check that the liquor distribution is as even as possible, i.e. that every spray is working, distributor pans are level and the liquor feed from the header is equally balanced.

If the pumps used for the circulation of liquor are self-priming, care must be taken that all suction lines are free of leaks and this possibility should be reduced by keeping the number of joints to a minimum.

When plastics insulation is being applied it should be so designed that it gives the maximum efficiency and at the same time provides accessibility to any points, e.g. bolted flanges, which may be required to be opened up periodically for inspection.

13.3 Instruments

Because of the necessity for maintaining temperature and pressure conditions constant under normal running and of giving indications of momentary abnormalities, warning devices are necessary.

It is important to have a temperature alarm device on the lead main between the spray tower and packed towers to prevent overheating and distortion of the lead equipment should the liquor supply to the spray tower fail—this alarm is usually arranged to switch on an emergency water supply (Figures 13.1 and 13.3). In Figure 13.2 the plate type tower incorporates a temperature alarm positioned just below the bottom plate of the scrubber section which switches on an emergency water supply if the liquor supply stops for any reason.

The pressure at the inlet of the dust precipitator usually controls the speed of the booster fan by adjustment of the slip of a Fluidrive coupling.

The electrical precipitation high-tension sets usually incorporate automatic current control when arduous operating conditions are expected. Another protective device is automatic reclosing which recloses the ON switch should the set trip-out because of temporary overload, due to any cause—this device performs this operation several times at pre-set short intervals, but if even this fails a Klaxon gives further warning to the operator.

13.4 Starting Up an Installation

Most of the difficulties in starting up arise from the fact that the equipment is not at its equilibrium temperature condition and hence the dust is apt to be sticky and difficult to remove through dust valves, conveyors, etc. This trouble can only be overcome by patient and continuous working on the poke-holes and valve inspection doors to remove any lumps.

It is important to heat up the dust precipitators before admitting SO_2 gas to them and this can most conveniently be done by means of a separate small furnace which can be readily isolated from the gas system just before putting the whole plant into operation. Extreme care is necessary when using this heating system so as not to produce soot, otherwise in an extreme case it may be necessary to isolate the precipitator again and clean the plates and wires. The dust precipitators should not be switched on until the temperature has reached 280°–300°C, otherwise the dust tends to stick to the electrodes and later cause trouble with build-up. The voltage settings need readjustment as the plant warms up.

The mist precipitators should be switched on before any gas is passed through, to ensure a clean atmosphere in the precipitator and, as the gas flow commences, the voltage will have to be adjusted to its optimum value.

The liquor circulation rates over the towers at the start-up may need readjustment when conditions are stabilized, in order to give the correct acidities or temperature condition through them.

13.5 Plant Control

It is very important with all these units to have a plant record sheet on which all temperatures, pressures, electrical readings, acid strengths, flows, etc., are entered by the plant operators and, in addition, to use recording instruments. From a study of these records it is possible to pin-point any troubles in the early stages and take the necessary corrective action.

Chemical testing carried out by the laboratory staff will provide the basis for the chemical control and such tests as the determination of the suspended matter in the weak acids will provide information on the change in the efficiency of the dust precipitators—this test should be made at the same time each day and preferably just before any hand rapping programme is carried out. Acid strength determinations at the various points will indicate whether excessive carry-over or excessive dilution is taking place.

Efficiency tests on the dry purification section can be made using the method described in Chapter 14, Part A. The efficiency of the wet gas precipitators can best be determined by using a small glass precipitator on a side stream from the main gas duct, allowance being made for any SO_2 oxidized to SO_3 in the test precipitator.

Complete materials balances are very difficult to carry out satisfactorily and when completed may give widely differing results dependent upon the length of time spent in making them.

Acid carry-over and moisture determinations on the gas from the drying tower should be determined periodically, especially if any large changes have been made in the plant load.

13.6 Equipment Costs

It is difficult to draw up a true comparison of the costs of the various types of gas cleaning, including dust removal equipment, to perform approximately the same duty as the cost of necessary ancillary equipment is often as great as the cost of the basic equipment and must be included thus: (i) the cost of any foundations or supprting structures required would vary considerably and may be influenced by connecting equipment; (ii) the dust disposal system necessary may be quite complicated if the dust recovered is valuable; and in addition units such as fans, etc., may have to be used to maintain balanced conditions at intermediate points or overcome excessive pressure (or suction) changes caused by the dust cleaning unit.

Consideration of these and other items which may affect the layout or size of the units will indicate that the most economic final cost of an efficient plant can best be obtained by discussions with several suppliers after study of the costs given in Chapter 12; thereafter use of method study and models as indicated in Chapter 1 will help to keep capital costs to a minimum.

PART B ELECTROSTATIC PRECIPITATORS FOR LARGE BOILERS, INCLUDING COMBINATIONS WITH CYCLONES

H. J. LOWE AND J. DALMON

13.7 Introduction

The fuels commonly used in large boilers are coal, oil and natural gas, though the latter has only recently become available in the United Kingdom. With the efficient combustion that can be achieved in these boilers, the emission of solids is only a major problem with coal and this Chapter is mainly devoted to the methods of removing solid particles from the effluent gases of coal-fired boilers so that they shall not create atmospheric pollution.

Although the quantity of ash in oil is very small, great care has to be taken to avoid smut emission and persistent, visible plumes from oil-fired boilers; U.K. experience of these problems is briefly outlined in Section 13.12.

With efficient combustion there should, of course, be no solids emission from a boiler burning natural gas.

13.8 Emission from Coal-fired Boilers

A considerable quantity of ash is carried out of a boiler furnace in the flue gases when coal is burned in pulverized form. This ash is usually called either fly-ash or pulverized fuel ash (P.F.A.). The carry-forward varies considerably with the type of firing and typical figures are 15–20 per cent for cyclone furnaces, 45–55 per cent for slag tap furnaces and 80–85 per cent for modern, fully water-cooled, dry-bottom pulverized-fuel furnaces. Dust burdens of about 25 g/m³ n.t.p. are usual from the latter type of furnace burning high-ash coals, with corresponding amounts for the other types; typical gradings are shown in Figure 13.4. It should perhaps be mentioned that it is Continental

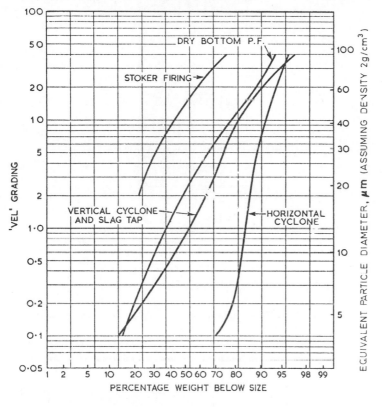

Figure 13.4 Typical dust gradings from various types of boiler. (A one vel particle has a terminal velocity of 1 cm/s in air)

practice to refer to ash retention, rather than carry-forward, and that the dust burden from slag tap boilers where dust re-firing is employed can be higher than that from straightforward dry-bottom furnaces.

13.9 Electrostatic Precipitation

The principal means of removing fly-ash from flue gases is the electrostatic precipitator of which the two main types are tubular and plate (see Figure 13.5). The basic principles of operation are quite simple: the dusty gas flows through a series of parallel tubes or plates, which are known as 'collecting electrodes'; the dust receives ionic charge from corona on the 'discharge

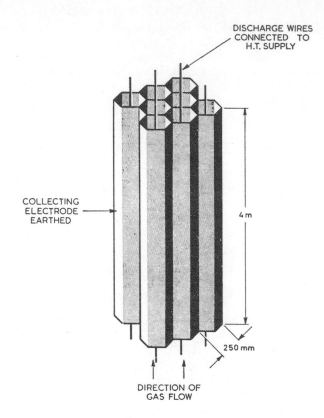

DISCHARGE WIRES
CONNECTED TO
H.T. SUPPLY

COLLECTING
ELECTRODE
EARTHED

4 m

250 mm

DIRECTION OF
GAS FLOW

Figure 13.5a Tubular precipitator showing typical dimensions

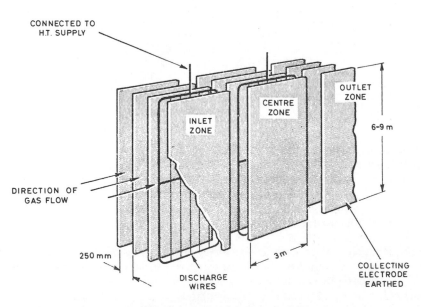

CONNECTED TO
H.T. SUPPLY

OUTLET
ZONE

CENTRE
ZONE

INLET
ZONE

6-9 m

DIRECTION OF
GAS FLOW

250 mm

3 m

DISCHARGE
WIRES

COLLECTING
ELECTRODE
EARTHED

Figure 13.5b Plate precipitator showing typical dimensions

electrodes' which are interposed between the collecting electrodes and maintained at a high, usually negative voltage—typically, 40 to 50 kV; the electrostatic field causes the charged dust to migrate towards the collecting electrodes where it is deposited and subsequently dislodged to fall into hoppers by periodically rapping the electrodes.

A 'tubular' precipitator consists of vertical hexagonal tubes, arranged side by side, through which the gas passes vertically upwards. The tubes are about 250 mm diameter and 4 m long and each contains an axial discharge electrode. A typical precipitator for the smaller type of power station boiler serving a 60 MW generating set (70 kg steam/s) would contain 1500–1800 tubes in parallel.

A good feature of these precipitators is that gas cannot bypass the treatment zone; on the other hand it is difficult to obtain uniform gas distribution among the tubes and re-entrainment of precipitated dust tends to be high since it has to fall against and through the incoming gas stream before entering the hoppers. Additionally, tubular precipitators are difficult to rap effectively and their limited treatment length restricts their collection efficiency to about 98·5 per cent. For these reasons, large modern boilers are almost invariably provided with 'plate' precipitators, which have the added advantage of being more compact and, hence, easier to accommodate in a limited space.

The plate precipitator comprises a number of parallel, vertical plates between which the gas passes horizontally. The plates are about 250 mm apart and 6–9 m high, and the discharge electrodes hang centrally between them at about 250–300 mm intervals. Plate precipitators are usually divided into a number of zones in series, each of which may be separately rapped and energized—a feature which contributes to their high efficiency and which it is not possible to embody in the normal form of tubular precipitator. The precipitator for a 500 MW unit would typically comprise three casings in parallel, each containing four zones in series. Each zone would have about 60 gas passages in parallel and the total plate area for all zones would be of the order 40000 m^2.

The efficiency required of flue-gas cleaning equipment is largely determined by the amount of plant to be installed on the site and by the chimney height; about 98 per cent would have been typical for moderate size power stations of 200 MW output, but 99·3 per cent has been specified by the Alkali Inspectorate for all stations of 1000 MW and above in Britain. These figures refer to full-load conditions and the performance at lighter loads will be significantly better.

The cost of dust collectors is considerable and the precipitators for a 2000 MW station, together with the associated dust handling plant, amount to about £3 million, i.e. about 3 per cent of the complete boiler installation. The proportional cost of smaller installations is, of course, likely to be rather higher.

Table 13.9 gives typical sizes for the dust collecting plant for a range of power station boilers; it also illustrates the marked increase in unit size which has taken place over the past decade or so.

Precipitator designs are usually based on the Deutsch formula[1], which may be expressed as follows:

$$\text{Efficiency} = 1 - \exp(-F_c)$$

416

Table 13.9 COMPARISON OF VOLUMES OCCUPIED BY BOILER PLANT AND DUST COLLECTING PLANT

Size of power plant, megawatts$_E$	60	120	200	350	500	500	500
Steam, kg/s	70 non reheat	110 reheat	170 reheat	310 reheat	435 reheat	435 reheat	435 reheat
Area of boiler plant, m²	600–850	950–1300	1600–1850	2150–3000	2800–4200	2800–4200	2800–4200
Maximum height of boiler plant, m	44	48	49	52	67	67	67
Type of dust collecting equipment	Precipitator only	Precipitator only	Cyclones and Precipitator	Cyclones and Precipitator	Cyclones and Precipitator	Cyclones and Precipitator	Precipitator only
Overall efficiency, per cent	96·5–98·5	97·5	99·3	99·3	99·3	99·3	99·3
Area of precipitator only, m²	195–255	230	330–380	540	780	780	780
Length of precipitator, m	14–19	11–14	12–13	13–14	16	16	16
Additional length for mechanical precollector, m	—	—	6	6	6	6	—
Height of precipitator body, m	7–9·5	8·5–15	11–14	11–14	12	12	12
Overall height from ground, m	17–20	17–24	21–24	21–24	24	24	24

where F is the specific collecting surface, that is the projected collecting electrode surface area per unit volume of gas treated per second, and c is the 'effective migration velocity' (e.m.v.) of the particles. Any self-consistent system of units may be used in the above equation.

The effective migration velocity depends mainly on particle size and on the strength of the electric field between the electrodes, and to a lesser extent on gas viscosity, gas velocity and composition of the particles. A typical curve showing the influence of particle size in power station precipitators is given in Figure 13.6, which is based on measurements made by the Central Electricity Research Laboratories at Leatherhead. It will be observed that the fine dust is less effectively collected than the coarse and the minimum for about 4 μm particles should be noted. This is believed to arise from a change in the charging process for sub-micron particles[2]

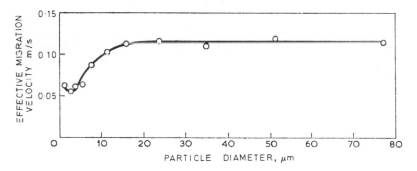

Figure 13.6 Typical relationship between effective migration velocity and particle size

Re-entrainment of precipitated dust will lower the average e.m.v. This can be caused either by the scouring action of the gas stream or by electrical forces, and will be most serious for coarse conducting particles[3]. A number of special collecting electrodes have been developed to minimize the effect of re-entrainment and these were helpful in the early pulverized fuel installations which produced relatively coarse fly-ash containing many coke particles. There is little evidence, however, that they are effective in modern installations where the ash usually contains only 1 or 2 per cent of carbon; indeed the tendency of collecting electrodes in the most modern plants has been towards flat plates with small ridges for stiffening.

Likewise, there are many types of discharge electrodes—round wires, square wires, concave-sided wires, barbed wires and barbed steel strip. There is, however, little evidence that any one type is significantly better than the others, provided that the high voltage supply matches the discharge characteristics of the electrodes, e.g. barbed electrodes will generally require a larger current than round wires, but at a lower voltage.

While conducting dusts are liable to re-entrainment, highly resistive dusts can also be troublesome. For many years this was attributed to 'back ionization'[4], i.e. the excessive voltage developed across a layer of highly-resistive dust on the collecting electrode causes electrical breakdown within the layer; as a result, positive ions are emitted and these tend to counter-balance the normal charging process by negative ions from the discharge electrode. The effect may readily be demonstrated in the laboratory, but it does not provide an entirely satisfactory explanation for abnormal electrical behaviour in British power station precipitators which usually takes the form of low discharge current, whereas back-ionization is characterized by abnormally high, stable discharge. A more plausible explanation is that a thin layer of highly resistive dust on the discharge electrode can markedly suppress the corona[5], by modifying the local electric field.

The electrical resistivity of P.F.A. appears to be mainly determined by the adsorbed salts on the surface of the particles; sulphur trioxide, which is formed in small quantities during combustion, seems to be a particularly active agent. There has been increasing evidence of abnormal electrical behaviour in British power station precipitators in recent years and this may well be due to the increasing ash content of the coal and to the finer grinding which is now used to achieve more complete combustion; thus, the available sulphur trioxide may be insufficient to give the dust adequate surface conductivity. A great deal of work is being carried out on the injection of sulphur trioxide and other 'conditioning agents' to restore the conductivity of high resistivity dusts, but the results have so far been inconclusive— significant improvements having been reported in some cases[6] but not in others[7]. It is certain, however, that most conditioning agents tend to be difficult to handle, are liable to cause corrosion and fouling in the duct work and air heaters, and the point of injection can be critical; their use is best regarded as still being in the experimental stage[8].

It should perhaps be added that a resistivity of 10^8 Ωm is often quoted as the threshold above which difficulties may be expected, although there is ample evidence that dusts with a resistivity of 10^{10} Ωm and above can be successfully precipitated. Also, the measurement of resistivity is fraught with practical difficulties; it is virtually impossible to reproduce in the laboratory a sample of dust with the same compaction and surface properties as it had when precipitated on the electrodes[9], and an agreed method of measuring resistivity would be essential if it were to be made a limiting factor in the guaranteed performance.

It is usual to specify the required performance of a precipitator in terms of the efficiency of dust collection by weight and to ask the designer to provide correction curves over the following ranges of operating conditions:

Gas flow:	Estimated flow at continuous maximum rating + 10 per cent, − 20 per cent.
Gas temperature:	100°–180°C
CO_2 content:	10–15 per cent
Dust burden:	7–35 g/m^3
Carbon content:	0–25 per cent
Sulphur in coal:	0·4–3·0 per cent

Precipitators are sensitive to gas velocity; it is therefore usual, during commissioning, to check the specified performance at both normal and 'low CO_2' operating conditions—the latter corresponding to about 10 per cent increase in velocity. It is good practice to repeat these tests, without preliminary servicing, about a year later to confirm that performance is maintained in normal service.

Typical values of e.m.v. are 0·09–0·12 m/s for precipitators alone and

0·07–0·09 m/s for precipitators with mechanical pre-collectors. Much higher values are often achieved on pilot plants because of the better gas distribution and more intense electrical discharge which can be maintained in the smaller units; this discrepancy underlines the need for caution in applying experimental results to full-scale installations.

13.10 Practical Considerations

13.10.1 Casings

Until recently, reinforced concrete was almost invariably used for the casings of British power station precipitators. Mild steel casings have, however, been used in many of the later stations; they have obvious advantages where speed of erection, space limitations during erection or total weight are important considerations. Both types are technically acceptable and the choice is usually made on economic grounds.

When properly designed and constructed concrete casings give good service on boilers burning coal with a sulphur content of up to 3 per cent. Allowances must, of course, be made for the reduced strength of concrete at higher temperatures (Figure 13.7), and care should be taken to cater for thermal strains—especially at the connections between the heated case and the unheated supports. The scantlings should be in accordance with *British Standard Code of Practice No. CP.*114:1957.

It is current practice to insulate thermally and weatherproof concrete casings in order to prevent condensation and corrosion. These matters obviously require special attention with steel casings, to the extent that any heat bridges between the casing itself and the external cladding should be avoided.

Particular care should be taken to minimize leakage at expansion joints, access doors and dust extraction valves, since the precipitator normally precedes the induced draught fans and is under a suction of about 15 to 35 mb. Inleakage should not be allowed to exceed 5 per cent, although values as high as 10 per cent are not exceptional on older plant; it reduces the stability of the high voltage discharge, increases the power consumption of the i.d. fans and incurs the risk of acid condensation.

Dust hoppers must be lagged and it is now usual to 'heat trace' the bottom metre depth to prevent condensation and consequential consolidation of the dust. For easy emptying, the sides should be as steep as possible; certainly greater than 60°.

Hopper capacity should be sufficient to store a 24-hours' accumulation of dust, though this may be reduced to 12 hours if a continuous ash extraction system is fitted. Dust level indicators are essential if overfilling of the hoppers —with consequential short-circuiting of the high voltage electrodes—is to be avoided. These must be robust if they are to withstand the inevitable knocks which occur during overhaul; the capacitance type are generally preferred in British power stations although the more expensive gamma-ray type is recommended where extreme reliability with virtually no maintenance is required. With the latter, the Ionizing Radiations Regulations[10] must be strictly observed.

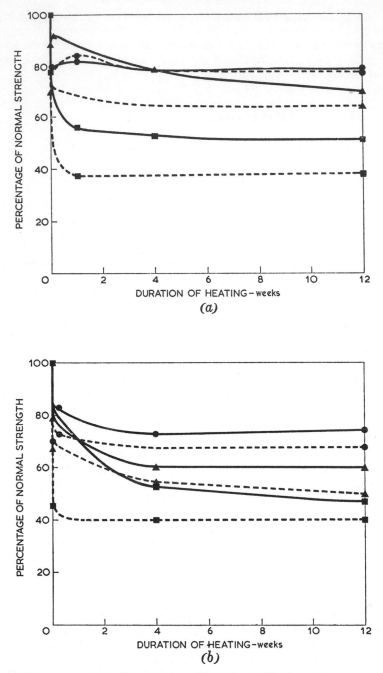

Figure 13.7 Effect of long duration heating on strength of concrete. (a) Mix ratio 1:3. Normal strength (before heating) 43 MN/m² (50 mm diameter cylinder). (b) Mix ratio 1:6. Normal strength (before heating) 24 MN/m² (50 mm diameter cylinder).

——— Specimens crushed hot. ––– Specimens crushed after cooling.

● = 90°C; ▲ = 200°C; ■ = 300°C

13.10.2 Gas Distribution

It is necessary for gas distribution to be uniform if optimum performance is to be obtained from the precipitator. Inlet ducting should be carefully planned to avoid sharp bends and rapid expansions, and model tests can usefully be carried out at the design stage to ensure that the gas distribution arrangements are adequate. Methods of controlling gas distribution usually take the form of splitters or turning vanes at the beginning of the inlet taper, followed by two or three perforated baffles immediately before the inlet zone[11]. Site tests should be carried out during commissioning to ensure even gas distribution.

Bypassing of the precipitating zone is, of course, intolerable in high-performance plants. This can occur in plate-type precipitators by gas flowing through the space above and below the electrodes, and adequate baffles and/or deflector plates should be provided to reduce this to negligible proportions. It is also likely to occur if dampers are fitted to allow the precipitator to be bypassed during the lighting-up period. This practice has been found quite unnecessary in British power stations, and bypasses are no longer provided.

13.10.3 Rapping Gear

Dust can be effectively dislodged from collecting electrodes or discharge wires by the shearing action of a sharp impulse. This may be applied by either raising the electrodes slightly and letting them fall against a stop or by striking them with a hammer which may be operated electromagnetically, pneumatically or by a cam. High-frequency electromagnetic vibrators which shake rather than strike the electrodes are not so effective and can cause fatigue failure of components.

It is generally acknowledged that the effectiveness of rapping is mainly determined by the peak acceleration of the electrode in its own plane, i.e. producing shear in the dust layer. The force required to dislodge dust is strongly dependent on the particle size distribution and the surface properties of the dust; values for various dusts are not well established but, as a guide, an electrode shearing acceleration of at least 240 m/s^2 appears necessary for adequate removal of fly-ash. It is, of course, important that a sufficient rapping impulse should reach all parts of an electrode surface.

Zonal control of rapping should be provided. Collecting electrodes near the inlet, where the dust burden and rate of precipitation are high, need rapping at about 10–20 min intervals, but the outlet zone needs rapping only about once an hour. These intervals are not critical. Frequent rapping is detrimental to performance since some re-entrainment is inevitable when dust is shaken from the electrodes; thus it is preferable to rap electrodes one at a time, rather than the whole zone together, in order to minimize visible puffs from the chimney.

Only a small amount of dust is precipitated on the discharge wires, but it can have a detrimental effect on the corona discharge if it is allowed to build up[5]. The discharge wires should, therefore, be rapped frequently, say, every one or two minutes.

13.10.4 High Voltage supplies

Large flue gas precipitators normally operate with a negative voltage of 40–50 kV applied to the discharge electrodes and a corona current equivalent to about 50–80 μA/m of discharge electrode (or 100–160 μA/m^2 of projected collecting surface area). The h.t. equipment should be generously designed since voltage and current vary considerably with combustion conditions.

Rotating mechanical rectifiers were once used almost exclusively but are now obsolete. Selenium rectifiers have been used for many years; they have proved reliable and do not require elaborate accommodation since both rectifier and h.v. transformer can be housed in a single, oil-filled tank which can be made weatherproof and mounted externally. Silicon rectifiers are now usual in large installations; they have a high electrical efficiency, may be installed with the same ease as selenium rectifiers and their early troubles due to reverse overvoltage transients appear to have been overcome with the controlled avalanche diode.

The h.t. supply to the electrodes should be sub-divided into as many zones as practicable, since the voltage that may be applied is limited by the flash-over voltage of the weakest point. The voltage to each zone should be controlled to maintain the highest possible stable discharge. Automatic equipments are now available to do this. They generally work by slowly increasing the voltage until either the current, because of flash-over, or the rate of sparking within the treatment zone exceeds a predetermined value. The voltage is then reduced a little and the cycle repeated. For smaller plants, where the cost of automatic voltage control equipment cannot be justified, arrangements should be made for the h.t. supply to be regulated from the boiler control panel since the voltage is likely to be set to a low value, and the precipitator worked at a mediocre level of performance, if the operator has to walk a considerable distance to make adjustments.

Insulators within the precipitator should be placed out of the gas stream to prevent surface contamination, particularly by oil and coal particles during lighting-up. A small in-leakage of air over the insulators also helps to keep them clean. All doors giving access to high voltage connections should be interlocked to ensure that the supply cannot be energized while they are open.

13.10.5 Radio Interference

Precipitators can cause radio interference, particularly when mechanical rectifiers are used. Adequate suppression circuits should be fitted to prevent feedback into the mains and the various sections of the plant should be bonded individually to a single low-impedance earth connection. In addition, the plant should be properly screened to prevent radiated interference.

13.10.6 Monitoring

The dust content of gas leaving a precipitator is usually monitored by an instrument measuring the percentage obscuration of a beam of light passing through it[12]. These instruments have not been entirely satisfactory in the past, and it is recommended that particular attention should be given to the following points: (a) location of the unit to ensure that the beam, which must be long enough to give adequate sensitivity, passes through a representative part of the duct; (b) cleanliness of the optical system; this has been a particularly troublesome feature in the past and has been largely overcome by the 'Everclean' window[13] (see Chapter 14C); (c) stability of the instrument with variation of supply voltage and ambient temperature; (d) the facility to check, while the boiler is on load, that the zero of the instrument corresponds to clean stack conditions and (e) alignment of the two components of the optical system.

If these precautions are taken, smoke density meters can give a useful guide to stack appearance though they should not be relied upon for an accurate indication of the performance of high efficiency plant.

It should, perhaps, be added that indicators are sometimes scaled in terms of Ringelmann number[14], as well as percentage obscuration. This can be misleading since the appearance of a plume containing light-coloured dust such as fly-ash is much influenced by the type of sky and by the relative position of the sun. The reader is referred to Chapter 19 and to *British Standard* 2811:1969, *Smoke Density Indicators and Recorders*, for further information.

A different approach, which has recently been adopted by the C.E.G.B., is to instal an additional instrument which measures the 'nuisance value' of the emitted dust. Nuisance is usually due to coarse dust falling locally and the sensitivity of the instrument is, therefore, biassed towards the coarse particles—contrary to the smoke density meter which is more sensitive (by mass) to the fines. In the C.E.R.L. flue dust monitor, Figure 14.36, this is achieved by allowing the dust to enter a stagnant chamber under its own momentum; the dust falls on to a glass plate and the optical obscuration is measured by a photocell. The plate is periodically cleaned and the instrument is self-zeroing.

13.10.7 Operating Procedure

It is sometimes advised that precipitators should be bypassed, or the high voltage supply not energized, until the gas temperature reaches about 80°C in order that insulators and electrodes shall not be contaminated with a sticky film of oil and coal. Experience in British power stations has shown that this precaution is quite unnecessary with modern plant, and present practice is to switch on the precipitators immediately before the boiler is lit, thereby preventing the substantial emission that would otherwise occur during the lighting-up period. Optimum performance is obtained by operating just below the flash-over voltage; this condition should be checked at frequent intervals, and whenever combustion conditions are changed. Hoppers should be emptied regularly: excessive dust levels can cause short-circuits between electrodes and, in the case of tubular precipitators disturb the gas distribution. Broken discharge electrodes should be removed at the earliest opportunity since they are likely to render the whole zone inoperative by short-circuit.

13.10.8 Annual Inspection

Precipitators should be carefully scrutinized during the annual inspection of the boiler. The alignment of electrodes should be checked and any excessive accumulation of dust should be removed, either by hand brushing or by washing. The latter method is preferred since brushing can cause damage to, and misalignment of, electrodes. The water should be directed from above, washing the lower parts first and working upwards. Washing must be carried out very thoroughly since damp fly-ash is liable to set like cement.

13.11 Combined Plants

For an interim period, about 1953–64, the dust collecting plant installed for high efficiency applications consisted of a mechanical collector (usually a large number of small cyclones in parallel) followed by an electrostatic precipitator; the arrangement was usually known as a 'combined plant'. It was argued that the mechanical collector protected the precipitator from gross disturbances during lighting-up and soot-blowing, and it was claimed that the combined plant was more economic. Mechanical precollectors were usually of either the 'multicellular' or 'aerodynamic' type and the pressure drop across them is about 3·75 m bar, compared with 1·25 m bar across precipitators. Their performance is strongly dependent upon dust grading, the coarse particles being collected preferentially.

Precollectors with a design efficiency of about 75 per cent were used in the first combined plants to be installed in British power stations in 1953, and their performance was extremely unsatisfactory. Dust tended to build up and choke the cyclones[15], and modifications in the form of vibrators and scrapers were introduced. These proved effective but the performance of the precipitators was then adversely affected, partly because fine dust is more difficult to precipitate and partly because it adheres strongly, and the rapping gear was unable to keep the electrodes clean. Additionally, the precollectors and, particularly, the fans in the secondary circuits tended to suffer severe erosion.

Precollectors of progressively lower efficiency (down to 30 per cent) were tried in an attempt to overcome these difficulties and to establish an optimum arrangement of combined plant. None proved entirely satisfactory and British power station practice reverted to the use of straightforward precipitators, i.e. without mechanical precollectors, from 1964 onwards.

It is worth mentioning that mechanical collectors have been fitted after the precipitators at an older station in order to improve the collection efficiency. This, too, was not entirely satisfactory, due mainly to blockage of the cyclones by the fine dust.

13.12 Emission from Oil-fired Boilers

The ash content of residual fuel oil is extremely low (less than 0·1 per cent) so that, with perfect combustion, the solids content of the flue gases would be less than that leaving efficient dust collectors on an equivalent coal-fired boiler. With incomplete combustion, however, the ash can be accompanied by a significant quantity of charred oil droplets, and this was so in the U.K. power station boilers converted from coal to oil firing in the 1950s. It was found, however, that the electrostatic precipitators on these boilers were capable of removing about 90 per cent of the char, which had a mean particle size of about 50 μm. It should be noted that, because the amount of particulate matter is small, rapping should only be carried out at infrequent intervals; also, because of the acid nature of the flue gas, good thermal lagging is particularly important and insulators should not intrude into the gas flow where they are liable to become coated with conducting dust.

An enormous amount of work has been carried out on the improvement of burners and the control of combustion to near-stoichiometric conditions, both to improve boiler efficiency and, particularly, to minimize the SO_3 content of the flue gas[16, 17]; SO_3 tends to be adsorbed on particles and can cause them to agglomerate and fall locally as acid smuts, or to create a persistant, visible plume. As a result of this work, it has been possible to reduce the dust collecting requirements on 500 MW boilers specifically designed for oil firing to multi-cyclone units of 50 per cent efficiency; it is expected that it will be possible to design and operate future generations of such power station boilers without grit arrestors.

PART C PROBLEMS IN THE CEMENT INDUSTRY

G. NONHEBEL*

13.13 Manufacture of Portland Cement

Portland cement is made from an accurately blended mixture, ground very finely, of calcareous and argillaceous materials, for example chalk and clay, limestone and shale, etc. If necessary sand is added to provide the required amount of silica. Ash from boilers fired with pulverized fuel is also used when it has a suitable analysis. The steps in the process are shown in Figure 13.8. The ground material is introduced into a long refractory lined tube (the kiln) as a suspension or in damp or dry form according to the process. At the opposite end to the entry of the raw materials a flame of oil or pulverized coal or gas is produced and the hot gases pass up the kiln against a flow of the roasting material. The kiln has a slight slope and is rotated slowly. Modern plants have rated capacities up to 125 tonnes/h and employ kilns up to 230 m long and up to 8 m diameter.

As the raw material passes down the kiln it is dried, heated, decarbonated and eventually sintered to a clinker at the hottest portion which is at about 1450°C. When the material becomes dry a certain amount of dust is produced, due to the cascading, which is suspended in the gases and of which a part

---

* Parts of this chapter are based on the chapter in the first edition by the late J. J. L. Murray and on a paper by E. Burke on Dust Control in the Cement Industry contributed to The National Society for Clean Air Conference, 1969.

comes out of the kiln. The amount depends largely on the friability of the raw materials.

The clinker emerges from the kiln at about 1100°C and is cooled by heat exchange with the air used for combustion. It is then ground with a small proportion of gypsum to give Portland cement, a powder.

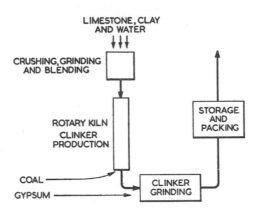

Figure 13.8 Cement manufacture by the wet process

It will be seen therefore that there are many problems with dust right through the manufacturing process, emissions at high level from the chimney and emissions at low level from the grinding, preparation and handling systems. We shall now consider four of the principal processes for the production of cement clinker.

The Wet Process. Until recently the most commonly employed process for cement manufacture was the wet process. Figure 13.9 illustrates a wet process kiln and ancillary equipment. The limestone and clay are ground, usually together, in water to a cream or slurry containing between 28 and 42 per cent of water depending upon the physical properties of the components. The slurry then goes to blending and storage tanks where adjustments to the composition may be made. Roughly one tonne of water is evaporated in the kiln per tonne of clinker produced.

From the storage tanks the slurry is fed to the back end of the kiln where it comes into contact with festoons of chains (illustrated in Figure 13.10). These assist in the drying and final breaking up of the wet sludge into suitable lumps of cake. This cake is then carried forward by the rotation of the kiln to the burning zone where the raw materials are combined to form cement clinker. During the passage of the solids through the kiln a certain amount of dust is produced and picked up by the hot draught. The first stage of flue gas cleaning thus takes place at the chain curtain where the entrained grit and dust are caught by adhering to the wet slurry-coated chains. The further dedusting required before the flue gases are discharged from the chimney are described in Section 13.13.

427

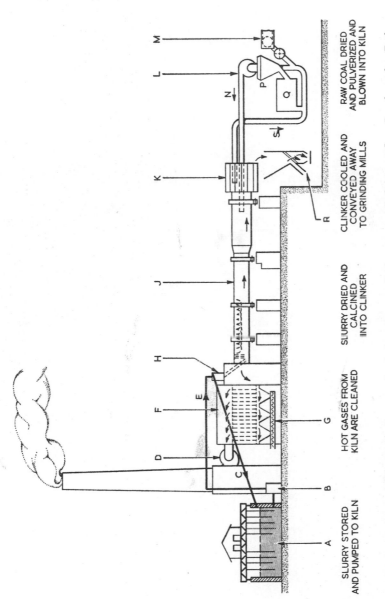

Figure 13.9 Diagrammatic layout of a cement works. A. slurry storage; B. slurry pump; C. slurry overflow; D. exhaust fan; E. slurry feed; F. electrostatic dust precipitator; G. dust conveyor; H. slurry feed to kiln; J. rotary kiln; K. recuperator; L. fine-coal plant; M. raw-coal feed; N. fine coal; P. classifier; Q. coal mill; R. clinker conveyor; S. hot air duct

SLURRY STORED AND PUMPED TO KILN

HOT GASES FROM KILN ARE CLEANED

SLURRY DRIED AND CALCINED INTO CLINKER

CLINKER COOLED AND CONVEYED AWAY TO GRINDING MILLS

RAW COAL DRIED AND PULVERIZED AND BLOWN INTO KILN

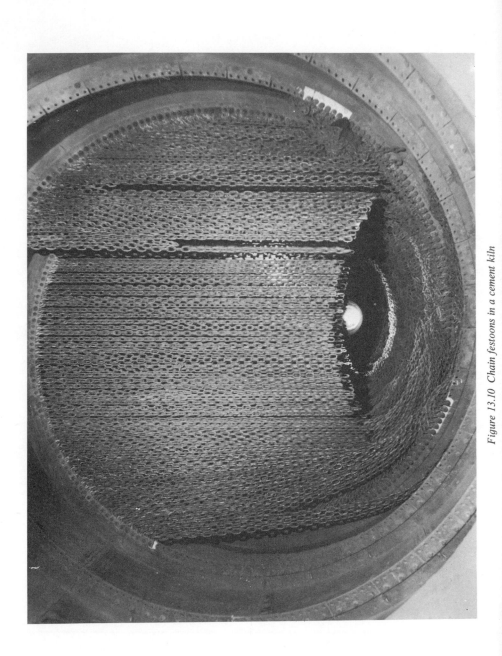

Figure 13.10 Chain festoons in a cement kiln

429

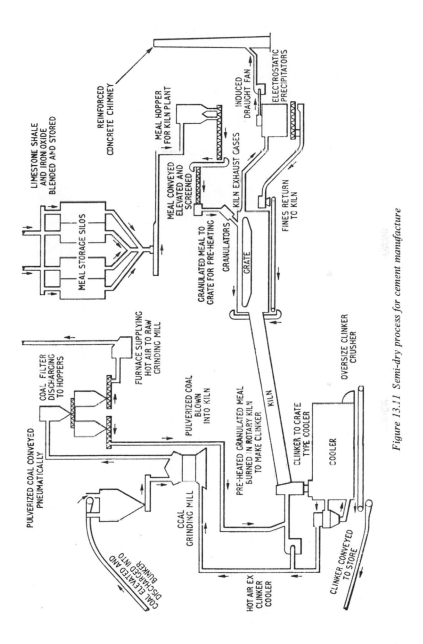

Figure 13.11 Semi-dry process for cement manufacture

There are three processes other than the wet process that are in use in the U.K. and they pose somewhat similar problems relating to dust. They are the following:

Lepol Process. The essential innovation here is that the raw material is first dried and ground and then nodulized with a small amount of water (Figure 13.11). The nodules are fed on to a moving grate and form a bed through which the kiln gases are drawn by a fan. When the nodules pass out of the grate they enter the kiln and from there the process is the same as for the wet process (see Figure 13.12), except that the chain curtain is omitted.

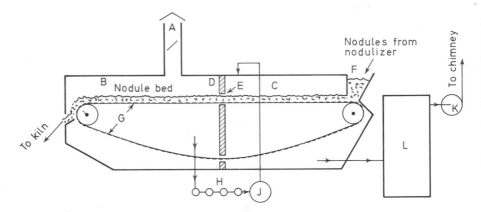

Figure 13.12 Diagram of double-pass Lepol grate

A. Auxiliary stack
B. Calcining chamber
C. Drying chamber
D. Fixed wall
E. Gap
F. Feed hopper

G. Moving grate
H. Multicyclone dust collector
J. Intermediate fan
K. Exit gas fan
L. Electrofilter

Due to the cascading of the material dust is produced but a large part of it is deposited in the bed of nodules which acts as a filter.

Davis Preheater Process. In this process the raw material is a suspension in water (slurry). This is suitable for raw materials with a high natural content of water such as chalk and clay. In this case, as with the wet process, the materials are ground wet but in contradistinction the slurry is then sub-jected to pressure filtration which removes the major amount of water. The resultant cake is then nodulized and introduced to form a bed in a rotating chamber. The gases are drawn through the bed by a fan and the dried nodules pass to the rotary kiln (see Figure 13.13).

Dust is produced in the kiln due to cascading and a large proportion is filtered out by the bed of nodules as in the Lepol process.

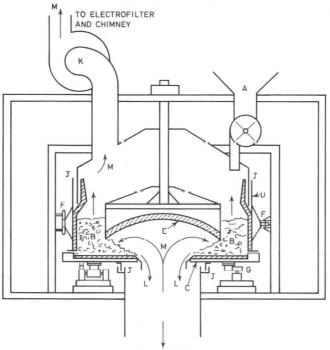

Figure 13.13 Diagram of Davis preheater

A. Nodule feeder
B. Nodule bed
C. Rotated hearth eccentric to bowl
D. Bowl
E. Suspended dome
F. Thrust bearings for bowl

G. Thrust bearings for hearth
H. Bearings for hearth
J. Water seals
K. Exit gas fan
L. Path of raw material
M. Path of gases

Suspension Preheater Process. In this process the raw material is dried and ground finely. Before passing into the kiln it is passed through a system of cyclones through which the kiln gases are drawn by a fan in counterflow. There is excellent heat exchange between the material and the gas. However, though the cyclones remove a good proportion of the suspended material a fair amount is still left. It is, therefore, necessary to provide large capacity in the dust filter and here only the electrostatic filter is acceptable. Figure 13.14 shows a diagram of one type of suspension preheater.

The object in these three processes is to improve fuel economy but the first two also assist in dust removal.

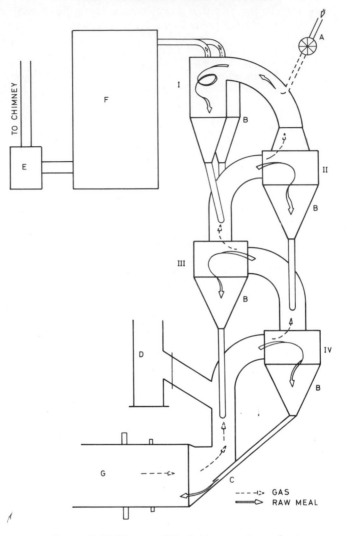

Figure 13.14 Diagram of Humboldt suspension preheater

A.   Raw meal inlet   E.   Exit gas fan
B.   Cyclones   F.   Electrostatic filter
C.   Input to kiln   G.   Kiln
D.   Bypass

Clinker coolers. Many kilns now have grate coolers instead of the old rotary coolers. In these the clinker passes on to a grate which by suitable motion causes the bed formed to move slowly from inlet to exit. At the same time cold air is blown through by fans. A part of this air is used for combustion but there is an excess which has to be wasted. The waste air carries clinker dust. As the dust is coarse a cyclone is usually adequate to deal with it.

13.14 The Main Problems

In so far as the general public is concerned, the main problem with cement manufacture is the removal of dust and fume from the flue gases leaving the kiln and discharged through the chimney. The dust burden entering the dust arrestors is high and the flue gases contain a high proportion of water vapour, especially in the wet process. This quickly condenses when it leaves the chimney giving a 'steamy' plume which travels a considerable distance before dissipating, especially in humid weather. The thermal buoyancy rise of wet plumes is far less than that of dry plumes because heat is absorbed in evaporating the water droplets formed when the gases have travelled a short distance from the top of the chimney.

Some water may condense on the residual dust escaping the arrestors thereby giving heavy particles and so increasing the rate of dust deposition on the surrounding district. Furthermore chlorides present in the raw material (such as those extracted near estuaries) are volatilized) mainly as K_2SO_4 and KCl) in the kiln and subsequently condense as a fine fume. These chlorides dissolve in the water droplets in the chimney plume and thereby reduce their rate of evaporation and therefore of dissipation. Their presence also reduces the performance of electrostatic dust precipitators. In fact in 1962 the large group of cement works producing 4·5 million tonnes/yr in an area of 8 miles^2 (21 km^2) on the south side of the Thames estuary experienced trouble with precipitator performance and plume dispersion which was attributed to the local clay workings entering deposits of estuarine clay. As a consequence the Alkali Inspector required change to Eocene clay extracted from the north side of the estuary. There are additionally some manufacturing process advantages. From this experience it appears that the chloride content of the kiln feed should be limited but the acceptable maximum is not known yet and will probably depend on the properties of the raw materials.

The dew point of the flue gases is raised well above that corresponding to their water content by their alkali salt content and by SO_3 derived by oxidation of a small portion of the SO_2 in the flue gases. The water dew point of flue gas from wet process kilns is in the range $42°$–$75°C$ but the actual dew point is raised by the SO_3 to well above $130°C$. It is necessary, therefore, to ensure that none of the internal surfaces of the dust arrestors, flues and chimney are cooled at any time below the dew point because the condensed water is corrosive to metal and to concrete. Dead spaces where dewing can occur must be particularly avoided since re-evaporation from such places will be slow; external heating may be necessary.

Dust deposited on the moisture film builds up with consequent chokage of gas passages. If cold air eddies form inside the top of even a well-lagged chimney, as have been found down to over two chimney diameters during strong winds, dewing and consequent dust deposition can occur. The dust deposits then break away from time to time and are emitted as 'blobs' which fall within the vicinity of the chimney base and become a considerable nuisance. Small pin-head blobs also form in cyclones and in flues after electrostatic precipitators.

From what has been said above it follows that there is a considerable advantage to be gained in respect of air pollution by use of processes in which the amount of water in the feed to the kiln is kept to a minimum. It is also necessary to reduce to a minimum the amount of in-leakage of air at various joints in flues, in dust arrestor hoppers and through holes formed by corrosion.

A problem with some raw materials is the emission of smell in the flue gases. This smell derives from traces of unburnt distillation products of organic matter. Occasionally there is a smell of H_2S. Smell is prevented by operating with 1 to $1\frac{1}{2}$ per cent oxygen (dry basis) at the kiln gas outlet.

Table 13.10 shows the analysis of flue gases from the wet process and other processes described in Section 13.13. Table 13.11 shows the normal range of particle size entering the dust arrestor from wet process kilns.

Table 13.10 ANALYSIS AND QUANTITIES OF FLUE GASES (RANGE) LEAVING KILN FROM FOUR PROCESSES USED FOR CEMENT MANUFACTURE

Constituent % by volume	Conventional wet process	Lepol process	Davis preheater process	Suspension preheater process
H_2O	43	18	20	8
O_2	0·8	5·8	6·8	1·8
CO_2	15	20	15	30
CO	0·1	0·1	0·1	0·1
SO_2	0·1	0·1	0·1	0·1
H_2S	Nil	Nil	Nil	Nil
NO and Cl	Traces	Traces	Traces	Traces
N_2 (by diff.)	41	56	57	60
m^3 (n.t.p.) per tonne of clinker leaving kiln	3800	2100	3300	1450
m^3 (n.t.p.) per tonne of clinker entering dust collector	Depends on inleakage at rotary seals and flue joints. May increase gas volume by 20%			
Dust content of gas to dust arrestor, g/m^3 (n.t.p.)	5–60	5–25	10–40	35–100

Note: The amount of NO depends on the flame temperature and the subsequent rate of cooling of the gases. No measurements have been reported.

Table 13.11 PARTICLE SIZE-GRADING OF DUST FROM WET PROCESS CEMENT KILNS ENTERING DUST ARRESTORS

Particle size, smaller than μm	High dust burden, 20 g/m³	Low dust burden, 5 g/m³	Very low dust burden, 0.5 g/m³
152	97	100	100
89	89	99	100
64	79	99	100
44	69	95	98
40	62	94	97
25	47	86	89
20	39	79	81
15	30	62	73
10	15	35	55
5	5	15	22
2	2	4	13

Prevention of the emission of dust at low level is relatively simple, though not cheap, though all the recovered dust can be returned to the appropriate part of the process. On the other hand only part of the collected flue gas dust can be returned to the beginning of the process because although it consists mainly of the original raw materials it does contain some alkali salts distilled from the hot part of the kiln. The proportion recirculated depends on its alkali content and is adjusted according to the reduction in the quality of the cement as recirculation is increased. When two-or-three-stage precipitators are used for dust collection, the dust collected in the second or third stage has been known to contain upwards of 15 per cent K_2O (mostly as sulphate) and can be sold as fertilizer.

13.15 Methods of Dust Removal from Flue Gases

There are only three practical dust arrestors for cement flue gases—cyclones, dry electrostatic precipitators and fabric filters using glass fibre fabrics. The latter are not favoured in the U.K. but there are many units in the U.S.A.

High-efficiency cyclones (Chapter 12) are reasonably satisfactory for small plants in the open country away from habitations. Small diameter cyclones should never be used if the dust is sticky because of a high content of alkali. On dusts that are not too fine, efficiencies as high as 80 per cent can be obtained but for very fine dusts it can drop to as low as 60 per cent. Careful experiments would be necessary for a plant in a new situation employing unfamiliar raw materials. These should include analyses for chlorides and examination of the dust liberated in an experimental kiln at the works of a kiln manufacturer. Even then cyclone dust arrestors might not ensure freedom from complaints of dust deposition. The great advantage of cyclones is that they do not break down and are comparatively cheap.

Electrostatic precipitators with two or three chambers in series, each separately energized will reduce the effluent dust concentration to less than 0.24 g/m^3 (n.t.p.) at which concentration the dust plume is practically invisible after all the water droplets have evaporated. Nevertheless designs and maintenance are seldom so perfect that no fall in efficiency occurs during years of operation.

Two solutions of this problem have been applied in practice. In one the electro-filter is made into a twin filter, the two running in parallel. One can be shut down for maintenance while the other takes the whole load for a short time at possibly a reduced efficiency but not necessarily so if the kiln through-put is reduced during this period. This avoids a kiln shut-down and it is fairly easy to obtain a satisfactory distribution of the gases between the two sections. This gas distribution is very important since the efficiency of the filter depends upon the velocity through it not being greater than its designed maximum. The other solution is to split the precipitator into a number of small units any one of which can be shut down for maintenance with little effect on the whole filter. In the one design one unit can be shut down, the top taken off, the old inside taken out and replaced by a new one and then put back in commission in quite a short time.

The problem here is to maintain an even distribution of the gases between, say, 6 or 8 units—not an easy job. Troubles with corrosion of precipitator chambers of concrete have been overcome by lining the chamber with acid resisting brick set in suitable cement.

Figure 13.15 is a photo of the emission from a cement plant employing the semi-dry process. This plant was commissioned in 1967. Another outstanding example of the efficiency of modern precipitators was obtained with a 7·4 t/h cement plant in Fiji. Here the plume from a short chimney beside a range of 250 m hills with mountains behind originally travelled for 8 km before dissipation in an atmosphere of 95 per cent humidity at 29°C. The raw materials consisted of coral, clay from a swamp in the sea lagoon and sand from an estuary. They were therefore highly contaminated

Figure 13.15 Aerial view of modern cement works in Weardale, Co. Durham. (By courtesy of Associated Portland Cement Manufacturers Ltd.)

with sea salt. Originally the only dust arrestment was by the chains at the kiln gas exit. After installation of a two-stage precipitator with an actual gas velocity of 1 m/s, the dust content was reduced to 0·24 g/m³ and the length of the plume in humid weather was reduced to only 400 m.

13.16 Low-level Emissions

Cement manufacture includes grinding and transport of materials. Whilst wet grinding is employed for the raw material mix, closed circuit air-swept mills are used for grinding coal and cement clinker. The dust from the mill vents is removed either by fabric filters provided the air is maintained above the dew point or, in the case of cement, by electrostatic precipitators. The air to the latter does not require to be heated, and as the total capital and running cost is lower than that of appropriate fabric filters, they are now being preferred.

Dry finely-divided material may be moved by screw or belt conveyors, elevators or pumps, or by flow in ducts or pipes after aeration. Where mechanical means such as band conveyors are used, difficulties with dust leakage may arise at transfer points and in such cases the provision of a suitable casing under suction, leading to a fabric filter, is usually effective. It is advisable that the possible points of dust leakage are placed in a suitably accessible position for easy maintenance.

13.17 Alkali Inspector's Requirements

Cement works are scheduled under the Alkali Act (Chapter 2). Notes on the requirement of Best Practicable Means were published in the Alkali Inspector's (104th) report for 1967. These include:

For kilns: Chimneys to be designed for efflux velocity of at least 50 ft/s (15 m/s). Ideally, emissions from more than one kiln on a site to be discharged from one chimney, preferably multi-flued. Chimneys to be adequately insulated to prevent internal condensation.

Minimum height of chimney to be based on a (published) scale and nomogram for several kilns. For a single chimney works, the heights vary from 200 ft (61 m) for a clinker output of 30 t/day to 550 ft (168 m) for an output of 360 t/day by the wet process and 450 ft (137 m) by a dry process.

Particulate emission to be less than 0·2 grain/ft³ wet gas, 60°F (0·48 g/m³ n.t.p.) for works producing up to 1500 t/day with a sliding scale down to 0·1 grain/ft³ (0·24 g/m³) for an output of more than 3000 t/day. Performance test sampling to be made once per month on Thames-side and every 2 to 3 months elsewhere.

The oxygen content of the kiln gas to be controlled to give an absence of H_2S—tests for H_2S to be made at least weekly.

For other operations: Dust emission from clinker cooler, grinding, cement packing, etc., to be reduced in new plants to less than 0·1 grain/ft³ (0·24 g/m³ n.t.p.). Plants to be tested at least annually. A high standard of good housekeeping to be maintained, e.g. roofs and roads to be kept clean.

PART D PROBLEMS IN BRASS FOUNDRIES

K. D. GREEN

13.18 Generation of the Fume

The necessity for collecting fume from brass foundries has become more important since the passing of the Clean Air Act 1956. It is unfortunate that no system has yet been evolved which will provide a complete answer to these problems.

The fume, which is mainly zinc oxide, is generated in varying amounts during the melting of brasses in open, electrically heated or oil-fired furnaces or crucibles. Zinc oxide, being generally light grey in colour, determines the colour of the fume generated, with one known exception, and that is in processes using swarf-containing machining oil. This swarf, when processed, produces a constituent that changes the colour of the fume from grey to black. This addition to the fume is from the oil which vaporizes above the crucible when stirring is carried on. The vaporized oil ignites above the crucible, and forms carbon particles in the sub-micron range. This adds a complication to the problem, because whereas the zinc oxide fume can generally be said to be below the Ringelmann 2 requirement of the Act, the presence of carbon black particles lifts it well above this range.

13.19 Analysis of the Fume

13.19.1 Size Analysis

Sampling the fume for the purpose of particle size analysis is uncomplicated, but it must be split into two functions:

   (i) Sampling for grits and dust down to 5 μm.
   (ii) Sampling for dust and fume below 5 μm.

It is not essential that the lower 5 μm limit is kept, but the grit and dust needs to be sampled isokinetically, whereas the fume behaves as a gas and can be sampled anisokinetically.

The fume can be analysed only by sedimentation and optical methods (Chapter 14). Air elutriation and apparatus employing centrifugal forces cannot be used for fume, but they are applicable to any dust that may be present. The most satisfactory (but slow) method would be to elutriate the fume in oil, since the normal difficulties or solubility would not then apply.

A typical analysis of the dust and fume which was sampled is given in Table 13.12. The analysis was determined by a particle count under a microscope.

13.19.2 Concentration of Fume

Concentrations of fume that will be presented to collection equipment will vary according to:

   (i) The capacity and number of crucibles or furnaces that operate.

(ii) The method of operation.
(iii) The quality of the charge (i.e. percentages of scrap, etc.).
(iv) The efficiency of the hood, canopy or extraction device.

Table 13.12 TYPICAL SIZE OF BRASS
FOUNDRY DUST AND FUME

Micron size	% Present at stated size
< 0·5	49·9
0·5–0·7	12·2
0·7–1·0	13·5
1·0–1·4	10·7
1·4–2·0	6·4
2·0–2·8	3·4
2·8–4·0	1·5
4·0–5·6	0·2
5·6–8·0	0·4
8·0–11·3	0·4
> 11·3	1·4
	100·0

Fume concentrations in the order of 1–15 g/m^3 n.t.p. may be expected.
The higher value is associated with a foundry using oily swarf in the charge,
and with an extraction device close to the top of the crucible or pot.

13.20 Applicable Equipment for Future Collection

13.20.1 Types of Collector

The performance of most of the particle collection devices applicable to the
problem are given below, for wet and dry systems. Fume in this section means
particles smaller than one micron.

(i) Wet Types. Spray towers: These suffer from the inherent inability of
being able to generate sufficiently high interception velocities between water
droplets and fume particles. On dust extracted in the process, this type will
be effective down to 2 μm, but on the fume, only approximately 75 per cent
effectiveness can be claimed even for multi-wash systems.

The design is simple and the cheapest of the systems involved. It is not
the cleanest method since disposal of the wet collected material also has its
problems.

Dust efficiency   80 per cent on particles less than 20 μm
                             less than 90 per cent particles greater than
                             50 μm
Operating pressure drop   2·5–18 mb

Impingement scrubbers: These are little better than spray towers, and have
a greater pressure drop. Difficulty is again experienced in producing a high
enough interception velocity, within the pressure drop usually associated
with this equipment. In types where the fume is forced through a depth of

liquid, the particulate fume behaves as a gas and effective wetting is prevented. The collection that does take place occurs in the turbulent period as the gas breaks the water surface.

Dust efficiency	97 per cent down to 5 μm
Fume efficiency	75 per cent overall on 1 μm and below
Operating pressure drop	1–18 mb

Venturi scrubbers: Providing high pressure drops are acceptable, namely 25–80 mb, high efficiencies can be obtained with venturi scrubbers for particles down to 1 μm size. Fume smaller than this will not be entirely collected, and the stack effluent will then still be coloured. This type of collector has, however, been successfully used on open hearth furnace fume.

Dust efficiency	90–99 per cent on particles less than 5 μm
Fume efficiency	86–97 per cent depending on the operating pressure drop

Disintegrators: This type of collector may be applied to the problem, but it is not as efficient as the venturi scrubber, nor the dry types mentioned. The cost of its operation is much higher than other types of equipment.

(ii) Dry Types. Bag filters: These will undoubtedly remove the majority of the fume, as bag filters are generally associated with collection of metallurgical fume and carbon black. The cost of maintenance is high and there are certain disadvantages.

Dust efficiency	95–99 per cent on particles less than 5 μm (Stairmand[12] plain bag and reverse jet type)
Fume efficiency	> 99 per cent
Operating pressure drop	1–15 mb (mechanical rappers)
	5–8 mb (reverse jet type)

Electrostatic precipitators: These have been successfully used on a composite problem in the steel industry (see Part E) and it is probable that the same degree of efficiency could be obtained on non-ferrous fume. Overall efficiency can be improved by irrigating the precipitators. Their overall disadvantage is the considerable capital cost. Although virtually 100 per cent efficiency is possible at great cost, performance of commercial plants is usually:

Dust efficiency	94–97 per cent
Fume efficiency	> 80 per cent
Operating pressure drop	0·5–1·5 mb

(iii) Destruction of Oily Fume by Incineration. As an alternative to collection, consideration should always be given to destruction by combustion of oily fumes from furnaces melting swarf—for example by passing the dirty gas through a refractory lined chamber containing appropriately designed oil burners. Recent investigations have shown that 97 per cent of the oily particles smaller than 1·5 μm can be removed and that the concentration of residual oil and zinc oxide particles from some types of furnace would be reduced to a density below that equivalent to Ringelmann 2. To ensure minimum fuel consumption it is obviously necessary to minimize the amount of excess air entrained by the fume extractor and to preheat the dirty fume by heat exchange with the purified gases leaving the combustion chamber.

13.21 Design Considerations

13.21.1 Temperature

The temperature of the fume over the crucible varies throughout the melting process. It is low at the start because the material charged is cold and fills the crucible, but it rises quickly once melting starts.

Gas temperatures with an open type of hood are 55°C at the commencement of the melt, rising to over 316°C when stirring takes place. Substantially higher temperatures occur for a short time when oil in the charge ignites below the hood. The resultant operating temperature at the collector depends on the length and size of the extraction ducting from the fume source, and the usual heat transfer calculations are necessary to predict the operating temperature at the collector.

Wet types of collectors are unaffected by temperature in either efficiency or pressure drop, but in the dry types, it is an important factor to be considered. Bag filters have a limited operating range, determined by the material from which the filter bags are made. Fibre glass allows operating temperatures up to 260°C, but this material is susceptible to fibre fracture during normal cleaning. Nylon is a particularly useful material up to 85°C. The other factor affecting both bag filters and electroststic precipitators is the operating velocity, as variations in this will produce changes in efficiency.

The extraction fan will, in general, be unaffected by the temperature, as it should always be designed for the cold condition of operation, i.e. assuming that no furnace is operating, but that air is still being drawn through the extract hoods.

13.21.2 Dew point

The dew point of the gas is not readily determined as so much depends on the coincidence of furnace operations. The gas which is to be cleaned does not always contain the same proportion of constituents and, therefore, its dew point will vary accordingly.

The humidity of the gases leaving a type of wet collector will depend on the efficiency of the spray eliminator, but it can be assumed 100 per cent for purposes of stack efficiency calculations.

13.21.3 Extraction

One of the problems associated with this subject is extraction. Any foundry concerned with the removal and collection of the fume, requires an extraction system of hoods, ducting and a fan. For the foundry to be clean and the air breathable, the extraction hood over the fume source performs an important function, and it will need to operate at maximum efficiency. It therefore becomes necessary to understand the general behaviour of the fume in relation to the furnace operation.

For the main part of the melting time, the fume is moderate in density. However, during 'stirring'—or time when the melting brass is agitated—

the fume generated is much more dense. It is during this period that the hood has to be efficient, for the fume expands rapidly due to its high temperature. In those foundries where swarf is melted during the 'stir', ignition of the vaporized oil takes place below the hood, with the result that some fume invariably finds its way into the foundry.

Of the three positions the furnace occupies during the overall time of the melt (charging, melting and fluxing, pouring) the melting and fluxing produces the extreme condition in both gas temperature and fume quantity.

Having now this appreciation of the operation, the pattern of which is not necessarily standard, the approach to the problem of extraction is made easier.

The type and design of hood will largely depend on the size of the furnace, and the limits of operation, but there are two approaches to the problem. The first is to collect the fume at a point close to its source, so that minimum excess air is entrained and the ultimate collector size is reduced. The second approach, which allows greater freedom of operation for the furnace operator, is to place a hood directly over the furnace so that the fume rises into it.

An oyster-back hood, or a h.v. ring main, is commonly found where the first approach is made. The latter method is effective where the amount of

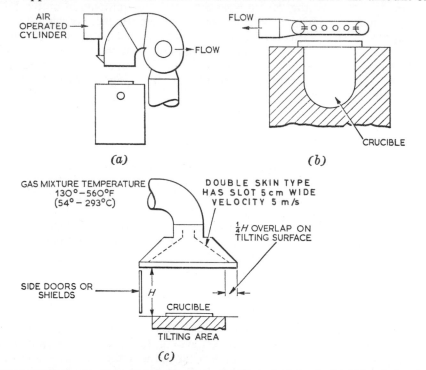

Figure 13.16 Arrangements for collecting fume. (a) Oyster-back hood; (b) high velocity ring main; (c) hood canopy

fume is small, but is less effective where oily swarf is melted. However, if the volume of fume can be determined, a balanced extraction reduces excess air to a minimum.

The open hood above the furnace is effective in most cases, and can deal with large quantities of fume. Up to 40 per cent excess air will be induced with this type of hood, upon which depends the effectiveness of containing the expanding fume. Figure 13.16 shows the possible designs covering the problem of extraction.

13.21.4 Ancillary Equipment

This comprises the ducting, extraction fan and fume stack. The ducting normally associated with this type of problem is manufactured in mild steel of 3–5 mm thickness. The ducting can be untreated internally, as there is little danger from corrosion with those systems employing dry collectors. However, it is advisable with wet systems to ensure that all ducting after the collector is protected internally with a corrosion-resistant paint or ceramic finish. Cleaning doors should be installed adjacent to points where dust is likely to built up. It is also advisable to add air infiltration ports for controlled supply of cooling air when excessive temperatures occur.

The extraction fan should be of a radial or radial tip design. Backward or aerofoil bladed fans are considered unsuitable. The fan can be sited before or after a dry collector, but because of the humidity of the gas, the fan must be sited before a wet collector, otherwise build-up will occur on the fan blades.

Vee rope drives for fans are recommended as opposed to direct drive arrangements, and motors should be supplied with ample margins on horsepower. Roller bearings are permissible for all drives, but cooling discs are recommended on the fan shafts for gases over 65°C. For high fan temperatures where the fan is sited close to an extraction point, water-cooled bearings are advisable. The circulating pump used in wet systems should be able to handle abrasive material, and should preferably be of a corrosion-resistant steel, with fresh water for gland flushing.

13.21.5 Choice of Collector

Experience has shown that, in general, the higher the efficiency of collection required, the higher will be the overall cost. With this in mind, the engineer when preparing general specifications for competitive tenders from suppliers, must consider the following,

   (i) the maximum collection efficiency required and the quality of the chimney discharge acceptable, bearing in mind the factory location;
  (ii) capital cost;
 (iii) running cost;
 (iv) space requirements.

A good guide to the first three points has been given in Chapter 12, and the relative costs are applicable with few exceptions.

Considering the fourth point, the engineer concerned can be the only judge of this. However, of the types given, the wet systems occupy the least floor area, although not necessarily the same applies as far as height is concerned, for the height will increase as washing stages are added. The venturi scrubber can be considered as having the highest volume flow/unit space.

Any ot the types of collector described in Section 13.20 may be applied to the problem. Of these, the most successful from an overall point of view will be the spray tower. It has a great deal to be said for its simplicity, moderate initial and running cost, small plan area and low maintenance if the particular design has been well tried on similar fume and dust problems.

If a spray tower is recommended, more than two washing stages are essential—less than this will not provide adequate cleaning. Spray eliminators, if provided, should be of an open pattern and not with narrow gas passages, for as was stated earlier, the fume that passes the last washing can lead to blockage. Adequate and accessible inspection doors are essential. All surfaces within the collector which are exposed should be protected by a suitable corrosion-resistant paint, plastics coating or rubber lining, although the latter two finishes are restricted to somewhat low temperatures.

13.21.6 Permissible Fume Emission

Brass foundries now come within the scope of the 'scheduled processes' registered under the Alkali Act (Chapter 2). The requirement is, therefore, that the best practical means for fume removal must be adopted to the approval of the Alkali Inspectorate, taking local factors into account. The target given in the Inspector's report for 1966 is a reduction of fume ($< 10 \ \mu m$ in size) to $0.12 \ g/m^3$ n.t.p.

Certainly, from the author's experience, fume emitted in the order of $0.34 \ g/m^3$ n.t.p. is not acceptable. This emission rate represented fume in which the fraction below $1.5 \ \mu m$ was 86 per cent as determined by a particle count under the microscope.

The concentration of the suspended solids emitted will depend on the following:

   (i) efficiency of extraction;
   (ii) efficiency of collection;
   (iii) the size of fume generated by the furnace and its operation.

From a health point of view, the most important quality is that the emission should never be in a sufficiently high concentration at ground level to be injurious to health. Therefore, rather than consider the amount discharged per hour, or the concentration leaving the stack, a measurement for zinc oxide should be made at a point downwind from the stack (allowing for local conditions) at which either the theoretical, or preferably the practical, maximum concentration occurs. If then the measurements giving the contamination in terms of weight/unit volume exceed the maximum concentration reckoned to be injurious to health, the plant should be considered ineffective or in need of improvement (Chapter 19).

There are many practical considerations that affect the application of such a ruling, but conversely, providing this concentration of fume is never reached at the ground level position determined, then the effect on health is going to be less. The above consideration does not, of course, take into account the fact that a black plume of smoke is an unpleasant sight in any surrounding. The problem of visibility of plumes is discussed in Chapter 19.

13.21.7 Control

Controlling dust-collecting equipment of this kind is important, so that the plant works at maximum efficiency in both extraction and collection. The most usual form of control as far as balancing the system is concerned is by the use of a damper. These will be fitted in each furnace connection so that when the particular furnace is inoperative it can be isolated, thereby reducing the total volume of gas to be cleaned. In both wet and dry systems, this control is obviously an important factor, and furnace operators must be trained to understand its value.

The types of control that can be made automatic are those connected with air infiltration and with the addition of neutralizing reagents to the recirculating water to maintain an alkaline condition. In the case of air infiltration, dampers can be operated by servo motors acting upon a signal from a thermostat. pH control of the recirculating water requires consultation with manufacturers of this type of equipment.

13.21.8 Chimney

The chimney or stack, which in all cases will be used for the discharge of the cleaned gas to atmosphere, is most important, and every consideration should be given to its correct design. This point assumes more importance if the collector is not entirely efficient, and it becomes essential that the effluent gases are discharged at a sufficient height and with sufficient velocity to allow ample dispersion of the fume, thereby reducing the possible danger to health, see Chapter 19.

The Alkali Inspector's report for 1966 gives a table for Copper Works relating chimney height to rate of melting expressed as aggregate capacity of all the furnaces on a works site in tonnes/24 hours as follows:

Tonnes/24 hours	50	100	150	200	250	300
Basic height of chimney, metres	31	44	54	62	70	77

13.22 Design Example

(i) The particular plant was required for the collection of fume from a brass foundry making ingot bars 50 mm diameter × 1·8 m long, and situated in a residential district. The crucibles were oil-fired, and there were five, each being 1 tonne capacity.

The extraction hoods were designed to swing from a standpipe, because the furnace was of the type that tilted to pour. Each standpipe was connected to the main duct running below the furnace level. The collector employed in this case was a vertical spray tower, the reason for this selection being that no machined swarf was used in the charge, which is mainly factory scrap.

The spray tower was designed for 55000 m³/h, and had a resistance of 1·7 mb. The gas entered from the top passing down a central duct in the collector. The gas then changed direction, and passed upwards through two water curtains and impingement baffles. A spray eliminator conditioned the gas leaving the washer.

The extraction fan mounted after the washer was subject to occasional build-up by the uncleaned fume. A circulating water system was employed with purge and make up of clean water to keep the concentration of solids below an acceptable level, usually set by the local authorities at a permissible increase of pollution downstream of the location of 30 p.p.m. (Stricter conditions were required in 1970.)

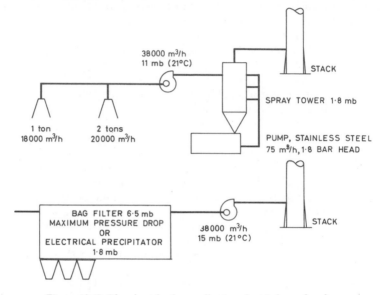

Figure 13.17 Flowsheet for fume collection plant in brass foundry

The recirculating pump was made from corrosion-resistant steel, and the settling tank was constructed from brick and concrete. The exhaust stack was mounted on the outlet of the extraction fan.

A typical flowsheet is shown in Figure 13.17.

(ii) A small brass foundry has two electrically heated furnaces of 1 and 2 tonne capacity. An existing fume extraction scheme is efficient, and a replacement scheme is required with the addition of a collector. Machined swarf is part of the charge, which otherwise is made up of the factory rejects and scrap.

Site tests on the 2 tonne furnace reveal standpipe temperatures of 55°C during melting, and 295°C for the stirring period. The extraction scheme being in action dilutes the fume and temperature. For a canopy type of extract hood, a face velocity of 1·6 m/s would result in 18000 and 20000 m³/h respectively, but if a high velocity ring main were used, the extraction volume could be reduced by 40 per cent. The ducting would be designed for 15 m/s, which is permissible for even long duct runs. The collector, which would be positioned after the fan, would be a bag filter of the reverse flow pattern. The overall size of the unit would be approximately 5·5 m long × 2·5 m wide × 6 m high with a filter cloth of either Orlon or Terylene which can operate at temperatures of 120°–150°C respectively. An automatic air infiltration point would be incorporated at the collector inlet to protect the filter elements. The elements would need earthing to prevent electrostatic charges which, on discharge, might set fire to the bags. The chimney, mounted separately, would be built to discharge at a height already discussed.

PART E DUST AND FUME CLEANING IN IRON AND STEEL WORKS

J. H. FLUX

13.23 Sources of Pollution

There has been a radical change during the last twenty-five years in the main sources and types of pollution from steelworks. The use of raw coal as a fuel has virtually disappeared with obvious advantages but newer steelmaking techniques, particularly the Basic Oxygen Furnace (B.O.F.) unit (or L.D. converter), developed following work at the Austrian steelworks at Linz and Donawitz and the high powered electric arc furnace. Both of these processes use large quantities of oxygen for refining liquid iron and steel and have introduced a serious problem by the generation of vast quantities of sub-micron oxide fume.

An indication of the sources of pollution in iron and steelmaking is given in Figure 13.18 and Reference 20 and these may be conveniently grouped into the following major areas of pollution:
1. Coke oven plant.
2. Ore preparation and sintering plant.
3. Iron making.
4. Steel making.
5. Deseaming processes.

The industry is responsible to the Chief Alkali Inspector for its measures to combat atmospheric pollution and the current standards are:

Grit and dust emission. Not more than 0.48 g/m^3 n.t.p., although an indication has already been given that for larger sinter plants the 0.48 g/m^3 limit will be reduced to 0.12 g/m^3.

Fume and dust emission. Near invisibility with a design maximum of 0.12 g/m^3 n.t.p.

13.24 Coke Oven Plants

The blast furnace will continue to be the major iron producing unit for the foreseeable future and therefore coke ovens will remain an integral part of ironworks plant. Operations in a coke oven battery which might be the source of a nuisance and techniques adopted for collecting and cleaning are as follows.

(i) *Coal handling and storage.* Troubles from these can be eliminated by ensuring that the moisture content of the coal is of the order of 10 per cent

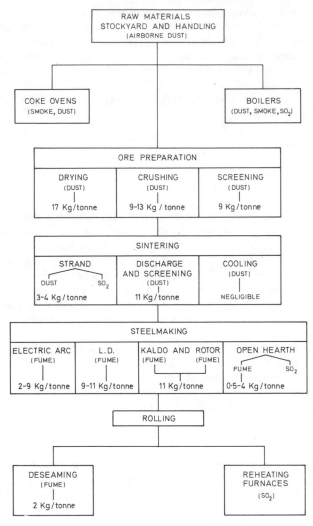

Figure 13.18 Sources of pollution in iron and steelworks

which is an acceptable figure for carbonization. Further, if recent developments in coal preheating techniques are used on a commercial scale even higher moisture contents of the coal can be adopted.

(ii) Charging the ovens. The charging of the ovens has always presented a serious problem but smokeless charging cars are now being brought into use. The arrangement provides for controlled conveyance of the coal into the ovens with adequate suction to draw off the mixture of green gas and air displaced by the coal. This gas is burnt on the car by injecting butane (or propane) into the draw-off pipe which is spark ignited. Combustion of the smoke-laden gas is substantially completed in a 3 m length of pipe. This is

followed by injecting water into the induced draught fan to wash the gases prior to discharge to the atmosphere so that the only visible emission is a small plume of clean steam which dissipates quickly.

Pilot installations are now undergoing rigorous trials and it is to be expected that this principle will be adopted universally. The car will eliminate the necessity for the double collecting main now in use to minimize pollution during charging. The double collecting main should have made a substantial contribution but because of the exposed heat the operators were reluctant to carry out adequate maintenance and it became ineffective. Also there is the trend to large capacity ovens (26 tonnes instead of 13 tonnes) and this will therefore reduce the number of times new batteries will be charged.

(iii) Smoke emission during carbonization Self-sealing doors are now provided which do not require excessive maintenance and by reasonable attention to detail there should be no smoke emission from the ovens whilst the charge is being carbonized.

(iv) Discharging and coke quenching. Provided the coal is correctly carbonized there need not be an excessive emission of smoke and grit during the discharge of coke from the oven. Coke car hoods and coke guide shields are available but are not really necessary because the recent adoption of superior oven wall heating equipment and better control of coal to oven quality ensures that the coal has been correctly carbonized. Grit from the quenching operation can be effectively stopped by grids in the quenching tower and although there is noticeable steam plume from wet quenching this is more effective for the prevention of a grit emission than dry quenching processes. For further information see Reference 21.

13.25 Ore Preparation and Sintering Plant

Although dust can be generated at all stages of iron ore handling and preparation it is possible to ensure that any discharges to the atmosphere are kept within tolerable limits. The ore is handled in a moist condition and it is standard practice to provide wind protection on elevated conveyors and, if necessary, to provide dust extraction and bag filter equipment at transfer points although, generally speaking, adequate suppression can be achieved by additional spraying with water to which a suitable surface tension reducing agent has been added. Ore drying which can lead to a substantial dust emission is required only for a few selected home ores and with the increasing use of foreign ores this practice is going out of use. However, any dust emission from this stage of the process can be effectively cleaned by electrostatic precipitators.

Thus the major pollution potential is the sinter plant. Sintering converts iron ore into a more easily digestible physical form for the blast furnace and, in addition to grit and dust, sulphur dioxide is generated from both the fuel and the ore. A two-part cleaning installation is required. Dust has to be recovered from the strand gases which contain the SO_2 and which are eventually discharged from a tall chimney. A separate system is used at the end of the strand where the sinter is broken, screened and cooled. The high efficiency cyclone has been extensively used for this purpose and was capable of reducing the solid emission to less than 0.46 g/m^3 n.t.p. However, with more stringent regulations the target is now being set at 0.12 g/m^3 and for this electrostatic precipitators are essential.

13.26 Iron Making

As previously stated, the blast furnace will be the major iron making unit for the foreseeable future and the associated production and works' use of blast furnace gas entails the removal of the dust and fume. If the gas were not effectively cleaned, dust deposition in mains, controllers and burners would cause considerable plant failure and greatly increase maintenance costs.

A typical cleaning plant would consist of a low pressure-drop water washing tower to remove the major part of the solid matter followed by an electro-static precipitator to clean the gases to less than 0.01 g/m^3. Since the production of gas is continuous and the precipitator has to be cleaned, by water flushing, at regular intervals, it is normal to have a combination of washers and precipitators interconnected so as to permit gas cleaning at all times.

Bleeding gas to atmosphere is kept to a minimum to avoid waste but if it should be necessary to do so, the dust content of the gas should comply with the standards set by the Chief Alkali Inspector.

13.27 Steel Making

The two dominant methods of steelmaking for the immediate future will be the B.O.F. process for refining liquid iron and the electric arc furnace for re-melting steel scrap. An essential feature of both methods is the use of oxygen for metallurgical purposes with the resultant production of large quantities of sub-micron iron oxide fume (Figures 13.19 and 13.20). The quantity varies according to the process requirements but typical ranges are:

B.O.F.	9–11 kg/tonne steel produced
Electric arc furnace	2–9 kg/tonne steel produced

The collection and filtration of this fume represents the greatest challenge that the industry has faced since serious attention has been given to the minimization of atmospheric pollution. The fume leaves the furnace at high temperature in a potentially dangerous gas mixture of carbon monoxide in the case of the B.O.F. and carbon monoxide and/or hydrogen in the case of the electric arc furnace. Further, neither process includes an integral waste gas collecting flue as in the open-hearth furnace and, consequently, collection and conditioning of the waste gas are essential steps in the overall cleaning process.

The other major steelmaking process, the open-hearth furnace, can present some difficulties but sufficient experience has been gained to show that by the use of correctly-sized electrostatic precipitators after a waste-heat boiler to cool the gases, the collection of fume to the desired standard is no longer a

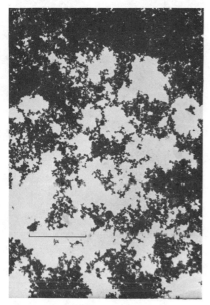

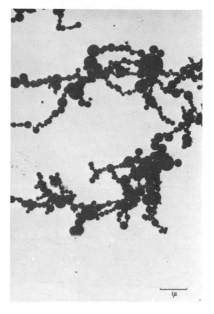

Figure 13.19 Iron oxide fume from electric arc steelmaking.

Figure 13.20 Iron oxide fume from B.O.F. steelmaking.

serious problem. In any case the open-hearth furnace represents a dwindling proportion of steel production. The remaining processes referred to in Table 13.1 (Kaldo and Rotor) have not made a serious inroad into steel production and are unlikely to survive against the more established B.O.F. practice. Claims have been made for the introduction of the Spray Steelmaking process which is the continuous refining of liquid iron by oxygen but a commercial plant has yet to be installed. It is claimed also that by this process the fume problem is noticeably less than that from the B.O.F. but, even so, fume removal and collection very much on the lines required for the latter process would berequired.

13.28 Waste Gas Collection

13.28.1 The B.O.F. Process

The B.O.F. process or the top blowing of a converter by oxygen was introduced in 1953 and now represents approximately 50 per cent of world steelmaking capacity. The plant comprises a pear-shaped vessel with a capacity of up to 300 tonnes situated under a collecting hood or stack (Figure 13.21) and the procedure for collecting and handling the fume has been changed as operating experience has been gained with larger and larger units.

The fume is discharge from the converter in an atmosphere of about 90 per cent carbon monoxide at a temperature in excess of 1600°C. Originally the gases were allowed to burn in the stack. This demanded elaborate cooling arrangements, particularly if optimum recovery of the heat potential in the gas was required, and the use of waste heat boilers in the stacks became established practice. However, as the steam generated was intermittent it was necessary to provide steam accumulators and/or auxiliary firing of the boilers to ensure a constant supply of steam. The result was that the operation of the waste heat recovery system tended to dictate the operation of the steelmaking vessel. This, together with the differing times required for maintenance of the boiler and the vessel, resulted in an undesirable combination.

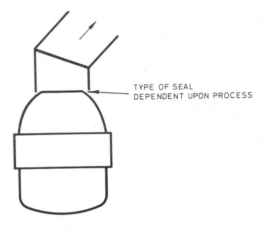

Figure 13.21 Collecting hood for B.O.F. steelmaking

There has therefore been a change to systems in which the combustion of the gas in the stack is severely restricted or virtually eliminated. This results in a smaller volume of lower temperature gas which has to be cleaned, with substantial savings in capital and operating costs. It has been found also that the dust in the unburnt gas contains a higher proportion of FeO and metallic Fe which form larger particles and are easier to remove than the Fe_2O_3 normally encountered. The cleaning of the unburnt gas also permits the recovery of a carbon monoxide-rich gas with a typical calorific value of $8\cdot9$ MJ/m^3 with a production rate equivalent to 422 MJ/tonne steel produced.

The three commercial arrangements are described below.

13.28.1 I.R.S.I.D.–C.A.F.L. Process

This process is known by the initials of the French organizations who developed the method.

The general principle adopted is to adjust the pressure in the stack continually to prevent either waste gas leaking out to atmosphere or air being induced through the open joint between the converter mouth and the base of the collection hood. To do this the draught must be under accurate and continuous control since the volume of waste gases is constantly changing even under conditions of constant oxygen blowing rate.

In order to facilitate gas recovery and control of draught, the hood has been equipped with a movable skirt which can be lifted in order to permit charging of the vessel.

Reliable safety measures are fundamental to this process which can be considered in two stages—the main blowing period, and the purging periods at the beginning and end of the blow. During the blowing period, CO-rich gases with CO_2, N_2 and traces of O_2 pass continuously through the system. When air enters zones above 600°C, e.g. at the open joint, there is no danger of explosions since combustion is spontaneous: it is sufficient to ensure that there is no in-leakage of air into cold zones below 600°C. For the beginning and end of the blow a complete purge of the system is carried out with oxygen-free gas, and for this purge to be effective, it is essential that the gas dusting be designed to eliminate dead zones where pockets of potentially explosive gases might accumulate.

13.28.2 Krupp Process

This system differs from the I.R.S.I.D.–C.A.F.L. process in that, to assist the balancing of gas flow through the system and to limit either air in-leakage or 'blow out' of waste gases air or burning waste gases are sucked into an annular ring on the periphery of the hood to form a protective curtain round the main column of gas. From the vent at the base of the hood the gas used for sealing is ducted to a small cleaning unit independent of the rest of the system.

The remainder of the plant is similar in principle to the I.R.S.I.D.–C.A.F.L. system. Over the converter mouth, there is a cooled gas off-take hood and cooling stack followed by a gas humidifier, pre-cleaner and a high efficiency cleaner.

13.28.3 O.G. Process

The O.G. (oxygen-gas) process was developed in Japan and nitrogen is used to provide a safety curtain between the converter mouth and the base of the collection hood (replacing the air ring of the Krupp method) and to act as a purge at the beginning and end of the oxygen blow (replacing the purge of combusted gas used both in the I.R.S.I.D.–C.A.F.L. and Krupp methods).

Like the I.R.S.I.D.–C.A.F.L. and the Krupp methods, the O.G. process uses a pressure controller located in the hood to equate the draughting of the system with the volume of gases evolved from the converter. Nitrogen is also used to expel all stagnant air from the system prior to the oxygen blow and to drive all remaining carbon monoxide gas from the equipment at the end of the blow. Further, as at the beginning and end of the oxygen blow, the ratio of CO to O_2 approaches the explosion limit, the converter gases are diluted with nitrogen. Nitrogen is also used to prevent air in-leakage at the hood openings for the oxygen lance and the raw material feeds.

13.29 Waste Gas Collection—Electric Arc Furnace

There is no universal solution to waste gas collection because of the wide range of rates of production involved which can vary from 5 tonne furnaces producing 1 tonne steel per hour to 150 tonne furnaces producing over 50 tonne steel per hour, with fume emission of up to 9 kg per tonne of steel.
   Three methods of collection are possible:

(i) Hooded (Figure 13.22). This was the original method but with high rates of working and also oxygen blowing, hoods became ineffective and their use is now restricted to furnaces of less than about 5 tonne capacity.

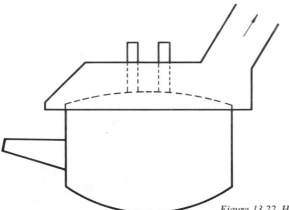

Figure 13.22 Hooded extraction electric arc furnace

With the hooded system a large volume of excess air is collected and thus the temperature is sufficiently low to allow the fume to be passed directly to a bag filter.

(ii) Direct Extraction (Figure 13.23). To meet the challenge of the high-powered furnace the arrangement of directly extracting the fume through a special connection to the furnace was introduced. By this system the volume

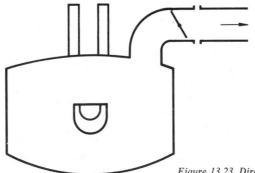

Figure 13.23 Direct extraction electric arc furnace

of gases to be cleaned is reduced to a minimum but as the gases leaving the furnace can contain large proportions of carbon monoxide and hydrogen there is an explosion hazard. To eliminate this a separate combustion chamber is used with forced air for combustion. The eventual volume of waste gases to be handled is of the order of 10–15 times the volume of oxygen injected into the furnace and the temperature of the waste gas necessitates a cooling and conditioning stage prior to the cleaner.

(iii) Semi-direct Extraction (Figure 13.24). With direct extraction, furnace pressure control equipment is required to minimize air infiltration into the furnace. This has to be completely eliminated during the refining stages in

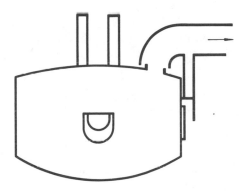

Figure 13.24 Semi-direct extraction electric arc furnace

the making of alloy steels and so an alternative arrangement, semi-direct extraction, was introduced. Essentially, the direct connection with the furnace is replaced by a collecting hood over a discharge port in the roof of the furnace. The gases leave the furnace at varying rates depending upon the pressure in the furnace but the absence of a positive suction eliminates air infiltration.

The gases burn in the space between the furnace and hood but, as in all hooded systems, excess air is drawn in and so a much higher volume of cooler waste gases is presented to the cleaning unit. The gas volumes are approximately $2–2\frac{1}{2}$ times those for direct extraction and therefore the cost for the larger cleaning unit has to be weighed against the advantages gained by the elimination of the combustion chamber and expensive gas conditioning. In practice it has been found that for installations working at the same rate, the capital cost of both schemes is virtually the same.

13.30 Waste Gas Cooling and Conditioning

This covers the adjustment of temperature and humidity of the gases. With the waste gases leaving the furnace at temperatures up to 1600°C or even higher, some form of cooling is obviously essential and the simplest way is by the injection of water as this keeps the total volume of gases to be cleaned to a minimum. However, if a dry precipitator or bag filter is used, extreme care must be taken to ensure that the temperature of the gases stays always above the dew-point temperature. With these types of cleaner it is imperative that there should be no deposition of moisture.

In the case of the bag filter with an upper temperature limit of approximately 250°C the use of water conditioning obviously presents many control problems and often it is better to effect cooling by the introduction of large volumes of dilution air.

In the case of the dry electrostatic precipitator it has been shown that, apart from the corrosive effects on the structure, warm moist iron oxide will bond to the collecting electrodes and the casing of the precipitator and that this deposit is extremely difficult to remove. This does not apply to a wet precipitator where saturation is called for and here, ironically, it is often difficult to achieve complete saturation at all times. Experience has shown that comparatively fine atomization of the water is essential together with a reasonable allowance for time of contact between the gases and the water. The fine sprays demand that filtered water should be used.

13.31 Fume Cleaning

For the removal of the fine iron oxide fume from the B.O.F. and electric arc furnace a high efficiency cleaner is required and thus the choice is restricted to bag filters, electrostatic precipitators and venturi scrubbers. Bag filters have found some favour in the U.S.A. for use with electric arc furnaces but in the U.K. they are used on small arc furnace installations only. The electrostatic precipitator and venturi scrubber are used for both the electric arc furnace and the B.O.F. furnace.

Dry or wet electrostatic precipitation may be used but where fluorspar is used as a slag-making material in the steelmaking operation a wet precipitator may be preferred because this eliminates any final discharge of fluorine to the atmosphere. The venturi scrubber is becoming universally accepted for small- to medium-sized electric arc furnaces up to approximately 50 tonne in capacity and its use is preferred also for the minimum gas methods of gas collection from the B.O.F.

The objections to a bag filter are the comparatively low temperature (approximately 250°C) to which the gases must be reduced before treatment and this can require the introduction of large volumes of dilution air, resulting in a large and expensive cleaning unit.

The fundamentals of the electrostatic precipitator have been discussed in Chapters 12 and 13B but certain additional precautions have to be taken when applying these to steel works' applications. These include:

(i) Gas distribution. This particularly applies to an installation on an existing site where it may not be possible to make an ideal arrangement to ensure uniform velocity of the gas through the system. If there is any doubt it is important that a model of the precipitator and inlet flue system should be made. Established techniques exist for relating model and plant conditions so that flow splitters and baffles can be designed and installed in the system during erection with a consequent substantial reduction in the time required for commissioning the full scale plant.

(ii) Electrode design. A high efficiency design is most desirable and the use of barbed wire and a fabricated strip with points was adopted some years ago. However, in both cases uniform tensioning presents difficulties. If the electrodes are not uniformly tensioned oscillations can be set up with consequent breakage resulting in excessive maintenance and down time. There has been a trend therefore towards the use of a more rigid rod but this should be shaped in a star or similar configuration to permit point discharge.

(iii) Drift velocities. Experience has shown that this should be of the order of 8–10 cm/s for typical oxygen steelmaking processes.

The main problems which can be experienced with venturi scrubbers is the build up of deposits particularly of calcium carbonate (arising from the additions of lime to the furnace), iron oxide and fine slag particles either immediately before or in the scrubber itself. These deposits can be hard and, in certain cases, difficult to remove but it has been found that water treatment and cleaning of the interior by high pressure jets at regular weekly or monthly intervals are generally adequate to ensure continuity of operation.

13.32 Deseaming Processes

The deseaming process is used to remove surface defects from ingots by an oxygen flame and, as such, generates sub-micron fume together with slag and scale. The emission is entrained in large volumes of low temperature air and the high pressure water jets used to flush away the slag and scale particles tend to cause some agglomeration of the fume although this is insufficient to justify dispensing with high efficiency cleaners such as the electrostatic precipitator. Large volumes of water vapour are included with the collecting air so that the temperature of the gases at the inlet to the filter are only just above the dew point and a wet precipitation is preferred in spite of the consequent problems in the disposal of a wet slurry.

New requirements on the Iron and Steel Industry were published by the Alkali Inspector in his 1970 Report (H.M.S.O. 1971).

14

Testing Performance of Equipment for Grit and Dust Removal

General Introduction

Testing performance of dust arrestors involves sampling of gases carrying grit and dust for overall efficiency of collection by weight and, more particularly, for determination of concentration of solids escaping. In addition, it is necessary to determine the size analysis of the solids leaving the arrestor and in some cases the size analysis of the entering solids.

Part A of this chapter deals with the techniques employed to sample gases for determination of the weight concentration of their dust burden; size analysis is described in Part B, whilst Part C deals with monitoring of chimney emissions.

The accurate collection of a representative sample of dust-bearing gas for the determination of the weight concentration might seem easy; actually many hundreds of papers on the subject have been written on both practical and statistical aspects. The difficulties are firstly that the gas velocities and dust concentrations are not uniformly distributed across the duct as in practice the gas stream has always passed round one or more bends—an example of this distribution has been given in Chapter 1, Table 1.2. Secondly, centrifugal forces will throw the heavier particles to the outside of the bends and consequently the size-analysis of the dust burden will vary across the flue. Thirdly, some form of size-analysis of the dust collected by the sampling apparatus is usually required, irrespective of whether the main gas stream is used for process purposes or discharged to atmosphere; it is therefore necessary to collect the dust from the gas sample in such a way that size-analysis is not rendered impossible, for example by extreme compaction on a filter, or by solution in a wet collector.

Consideration of the conditions at the mouth of a sampling probe indicates, as shown in Figure 14.1, that the coarser particles are relatively unaffected by the divergence of the gas flow lines compared with the finer particles. Consequently, in order to obtain a representative sample of dust in a gas stream which is correct in respect of size analysis and concentration, it is essential that the sample of gas be withdrawn at the same velocity as the gas stream at the point of sampling; this is known as isokinetic sampling. A full theoretical treatment of the errors in concentration and mass flow due to sampling at an incorrect velocity has been given by Badzioch[1]. It may be concluded that it is impracticable to attempt to correct such errors by

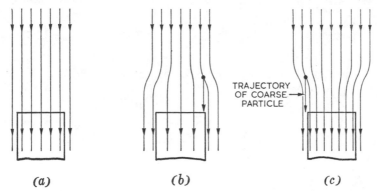

Figure 14.1 (a) Isokinetic sampling; representative concentration and grading. (b) Sampling velocity too low; excess of coarse particles. (c) Sampling velocity too high; deficiency of coarse particles

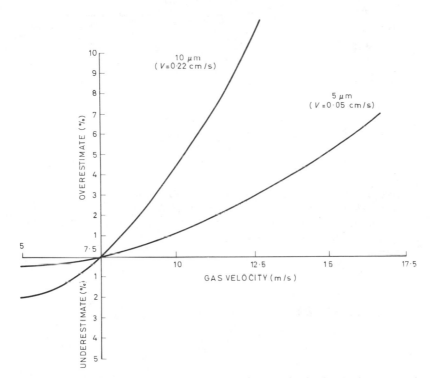

Figure 14.2 Errors in concentration of particles sampled at a fixed velocity of 7·5 m/s with a nozzle of 25 mm diameter. Density of dust is 1 g/cm³

calculation. Figures 14.2 and 14.3 taken from his paper show that errors are much smaller for the coarser particles and are numerically smaller when the sampling velocity exceeds the gas velocity.

Another difficulty in sampling occurs when the gas flow is not parallel to the wall of the duct and occasions arise when some form of flow straightener

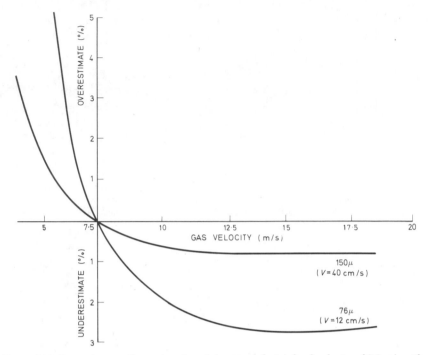

Figure 14.3 Errors in mass flow rates of particles sampled at a fixed velocity of 7·5 m/s with a nozzle of 25 mm diameter

is essential; with low gas velocities in chimneys reverse flows of gas are not unknown.

In conclusion, it should be emphasized that failure to observe correct conditions when sampling dust from gas streams can lead to errors of over 100 per cent in the determined concentration. The accurate measurement of dust concentration is therefore a costly, complicated and time-consuming operation.

PART A SAMPLING OF DUST-LADEN GAS

A. LITTLE

14.1 General

The testing of performance of grit, dust and fume collectors falls into two distinct categories; the testing of installed equipment and the testing of proprietary equipment usually by research organizations in laboratories. The former category is important to those who are in charge of full-scale dust arrestors. When such equipment is newly purchased, it is important to verify that the equipment performs satisfactorily or, as it is more commonly stated, meets its guarantee. It is also necessary to check that it continues to operate satisfactorily during a reasonable life. The second category is important to those who are developing equipment for future sales and to those who need to select from a number of apparently suitable installations the type which is most suitable for the particular duty being considered. The methods of testing in the two categories differ mainly in elaboration in that the installed equipment will be in operation treating a dust-laden gas, which may in addition be hot and wet, whereas the laboratory tests are usually conducted by dispersing recognized test powders or fumes into air which is subsequently drawn through the arrestor on test.

14.2 Sampling Systems

The concentrations of particles in gases at the inlet to arrestors can range from as high as 1000 g/m^3, e.g. flash drying systems, to as low as 0·25 mg/m^3, e.g. in atmospheric air cleaning, and it is generally accepted that no single sampling apparatus is capable of dealing satisfactorily with such a range of conditions. It is necessary to have an assembly of basic equipment which, although frequently used in a standard or semi-standard form, may be readily adapted by substituting suitable ready-made accessories to allow unusual problems to be tackled easily. The basic equipment comprises a set of nozzles; a sampling tube; a miniature collector to retain the particles; means for determining the amount of gas sampled; means for determining gas velocities in ducts, e.g. Pitot tubes, anemometers or velometers; means for withdrawing samples of gas through the system; thermometers; manometers; cooling coils; catchpots and connecting tubing; stop-watches are also required. This equipment must be assembled compactly in a safe working space near access holes suitably located in the ducts leading to and from the dust collector. Since the purpose is primarily to measure the weight of dust per unit quantity of gas, other equipment needed in a nearby laboratory comprises a suitable balance and filter drying equipment.

A general purpose form of the sampling equipment[2] used in the Agricultural Division of I.C.I. is shown in Figure 14.4. It consists of a nozzle attached to a heated sampling tube followed by a glass-wool filter, cooling coil, catchpot, an orifice-plate flowmeter, and an ejector or exhauster. Appropriate manometers and thermometers are provided so that the necessary calculations for correct isokinetic sampling may be made. Special glass-wool resistant to acid gases is essential; the first layer has fibre diameters of 6–7 μm and the second layer fibres of 2 μm average diameter. Both layers are packed to a density of 0·06 g/ml.

Many other systems have been developed for more specialized duties based in some degree on the above apparatus. Five such systems intended for flue gas sampling are listed in British Standard 3405[3]; there are several others, none of which is excluded provided it is used for the purpose for which it was developed. One modification is to incorporate the filter in a probe-head near the nozzle, and before the probe-head is used it is allowed to warm up in the hot gas stream; this eliminates the need to heat the tube and excludes the rather heavy transformer needed for electrical heating; incidentally the basic components of the equipment, orifice plate, flowmeter,

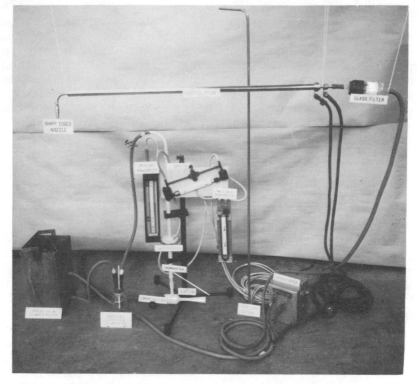

Figure 14.4 General purpose heated sampling probe.

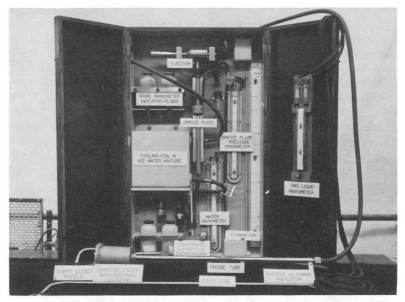

Figure 14.5 I.C.I. packed cartridge filter sampling apparatus. (Courtesy of Imperial Chemical Industries Ltd.)

cooling oils, catchpots, etc. are all more lightly constructed and more compactly assembled in a wooden box (Figure 14.5).

Another system involves a redesigned probe-head incorporating a small axial cyclone followed closely by a glass-wool filter. A further arrangement involves the use of an efficient miniature cyclone as the probe-head, but this inevitably means that the gas passing through the rest of the equipment is still not perfectly clean and special care is needed to ensure correct results. Yet another sampling system reverts to the use of an external glass-wool filter following an unheated sampling tube since it is intended for use with hotter gases containing little water vapour.

From the above brief summaries, it is clear that the essential factors are (a) to draw a sample of gas isokinetically from a duct or chimney, (b) to collect all the particles in the sampled gas in such a way that the weight collected may be determined, (c) to measure the amount of gas sampled fairly accurately, always ensuring that any condensable gases do not interfere with the measurement, (d) to make the equipment as light and compact as possible, having regard for the need to use it frequently in relatively inaccessible places such as a platform, say, 50 m up the side of a 100 m chimney.

Special problems of variations of dust and gas flow across a flue and of variations of dust flow with time are discussed in detail by Hawksley[4]; during sootblowing of a boiler the instantaneous mass emission rate can increase up to 300-fold.

Experiments have indicated that a mixing baffle can sometimes be employed to obtain uniform gas flow and to ensure that the dust sample extracted shall be representative[5]. Such mixing baffles (usually half-area) installed in plant ducting may be made similar to butterfly valves so that they can be turned through 90°, thus eliminating the pressure drop when not required. In use, a half-area mixing baffle would impose a pressure drop of 5·5 velocity heads, i.e. for air at 1 bar abs. and 20°C travelling along a duct at 10 m/s a half-area mixing baffle would impose a pressure loss of 3·3 mb. With a mixing baffle in position the sample is withdrawn at a point three duct diameters downstream from the baffle (Figure 14.6).

14.3 Planning Tests of Performance

14.3.1 General

Any well-conducted test on an installed arrestor should end with the following minimum information:

(i) Gas throughput (± 10 per cent);
(ii) Inlet dust concentration (± 10 per cent);
(iii) Exit dust concentration (± 10 per cent);
(iv) Basic data relevant to the particular arrestor; thus for electrostatic precipitators the usual information would comprise the primary potential; the primary current and the secondary current (sometimes it is also possible to measure the secondary potential); the rapping cycles in use and how the particular test periods were related to the rapping cycles, also plant design details.

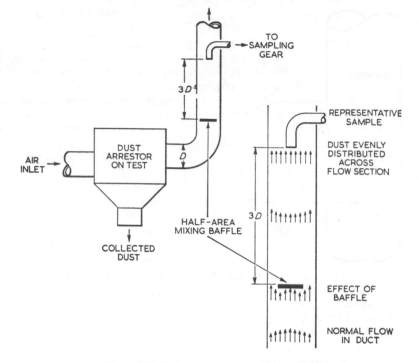

Figure 14.6 Dust arrestor on test; laboratory rig

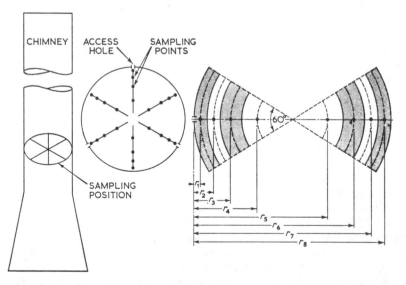

Figure 14.7 Twenty-four-point sampling in circular chimneys or flues, B.S. 893[6]. r = radius of circle corresponding to cross-section of chimney or flue. The points are at the centres of equal areas. $r_1 = 0.07\ r$, $r_2 = 0.21\ r$, $r_3 = 0.39\ r$, $r_4 = 0.65\ r$, $r_5 = 1.35\ r$, $r_6 = 1.61\ r$, $r_7 = 1.79\ r$, $r_8 = 1.94\ r$. (By permission of The British Standards Institution)

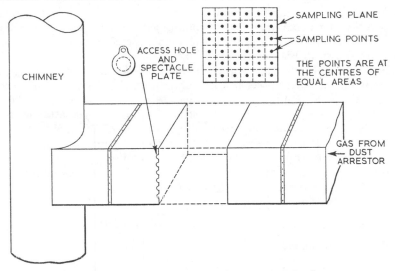

Figure 14.8 Thirty-six-point sampling in rectangular flues

(v) In the case of boilers it should be stated whether sootblowing took place during the test.

Supplementary data relate to:

(a) Determination of the total weight of dust collected by the arrestor; this is not always obtainable without considerable modification to the dust discharge system and may therefore be too expensive.

(b) Size analyses of the various samples; these are not always required but, when they are, the sampling should be carried out to produce samples suitable for size analysis subsequent to the test, e.g. not contaminated with glass fibre and not strongly compacted.

14.3.2 Sampling Positions, Sampling Points and Access Holes

Since most sampling systems require the measurement of the gas velocity in the ducts or chimneys, this is a convenient way to determine the gas rate where the gas is not otherwise metered. Thus the position in the ducting and the individual sampling points are chosen with the object of determining both the gas rate and the dust concentration. To meet these requirements the position in the dust collection system most suitable for sampling should be in a straight length of ducting as far as possible from any obstruction, damper or valve likely to cause a disturbance of the gas flow; vertical ducts are preferable. Because plants are seldom built with the requirements of dust sampling in mind, the usual situation is far from ideal and often sufficient accuracy can be obtained only by sampling at a large number of points at the best available sampling position. In extreme cases it may be necessary to reconstruct the ducting but clearly economic factors will have a very strong bearing on any such decision.

Having chosen the most suitable position, the cross-section of the duct is suitably divided into a sufficient number of equal areas and the centres of these areas are the sampling points. Generally the cross-section is divided into twenty-four equal areas but as mentioned earlier, greater sub-division is sometimes required. Typical arrangements for circular and rectangular ducts are shown in Figures 14.7 and 14.8

The access holes are also shown in the same figures and the particular positions for the access holes must be chosen, having regard to the need to provide adequate platforms (where they do not already exist) capable of supporting the weight of sampling equipment and two operators in safety. Certain services must also be provided at the platform (e.g. compressed air, electricity or steam as the particular sampling equipment requires), and provision of ice or solid carbon dioxide for the cooling coil.

All the above requirements must be available for both the inlet and exit ducts and where there is a multiplicity of ducts all should be sampled simultaneously or in a sequence so that the final objective is not jeopardized.

14.3.3 Preliminary Tests

Having completed the above arrangements, it is always advisable to make preliminary tests in which samples are collected for short periods from the centres of the inlet and exit ducts in order to determine the magnitude of the concentrations, and so decide the most suitable total test period, the required sampling time at each sampling point and the co-ordination of inlet and exit sampling periods with each other and with any other periodic factors affecting the particular arrestor on test. To illustrate a situation involving this detailed planning an actual test on a cyclicly rapped three-section precipitator required a total test period of 4 h, because during this period each section had been off-line once for 5 minutes' rapping. The exit sample was arranged to cover the same period and the sequence of sample with-drawal from individual sample points in the cross-section was arranged to give a truly representative sample both of that portion of the test period when all the precipitator sections were working and also of the portion when only two sections were in use. The inlet sampling was not so critical and for simplicity each sample point was sampled for 2 min; with 36 points this involved 72 min of sampling. There were three such sampling periods evenly disposed to fall in the middle of the periods for each of the three precipitator sections. Only with such practical detailed planning can a test be considered successful.

Having obtained the information detailed earlier, it is possible to combine the information to give the overall collection efficiency and other factors peculiar to the particular arrestor on test, e.g. for precipitators, it is useful to calculate the effective drift velocity (sometimes called migration velocity) of the particles. The expression of the results is covered in Section 14.5.

14.3.4 Test Procedure at a Sampling Position

In this section the test procedure for the I.C.I. packed cartridge filter sampling apparatus will be described and since much of it is common to other equipment, it should be a sufficient guide to those engaged in performance testing.

Further, it will be assumed that no previous experience of sampling the particular duct exists and this then will require a preliminary test. The equipment is shown in Figure 14.5. Full details of the construction and use of similar apparatus are given in B.S. 3405, Appendix C[3]; these are not repeated in the revised edition of 1971. First of all it is necessary to determine the amount of water vapour in the gases, whose nature and analysis must also be known; these are necessary to provide the values for the water vapour content, C, and the gas density ρ_0 (Section 14.3.5). To obtain the latter a gas analysis may be required and to determine the former wet and dry bulb thermometers may be used, incorporated in a gas sampling system as shown in Figure 14.9. Referring to this figure, a sample of the gas from near the centre of the duct is drawn through a filter, then passed through the wet and dry bulb thermometer holder so that the gas speed near the bulbs is about 3 m/s. After reaching steady conditions, the temperatures recorded by the wet and dry bulb thermometers are used in conjunction with a nomogram to determine the water vapour content. Having determined C and ρ_0 the pitot tube is connected to the water manometer and inserted in the duct at or near the centre point of the duct and having suitably lined up the pitot head with the gas stream (B.S.3405, Appendix C)[3], a reading of the pitot-static pressure difference is taken with a suitably sensitive manometer. A preliminary survey is then carried out with the pitot placed at each selected sampling point in turn. The usual precautions in the use of the pitot tubes in dust-laden gas must be observed[3]. The suitability of the position for sampling can be decided to some extent from the uniformity of the velocity distribution. From the pitot reading for a point near the centre of the duct the gas velocity is calculated (or read off a graph) and the most suitable nozzle is selected (from 6) so that the sampling rate into the nozzle is near but less than 5 m³/h. This particular nozzle is screwed on to the sampling tube and plugged. The probe head containing a clean, dried, weighed filter cartridge is then inserted into the gas stream and allowed to warm up for

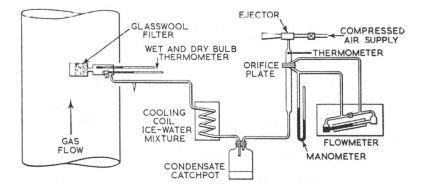

Figure 14.9 Gas-sampling system for determining the water-vapour content of the gas

10 min. During this time the rest of the equipment can be checked including a check for leaks, i.e. on operating the ejector to create a suction in the equipment there should be no flow because the nozzle is plugged. When the probe head is warm it is withdrawn, unplugged, re-positioned at the sampling point and sampling is started at a rate previously calculated from the formulae in Section 14.3.5. With this equipment the rate shown on the flowmeter is calculated with a fixed pressure of 800 mb abs. applied by a screw clip upstream of the orifice plate. The sampling is continued and as the filter-cartridge collects dust, pressure drop across it increases and the overall pressure is maintained at 800 mb abs. by gradually releasing the screw clip. Sampling is continued for 10 min or until it is no longer possible to control the rate by releasing the screw clip, whichever is the sooner; then the probe head is withdrawn, dismantled, the cartridge re-dried and weighed as quickly as possible. From the duration of this preliminary test and the flow rate, suitably corrected for pressure, temperature and the moisture content of the gas, the amount of gas sampled can be calculated. Combination of the weight collected with the amount of gas sampled gives the dust concentration. The order of this figure affects the time of sampling at each point in the test proper and in a few cases even leads to a change of components in the equipment or its replacement by other more suitable apparatus. Nevertheless, very often the equipment is suitable and, when a convenient sampling time per sampling point has been fixed, the main test can be started. From the preliminary test, guidance in organizing the sampling is obtained. It is known approximately how much dust can be collected in a cartridge and it is generally arranged that the sampling be conducted so that one cartridge is used for each row of points, e.g. with a rectangular duct with four access holes to four sampling lines, each with six sampling points; a total of twenty-four points may be covered with four cartridges. Where the dust concentrations are low enough a single cartridge may suffice for all 24 points; this is often the case in arrestor exit ducts.

Having planned for the inlet and exit ducts, sampling is conducted to fit in with any periodic operation of the plant. In order to avoid upsetting the work schedule by the time needed to warm up the probe head it is usual to have another probe head and sampling tube already prepared, plugged and warming up in one of the other access holes. With a little experience the system is easy to work and good results are obtained.

14.3.5 An Example of a Sampling Test

An example of a sampling test and the calculation of the result is given below.

Flue gas at 300°C and containing grit and dust in suspension is passing through a flue of 1500 mm diameter. It is suspected that the total solid burden is about 35 kg/h, and it is assumed that the gas has the same density as air and contains no water vapour. In the pitot survey, the pitot readings (h) ranged from 0·086 to 0·125 mb, the mean value of $\sqrt{h}$ being 0·323. The most suitable nozzle size is selected by substituting $T°C$, the highest measured value of h(mb) and $d = 25$ mm in the following formula.

$$Q_m = 0{\cdot}727(d)^2 \sqrt{\frac{h_{\max}}{273 + T}} \, \text{m}^3/\text{h} \tag{14.1}$$

Thus $Q_m = 6\cdot71$ m^3/h at 1 bar abs. and 20°C.

For a flow rate of 5 m^3/h the required value of d is given by:

$$d = 25\sqrt{\frac{5}{Q_m}} = 25\sqrt{\frac{5}{6\cdot71}} = 21\cdot6\text{ mm} \tag{14.2}$$

Of the six nozzles available the nearest smaller nozzle is 19 mm diameter. Substituting this value (19 mm) for d in equation (14.1) it was found that the correct flowmeter settings ranged from 3·2 to 3·9 m^3/h. Equation (14.1) is derived from a more detailed formula[2] which takes account of the conditions given in the example[7].

For this order of dust concentration one filter sufficed, the nozzle being held at each of the twenty-four sample points for two minutes (total 48 min). The weight of sample collected was 4·68 g. The volume of gas sampled is given by taking the mean velocity of the gas and combining it with the sampling nozzle size, correcting the gas volume to n.t.p. (0°C, 1·013 bar). Thus:

$$\text{gas velocity } v = 0\cdot755\sqrt{h(273+T)}$$
$$= 5\cdot84\text{ m/s}$$

Volume of gas sampled

$$N = \frac{5\cdot84\pi}{4}\left(\frac{19}{1000}\right)^2 \times \frac{48 \times 60 \times 273}{573}$$
$$= 2\cdot27\text{ m}^3\text{ at n.t.p.}$$

where sampling time = 48 min (2 min per point).
Gas flow rate in flue

$$Q_f = \frac{5\cdot84\pi}{4}\left(\frac{1500}{1000}\right)^2 \times \frac{3600 \times 273}{573}$$
$$= 17\,700\text{ m}^3/\text{h at n.t.p.}$$

Thus concentration of solids in the flue gas

$$C = \frac{4\cdot68}{2\cdot27} = 2\cdot06\text{ g/m}^3\text{ at n.t.p.}$$

and
the rate of solids emission

$$M = \frac{2\cdot06 \times 17\,700}{1000} = 36\cdot4\text{ kg/h}$$

14.4 Equipment for Extreme Dust Concentrations

14.4.1 General

The technique described in the previous section applies to medium dust concentrations and modifications to the equipment are needed for extremely high or extremely low dust concentrations. For the purpose of this chapter dust concentrations will be defined as high when greater than 50 g/m³, medium in the range 0·1 to 50 g/m³ and low when the concentration is smaller than 0·1 g/m³.

14.4.2 High Dust Concentrations

With a dust concentration of the order of 50 g/m³ the filter cartridge, which will hold up to 10 g, will be used up in just over 2 min sampling time, which is a reasonable residence time at a single sample point. In turn, this would require 24 cartridges to cover 24 points. Thus it can be seen that the system begins to become unworkable for concentrations approaching 50 g/m³. A modification which may be used is to precede the filter cartridge by a miniature high efficiency cyclone designed to collect about 95–98 per cent of the dust and in this way the range of the apparatus is extended to about 1000 g/m³ (Figure 14.10). At this point it should be noted that the cyclone will be collecting almost 1·0 kg every 12 min, the hopper must therefore be appropriately sized and/or changed frequently; otherwise collected dust will be re-entrained. For dust concentrations higher than 1000 g/m³ it is necessary

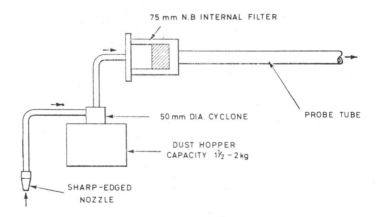

75 mm N.B INTERNAL FILTER

50 mm DIA. CYCLONE

PROBE TUBE

DUST HOPPER
CAPACITY 1½ – 2 kg

SHARP-EDGED
NOZZLE

Figure 14.10 Modified sampling equipment for high dust concentrations

to sample a much larger gas volume into a larger cyclone, say 200 mm diameter, with its own exit pipe which may be sampled using the original equipment in which the filter cartridge is located at the downstream end of a heated sampling probe as in Figure 14.4.

14.4.3 Low Dust Concentrations

At 0·1 g/m³ the filter cartridge collects dust at about 0·5 g/h and at lower concentrations the accuracy of drying and weighing begins to play an appreciable part in introducing errors. For concentrations lower than 0·1 g/m³ the filter cartridge is replaced by a holder containing two 55 mm What-man No. 31 filter papers face to face (Figure 14.11). Before use the papers are placed on opposite pans of a balance sensitive to 0·1 mg and their difference in weight is observed. In use the filter treats about 1 m³/h of gas and at 0·1 g/m³ the upstream paper collects 100 mg/h which is easily detected. The balancing method is claimed to be accurate to 0·2 mg. Clearly such papers can be used only in a certain temperature range and sometimes it is necessary partially to cool the sampled gas before it reaches the filter papers.

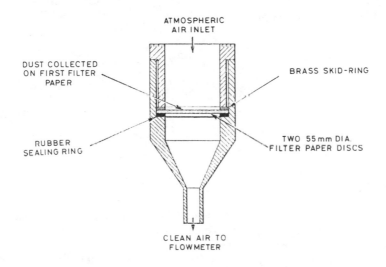

Figure 14.11 Diagram of filter-paper holder

The essence of this filter paper technique is that each paper has received and is receiving identical treatment the whole time; in this way the difficulties associated with weighing a single pre-dried filter paper are eliminated. The method has been used to test air-cleaning installations; by sampling for 20–24 h concentrations as low as 0·25 mg/m³ have been measured to ±10 per cent accuracy.

14.5 Expression of the Results of Tests

Whatever form of sampling equipment is employed it is desirable to use a suitable report form; an example of a simplified report form is given in B.S.3405[3]. The report generally ends with the following two items:

Rate of solids emission (M)	kg/h
Rate of grit emission (M_g)	kg/h

(Grit: solid particles retained on a 200 mesh B.S. sieve, nominal aperture 75 μm.)

Sometimes the amount collected by the dust arrestor is also determined and the results thus conclude with

I = inlet dust rate   mass/h
B = collected dust rate   mass/h
E = exit dust rate   mass/h

These may all be expressed as dust concentrations, if desired, taking care that correction is made for any air leaks into the arrestor, fairly common in arrestors operating under suction.

Three efficiencies can now be calculated.

$$\eta_1 = 100\left(\frac{I-E}{I}\right)$$

$$\eta_2 = 100\left(\frac{B}{I}\right)$$

$$\eta_3 = 100\left(\frac{B}{B+E}\right)$$

For a perfect matter balance $I - E = B$ and these three efficiencies are identical.

In practice, a perfect balance is seldom achieved and the true efficiency is taken to be either η_1 or η_3, the former being preferred.

With experienced sampling teams the values of I and E for repeat tests can usually be obtained to within 10 per cent and whenever this figure is exceeded it is generally necessary to carry out further tests.

14.6 Special Laboratory Testing

Some simplification of technique is possible when assessing the performance of an arrestor in a semi-technical laboratory.

To test an arrestor using laboratory techniques, the test powder (such as that characterized in Table 12.9) is dispersed into a stream of air entering the apparatus. Some of the powder is collected and the rest escapes with the exit air. The air leaving the arrestor is sampled, thereby determining the exit concentration, and because the air is cool and fairly dry the sampling system is very simple. The weight of material fed during the test is known and the weight of powder collected by the device is determined after the test. Samples representative of the inlet dust and collected dust are size-analysed together with the sample of the exit dust. In such a test it is possible to determine the inlet dust concentration, the exit concentration, the efficiency of collection and also the efficiency of collection at various particle sizes, usually expressed in a grade–efficiency curve. Clearly with the testing system described above, many data can be collected about the apparatus on test, e.g. how the grade–efficiency curve varies with the air flow. This technique can be applied only to relatively small-scale equipment but, because the bigger arrestors are usually composed of a multiplicity of smaller units, it is generally possible to carry out pilot tests. Examples of such pilot units are: cyclones up to 900 mm diameter taking up to 4000 m^3/h; venturi scrubber (4000 m^3/h); twin-bag filter (50–70 m^3/h); Doyle scrubber (2500 m^3/h); Rotoclone (2500 m^3/h); Peabody scrubber (4000 m^3/h); and on a rather larger scale a pilot electrostatic precipitator (up to 25000 m^3/h).

A simple rig to test an arrestor has been shown (Figure 14.6). It will be seen that a half-area mixing baffle is used in the exit duct so that only a single centre-point sample need be taken to represent the escaping powder.

14.7 Modified Sampling Techniques for Particular Plant Processes

14.7.1 General

The apparatus described in the earlier sections is suitable for a wide variety of applications where the gas is relatively innocuous and is at or near atmospheric pressure. Special precautions must be taken and the apparatus modified for certain plant conditions, e.g. toxic gases, inflammable gases and high pressure; it is proposed therefore to discuss several special cases for general guidance.

14.7.2 Toxic Gases or Dust

If the duct to be sampled contains toxic gases or dust in quantities sufficient to be dangerous if blown to atmosphere the apparatus and method may be modified as follows:

(i) A sampling nozzle may be located in the duct so that the probe tube protrudes through a suitable gland and is itself fitted with a suitable valve. Clearly this can be done only during a plant shut-down.

(ii) When required for use the probe and nozzle may be cleared by means of compressed air (or nitrogen) blown into the duct. After this, with the valve closed, the filter is connected to the probe and the rest of the apparatus is as shown in Figure 14.5 except that a suitable electrically operated pump is used instead of the ejector and the gas is returned to the duct via another valve and a tee piece fitted to the duct. In some cases to avoid condensation in the filter it may be necessary to insert an electrically heated tube between the filter and the probe (Figure 14.4).

(iii) The sampling rate may be predetermined by computing the mean gas velocity in the duct from plant data and sampling approximately isokinetically at the centre point of the duct.

(iv) With a suitable gland for the probe tube a limited search along a diameter of the duct is possible but in this case the probe must be marked to indicate the position of the nozzle inside the duct.

(v) At the end of the test the apparatus will be full of toxic gas and must be purged by means of compressed air (or nitrogen). Conveniently, this is done through a tee piece located between the filter and the valve on the probe tube; in this way the purging gas will not blow the collected dust out of the filter. With the probe valve closed and purge gas flowing the flowmeter will indicate the flow of purge gas in the correct direction.

(vi) The filter cartridge is removed and weighed in the normal manner; if the dust is toxic the operator should, of course, take all appropriate precautions, including special precautions when disposing of the dust. With radioactive dust the accumulation at the filter can constitute a serious hazard and the appropriate clothing and facilities for protection of the operator must be available and used.

(vii) Sometimes plants dealing with toxic gases and dusts are fitted with special permanent purge and disposal lines, in which case it may be more convenient to discharge the sampled gas into the purge system.

14.7.3 Inflammable Gases

If the duct contains inflammable gases the procedures outlined in Section 14.7.2 are generally appropriate though it is obvious that there should be no smoking, and no matches, and that fire service arrangements should be available. Disposal of the sampled gas may be by returning it to the duct or by any permanent purge system. When purging the lines it is obviously unsuitable to use compressed air; nitrogen from a h.p. nitrogen cylinder is most frequently used for this purpose.

14.7.4 Gases at Pressure

When the duct to be sampled is at pressure the apparatus and procedure are modified to include suitable components. The principles may be illustrated by describing an actual case where the duct pressure was 28·6 bar abs. and the temperature was about 200°C. The gases in the duct contained approximately 50 per cent water vapour, the remaining gas being 22 per cent hydrogen, 23 per cent carbon monoxide, with 4 per cent carbon dioxide and small quantities of other gases. The purpose of sampling was to determine the concentration of carbon particles, mostly sub-micron in size, present in the gas stream.

During a plant shut-down a 6 mm diameter sharp-edged sampling nozzle was fitted into the 200 mm gas main arranged to point upstream along the centre line of the gas main, the intention being to sample 1/1100th of the main gas flow (ratio of nozzle area to duct area). The probe tube was brought out through the wall to a stop valve and a 'Klinger' cock in series, this part of the equipment being fitted permanently to the duct. These fittings and the remainder of the apparatus are shown in Figure 14.12. Referring to the figure, two cooling coils were necessary to condense the large quantities of water vapour present in the gases. Each cooling coil consisted of a 7-turn helix of 13 mm nominal bore standard wall borosilicote glass tubing, coils pitched 25 mm apart. The coil, 140 mm mean diameter, was immersed in a mixture of water and 'Drikold' in a container (230 mm × 280 mm deep) fitted with a suitable carrying handle. Frequent replenishment of the 'Drikold' (a commercial form of solid carbon dioxide) water coolant was required. When the apparatus was used, the water condensed out of the gases accumulated in the large catchpot and was found to contain practically all the carbon particles. The cool, clean, dry gases passed on to the guard

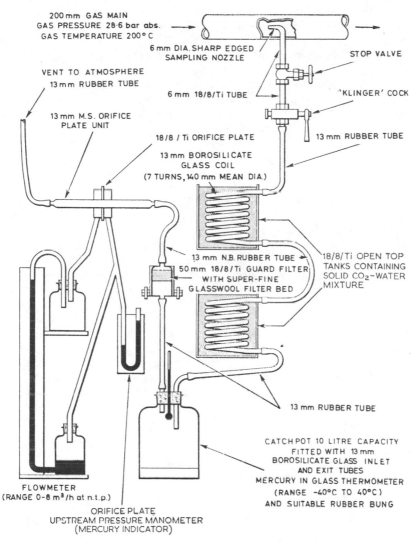

Figure 14.12 Apparatus used to measure carbon content of gas at 28·6 bar abs. pressure

filter containing superfine glass wool and then to the flowmeter and vent system. Because the duct gas contained large amounts of water vapour it was essential to use the more complex formula for sampling rates given in Ref. 2 and with this formula the density of the dry gas is required, i.e. 0·77 kg/m³ (dsy at n.t.p.). There was no ejector or pump in the system since there was a high gas pressure in the main. Prior to operating the sampling system the permanent fittings, i.e. the nozzle and valves, were thoroughly purged direct to the vent system.

The particular sampling nozzle size was determined to give approximately isokinetic sampling with the gas flow rate at a reasonable value for the flowmeter installed in the sampling apparatus (Figure 14.5).

With the fittings fixed to the duct to give centre-point sampling it is not possible to carry out a search along a diameter of the gas main and for fine carbon particles this is scarcely necessary. If a search is needed a gas-tight gland is required at the point where the probe tube passes through the wall of the gas main and it is necessary to mark the probe tube to indicate the position of the sampling nozzle with respect to the centre line of the gas main. If sampling on two diameters of the duct is required an extra nozzle, probe tube, gland and valves must be provided near the initial sample point at a position one duct diameter downstream from it.

In this work the guard filter was found to be quite clean and the sample was extracted from the catchpot liquor by filtration through dried and weighed filter papers (Whatman No. 42), the contaminated papers being re-dried and weighed to give the weight of carbon collected during the test. The concentration was obtained by dividing the weight of carbon by the volume of gas sampled corrected to standard conditions. Typical figures were in the range 5–25 mg/m^3 at n.t.p.

With systems of the type shown in Figure 14.12 there is a possibility of chokes at the stop valve or 'Klinger' cock. In this case the system was workable owing to the finely divided nature of the carbon particles and also to the presence of large quantities of water in the gases which were fully saturated. In cases where larger particles are known to be present in relatively dry gas, more complicated arrangements must be made involving the provision of a sampling nozzle and filter holder capable of withstanding the duct pressure and followed by suitable valves. With this system the gas would be filtered at pressure and there would be no danger of choking the let-down valves through which the sampled gas, now clean, would flow to be metered at atmospheric conditions. It should be noted that such systems involve using a pressure vessel as filter holder and are generally quite expensive.

PART B SIZE ANALYSIS OF DUST

A. LITTLE

14.8 General

As with sampling, no single size analysis system can meet every case. In fact long experience in the field generally leads to a laboratory housing a selection of equipment intended for various types of measurement. In the field of gas purification the most important parameter describing the behaviour of a particle is its free-falling speed in gas. Since this is often too difficult to measure in the particular gas, it is desirable to determine the free-falling speed in air;* this is generally referred to as size analysis by air elutriation. Air elutriators have several serious disadvantages however and

---

* *Use of Vel Gradings*: in connection with the removal of dust from flue gases, the Central Electricity Research Laboratory have found it convenient to express particle size-gradings in terms of the terminal velocity of the particles in centimetres per second in air at 15°C. These are called 'Vel Gradings', one vel being 1 cm/s (see page 413).

the usual practice is to determine the free-falling speeds of particles in liquids, particularly in water, methanol and ethyl alcohol. For particles larger than 75 μm (equivalent to 200 B.S. sieve) it is customary to employ sieves, which are sufficiently accurate for this size range. Thus a common situation in this work is to have a size analysis partly obtained by sieving and partly by, say, sedimentation, the latter usually representing the bigger proportion of the analysis. When the two portions of the analysis are plotted on the same graph with particle diameter for the abscissa and the cumulative percentage smaller than the particle size for the ordinate, a break at the 75 μm size is sometimes observed due to the change from sieves to sedimentation. Nevertheless, since dust arrestors are usually quite efficient in this region, no great error is introduced by drawing the best smooth line through the points, then reading off the accepted analysis from the smooth line where the results are required in tabular form. Thus it is convenient to describe the techniques for size analysis in the order—sieving, air elutriation, sedimentation, optical microscope, then the remaining techniques.

Since the Stokes' free-falling speed varies as the square of the particle diameter, it is convenient to express and therefore determine size analyses in a $\sqrt{2}$ geometric progression as cumulative percentages below sizes of a consecutive $\sqrt{2}$ series with 75 μm as the dividing point between sieving and sub-sieve methods. For grit and dust particles in the context of this book the series is:

> Grit   850, 600, 425, 300, 212, 150, 106, 75 micron
>   (to nearest B.S. sieve aperture)
> Dust   75, 53, 37·5, 26·5, 18·7, 13·3, 9·4, 6·6, 4·7, 3·3, 2·3, 1·7 micron

By convention, particles larger than 75 μm are classified as grit, those smaller as dust[7].

14.9 Selected Size Analysis Techniques

A list of the more important apparatus described later is given in Table 14.1 which includes some guidance on the amount of sample, the time required for an analysis, and the useful size range for the apparatus.

14.10 Subdivision of Samples of Powder

The amount of sample required for each type of equipment is given in Table 14.1. As it is probable that the sample of powder will be larger, it is necessary to provide means for sub-dividing it so that the final small sample is representative of the original[8]. A convenient method is to employ a moving-hopper sample divider (Figure 14.13) in which a hopper oscillates to deliver material alternately to two hoppers situated below the first. By suitable adjustments to the movement, the sample can be divided almost equally into two portions each comprising a larger number of small portions of the original sample. One of the samples in the lower hoppers is then taken and divided into two portions, this process being repeated until the operator is

Table 14.1 METHODS OF PARTICLE-SIZE ANALYSIS

Method	For use in the size range	Amount of sample required	Time required for analysis	Remarks
Sieving	Above 75 μm	10–20 g	about 1½ h	Cheap; rapid; most commonly used in this range
Gonell elutriator	75–10 μm	2–5 g	8–30 h	Useful for fragile powders. Fine, sticky powders are not adequately dispersed. Fractions may be retained if required
I.C.I. miniature elutriator	60–10 μm	0·1–0·2 g	6 h	Cheap; useful for fine sticky powders where air free-falling speeds are required and only a small quantity of material is available for analysis
Roller particle size analyser	75–5 μm	10–15 ml (volume)	4–24 h	Useful when free-falling speeds are required directly. Fractions may be retained if required
I.C.I. sedimentation apparatus	104–2 μm	0·3–0·7	4–5 h	Cheap; several units may be operated simultaneously by one person. Applicable to insoluble powders only
I.C.I. X-ray sedimentation apparatus	75–2 μm	usually 0·3–1·2	1–2 h	Provides a rapid, accurate and continuous analysis of any non-soluble, dispersible powder. The powder must have a reasonably homogeneous X-ray absorptivity. The weight of sample required depends upon the X-ray absorption of the powder on test
I.C.I. photosedimentation apparatus	104–2 μm	40–60 mg	4–6 h	Useful as a standard for checking simpler routine methods of size analysis. Free-falling speeds are determined directly for individual particles. Test powders are used of reasonable light reflectivity, e.g. silica and glass spheres
Optical microscope	75–1 μm	1–2 mg	1–4 h	A well-known technique requiring care and attention on the part of the operator to avoid subjective errors. High-grade optical equipment is essential for work of this character
I.C.I. rapid air elutriator	370–80 μm	0·5–1·5 g	about 30 min	For determination of free-falling speeds of loose aggregates in air in the range 0·3 to 2·4 m/s
Electron microscope	4·0–0·001 μm	1–2 mg	1–4 h	The additional technique necessary beyond the normal operation of the electron microscope is similar to that of the optical microscope
Schöne water elutriator	104–20 μm	0·5–1 g	1–2 h	Cheap. Restricted to insoluble powders

left with a suitable size of sample. It is customary to use the contents of the two base hoppers alternately. The laboratory moving-hopper sample divider shown in Figure 14.13(b) may be used to reduce samples weighing up to 1 kg to less than 1 g, though some attention must be paid to the size of the largest particles in the sample, i.e. it may be necessary firstly to reduce the sample to the range 10–20 g suitable for sieving. After the sieving is completed the fraction below the sieving range may be further sub-divided to produce a sample suitable for the next stage of size analysis. Full information on the construction and use of this apparatus is given in B.S. 3406: Part 1[8].

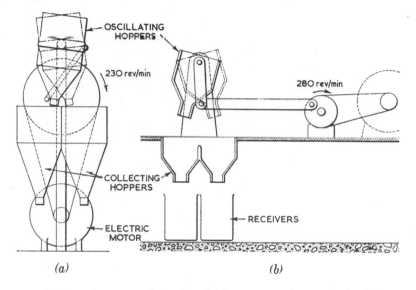

Figure 14.13 Moving-hopper sample dividers (a) Large moving-hopper-sampler. (b) Moving-hopper sub-divider for laboratory samples

Larger machines of similar design may be used to sample down 50–100 kg bags of powder to about 1 kg samples which can then be further sub-divided in the small machine.

The technique is very reliable, as revealed by a series of test analyses carried out at each of several stages of sub-division of a gross sample.

14.11 Size Analysis by Sieving

14.11.1 General

In this field there is little point in considering particles larger than 1 mm (1000 μm) and the following is therefore restricted to the size range covered by the British Standard Fine Test sieves, specified in B.S. 410[9]. Previous to 1969 British sieves were described in numbers per inch. The new numbering in microns conforms with the draft proposals before the International

Table 14.2 CONVERSION CHART FOR SIEVE APERTURES
(AFTER B.S. 410: 1969 AND 1962)

Size of Aperture μm	Britain — British Standards fine special test sieves*	America — American Standards Association ASA.Z23.1:1961 also ASTM E-11-61	France — Association Française de Normalisation (AFNOR) NF K11-501:1938	Germany — Deutscher Normenausschuss (DNA) (1957) DIN.4188 (1960) mm
1000	1000 (16)	18	31	1·0
850	850 (18)			
841		20		
800			30	0·8
710	710 (22)			
707		25		
630			29	0·63
600	600 (25)			
595		30		
500	500 (30)	35	28	0·5
425	425 (36)	40		
400			27	0·4
355	355 (44)			
354		45		
315			26	0·315
300	300 (52)			
297		50		
250	250 (60)	60	25	0·25
212	212 (72)	70		
200			24	0·20
180	180 (85)			
177		80		
160			23	0·16
150	150 (100)			
149		100		
125	125 (120)	120	22	0·125
106	106 (150)	140		
100			21	0·10
90	90 (170)			0·09
88		170		
80			20	0·08
75	75 (200)			
74		200		
71				0·071
63	63 (240)	230	19	0·063
56				0·056
53	53 (300)	270		
50			18	0·05
45	45 (350)			0·045
44		325		
40			17	0·04
38		400		

*Old numbering in brackets in meshes per inch.

Standards Organization. As older literature references use out-moded numbering, Table 14.2 gives for convenience the sieve numbering and micron apertures of American, French, German and former British sieve series. The ratio between successive sieves in the series is approximately $\sqrt[4]{2}$; alternate sieves have a ratio roughly $\sqrt{2}:1$ and every fourth sieve 2:1. All the meshes except the 45, 53 and 63 μm sieves are plain weave; the other three may be twill weave. It should be noted that plain and twill weave sieves of the same nominal aperture will yield slightly different analyses when the same test procedure is adopted.

The allowable tolerance on aperture varies with the mesh number and is summarized in Table 14.3 (minor discrepancies with the British Standard are due to grouping). Although it is too much to expect that all the other test sieve series produced by other organizations should have exactly the same specification, the above tolerances can be taken as a general guide to test sieve accuracy.

Table 14.3 TOLERANCES FOR BRITISH STANDARD TEST SIEVES (FROM TABLE 3 B.S. 410:1969)

Nominal width of aperture, μm	Tolerance on average aperture,[1] μm	Intermediate,[2] μm	Maximum positive tolerance on occasional large apertures,[3] μm
1000	30	90	150
850	30	79	128
710	28	71	114
600	24	66	102
500	20	55	90
425	17	51	81
355	14	43	71
300	15	40	64
250	13	36	58
212	12	13	53
180	11	31	51
150	9·4	29	48
125	8·1	27	46
106	7·4	25	43
90	6·6	25	43
75	6·1	24	41
63	5·3	23	41
53	4·8	21	38
45	4·8	21	38

[1] The average aperture width shall not be greater or smaller than the nominal width by more than this amount.
[2] Not more than 6 per cent of the measured apertures shall be above, and not more than 6 per cent of such apertures shall be below the nominal width by more than this amount.
[3] No aperture shall exceed the nominal width by more than this amount. There is also available a more precise series of sieves with close tolerances half those given in this column.

The normal B.S.F. sieves are 200 mm diameter and 25 or 50 mm deep. There is also a series of 100 mm diameter and 20 or 40 mm deep; this series is particularly useful for smaller quantities of material and possible wet sieving. The sieves are designed to fit together forming a nest of sieves in which the sieves become progressively finer the lower they are in the nest.

It is not necessary always to use all the sieves in the series; commonly alternate sieves are used and sometimes only every fourth sieve.

The sieving process itself may be carried out by hand or by mechanical sieving; standardized procedure is fully described in B.S.1796[10]. Despite the tedious nature of the process, hand-sieving is often fairly reliable but is obviously dependent on the diligence of the operator. However, with some materials there is no other method and a brief description of the technique will be given.

14.11.2 Hand-sieving

To carry out hand-sieve testing it is necessary to split the nest of sieves into small nests, including not more than three sieves in any one group. The previously dried and weighed sample of the powder (about 12–20 g) is placed on the coarsest sieve, the nest resting on a close-fitting base and being closed by a lid. With very dusty powders it is often necessary to tape the joints between the sieves and the lid and base to prevent the escape of sub-sieve material which may become air-borne as the sieves are shaken. The nest is then placed on a smooth surface, usually wood, and given a rotary motion about 30 cm in diameter. After five or six such motions the nest is rapped alternately at two points roughly at opposite ends of a diameter for about ten raps; the operator then alternates between these two processes. After shaking and tapping for 5 min, the amount retained on the top sieve is weighed and if the reduction in weight is less than 0·2 per cent of the total sample weight, the process is said to be complete for that particular sieve. When the process is completed for each sieve in the first small nest, the operator transfers the powder in the base to the top of the next small nest of finer sieves and repeats the above procedure. Eventually the weight retained on each sieve in the selected series is determined and the amount in the base, i.e. that passing through all the sieves, is weighed. This material may then be transferred, after suitable preparation, to a sedimentation size analysis apparatus or air elutriator.

Even the above tedious procedure is not always successful and with certain powders (particularly organic) gentle brushing of the powder over the surface of the sieve greatly assists in breaking up soft aggregates and helps to prevent blinding of the meshes. Another technique sometimes adopted is to wash the fines through the mesh using a suitable liquid which neither dissolves the material nor attacks the wires in the sieve; this process may be combined with gentle brushing.

14.11.3 Mechanical Sieving

Machines for mechanical test sieving vary in the motion they impart to the nest of sieves but perhaps the commonest motion is one which imparts a horizontal rotary motion to the nest of sieves and raps them in a vertical plane once every revolution. By this motion a fresh set of particles is constantly presented to the sieve meshes and the rapping assists the fines through the mesh. Usually about 10–20 g of powder is used for the test in order to give reasonable quantities retained on the sieves for subsequent weighing. It will be seen that the process simulates that described for hand-sieving. Sieving machines usually take a nest containing about eight British Standard sieves and if attempts are made to load more sieves on to the machines their effectiveness is reduced. Several such machines are on the market and do not differ markedly from one another. Any machine may be checked against hand-sieving, using carefully prepared test powders and checking the sieving end-points by weighing the retained material. After experience has been gained in the use of a particular machine for repetitive work with particular powders, there is no longer need to check the sieving end-points and eventually a list of routine sieving times can be prepared for most of the relevant powders. In some cases the time of sieving can be reduced by removing the bulk of the fines initially in the finest sieve, then assembling the nest of sieves and completing the sieving in the normal manner. Alternatively the recently developed Alpine air jet sieving machine may be used—it is much quicker and is specially suitable for fine difficult powders.

The material passing through the finest mesh used (usually 200 mesh, 75 μm) is then prepared for further analysis by one of the methods described in succeeding sections.

14.12 Size Analysis by Air Elutriation

14.12.1 Introduction

In this method of size analysis the particles in the test sample are suspended in an air stream rising vertically in a tube. All particles with free-falling speeds less than the speed at which the air rises are carried out of the system. By increasing the air velocity in steps the sample is reduced stepwise and the weight carried off in the air stream is determined, leading to a full free-falling speed analysis. Although the free-falling speed in the gas is the parameter usually required in the field of gas purification, custom demands that the results be expressed in terms of size and this gives rise to the concept of the equivalent sphere. Briefly the equivalent sphere is that sphere of the same density as the particle which under identical conditions would have the same free-falling speed as the particle.* With the aid of this convention, gradings expressed in terms of free-falling speed may be tabulated in terms of equivalent particle diameters and this is a great aid to most users.

There are several types of air elutriator in use and they will be described briefly in the following order: the Gonell elutriator[11], the miniature elutriator[12] and the Roller particle size analyser[13]. Fuller information on the construction and use of these elutriators is given in B.S.3406[14] (see also B.S.893 on the Gonell elutriator[6]).

---

*This is not the Stokes' free-falling speed when the Reynolds number for the particle motion exceeds 0·2 (see also Section 14.18). Thus 5 per cent deviations of the true free-falling speeds from the speeds calculated from Stokes' law occur for quartz (2650 kg/m³) at particle diameters of 65 μm in water and 33 μm in air at 15°C: these diameters are smaller for denser particles.

To avoid doubt it is desirable to state when a size analysis is expressed in terms of Stokes' diameters or in equivalent diameters taking into account deviations from Stokes' law.

14.12.2 The Gonell Elutriator

The Gonell air elutriator[11] is suitable for size analysis of readily-dispersible powders in the range 10–75 μm. It consists of a vertical tube 1070 mm long internally polished, fitted with special detachable end pieces (Figure 14.14).

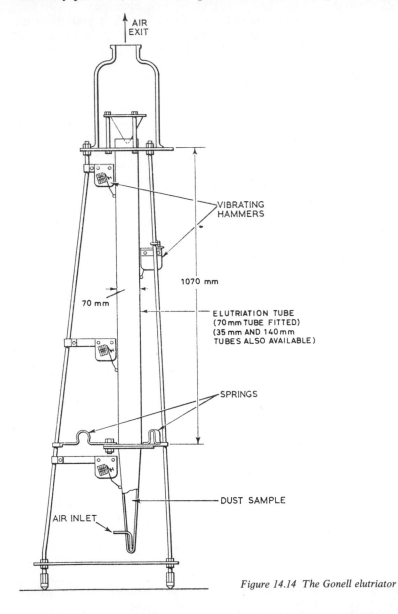

Figure 14.14 The Gonell elutriator

At the lower end there is a cone in which the dust sample (2–5 g) is subjected to the winnowing action of an air stream carrying the finer particles up into the tube where they commence to fall freely against the rising air stream.

Those particles falling faster than the air is rising in the tube return to the cone; those falling more slowly relative to the air, necessarily flow with the air up to a bell-jar attachment at the upper end of the tube where they settle. For any given air rate the amount elutriated is determined by weighing the material remaining in the cone and comparing it with the initial weight. Three tubes are provided, 35, 70 and 140 mm diameter respectively, and each may be used in conjunction with the full range of air rates available to give a wide range of air speeds in the tubes. Thus, commencing with the lowest air rate and increasing the rate in steps, a full free-falling speed analysis may be determined. In practice, it is found that longer periods are required for the lower flow rates and that these periods also vary with the particular powders being analysed. Depending on the purpose for which the analysis is required, different criteria may be adopted in deciding the end-point at any step in the elutriation. Commonly the end-point at any step is said to be reached when the difference in the percentage loss for two consecutive periods is not more than 1 per cent of the initial weight. Sometimes powder adheres to the walls of the tube and electrically operated rapping hammers are attached to the tube and the base cone to dislodge dust settling on the surfaces.

Periods of elutriation which are suitable for one dust may not suffice for another and with particular dusts experiments are necessary to establish suitable routine operation. In B.S.893[6] the periods of elutriation recommended for fly ash are as shown in Table 14.4.

Table 14.4 TERMINAL VELOCITIES AND PERIODS OF ELUTRIATION FOR FLY ASH IN THE GONELL ELUTRIATOR

Terminal velocity m/s	Periods of elutriation	
	Initial period min	Subsequent periods min
Up to 0·007	60	30
Between 0·007 and 0·025	45	20
Between 0·025 and 0·10	30	15
Between 0·10 and 0·20	20	10

In addition to the periods given in Table 14.4, further time must be allowed before weighing the material remaining in the cone to allow particles suspended in air near the top of the tube to settle down to the cone; this extra time period should at least equal the time taken for the gas to pass through the tube in the previous elutriation period.

If it is required with the use of all three tubes to obtain a size analysis comprising ten fractions, then nine terminal velocities must be used. Further, if three of these are in the first range and two in each of the other three ranges in Table 14.4 the total time required for the analysis, allowing only one 'subsequent period' for each step, would amount to 550 min, i.e. more than 9 h. This period is normal and difficult powders may require up to 30 h total, e.g. typical elutriation periods for fine limestone (a difficult powder) are given in Table 14.5.

Table 14.5 PERIODS OF ELUTRIATION FOR FINE
LIMESTONE ($\sigma = 2770$ kg/m^3)

Size range μm	Stokes' terminal velocity m/s	Approximate elutriation period min
Up to 9·4	Up to 0·008	480
9·4–18·8	0·008–0·029	330
18·8–37·5	0·029–0·115	300
37·5–53	0·115–0·230	230
> 53	> 0·230	180

In the latest British Standards on size analysis the convention of assuming Stokes' law* is adopted; also this is why the three Gonell tubes have diameters in the ratio 1:2:4. Thus it may be convenient to give Stokes' diameters when reporting results. If required, the true equivalent spheres corresponding to the elutriation air speeds used can be interpolated from Table 14.10.

14.12.3 The Miniature Elutriator

A miniature version of the Gonell elutriator has been developed by Imperial Chemical Industries Ltd.[12] for size analyses in the range 10–60 μm. Its performance has been found to compare favourably with other available elutriators and it has the added advantages that it is extremely compact, simple to use and relatively cheap. Only 0·1–0·2 g of sample is required for an analysis, which takes approximately 6 h for free-flowing powders. Certain sticky powders, e.g. fine chalk and adipic acid proved difficult to treat in this apparatus but for suitable materials it is a very convenient device.

The miniature elutriator consists of a brass tube 360 mm long and 25 mm diameter, polished on the inside. A conical piece 110 mm long is fitted to the lower end and an aluminium base containing the sample is screwed to the conical portion (Figure 14.15). The air for elutriation enters the conical portion of the device through a side arm and two jets are available for use with air rates in the ranges above and below 0·05 m^3/h respectively. The air flow is measured by means of a pair of flowmeters (one of range up to 0·12 m^3/h, the other up to 0·50 m^3/h). The elutriator tube is mounted vertically on a simple stand, the tube being attached to the stand by four flat springs. When lightly tapped the tube vibrates slightly thus assisting to dislodge any dust sticking to the polished surfaces.

In use the powder sample (0·1–0·2 g) is placed in the aluminium base, the combined weight is determined and the air rate corresponding to the lowest separation size is applied. Elutriation is continued for 15 min during which

---

*Stokes' law: v (m/s) $= \dfrac{5\cdot46 \times 10^{-13}(\sigma-\rho)\times(d^2)}{\eta}$

σ = density of particle, kg/m^3 $\qquad$ η = viscosity of fluid, Ns/m^2
ρ = density of fluid, kg/m^3 $\qquad$ v = Stokes' free-falling speed of particle, m/s
d = diameter of particle, μm

time the tube is tapped at intervals. After stopping the air flow, tapping is continued for a few seconds. The aluminium base and its contents are then weighed, the loss in weight due to elutriated dust being determined. The

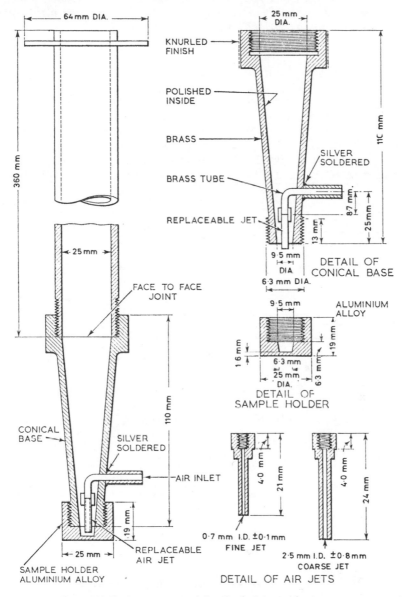

Figure 14.15 Arrangement and details of miniature elutriator

procedure is repeated at 15 min intervals, until two consecutive weighings show a loss equal to less than 1 per cent of the original sample weight. Having fixed the end-point for the lowest separation size, the air rate is increased to separate the next coarser fraction. The same procedure is adopted; however, it will be found that this separation and subsequent separations will reach their end-points more quickly than the first. Thus, step by step, a full size analysis can be obtained. As with the Gonell elutriator, results may be reported in Stokes' diameters or in equivalent sphere diameters interpolated from Table 14.10.

14.12.4 The Roller Particle Size Analyser

The Roller particle size analyser[13] classifies powdered materials in the range from 5 to 75 μm by a process of elutriation, similar to that in the two previous elutriators. In this case the finer particles are carried up the elutriation tube by the gas stream into a paper Soxhlet thimble.

The instrument (Figure 14.16) consists of an air inlet nozzle (a range of nozzle sizes is included to keep the inlet air velocity constant at about

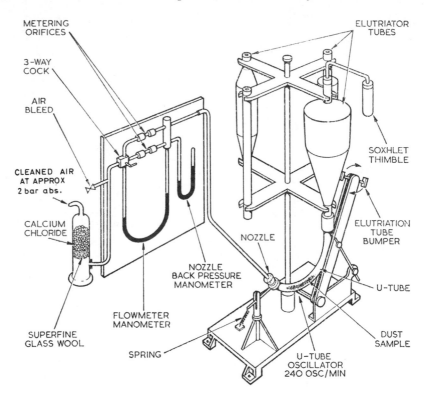

Figure 14.16 Roller elutriator (metal parts are earthed)

75 m/s and therefore almost independent of the air rate), an oscillating U-shaped glass sample container, four automatically-rapped stainless steel elutriation tubes of 228, 114, 57 and 28·5 mm i.d. respectively and a paper Soxhlet thimble to collect the separated fraction of powder from the air stream. The flow of air through the apparatus is metered by a calibrated

flowmeter. The oscillating action of the glass U-tube enables the powder to circulate in the high speed jet of air thus winnowing the lighter particles into the elutriation tube where the classification takes place. The size at which separation takes place depends upon the gas velocity prevailing in the elutriation tube. Care must be taken to ensure that grinding is not taking place in the sample container; there is a tendency for the vigorous dispersing action to disintegrate soft or granular particles.

About 10–15 ml of the powder to be analysed is weighed and placed in the U-tube connected to the largest elutriation tube (228 mm) for separating the finest fraction required, usually < 4·7 μm. The free-falling speed of a 4·7 μm spherical particle of the material under analysis is calculated using Stokes' law or interpolated from Table 14.10 and then the required air rate is computed. An air jet is fitted which will give an inlet air velocity of about 75 m/s under the prescribed conditions. The air rate is adjusted to that computed earlier; the U-tube oscillator and separation vessel rapper are switched on and the elutriation process is commenced.

The air flow is continued for 30 min periods initially, shortening to 15 min periods as the rate of separation reduces. At the end of each elutriation period the air supply is stopped, the mechanical gear switched off and after vigorously rapping the elutriation tube with a light mallet and allowing time for the particles to settle, the powder in the U-tube is weighed. The process is repeated until less than 1 per cent of the original weight of material is separated in a 15 min elutriation period; the separation is then deemed to be complete. The total weight removed from the test portion represents the fraction in the size grade 0–4·7 μm.

After doubling the air rate the above cycle of operations is repeated, the fraction separated being sized 4·7–6·6 μm, the grade limits being in the relationship 1 : $\sqrt{2}$. The next fraction 6·6–9·4 μm is obtained by employing the air rate previously used for the 4·7 μm separation and the second largest elutriation tube (114 mm). The process is continued, selecting suitable tubes and air rates until a full analysis is obtained. Since the tube diameters are in the ratio 1:2:4:8 it is convenient to report results in terms of Stokes' diameters; if required, the equivalent sphere diameters may be interpolated from Table 14.10.

14.13 Size Analysis by Sedimentation

14.13.1 General

The sedimentation technique[15] consists basically of suspending a small quantity of powder in a vertical sedimentation cell containing a suitable liquid. By agitation, usually by means of compressed air, the particles are dispersed until it can be assumed that each cubic centimetre of liquid contains a representative dispersed sample of the original powder. The agitation is stopped and the particles settle, each falling on average at its free-falling speed. With such a suspension, as time passes, the coarser particles settle out at the bottom of the cell; thus equal samples of liquid taken at intervals at a fixed depth contain increasing proportions of finer particles while the weight of material in the sample decreases. Knowing the depth of the sample point, the density of the particles, the density and viscosity of the liquid and the period up to the time of sampling, it is possible to calculate the equivalent size below which all the particles in the sample must be. With a series of such results the cumulative percentage smaller than selected sizes is easily obtained. The above general principles are basic to all sedimentation methods.

It is essential in the sedimentation technique to employ suitable suspending media and dispersing agents and a short list of the more common liquids is given in Table 14.6.

Table 14.6 EXAMPLES OF SUSPENDING MEDIA AND DISPERSING AGENTS FOR SIZE ANALYSIS BY SEDIMENTATION

Suspending medium	Dispersing agent	Typical application
Water (0·1% Calgon)*	Water (1·0% Calgon)	Limestone, clay, fine silica, chalk, alumina
Methanol	Fresh Calsolene oil†	Fly ash, pulverized coal, felspar
Methanol	Ethylene glycol	Coke breeze
Ethyl alcohol	Ethyl alcohol	Portland cement, gypsum, stucco

* Calgon is commercial sodium hexametaphosphate.
† The quality of Calsolene oil deteriorates with age; it should be tested to establish that it does in fact fully dissolve in methanol.

In selecting a suitable suspending medium and wetting agent it is first necessary to check that the liquids considered will not dissolve or in any way attack the powder to be sedimented; the ability of the liquids to disperse the powder is then determined by preparing test suspensions. It is particularly worth while investigating the possibility of using a low viscosity, volatile suspending medium (e.g. methanol) with a view to reducing the time required for an analysis. Suspending liquids and dispersing agents are discussed fully in B.S.3406: Part 2, Liquid Sedimentation Methods[16].

It is worth noting that in any sedimentation technique the initial dispersion is fundamental, as failure to disperse the powder fully will lead to an incorrect result. The usual dispersing technique is to stir into the powder sufficient wetting agent to reduce it to a viscous honey-like consistency and then slowly to mix in a quantity of the suspending medium. This suspension is then added to the sedimentation vessel.

14.13.2 The I.C.I. Sedimentation Apparatus

The I.C.I. sedimentation apparatus[17] provides a routine method of size analysis which is simple and easy to operate; it incorporates a number of features which are improvements on the basic technique described in the previous section.

It consists of a sedimentation tube with a sampling point at the base and a reservoir for clear liquid (Figure 14.17). When the first sample is withdrawn by operating the spring clip the whole of the powder sedimented so far is washed through the rubber sampling tube in a very short time by means of clear liquid from the reservoir. The apparatus has two advantages, (a) there is little disturbance of the column of settling particles while sampling and, (b) much lower concentrations of suspended particles can be used than is possible when only a portion of the sedimented material is extracted as in the original Andreasen apparatus.

The sedimentation apparatus is enclosed in a water-bath of large heat capacity to prevent rapid temperature changes in the sedimentation tube;

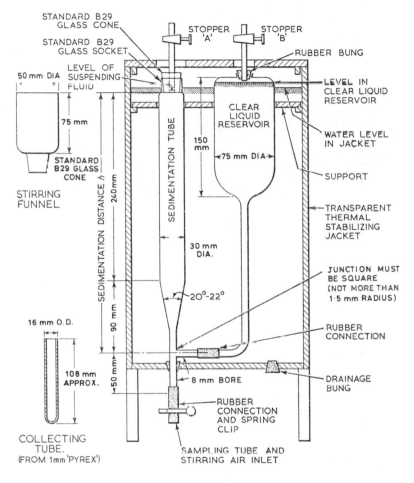

Figure 14.17 I.C.I. sedimentation apparatus

it is generally sufficient to use stagnant water without special thermostatic control, although it is advisable to house the apparatus in a draught-free location. Fuller information on the construction and use of this apparatus is given by Stairmand[17] and in B.S.3406: Part 2[16]. The apparatus has the advantage of simplicity and cheapness of construction and the principal dimensions are not critical. It is advisable, however, in order to avoid mass convection, to keep the diameter of the sedimentation tube 40 mm or less. If the height of the sedimentation tube exceeds 350 to 400 mm the time of sedimentation becomes unduly protracted and this is an additional disadvantage with certain powders which, though fully dispersed at the start, may become partially aggregated with time.

The appropriate dispersing agent for each liquid must be used (Table 14.6). The concentration of material in suspension varies over the range 0·05–0·5 per cent by volume but is usually of the order of 0·1 per cent.

The samples taken from the bottom of the sedimentation tube are necessarily associated with excess liquid and it has been found convenient to separate the sample from the collecting fluid by means of a small electrically operated centrifuge resulting in a considerable saving in time. The last remnants of liquid are driven off in a laboratory oven and the samples are then weighed. This variation from the basic technique (Section 14.13.1) means that the amount sedimented in a period of time is determined rather than the concentration in suspension at a fixed depth; consequently some calculation is needed to determine the percentages in various size ranges.

In the calculation it is assumed that Stokes' law applies, the settling column of suspension is cylindrical and that the suspended particles lie in a number of size grades; in any grade the particles are assumed to fall with the same speed as the geometric mean particle. Commonly the sample being sedimented will be the sub-sieve fraction of the full analysis and, although the finest sieve used might be 200 mesh (75 μm), some particles coarser than this size may be present due to a few wider apertures (see sieve tolerances, Table 14.3). To allow for such particles it is convenient to use the size grades in Table 14.7.

Table 14.7 GRADE LIMITS AND MEAN SIZES

Grade limits, μm	Geometric mean size, μm
75–104	89
53–75	63
37·5–53	44·5
26·5–37·5	31·5
18·7–26·5	22·2
13·3–18·7	15·7
9·4–13·3	11·1
6·6–9·4	7·9
4·7–6·6	5·6
3·3–4·7	3·9
< 3·3	1·7*

*For the last grade the arithmetic mean size is used.

It will be seen that the grades are in approximately $\sqrt{2}:1$ ratio, hence the mean free-falling speeds of the grades will decrease approximately in the ratio 2:1. The times required for the grades to fall out of suspension may be designated t_{89}, t_{63}, $t_{44·5}$, etc., and will also increase in the ratio 2:1. By taking samples at these times, it can be shown that the weight in each grade may be easily computed[17].

Although the time required for an individual analysis may be extensive one operator and an assistant can handle five sets of equipment comfortably by staggering the sedimentation starting times.

14.13.3 The I.C.I. X-ray Sedimentation Apparatus

The original sedimentation system due to Andreasen suffers in that the settling liquid is disturbed when the sample is taken, while the I.C.I. Standard sedimentation apparatus has the disadvantage of the cone at the base of the tube. To overcome these disadvantages some way of continuously weighing the material in suspension without disturbing the liquid or requiring a cone was needed; the X-ray method meets this need[18,31].

The cell in which the sedimentation is occurring is placed next to another cell equal in all respects except for the presence of the settling particles (Figure 14.19). Rays from an X-ray source pass horizontally through both cells at a fixed depth and two identical detectors determine the amount of radiation passing through each cell. The degree of attenuation of the X-ray beam which passes through the cell containing the powder compared with the other beam is recorded as an ink trace on paper. An example for fine

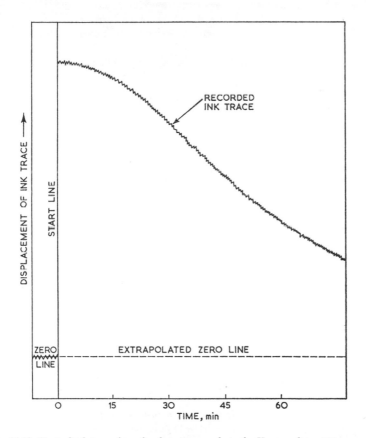

Figure 14.18 Typical ink trace for a fine barytes sample in the X-ray sedimentation apparatus

barytes is shown in Figure 14.18. At the start of the test, with the powder fully and uniformly dispersed in the cell, the attentuation is maximum and also is the displacement of the ink trace. As particles fall out of suspension the attenuation of the X-ray beam is reduced and the trace moves accordingly. In fact the displacement of the pen from the zero line is a measure of the weight of material in suspension at the fixed depth. By choosing suitable

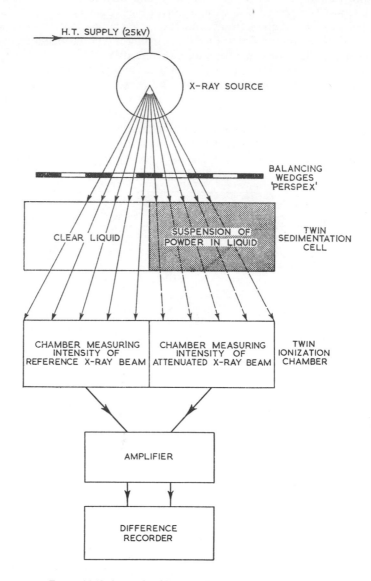

Figure 14.19 Principle of X-ray sedimentation apparatus

times at which to measure the movement the results of the size analysis can be computed. The results may be expressed in terms of Stokes' diameters or in terms of equivalent spheres using the appropriate table in Section 14.18.

Provided the material to be size analysed is homogeneous there is little restriction in the use of the equipment. The range of materials successfully analysed include the following:

alumina	dolomite	plaster
aluminium phosphate	felspar	silica
anhydrite	firebrick	silicon carbide
barium titanate	fuller's earth	sodium cyanide
barytes	gypsum	stucco
cement	kaolin	tungstic acid
chalk	kieselguhr	zinc
clay	limestone	
cobalt	phosphate rock	

14.14 Size Analysis by Optical Microscope

In size analysis by optical microscope a very small representative portion of the dust is thoroughly dispersed in a suitable liquid containing a dispersing agent, and a small drop of the liquid is placed on a clean microscope slide, then covered with a cover slip. The slide is viewed through an optical microscope with the magnification adjusted to suit the particular range of particle sizes being considered. The microscope includes in its eyepiece a graticule[19] showing numbered circles with which individual particles may

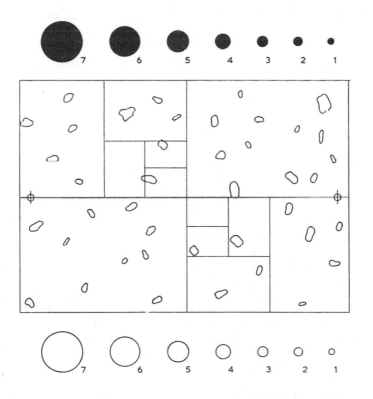

Figure 14.20 A typical field in a microscope count. (Graticule according to B.S. 3625: 1963)

be compared. A typical field is shown in Figure 14.20. By systematic comparison of individual particle projected areas with the graticule, counting the number in various size ranges, counting a large number of fields and making suitable correction for the various magnifications used, it is possible to compute a size analysis by number for the sample under examination. Further, if the assumption is made that the density does not vary with the particle size and, taking account of any shape factors relevant to the particular dust, it is possible to transpose the analysis from a size analysis by number to a size analysis by weight. It is essential when a weight analysis is required that at least the statistical minimum of large particles is counted[20].

There are many variations in practice on the above general method, e.g. the microscope may be of the projection type producing a much enlarged image of the field and the graticule on a suitable screen, or, the graticule may be drawn on the screen itself. In order to reduce the tedious work of counting, automatic scanning equipment has been devised, but inevitably such equipment is expensive and needs fairly frequent servicing.

A description of the technique of size analysis by microscope is too lengthy to give here and the reader is referred to papers by Fairs[21] and to British Standards[19,20] which amplify and extend his work.

14.15 Miscellaneous Techniques for Size Analysis

The foregoing sections have dealt with the more common techniques for size analysis; there are, however, several other systems which may be mentioned briefly.

14.15.1 Air Elutriation of Agglomerated Dust

The rapid air elutriator[22] is an instrument designed to evaluate the free-falling speed distribution of dust agglomerates emitted from power station stacks. Instead of dispersing the dust for analysis it is preserved in the agglomerated state in which it is collected from the gas stream. The size analysis of the agglomerates in terms of free-falling speed obtained by using this technique is required for assessing the rate of dust deposition in the neighbourhood of the stack. The elutriator covers the range of free-falling speeds 0·3 to 2·4 m/s corresponding to particles of density 2000 kg/m^3 from about 80 μm to 370 μm falling freely in air at 20°C.

The sample of agglomerated dust is supported in the gas stream by a silk gauze stretched across the 300 mm long elutriator tube (Figure 14.21). The upper exit end of the tube is connected to a Soxhlet extraction thimble which collects the elutriated fractions of the sample under analysis. Starting with a gas velocity of 0·3 m/s elutriation is carried out for 30 sec and then the weight of dust carried into the Soxhlet thimble is determined. The process is repeated to give fractions in the ranges < 0·3, 0·3 to 0·6, 0·6 to 0·9, 0·9 to 1·2, 1·2 to 1·5, 1·5 to 1·8, 1·8 to 2·1, 2·1 to 2·4, > 2·4 m/s from which a cumulative analysis may be derived.

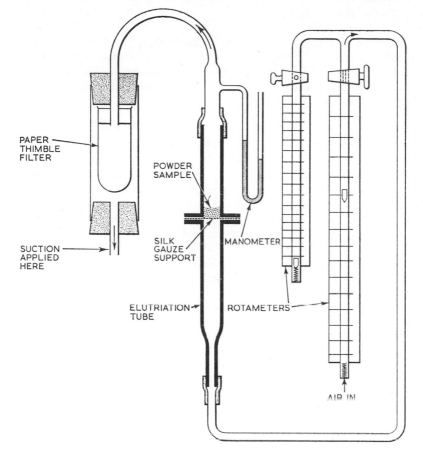

Figure 14.21 General arrangement of rapid air elutriator

14.15.2 Sedimentation in Air

Clearly the general principles of sedimentation outlined in Section 14.13 also apply to sedimentation in air and equipment has been developed for this purpose[23,24].

14.15.3 Electron Microscope

The electron microscope may be used instead of the optical microscope in the range below 4 μm. The smallest size the optical microscope can define for size analysis is about 1 μm whereas the limit for the normal electron microscope is at present about 0·001 μm. The electron microscope is therefore necessary for size analyses of fumes such as those from iron oxide from oxygen-blown steel furnaces. Descriptions of operating techniques have been given by Walton[25] and Cartwright[26].

14.15.4 Water Elutriation

The principles outlined under air elutriation (Section 14.12) also apply to water elutriation; apparatus such as the Schöne elutriator[27] has been developed for the clay industries but has little application for the size analysis of gas-borne dusts owing to its slowness and the difficulties in dispersion of the sample.

14.15.5 Automatic Particle Size Analysers

Several forms of apparatus have been described for automatically counting particles within particular size ranges. None of them is yet in a sufficiently advanced form of development to be regarded as an instrument for absolute determinations of size analysis, but some of them have been usefully applied to routine monitoring of particular materials.

14.15.6 Light Extinction Techniques

Several size analysis instruments have been developed employing the light extinction technique, i.e. the rate of sedimentation of a suspension is measured photoelectrically by the decrease of obscuration of a beam of light passing through the sedimentation cell. Work by Rose[28] shows, however, that the fundamental Lambert–Beer law for light extinction must be modified for sedimenting particles sized in the range below 20 μm; incidentally this turned attention to the use of shorter electromagnetic waves, e.g. X-rays as described in Section 14.13.3.

14.16 Relative Use of Size Analysis Equipment

The apparatus described in previous sections is that used extensively in the industrial laboratory with which the author is concerned for service work on research and process investigations. Descriptions of some other forms of apparatus will be found in B.S.3406: Parts 2–4. Speed is of importance and accuracy must be sufficient for the purpose for which the analysis is required. Several proprietary analysers have been tested but not found sufficiently accurate for all types of dust to justify their use in a laboratory servicing numerous types of manufacture. Such apparatus may well have advantages, however, for routine control of process operations.

The relative use of the apparatus described in this chapter for a 15-year period, is given in Table 14.8. The X-ray sedimentation apparatus is a recent development which has tended to displace the cheaper I.C.I. sedimentation apparatus as it is more accurate and requires very little time in analysis and computation. The photosedimentation apparatus mentioned in Table 14.1 is not described further as it is primarily an instrument for checking other methods of size-analysis. Readers interested are referred to the original publication[29].

The agreement between the types of apparatus described in this chapter

Table 14.8 DISTRIBUTION OF SIZE ANALYSES AMONG THE
MAJOR TECHNIQUES IN A PARTICULAR LABORATORY

Size analysis equipment	Total size analyses in period 1953–67, inclusive	
	Number	%
I.C.I. sedimentation apparatus	5150	37·0
Sieving only	4759	34·2
I.C.I. X-ray sedimentation apparatus	2417	17·4
Optical microscope	550	3·9
Roller particle size analyser	498	3·6
Gonell elutriator	260	1·9
Miscellaneous	275	2·0
	13909	100·0

together with that of some other apparatus is discussed in B.S.3406 Parts
2–4[14,16,20], for silica powder. A general bibliography on techniques of size
analysis is given under References 32, 33, 34.

14.17 Evaluation of a Size Analysis Apparatus

It cannot be too often emphasized that accuracy and reproducibility or
precision are not the same thing: a measurement may be reproducible to a
high degree of precision but may be in error through a constant bias. All

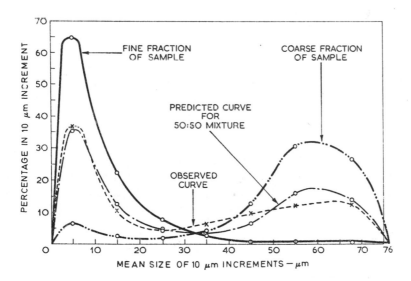

Figure 14.22 Calculated and experimental size analyses

newcomers to the field of size analysis should test their apparatus and operating technique for freedom from bias.

A method described in B.S.3406: Part 2 (to which reference should be made for further details[16]) for checking techniques is to prepare, by some convenient process such as elutriation, bulk samples of two or more size fractions of a suitable powder having particles which are not far from spherical. Each fraction is then analysed separately. The fractions are then mixed thoroughly in equal proportions and the mixtures also analysed. The size analysis calculated from the composition of the mixture and the analysis of the fractions is then compared with the determined size analysis of the mixture (Figure 4.22).   Differences between calculated and experimental size analysis may be due to errors in the subdivision apparatus or the size analysis apparatus or the operational technique. B.S.3406 suggests that the difference between directly determined and predicted size analyses by sedimentation techniques should not exceed 10 per cent of the total at any point when the analyses are plotted on a cumulative basis.

14.18   Free-falling Speeds of Spheres in Air, Water and Alcohols

In order to avoid tedious calculations, tables of free-falling speeds are given in the following pages covering the size ranges particularly important in gas purification. In preparing these tables it was necessary to use graphs showing the deviation from Stokes' law for the coarser particles and in view of this the figures are accurate only to about 3 per cent. Nevertheless, the tables allow easy interpolation and are sufficiently accurate for most purposes. An

Table 14.9 DENSITY AND VISCOSITY OF
FLUIDS USED IN SIZE ANALYSIS

Substance	Density, ρ kg/m^3 at 20°C	Viscosity, η Ns/m^2 at 20°C
Air	1·205	183×10^{-7}
Water	1000	10^{-3}
Methanol	790	$5·9 \times 10^{-4}$
Ethyl alcohol	800	$1·2 \times 10^{-3}$

alternative procedure has recently been given by Heywood[30] for calculating the uniform velocity attained by particles in fluids when the postulates of Stokes' law are not fulfilled. In carrying out the calculations the data in Table 14.9 have been used.

Table 14.10 FREE-FALLING SPEEDS (FT/S) OF SOLIDS IN AIR AT 1 ATM.
AND 20°C

To obtain m/s, multiply ft/s by 0·3048

Diameter of particle μm	Density difference $(\sigma - \rho)$ kg/m^3				
	1000	2000	3000	4000	5000
1	0·000 097 5	0·000 195	0·000 293	0·000 390	0·000 488
2	0·000 390	0·000 780	0·001 17	0·001 56	0·001 95
3	0·000 878	0·001 76	0·002 63	0·003 51	0·004 39
4	0·001 56	0·003 12	0·004 68	0·006 24	0·007 80
5	0·002 44	0·004 88	0·007 31	0·009 75	0·012 2
6	0·003 51	0·007 02	0·010 5	0·014 0	0·017 6
7	0·004 78	0·009 56	0·014 3	0·019 1	0·023 9
8	0·006 24	0·012 5	0·018 7	0·025 0	0·031 2
9	0·007 90	0·015 8	0·023 7	0·031 6	0·039 5
10	0·009 75	0·019 5	0·029 3	0·038 0	0·048 8
11	0·011 8	0·023 6	0·035 4	0·047 2	0·059 0
12	0·014 0	0·028 1	0·042 1	0·056 2	0·070 2
13	0·016 5	0·033 0	0·049 4	0·065 9	0·082 4
14	0·019 1	0·038 2	0·057 3	0·076 4	0·095 6
15	0·021 9	0·043 9	0·065 8	0·087 8	0·110
16	0·025 0	0·049 9	0·074 9	0·099 8	0·124
17	0·028 2	0·056 4	0·084 5	0·112	0·141
18	0·031 6	0·063 2	0·094 6	0·126	0·157
19	0·035 2	0·070 4	0·105	0·140	0·174
20	0·039 0	0·078 0	0·116	0·154	0·191
25	0·060 9	0·120	0·178	0·236	0·293
30	0·086 7	0·170	0·253	0·334	0·413
35	0·117	0·229	0·338	0·446	0·552
40	0·151	0·295	0·435	0·572	0·706
45	0·189	0·368	0·541	0·709	0·874
50	0·230	0·447	0·656	0·856	1·05
55	0·275	0·533	0·777	1·01	1·24
60	0·324	0·623	0·906	1·18	1·44
65	0·376	0·719	1·04	1·35	1·64
70	0·431	0·818	1·18	1·52	1·84
75	0·488	0·922	1·32	1·70	2·06
80	0·547	1·03	1·46	1·88	2·28
85	0·609	1·14	1·62	2·07	2·49
90	0·672	1·25	1·77	2·25	2·70
95	0·738	1·36	1·92	2·44	2·92
100	0·806	1·48	2·07	2·62	3·14

Table 14.11 FREE-FALLING SPEEDS (FT/S) OF SOLIDS IN WATER AT 20°C
To obtain m/s, multiply ft/s by 0·3048

Diameter of particle μm	Density difference $(\sigma - \rho)$ kg/m^3				
	1000	2000	3000	4000	5000
1	1.79×10^{-6}	3.57×10^{-6}	5.36×10^{-6}	7.14×10^{-6}	8.93×10^{-6}
2	7.14×10^{-6}	1.43×10^{-5}	2.14×10^{-5}	2.86×10^{-5}	3.57×10^{-5}
3	1.61×10^{-5}	3.21×10^{-5}	4.82×10^{-5}	6.43×10^{-5}	8.03×10^{-5}
4	2.86×10^{-5}	5.71×10^{-5}	8.57×10^{-5}	1.14×10^{-4}	1.43×10^{-4}
5	4.46×10^{-5}	8.93×10^{-5}	1.34×10^{-4}	1.79×10^{-4}	2.23×10^{-4}
6	6.43×10^{-5}	1.29×10^{-4}	1.93×10^{-4}	2.57×10^{-4}	3.21×10^{-4}
7	8.75×10^{-5}	1.75×10^{-4}	2.62×10^{-4}	3.50×10^{-4}	4.37×10^{-4}
8	1.14×10^{-4}	2.28×10^{-4}	3.43×10^{-4}	4.57×10^{-4}	5.71×10^{-4}
9	1.45×10^{-4}	2.89×10^{-4}	4.34×10^{-4}	5.78×10^{-4}	7.23×10^{-4}
10	1.79×10^{-4}	3.57×10^{-4}	5.36×10^{-4}	7.14×10^{-4}	8.93×10^{-4}
11	0·000 216	0·000 432	0·000 648	0·000 864	0·001 08
12	0·000 257	0·000 514	0·000 771	0·001 03	0·001 29
13	0·000 302	0·000 603	0·000 905	0·001 21	0·001 51
14	0·000 350	0·000 700	0·001 05	0·001 40	0·001 75
15	0·000 402	0·000 803	0·001 20	0·001 61	0·002 01
16	0·000 457	0·000 914	0·001 37	0·001 83	0·002 28
17	0·000 516	0·001 03	0·001 55	0·002 06	0·002 58
18	0·000 578	0·001 16	0·001 74	0·002 31	0·002 89
19	0·000 644	0·001 29	0·001 93	0·002 58	0·003 22
20	0·000 714	0·001 43	0·002 14	0·002 86	0·003 57
25	0·001 12	0·002 23	0·003 35	0·004 45	0·005 54
30	0·001 61	0·003 21	0·004 78	0·006 34	0·007 87
35	0·002 19	0·004 33	0·006 44	0·008 52	0·010 6
40	0·002 85	0·005 61	0·008 32	0·011 0	0·013 7
45	0·003 58	0·007 03	0·010 4	0·013 8	0·017 1
50	0·004 38	0·008 60	0·012 7	0·016 8	0·020 8
55	0·005 26	0·010 3	0·015 2	0·020 1	0·024 8
60	0·006 21	0·012 2	0·018 0	0·023 6	0·029 2
65	0·007 24	0·014 2	0·020 9	0·027 4	0·033 8
70	0·008 35	0·016 3	0·023 9	0·031 3	0·038 6
75	0·009 51	0·018 5	0·027 1	0·035 4	0·043 5
80	0·010 7	0·020 8	0·030 5	0·039 8	0·048 7
85	0·012 1	0·023 3	0·033 9	0·044 2	0·054 1
90	0·013 4	0·025 8	0·037 5	0·048 8	0·059 6
95	0·014 8	0·028 4	0·041 2	0·053 5	0·065 3
100	0·016 3	0·031 1	0·045 0	0·058 3	0·070 9

Table 14.12 FREE-FALLING SPEEDS (FT/S) OF SOLIDS IN METHANOL AT
20°C

To obtain m/s, multiply ft/s by 0·304 8

Diameter of particle μm	Density difference $(\sigma - \rho)$ kg/m^3				
	1000	2000	3000	4000	5000
1	$3\cdot04 \times 10^{-6}$	$6\cdot08 \times 10^{-6}$	$9\cdot12 \times 10^{-6}$	$1\cdot22 \times 10^{-5}$	$1\cdot52 \times 10^{-5}$
2	$1\cdot22 \times 10^{-5}$	$2\cdot43 \times 10^{-5}$	$3\cdot65 \times 10^{-5}$	$4\cdot86 \times 10^{-5}$	$6\cdot08 \times 10^{-5}$
3	$2\cdot74 \times 10^{-5}$	$5\cdot47 \times 10^{-5}$	$8\cdot21 \times 10^{-5}$	$1\cdot09 \times 10^{-4}$	$1\cdot37 \times 10^{-4}$
4	$4\cdot86 \times 10^{-5}$	$9\cdot73 \times 10^{-5}$	$1\cdot46 \times 10^{-4}$	$1\cdot95 \times 10^{-4}$	$2\cdot43 \times 10^{-4}$
5	$7\cdot60 \times 10^{-5}$	$1\cdot52 \times 10^{-4}$	$2\cdot28 \times 10^{-4}$	$3\cdot04 \times 10^{-4}$	$3\cdot80 \times 10^{-4}$
6	0·000 109	0·000 219	0·000 328	0·000 438	0·000 547
7	0·000 149	0·000 298	0 000 447	0 000 596	0 000 745
8	0·000 195	0·000 389	0·000 584	0·000 778	0·000 973
9	0·000 246	0·000 493	0·000 739	0·000 985	0·001 23
10	0·000 304	0·000 608	0·000 912	0·001 22	0·001 52
11	0·000 368	0·000 736	0·001 10	0·001 47	0·001 84
12	0·000 438	0·000 876	0·001 31	0·001 75	0·002 19
13	0·000 514	0·001 03	0·001 54	0·002 06	0·002 57
14	0·000 596	0·001 19	0·001 79	0·002 38	0·002 98
15	0·000 684	0·001 37	0·002 05	0·002 74	0·003 42
16	0·000 778	0·001 56	0·002 34	0·003 11	0·003 89
17	0·000 879	0·001 76	0·002 64	0·003 51	0·004 39
18	0·000 985	0·001 97	0·002 96	0·003 94	0·004 91
19	0·001 10	0·002 20	0·003 29	0·004 38	0·005 47
20	0·001 22	0·002 43	0·003 65	0·004 84	0·006 02
25	0·001 90	0·003 78	0·005 62	0·007 43	0·009 24
30	0·002 73	0·005 37	0·007 97	0·010 5	0·013 1
35	0·003 68	0·007 23	0·010 7	0·014 2	0·017 5
40	0·004 76	0·009 32	0·013 8	0·018 2	0·022 5
45	0·005 96	0·011 7	0·017 2	0·022 7	0·028 0
50	0·007 30	0·014 2	0·021 0	0·027 5	0·034 0
55	0·008 75	0·017 0	0·025 0	0·032 8	0·040 2
60	0·010 3	0·020 0	0·029 2	0·038 2	0·046 8
65	0·012 0	0·023 1	0·033 7	0·043 9	0·053 8
70	0·013 8	0·026 4	0·038 4	0·049 9	0·060 9
75	0·015 6	0·029 9	0·043 3	0·056 1	0·068 1
80	0·017 6	0·033 4	0·048 3	0·062 3	0·075 5
85	0·019 6	0·037 2	0·053 5	0·068 6	0·083 3
90	0·021 6	0·041 0	0·058 7	0·075 3	0·091 2
95	0·023 9	0·044 8	0·063 9	0·082 0	0·098 9
100	0·026 2	0·048 9	0·069 5	0·088 9	0·107

Table 14.13 FREE-FALLING SPEEDS (FT/S) OF SOLIDS IN ETHYL ALCOHOL
AT 20°C

To obtain m/s, multiply ft/s by 0·304 8

Diameter of particle μm	Density difference $(\sigma - \rho)$ kg/m³				
	1000	2000	3000	4000	5000
1	$1·49 \times 10^{-6}$	$2·97 \times 10^{-6}$	$4·46 \times 10^{-6}$	$5·95 \times 10^{-6}$	$7·44 \times 10^{-6}$
2	$5·95 \times 10^{-6}$	$1·19 \times 10^{-5}$	$1·78 \times 10^{-5}$	$2·38 \times 10^{-5}$	$2·97 \times 10^{-5}$
3	$1·34 \times 10^{-5}$	$2·68 \times 10^{-5}$	$4·01 \times 10^{-5}$	$5·35 \times 10^{-5}$	$6·69 \times 10^{-5}$
4	$2·38 \times 10^{-5}$	$4·76 \times 10^{-5}$	$7·14 \times 10^{-5}$	$9·52 \times 10^{-5}$	$1·19 \times 10^{-4}$
5	$3·72 \times 10^{-5}$	$7·44 \times 10^{-5}$	$1·12 \times 10^{-4}$	$1·49 \times 10^{-4}$	$1·86 \times 10^{-4}$
6	$5·35 \times 10^{-5}$	$1·07 \times 10^{-4}$	$1·61 \times 10^{-4}$	$2·14 \times 10^{-4}$	$2·68 \times 10^{-4}$
7	$7·29 \times 10^{-5}$	$1·46 \times 10^{-4}$	$2·19 \times 10^{-4}$	$2·91 \times 10^{-4}$	$3·64 \times 10^{-4}$
8	$9·52 \times 10^{-5}$	$1·90 \times 10^{-4}$	$2·86 \times 10^{-4}$	$3·81 \times 10^{-4}$	$4·76 \times 10^{-4}$
9	$1·20 \times 10^{-4}$	$2·41 \times 10^{-4}$	$3·61 \times 10^{-4}$	$4·82 \times 10^{-4}$	$6·02 \times 10^{-4}$
10	0·000 149	0·000 297	0·000 446	0·000 595	0·000 744
11	0·000 180	0·000 360	0·000 540	0·000 720	0·000 900
12	0·000 214	0·000 428	0·000 642	0·000 856	0·001 07
13	0·000 251	0·000 503	0·000 754	0·001 01	0·001 26
14	0·000 292	0·000 583	0·000 875	0·001 17	0·001 46
15	0·000 335	0·000 669	0·001 00	0·001 34	0·001 67
16	0·000 381	0·000 761	0·001 14	0·001 52	0·001 90
17	0·000 430	0·000 859	0·001 29	0·001 72	0·002 15
18	0·000 482	0·000 964	0·001 45	0·001 93	0·002 41
19	0·000 537	0·001 07	0·001 61	0·002 15	0·002 68
20	0·000 595	0·001 19	0·001 78	0·002 38	0·002 97
25	0·000 929	0·001 86	0·002 79	0·003 72	0·004 65
30	0·001 34	0·002 68	0·004 01	0·005 34	0·006 64
35	0·001 82	0·003 64	0·005 44	0·007 20	0·008 96
40	0·002 38	0·004 73	0·007 04	0·009 31	0·011 6
45	0·003 01	0·005 94	0·008 83	0·011 7	0·014 5
50	0·003 70	0·007 29	0·010 8	0·014 3	0·017 7
55	0·004 45	0·008 74	0·013 0	0·017 1	0·021 2
60	0·005 26	0·010 3	0·015 3	0·020 2	0·025 0
65	0·006 14	0·012 0	0·017 8	0·023 5	0·029 1
70	0·007 08	0·013 9	0·020 5	0·027 0	0·033 3
85	0·008 07	0·015 8	0·023 3	0·030 7	0·037 9
80	0·009 14	0·017 8	0·026 3	0·034 5	0·042 5
85	0·010 3	0·020 0	0·029 4	0·038 5	0·047 4
90	0·011 4	0·022 2	0·032 6	0·042 6	0·052 4
95	0·012 7	0·024 6	0·036 0	0·047 0	0·057 6
100	0·013 9	0·027 0	0·039 4	0·051 3	0·063 0

PART C ROUTINE MONITORING

D. H. LUCAS

14.19 Introduction

Flue gases and process gases commonly contain particulate matter which is valuable, objectionable, or both. The removal of the particulate matter by precipitators or by combustion control is often difficult and expensive and the plant involved is notoriously temperamental. It is therefore desirable to monitor effluent gases to ensure that the plant maintains the expected standard of performance and justifies the capital and running costs involved. The instrument will not only give indication of increased emission but the consideration of events when it occurs will often give a diagnosis. It is also desirable to monitor flue gases so that if the emission of objectionable matter has been prevented this may be convincingly demonstrated. From a legal point of view, but not necessarily from a technical point of view, this end is achieved by complying with the provisions of the Clean Air Act.

14.20 The Clean Air Acts

With regard to dust and grit, i.e. particles with sizes greater than 1 μm, the Acts require that measurements of emission by sampling and weighing methods shall be made from time to time, see Section 2.4.2(c).

However, both the Clean Air Acts and the Alkali Act refer to using 'the best practicable means' of reducing emission and the Chief Alkali Inspector has made it clear that the installation and use of continuously indicating/recording instruments will be considered an integral part of 'the best practicable means' where they are appropriate. The use of such instruments is therefore likely to be of increasing importance in the implementation of the Clean Air and Alkali Acts.

14.21 Ringelmann Number

The present regulations on smoke emission are based on the use of the Ringelmann number and it is essential to discuss this before considering its relationship to monitoring instruments.

The use of the Ringelmann chart is described[35] in B.S. 2742: 1969. The user is required to match the appearance of the smoke *immediately it leaves the chimney* viewed against the background of the sky, with a white card illuminated by the general light coming from all parts of the sky, the card being obscured by black lines to the extent of 20, 40, 60 or 80 per cent. The corresponding Ringelmann numbers are 1, 2, 3 and 4; 0 and 5 correspond to full white or full black. If the smoke involved is formed by the condensation of volatile hydrocarbons which have escaped combustion, i.e. if it is black smoke, it reflects no incident light and the blackness is only moderated by the brightness of the sky behind the smoke.

In framing a smoke regulation it might be desirable to specify that all flue gas should be above a certain quality, as regards the amount of smoke per cubic metre. This would be difficult to apply to the small source in which combustion control is more difficult. It might be desirable to specify that every source of smoke should be limited to a certain amount of smoke per hour. This would be unduly difficult to apply to the large source. In fact, since obscuration is a function of the diameter rather than the area of the chimney, the use of Ringelmann number 2 to specify smoke is a compromise between the two extremes of limiting the emission per cubic metre and limiting the emission per chimney to set figures. If we consider two sources—one ten times as big as the other, the use of Ringelmann number 2 as a controlling condition allows the larger source to emit about three times as much smoke as the smaller source but demands that its flue gas shall be about three times better in quality, i.e. it must have one-third as much smoke per cubic metre (this assumes the same emission velocity for both sources). Some compromise between the two extremes is probably necessary. This one is probably kinder to the small source than the national interest justifies.

It might be thought that if the Ringelmann number of the smoke at the top of the chimney is 2 and if a beam of light were directed through the smoke, 40 per cent of the light would be obscured. This is far from true. British Standards 2740 and 2811 imply[36] that measurements on different chimneys with different conditions show that the loss of light in the smoke over a path length equal to the diameter of the chimney will vary between 75 and 94 per cent when the Ringelmann number is 2. The data on which the standards were based must have been obtained with a bright sky behind the plume. The brightness of the sky compared with a white card can vary from a ratio of 6:1 to 0·6:1 in the normal range of weather conditions.

If the sky is six times as bright as the white card, Ringelmann 2 corresponds to a percentage obscuration of 90 per cent and an optical density of 1·0. If the sky is 0·6 times as bright as the white card Ringelmann 2 corresponds to 0 per cent obscuration! If the interpretation of Ringelmann 2 is to be made independent of the weather but with a minimum of change from past practice some density between 1·0 and 0 must be chosen. The Telesmoke instrument[42] developed by the Warren Spring Laboratory chose 0·44 as the optical density (i.e. 64 per cent obscuration) to represent Ringelmann 2 and it was proposed by Lucas[43] that the Ringelmann system should be rationalized around this figure. It corresponds to a sky brightness of 1·7:1 compared with the white card and if this is assumed for all assessment of Ringelmann numbers, the optical density or percentage obscuration, as read by an instrument, to correspond to Ringelmann numbers is shown in Figure 14.23. Since by definition the Ringelmann number applies to the smoke at the exit from the chimney the path length of the smoke density measuring instrument must be equal to the chimney diameter, or must be adjusted in proportion as shown in Figure 14.23. (Acceptance of this proposal is now being considered by the B.S.I.)

A further cause of discrepancy between visual and photocell indications is that the spectral response of the photocell may be different from that of the eye. If the photocell is more sensitive than the eye to infra-red it will usually indicate a lower optical density of the smoke.

The use of the Ringelmann chart for smoke which is not 'black' is still further complicated. If the smoke is loaded with steam or light coloured particles of ash then its brightness is affected not only by the sky background but also by light reflected from the ash or steam. Under certain conditions a heavily contaminated plume carrying a white dust may have a brighter appearance than the Ringelmann 0 card and the use of the Ringelmann chart becomes ridiculous. However, the difficulties discussed largely disappear if the quality of smoke emission is defined in terms of optical obscuration as measured before the smoke leaves the chimney. The use of tungsten light of a certain range of temperatures and photocells with a suitable spectral response would also need to be specified.

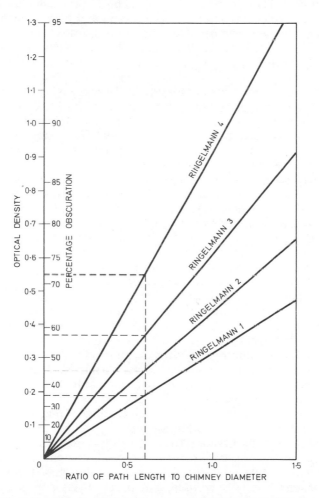

Figure 14.23 Calibration of optical density measuring instruments in Ringelmann numbers for differing optical path lengths. (Courtesy of Pergammon Press Ltd.)

The measurement of Ringelmann number is based on observing the flue gases before they are appreciably diluted by atmospheric air. The problems relating to the visibility and persistence of chimney plumes are, in fact, most complex. A theoretical discussion of the subject together with measurements of the appearance of plumes from pulverized fuel- and oil-fired power station chimneys has been given by Jarman[44].

14.22 Monitoring Instruments Based on Optical Density

There are many designs of instrument which are based on the principle of shining a light beam through some convenient part of the flue gas system on to a photocell and measuring the amount of light which is absorbed by the smoke or dust. They are particularly valuable in preventing the emission of soot particles which have escaped combustion and have condensed after leaving the combustion chamber. These are the basic cause of 'black smoke'. The necessity for preventing the emission of black smoke is two-fold: it is a valuable fuel which is going to waste; it is also a highly objectionable pollutant.

The sizes of smoke particles are usually in the range of 1 μm downwards and the smoke density type of instrument is highly sensitive to small quantities of material in this range. Instruments of this type invariably have a lamp and a photocell with associated measuring equipment. They may present their readings on an 'indicator' which is a moving pointer instrument, or on a 'recorder' which inscribes the readings on a chart, or both. In any of these cases they may be fitted with an 'alarm' which gives an audible or visible warning when the reading passes a preset position on the instrument scale. Alternatively the instrument may have no indicator or recorder and may merely give an alarm. In this case it may or may not have a recorder which records the number and duration of alarm periods rather than the smoke density.

While the principle of operation of instruments of this type is very simple they suffered in the past from a number of disadvantages which reduced confidence in them. Recently, however, there have been several developments in design which give a more satisfactory performance. One of the basic difficulties of the method is that the instrument is indicating a small difference between two larger quantities, namely the difference between the light transmitted when the chimney was clear on some previous occasion and the light transmitted through a smoky chimney, rather than giving a signal directly dependent on the amount of smoke present. It follows that any instability of the measuring system can produce errors which are independent of the size of the reading and may be relatively large. Thus, in the simplest types of instrument, any variation in the intensity of light being emitted by the lamp, due either to the ageing of the bulb or changes in the supply voltage, any variations in the sensitivity of the photocell, due either to ageing or changes of temperature, and any variations in the 'gain factor' of any measuring or amplifying system used, may produce very appreciable errors in the reading. In certain commercial instruments readings of up to 50 per cent obscuration may occur due merely to instrument drift. A further and most serious cause of error has been the build-up of an obscuring deposit on the windows or lenses through which the light enters and leaves the chimney duct, and the magnitude of the errors experienced is limited only by the frequency of cleaning the windows.

A further cause of error is any change in the optical alignment of the instrument during the heating up or cooling of the ducting on which the two main parts of the instrument are mounted.

A wide variety of designs is commercially available which cope with some or all of these causes of error in different ways. The simplest and cheapest device merely consists of a light beam directed through the chimney on to a barrier-layer-type photocell. This has the advantage that it needs no amplifier and will operate an indicating instrument directly. Nevertheless, the barrier-layer-type cell has largely lost favour because of its instability with change of temperature and with its age. The output of a selenium-type barrier-layer cell increases approximately 3 per cent for a 10°C change in temperature. The caesium/silver oxide type of photocell (photo-emissive) is

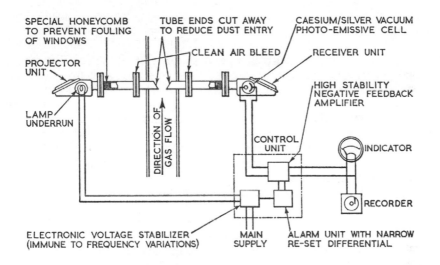

Figure 14.24 Typical installation showing some of the features which maintain good stability. (Reproduced by permission of Ronald Trist and Co. Ltd.)

now commonly used because of its better stability, but it required an amplifier and is therefore necessarily more expensive and unless the amplifier is suitably designed, it may itself introduce more drift than the photocell. For instance, 'chopper-type' amplifiers are used on some installations to give good long-term stability (Figure 14.24).

Other types of photocell are being used or considered; the cadmium sulphide cell, for instance (photo-resistive), has high sensitivity and good response to visiible light. The lead sulphide cell has certain applications but is more sensitive to infra-red radiation than to visible light.

Photo-transistors are very sensitive but their sensitivity and their 'dark current' are very temperature-dependent; they are also sensitive to infra-red. They may be used as switching devices but are unsuitable for measuring unless used with a specially designed circuit.

In the more stable instruments a constant voltage transformer or some other method is used to stabilize the current passing through the lamp,

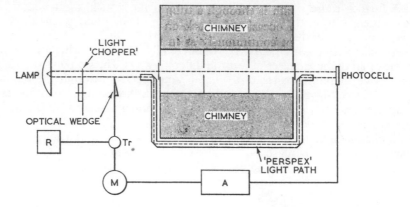

Figure 14.25 Research-type of instrument for measuring smoke density. (Crown Copyright: reproduced by permission of the Controller, H.M.S.O. and the Institute of Physics)

so that this does not vary with changes of supply voltage. Still further degrees of elaboration and precision are needed for special purposes. For instance, a Research Station studying smoke from domestic chimneys used a differential system to minimize the lamp and photocell errors[37]; in this instrument the light beam is passed alternately through the chimney and along a Perspex path which goes round the chimney, and the photocell is used to measure any difference between the two signals obtained. The measurement of smoke density is made by moving an optical wedge across the chimney light beam until the difference signal is zero (Figure 14.25).

An equally sophisticated device is now commercially available. It is shown in Figure 14.26. Light is supplied by a bulb 3 and two beams of light are selected by the mirrors 1 and 1' and are passed through the lens systems 2 and 2' through a single rotating disc 4 which chops the two light beams at different frequencies. They then pass through the half-silvered mirrors 10 and 10' through the lens 6 and 6' and then one beam passes through the flue gas stream to a corner reflector-type mirror 8 which always returns the light beam over its original path even though the mirror changes its alignment somewhat. The beam is finally reflected on to a photocell 11 by the half-silvered mirror 10. The other beam is similarly treated except that it reaches the corner reflector 8' without having to traverse any flue gas. The combined photocell signals are passed through an amplifier but are subsequently separated. This is made simple because their carrier frequencies are different. Since the comparison beam is subjected to nearly all the same features as the measurement beam, it is possible to correct for any errors which may result from changes in the light brightness, changes in photocell response and changes in amplifier gain. The zero reading of the instrument can be checked by inserting the corner reflector mirror 12 into the path of the measuring light beam. This can allow corrections to be made for all causes of error except the fouling of the mirror 8 and any change of alignment of the main unit. The fouling of the mirror 8 is minimized by a cylindrical labyrinth, but for really long-term use, this must be supplemented by protecting the mirror with a flow of filtered air.

Although most designs pass the light beam across the chimney or flue

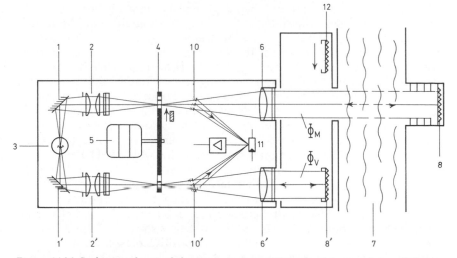

Figure 14.26 Sophisticated optical density instrument. (Reproduced by permission of Pearson Panke Ltd.)

1 and 1′, Mirrors; 2 and 2′, System of lenses; 3, Bulb; 4, Rotating disc; 5, Motor; 6 and 6′, Lens; 7, Gas stream; 8 and 8′, Reflection mirrors; 10 and 10′, Mirrors; 11, Photocell; 12, Mirror reflector.

duct, in some cases a sample of flue gas is removed from the chimney, passed through the measuring equipment and returned to the chimney as shown in Figure 14.27. This is convenient when it is difficult to gain access to suitable positions on the actual ducting or chimney, it also facilitates the setting up and zero checking of the instrument, and probably minimizes the likelihood of the optical system becoming obscured by sooty deposit.

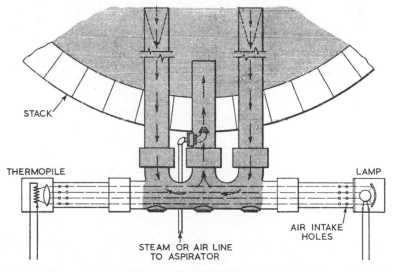

Figure 14.27 The measurement of the optical density of flue gas outside the chimney. (Reproduced by permission of Leeds & Northrup Ltd.)

The progressive obscuration of windows has undoubtedly been one of the most difficult problems associated with smoke density equipment. The trouble has been somewhat reduced in most instruments by arranging for external air to be sucked or blown across the windows. This has only been partially successful because the air itself is far from clean and often has been an imperfect barrier to the flue gases. In many cases windows have required to be cleaned once a shift. A recent development has been successful in maintaining cleanliness for very long periods, even under difficult circumstances. In this system[38] the window is set back from the cleaning air entrance a distance of about 30 cm and in addition a honeycomb (Figure 14.28(a)) of thin aluminium about 12 cm in length is sealed on to the window. The probability of a soot or dust particle diffusing the whole length of the main tube and also the length of one of the individual honeycomb tubes is so small that windows of this type are claimed to remain clean for years. The 30 cm length of wide tube is provided so that coarser particles can settle out before they reach the homeycomb. The design of this system is shown in Figure 14.28(b). It requires modification if the duct is under positive pressure instead of the more usual negative pressure and the modified design is shown in Figure 14.28(c). These designs are protected by a C.E.G.B. patent[34] but are commercially available under licence from a number of firms.

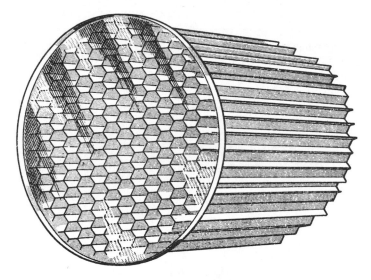

Figure 14.28(a) Honeycomb attached to glass window (as shown in Figures 14.31(b) and (c)). (Reproduced by permission of the Director of the Central Electricity Research Laboratories and the Institute of Fuel)

When the smoke being monitored is light in colour it is possible to make use of the light scattering or light reflecting property of the smoke. The photocell is set up so that it receives no direct light from the lamp: it then measures either scattered or reflected light when smoke is passing. This

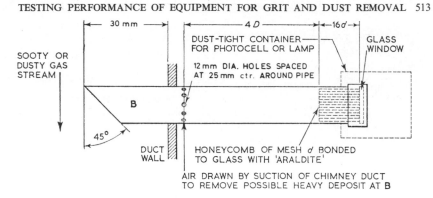

Figure 14.28(b) 'Everclean' observation window for use in ducts with negative pressure

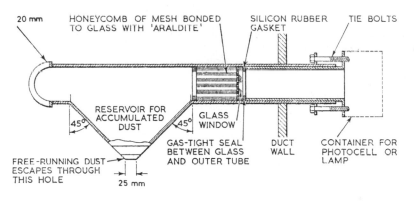

Figure 14.28(c) 'Everclean' observation window for use in ducts with positive pressure. (Illustrations reproduced by permission of the Director of Central Electricity Research Laboratories and the Institute of Fuel)

method reduces the difficulty of obtaining zero stability and is particularly suitable for very sensitive measurement of low density smokes. Apart from this advantage and the conjugate disadvantage that it can only be applied to smoke and dust of uniform colour, this type of instrument has similar characteristics to optical density type instruments. However, its readings cannot be directly related to Ringelmann number.

An instrument of this type has recently been developed by the North West Region of the C.E.G.B. with the name Fordust. It has a specially designed observation system to avoid the accumulation of dust on windows and is shown in Figure 14.29.

The South Eastern Region of the C.E.G.B. has developed a variant of the normal type of smoke density instrument, referred to as the S.E.R.O.P., which makes it possible to carry out a zero check of the instrument. Instead of mounting the light and photocell on opposite sides of a duct, the two are mounted on a rigid tube 1·2 m long which is inserted from one side of the duct only. In consequence, it is relatively easy to remove the instrument to carry out a zero check. The rigid tube is extensively cut away so that when it is

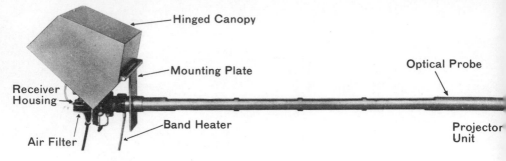

Figure 14.29 Instrument removable for zero check. (Reproduced by permission of Airflow Developments Ltd.)

inserted in the flue duct, flue gas can flow between the lamp and the photocell. A diagram of the instrument is shown in Figure 14.30. There has been a further C.E.G.B. development by the Research Laboratories at Leatherhead, known as the C.E.R.L. Self Checking Smoke Recorder. In this case a rigid tube is inserted right across the flue duct and the lamp and photocell are

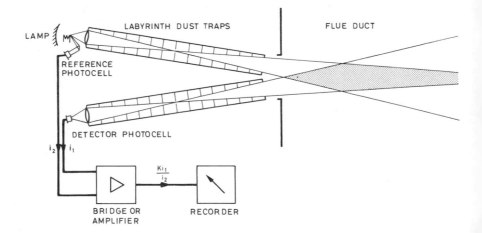

Figure 14.30 Optical arrangement for measuring light reflected from dust. (Reproduced by permission of Research Manager, C.E.G.B., N.W. Region Scientific Services Ltd.)

mounted directly on it. Flue gas enters and leaves the tube through relatively small sampling nozzles and the tube is normally full of flue gas. At pre-determined intervals, clean air is brought into the tube either by using duct suction or by using a fan, and the instrument then automatically records its effective zero. The true optical density can always be read from the chart.

The tube is also an ideal situation for the installation of Everclean Windows. The instrument is illustrated in Figure 14.31. It has an incidental advantage that if the sampling nozzles are deliberately reduced in size, the averaging

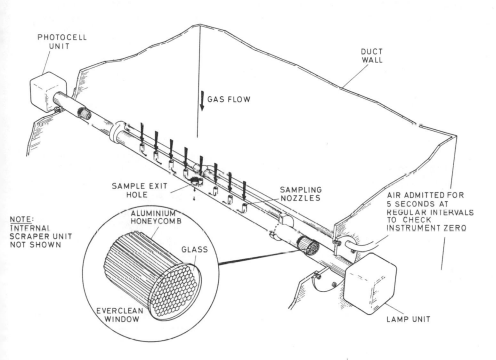

Figure 14.31 Self-checking smoke density recorder. (Reproduced by permission of Director, C.E.R.L.

time of the instrument can be increased to about 30 seconds and this smooths out most of the high frequency clutter which is typical of smoke density readings and the chart record is then much clearer and easier to interpret.

14.23 Monitoring Instruments not Based on the Optical Density of Flue Gas

The *raison d'être* of the types of instruments discussed so far is that they indicate the visibility of a plume which is the first and most obvious cause of public complaint, they are particularly sensitive to black smoke which should be suppressed because it is both desirable and economic to do so. However, the visibility of the plume is not the only or even the most bitter cause of complaint and it is essential to consider the other aspects of pollution by dust and grit and to realize that another type of instrument is required to deal with it.

14.24 The Nature of Pollution by Dust and Grit

Dust and grit particles have a range of size from 1000 to 1 μm and a range of free-falling speed from 10 m/s to speeds a million times less. The relative importance as pollutants of particles of different size is not defined by their obscuring power or by the visibility of the plume carrying them. It is common practice to give the weight of dust per unit volume of flue gas emitted as a criterion for a particular chimney. This is purely a function of convenience in measuring emission by the sampling methods described in Part A of this chapter. It is not based on any theory of pollution. In general, the most serious complaints of pollution are caused by the dust which settles on laundry, obscures the surfaces of houses and trees or enters open windows and makes internal furnishings dirty.

The pollution takes place in two stages. In the first stage the dust has to settle or impinge on some object, and in the second place it obscures some of the light which is normally reflected from the object. The tendency for a dust particle to settle or impinge on an object is a complicated function of the particle's size and density, the velocity of the air stream in which it finds itself and the size and nature of the object. However, taking a broad view of a whole range of circumstances it can be shown that the likelihood that a particle will reach a surface is proportional to its free-falling speed in air, and this is approximately proportional to the square of its diameter. (A small particle of dust will usually adhere to the surface it first touches; a larger particle may fall after impact. The nuisance caused is hardly different in the two cases.) Therefore, on a weight-for-weight basis, coarse particles are far more likely to cause complaint than fine ones. This is to some extent offset by the fact that after the particles have settled, the obscuration is a function of the surface area of the settled particles and in this respect fine particles are more serious. When one considers the net result of these two functions it can be shown that the nuisance value of dust increases proportionately with particle size and it can be said very approximately that a given weight of 100 μm dust is 10 times more of a nuisance than the same weight of 10 μm dust.

If an optical density type instrument is used to monitor dust it responds to the total projected area of the dust particles. This is proportional to the total surface area of the particles. Again using a weight-for-weight comparison 10 μm dust gives 1/10 the reading of 1 μm dust and 100 μm dust gives 1/100 of the reading. This, of course, is varying in the opposite sense to the nuisance value of the dust.

It is important to recognize that the size to be considered is not necessarily the size of the constituent particles. It is well known that the dust emitted by electrostatic precipitators is usually very much finer than the dust presented to the precipitator, but it is now becoming recognized that much of this emitted dust is in the form of agglomerates. These are a particularly serious form of dust emission since they have the same ability as coarse dust to impinge on objects and the great obscuring power peculiar to fine dust.

Again the optical density-type instrument responds to the concentration of dust in the flue gas. The likelihood of nuisance is dependent on the *amount* of dust emitted by the chimney and not on the concentration alone. The true nuisance value is the product of the concentration of dust, and the gas velocity; and of course other factors such as the area of cross-section of duct and dust grading as already discussed.

14.25 Dust Nuisance Monitor

An instrument has been developed[39], the C.E.R.L. dust monitor, which takes account of these arguments; it monitors the amount of dust passing through a chimney, but places increased emphasis on the coarser particles of dust. The sampling head of this instrument which is inserted into the duct leading to the chimney is shown in Figure 14.32. The small nozzle faces into the gas stream, but since the nozzle leads to a closed chamber there is no net

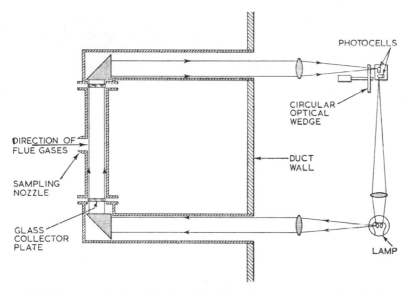

Figure 14.32 Diagrammatic view of dust monitor. Note: *For convenience in drawing the nozzle has been turned through a right angle. (Reproduced by courtesy of the Director of Central Electricity Research Laboratories, Evans Electro Selenium Ltd. and the Foster Instrument Co.)*

movement of gas through the nozzle. Nevertheless, since the dust particles are moving at high velocity they succeed in entering the nozzle and settle at the bottom of the closed chamber. The chance that a particle will penetrate the nozzle is dependent on its size and the instrument therefore selects the dust according to the likelihood that it would settle or impinge on some external object. Subsequently the obscuring power of the collected dust is measured by means of a light beam and photocell. The operation of the instrument is therefore strictly analogous to the sequence of events by which dust causes nuisance.

  In an improved version of this instrument the optical density of the dust is measured by a photocell in a Wheatstone Bridge, which is designed to have a linear response as the signal level increases. The signal level is continuously recorded on a chart recorder, and at a pre-arranged time, usually after 15 minutes, a blast of compressed air blows away the collected dust and the signal returns to zero. The form of the chart record is therefore a saw tooth with the peaks of the tooth giving the quarter-hour average of the instrument reading. The lower points of the saw tooth should lie on the chart zero, but if they do not, they give a reliable indication of the instrument's effective zero.

If the gas velocity in the duct increases while the concentration and grading of the dust remain unchanged the reading of the instrument increases. It records the product of concentration and gas velocity as discussed in the previous section and satisfies both the conditions required to express the likelihood of the dust causing a nuisance. This instrument is covered by a C.E.G.B. patent[40] but is commercially available. Currently a device is being tested which will integrate the signals from an instrument so that 8- or 24-hour averages can be obtained, and so that the long-term averages for a number of instruments in the same plant can be printed out centrally.

A comparison of the response of the two types of instrument so far considered is given in Figure 14.33. Of course, if it can be assumed that the grading of emitted dust is completely fixed, both types of instrument can be

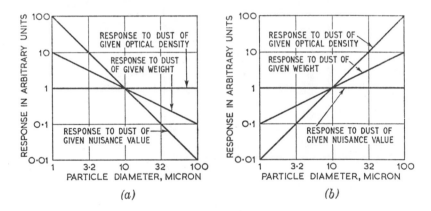

Figure 14.33 (a) Response of optical density-type instrument to dust particles of different size. (b) Response of nuisance value-type instruments to dust particles of different size.

Notes: (i) All curves made arbitrarily equal at 10 μm; (ii) optical density $\propto \sum D^2$ for all particles in unit volume; (iii) 'nuisance value' $\propto \sum \rho D^4$ for all particles in unit volume.

calibrated to read weight of dust emitted. Since this proviso is never met in practice, the weight of dust is a parameter which is not measured by either instrument.

14.26 Dust-Collecting Thimble

A simple and convenient device has been described[41] which consists of a cylinder approximately 25 mm in diameter and 150 mm long which is closed at one end and open at the other. It is introduced into the flue duct so that the gas flow is directly into the open end of the cylinder. It is suitable for horizontal or vertical (down) flows of gas. It has been found advantageous to provide the cylinder with a circumferential lip, so that the dust which enters the thimble is retained even though the thimble is subject to vibration. The thimble is inserted into the flue gases for a fixed time and the collected dust is then weighed, or measured volumetrically.

The instrument has, of course, a great deal in common in its performance with the automatic instrument described above. If the collected dust were measured optically by an absorptiometer instead of being weighed, the results obtained should be strictly comparable. The thimble has the advantage of cheapness and simplicity, while the dust nuisance monitor carries out the same functions automatically and without the necessity for manual operation.

14.27 Conclusion

There have been many developments in the nature and in the detailed design of monitoring instruments for particulate matter in flue gas. Two main types of instrument exist and are necessary. One monitors the visibility of the plume and is relevant to complaints of obscured sky and loss of sunlight; it is most sensitive to fine particles, and, if well designed, is appropriate for the control of smoke emission. The other instrument monitors the nuisance value of dust and grit and is relevant to complaints of obscured windows, paint, laundry, etc., and deposits of grit; it is most sensitive to coarse particles and agglomerates.

15

Mist Removal

PART A **REMOVAL OF ACID MISTS FROM CHEMICAL PROCESSES**

G. LOWRIE FAIRS

15.1 Physical Properties of Condensation Mists Affecting Their Particle Size

Many plant gases contain mists produced by condensation of acid particles. Such mists are usually very fine, much finer than those produced mechanically by carry-over from evaporators or distributors of absorption towers, and are consequently more difficult to scrub effectively. Condensation mists may either be present in tail gases, where they may constitute a nuisance, or they may have to be removed at an intermediate stage in a chemical process, as for example to avoid catalyst poisoning in contact sulphuric acid plants. This chapter is restricted to the consideration of condensation mists, methods of treating carry-over spray being discussed in Chapter 16.

Efficient scrubbing of condensation mists presents a number of problems additional to those occurring when handling solid gas-borne particles of comparable size. It is therefore important to describe those properties of aqueous acid mists that affect their fineness and stability, since much of this information is as yet unpublished. Such data have an important bearing on the selection and design of appropriate scrubbing equipment.

15.1.1 Stability of Mists

One of the main reasons why an aqueous mist is more difficult to handle than a dust is that its particle size does not necessarily remain stable, being profoundly affected by changes of temperature and humidity of the suspending gas. Furthermore, even if the size distribution of a particular mist is known, it cannot be assumed that the mist from a second plant of similar design and output will be the same and it would be most unwise to do so. There are in fact numerous examples of generally similar plants whose tail gas mists are either very different or are present in one and absent in the other. A typical example is shown in Table 15.1.

15.1.2 Influence of Solid Nuclei in the Suspending Gas

The fineness of acid mists is greatly influenced by the number of solid nuclei present in the suspending gas at the time of formation. This was noted in unpublished work by Fox shortly after World War I, when developing the Calder–Fox Scrubber. Although there was at that time no means of measuring the particle sizes of mists, he observed that the mist evolved from sulphuric acid concentrators of the Cascade type was easier to scrub than that from Gaillard and Kessler concentrators. Furthermore he demonstrated in the

Table 15.1 FINENESS OF SULPHURIC ACID MIST VENTED FROM REACTION VESSELS IN TWO SIMILAR PLANTS

Particle size, μm	Weight percentage less than stated size	
	Plant 1	Plant 2
26	—	100
13	100	80
6·6	87	24
3·3	58	1
1·6	24	—
0·8	6	—

laboratory that freshly prepared sulphuric acid mist was made more difficult to scrub by injecting tobacco smoke into it, thus providing many additional nuclei for droplet formation. Investigations by Fairs[1] established that mists from the indirectly fired Cascade concentrator are actually coarser than those from Gaillard and Kessler concentrators, which being directly fired produce large numbers of solid nuclei and consequently finer mists in the tail gases.

15.1.3 Mechanical Growth

Since it is easier to scrub large droplets, it is reasonable to suggest that condensation mists should be grown before scrubbing. Certain methods of mechanical agglomeration have been developed on a commercial scale

Table 15.2 GROWTH OF HYDROCHLORIC ACID MIST BY PASSAGE THROUGH AN AIR EJECTOR

Particle size, μm	Weight percentage less than stated size	
	Before ejector	After ejector
105	—	100
53	—	50
26	—	10
13	100	0·6
6·6	63	—
3·3	17	—
1·7	1	—

(Section 15.7.3) but all are very expensive to operate because of the large power inputs required. However, hydrochloric and chlorosulphonic acid mists can usually be grown substantially, merely by passage through a fan or ejector. It is therefore important, when dealing with such mists, to arrange that the scrubber follows the fan or ejector and does not precede it. An example of the growth of hydrochloric acid mist in an ejector is given in Table 15.2.

15.1.4 Physical Growth

On the other hand it is rarely found that sulphuric acid mist can be grown mechanically by such simple means and methods when large power inputs are required. If, however, the particles have not reached equilibrium with the water vapour in the suspending gas and are in a relatively anhydrous condition it is often possible to grow the particles by humidification (e.g. by passing the gases up a packed tower irrigated with water) and thus render them much more easy to scrub. This is illustrated by the size analyses of an oleum mist before and after humidification.

Table 15.3 EFFECT OF HUMIDIFICATION ON THE GROWTH OF NEWLY FORMED OLEUM MIST

Particle size, μm	Weight percentage less stan stated size	
	Before humidification	After humidification
26	—	100
13	—	69
6·6	100	22
3·3	70	7
1·6	40	2

Shock cooling of mists by drawing large volumes of cold air into ventilating hoods over vats of fuming acids results in very fine mists. It is a frequent practice in industry but should be avoided whenever possible. Fox invetigated the 'conditioning' of sulphuric acid concentrator mists by controlled cooling and recommended rapid cooling of the gases to about 180°–200°C at which temperature the vapour pressure of the acid is negligible. Thereafter the rate of cooling to about 130°C was to be as slow as possible. Metallgesellschaft, A.G.[2] in describing a wet contact process emphasize the importance of slow cooling of the gases in the region of 140°–150°C if satisfactory condensation is to take place.

15.1.5 Other Factors Influencing the Ease of Collection of Acid Mists

Certain substances such as ammonia and ammonium compounds have an inhibiting effect upon the growth of sulphuric acid mist particles, and the presence of such inhibitors, whether in the acid or the suspending gas, can be taken as an indication that the mist will be fine and very difficult to scrub. This fact should be borne in mind, as the addition of ammonia is sometimes advocated in the treatment of sulphur-bearing tail gases.

It is not always realized that fine acid mists are not readily absorbed even in alkaline solutions, and surprise is sometimes expressed that a packed tower designed to absorb acid vapour will not remove mist as well. In all cases where appreciable quantities of acid mist have to be handled as well as vapour, it is essential to provide a mist scrubber in addition to the absorption tower.

15.1.6 Visibility of Acid Mist Plumes

Since the Clean Air Act, 1956, came into force the public and those connected with Public Health Administration are giving increasing attention to the appearance of gaseous effluents from chemical plants. Many such effluents consist almost entirely of condensed steam, but unfortunately steam plumes are made more persistent by the presence of acid mist droplets. It was found that, when the acid mist was removed from the tail gas from one of two adjacent waste acid strippers, the length of the steam plume was only one quarter that from the untreated unit even although the gas volume rate, handled was three times as great.

The visibility of a plume, i.e. its light-scattering effect, is a function of the projected area of the suspended particles, but below about 20 μm this scattering is greatly accentuated and reaches a maximum for particle sizes about the wavelength of light. A mist containing 1 g/m^3 and consisting entirely of 1 μm particles would have ten times the projected area of one of the same concentration but containing only 10 μm particles. The light-scattering of the finer mist would, however, be still further accentuated as indicated above. Thus the obscuring power of a fine mist may be out of all proprtion to its acidity, and many cases are known of tail gases of fine particle size and extremely bad appearance which have much lower acidities than others which are much less visible because their particles are larger. A further factor, as is pointed out by Green and Lane[3] is the psychological effect of threshold contrast, which will vary according to atmospheric conditions, an average value of 2 per cent being suggested. The degree of obscuration presents a somewhat awkward problem because it is difficult to assess the importance of plume appearance when applying the provisions of the Alkali Act. There is no doubt, however, that a much stricter attitude is being adopted by H.M. Alkali Inspectorate, as reference to the annual reports will show.

For recent research on the appearance of fine particulate matter against various sky backgrounds, see Jarman, Chapter 14, Ref. 44.

15.2 Sampling and Size Analysis of Mists

The successful design of mist scrubbers has been impeded in the past because of a lack of data on the particle size distributions of the mists to be handled. All mist scrubbers have particle size ranges to which they are specially applicable and their selection and design depends on the size distribution of the particles which they will be called upon to handle. Since these size distributions can vary considerably from plant to plant it follows that the only really reliable basis for design is an actual size analysis of the mist in question. Obviously this criterion can only be applied when the mist actually exists and, when designing mist removal equipment for chemical plant which is not yet erected, the chemical engineer is forced to make an estimate on the basis of previous experience, making suitable provision for modifications should the mist prove finer than expected. Moreover regular monitoring of the performance of installed equipment is highly desirable. Before describing the various types of scrubbing equipment therefore it will be useful to indicate briefly how mists may be sampled and sized.

15.2.1 Sampling for Size Analysis

Sampling mists is a more exacting process than for solid particles, because growth and shrinkage of the particles by condensation or evaporation has

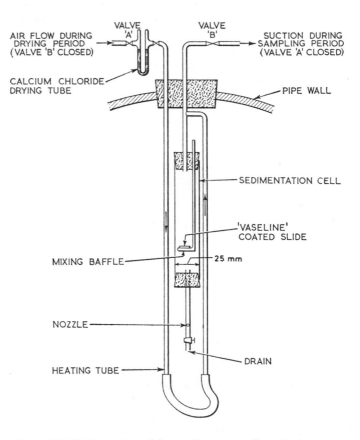

Figure 15.1 Sedimentation cell for sampling mists at elevated temperatures

to be prevented. Sampling must be carried out isokinetically[5] in a stack or duct at a point well away from bends or other sources of disturbance of the gas flow. The extracted sample is passed into a cell in which the mist is isolated and allowed to settle on to a microscope cover-slip coated with a thin film of petroleum jelly deposited from saturated xylene solution.

The original type of cell is described by Fairs[1] and is designed primarily for sampling above atmospheric temperature. It is inserted into the gas main and consists of a combined sampling nozzle, sedimentation cell and heater tube and is illustrated in Figure 15.1. If the sampled gases are not dry, a reverse stream of dry air is blown through the cell when sedimentation is complete to prevent condensation on the deposited particles when the cell is removed from the duct.

A second type of cell, used externally to the duct, is primarily intended for sampling at atmospheric temperature, though it can be used for high

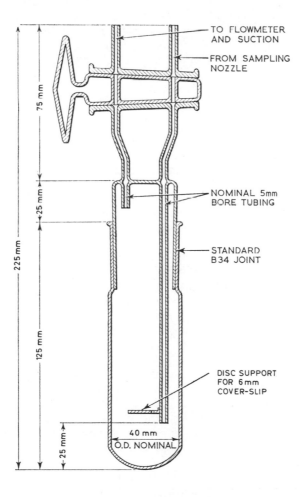

Figure 15.2 Sedimentation cell for sampling at atmospheric temperatures

temperature sampling if immersed in water at the appropriate temperature in a Dewar flask. It is illustrated in Figure 15.2 and is generally similar to the cell previously described. The double tap controlling the inlet and outlet is useful where the sampled gases are under suction since it ensures the simultaneous closing of both lines when isolating the sample.

15.2.2 Size Analysis of Mists

Size analysis of mists is carried out by microscope since sedimentation and elutriation methods are obviously inapplicable. The particles deposited on the coverslip are measured by comparison with calibrated circles on a graticule mounted either in the eyepiece or projection screen. The counting and sizing procedure is controlled to give an analysis of known statistical accuracy. The technique is described by Fairs[4] and forms the basis of British Standard 3406, Part 4 (Chapter 14).

While it must be understood that when designing mist scrubbers there is no substitute for an actual size analysis a few size analyses of acid mists are given in Table 15.4. While emphasizing that they are specific to the plants concerned they will give some idea of the order of fineness of condensation mists. The significance of the amount of mist finer than 3 μm will be apparent when the performance of the Calder–Fox scrubber is discussed (Sections 15.4.2 and 15.4.4).

15.2.3 Determination of Weight Concentration of Acid Mist in Gases

When determining the efficiency of any piece of gas-cleaning equipment it is necessary to measure the concentration of acid mist in the inlet and outlet gases. Samples are best obtained by means of a small electrostatic sampler or a glass fibre filter.

A suitable electrostatic sampler is illustrated in Figure 15.3 and consists of a platinum electrode with a spiral gauze welded to it hanging centrally in a glass tube, 25 mm diameter, which is in turn surrounded by a copper sheath or covered with tin or aluminium foil. The central electrode is energized by a coil or electronic powerpack capable of producing 20–50 kV. The multi-pointed electrode gives a very intense corona, which in a sampler 0·5 m long, is capable of completely demisting $\times 3 \times 10^{-4} - 1\cdot2 \times 10^{-3}$ m^3/s of gas.

Glass fibre filters and holders have been described by Stairmand[5]. Superfine glass wool (unbonded) made by Fibreglass Ltd. has a very small fibre diameter (2–5 μm) and will filter the finest mists completely. A depth of 25 mm packed into a 50 mm diameter filter holder to a density of 0·08 g/cm^3 will be adequate. In this connection it should be noted that the glass wool normally used in laboratories is useless for mist sampling, as the fibres are much too thick.

In both cases a measured volume of gas extracted isokinetically from the gas main is drawn through the apparatus which is afterwards washed out and the amount of acid collected determined.

Table 15.4 EXAMPLES OF SIZE ANALYSES OF VARIOUS TYPES OF MISTS

Weight percentage less than stated size

Particle size microns, μm	1 H₂SO₄ in tail gas from Kessler concentrator	2 H₂SO₄ in tail gas from waste acid stripper	3 H₂SO₄ in tail gas from calciner	4 H₂SO₄ in tail gas from 'anhydrite' contact plant	5 H₂SO₄ in tail gas from contact/ sodium bisulphite plant	6 Shock-cooled HCl Plant A	7 Shock-cooled HCl Plant B	8 Chloro-sulphonic acid following quenching of excess acid in water	9 Humidified P₂O₅ fume	10 Formic acid tail gas after vacuum stills
19	—	—	—	—	—	100	—	—	—	—
13	—	—	—	—	—	79	100	—	—	—
9·5	100	—	100	—	—	47	91	—	100	100
6·5	90	—	78	—	—	24	74	—	98	77
4·7	69	—	25	100	—	13	49	100	57	38
3·3	60	100	5	70	100	6	23	90	25	18
2·3	32	72	—	29	54	2	7	74	8	9
1·6	18	30	—	6	10	1	2	58	2	4
1·1	9	6	—	1	3	—	—	32	—	1
0·8	—	1	—	—	—	—	—	7	—	—

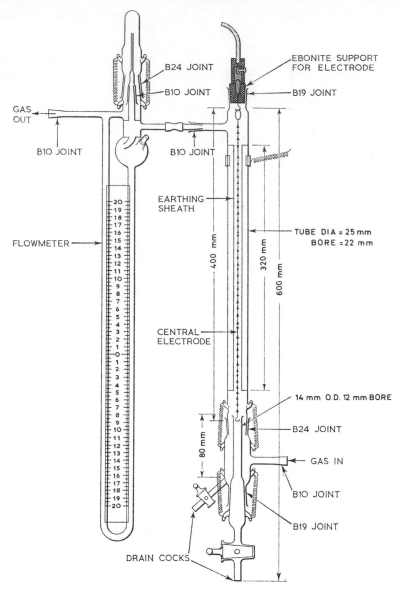

Figure 15.3 Electrostatic sampler for mists

15.3 Equipment for Removal of Acid Mists

At a very early stage in the industry steps had to be taken to reduce the acidity of tail gases from chemical plants. Hardie[6] records that James Muspratt was convicted at Liverpool Assizes in 1838 for creating and maintaining a nuisance within the Borough to the annoyance and injury of the inhabitants thereof by the evolution of muriatic acid from a LeBlanc plant. As the industry grew legislation was passed in the form of the Alkali Acts of 1863 and 1874 whereby tail gases containing such fumes as hydrochloric and sulphuric acids, oxides of nitrogen, and hydrogen sulphide, were scheduled and manufacturers were instructed to use 'the best practicable means' for preventing the discharge of such substances to the atmosphere. 'The best practicable means' has remained the criterion for assessing the acceptability of acid mist effluents and as new and better methods of mist treatment have been developed so have more stringent standards of scrubbing been demanded, particularly since the advent of the Clean Air Act.

For this reason the descriptions of scrubbers in this chapter are restricted to high-efficiency equipment appropriate to present-day standards. The selection of appropriate equipment will depend upon the fineness of the mist to be scrubbed and the efficiency of scrubbing required, bearing in mind the economic considerations of capital and running costs and depreciation. It should be noted that except in the case of electrostatic precipitators there is an appreciable pressure loss across all high efficiency scrubbers and unless an adequate pressure head is available on the main plant a fan or other means will have to be provided to operate the scrubber.

As mist collectors may sludge up periodically, spare capacity will be required to allow units to be taken off line in rotation for cleaning.

15.4 Calder–Fox Scrubber

In an attempt to produce a more compact scrubber than the old low-velocity coke box scrubber, Fox and Calder, working at the Chance & Hunt factory at Oldbury developed a 'high speed' scrubber.

The broad principle of operation was to subject the mist-laden gas to a strong centrifugal force by causing it to pass through a pair of perforated plates with a small clearance between them, the orifices in the first plate being staggered in relation to those in the second (Figure 15.4). This results in all mist particles larger than a certain critical diameter continuing in a

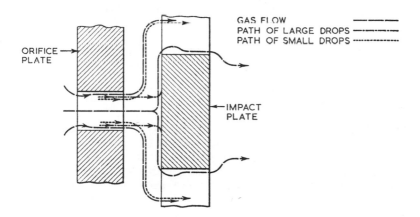

Figure 15.4 Path of particles in Calder–Fox scrubber

relatively straight course after leaving the orifice plate and impinging on the surface of the impact plate where they form a film which drains by gravity. The smaller particles turn through a right angle with the gas stream and travel untrapped through the slots in the impact plate. The historical development of the Calder–Fox scrubber is fully dealt with elsewhere[1].

15.4.1 Details of Design

The general arrangement of the present-day scrubber is shown in Figure 15.5. It consists of a casing to hold the scrubber plate assemblies with suitable reducing members at each end to couple it into the gas main.

The main plate assembly consists of orifice and impact plates. Each has a series of vertical slots, those in the impact plate usually being twice the width of those in the orifice plate and staggered in relation to them. The

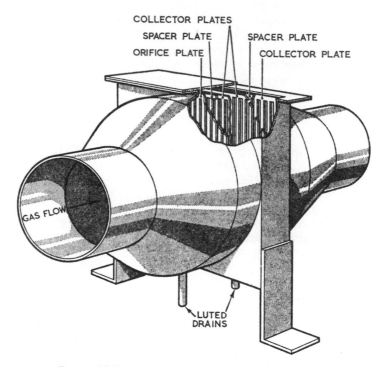

Figure 15.5 Pictorial arrangement of Calder–Fox scrubber

impact strips are thus located directly opposite the orifice plate slots and are proportioned to give a slight overlap. The plate separation is, in general, equal to the width of the orifice plate slots, and this slot width controls the fineness of particle which can be trapped (Section 15.4.2). The gas velocity necessary to produce a given performance determines the slot area and therefore the total plate area; thus in low pressure drop scrubbers dealing with coarse mists the plate area may be quite large in comparison with the cross-sectional area of the gas main. In such cases it may be preferable to arrange the plate assemblies in the scrubber body in V-formation and, by suitably adjusting the angle between the two halves, the cross-sectional area of the scrubber may be reduced to that of the duct if so desired[1].

If there is any possibility of re-entraining trapped mist it is necessary to install collector plates downstream of the main plate assembly. Re-entrained mist is usually coarse and these collectors can therefore be designed with a very low pressure drop, the slot area being not less than that of the impact plate. The arrangement shown in Figure 15.6 shows collector slot widths five times those in the impact plate, the pressure drop across the collectors being about 20 per cent of that across the main plate assembly.

The main plates are arranged to give maximum free area consistent with reasonable overlap between the slot systems. The actual free area of the slot system in the orifice plate is 20 per cent, the overall free area being about 15 per cent depending upon the width of solid frame around the slots.

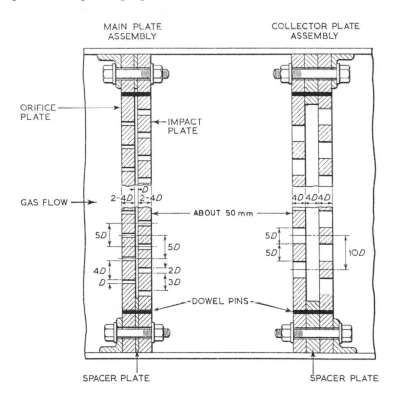

Figure 15.6 Typical arrangement of Calder–Fox Plates (plan view). All dimensions given in terms of orifice plate slot width D.

Originally plates were made with circular orifices rather than slots but these are now regarded as obsolete since the free area is only about 5–9 per cent.

The separation between orifice and impact plates has—within limits— little effect upon performance, although considerable increase in pressure drop will result if the separation is less than half the orifice plate slot width.

Large plate separations will obviously have an adverse effect and a plate separation equal to the orifice plate slot width is recommended for general use. Experience suggests that 1·6 mm is the minimum plate separation and orifice plate slot width which can usefully be employed, and this is the figure normally used for fine mists.

It is usually possible to fabricate the scrubber plates by milling slots from a sheet of suitably resistant material. When, however, a plastics material is used, distortion of the slots may take place either during fabrication or in use, so that unrestricted passages through the plate assembly may occur at various points. In such cases the slot length should not exceed 100 mm and if longer slots are required they should be made up in banks 100 mm long or less with strengthening bars between. In order to preserve the correct location of the main and collector plate assemblies each set should be dowelled together with the appropriate spacer plate and inserted into the scrubber body as a complete unit. Careful dimensional inspection during erection is essential.

In cases where operating conditions preclude the use of metal or plastics scrubber plates, the slot system can be built up from strips of extruded unglazed porcelain with suitable spacers and mounted in corrosion-resistant frames. Since these strips can be fabricated to tolerances of about ±0·2 per cent it is possible to construct satisfactory scrubber plates with slots as narrow as 1·6 mm. A suggested arrangement for a complete plate assembly fabricated entirely from strips 4·5 × 6 mm cross-section is given in Figure 15.7. Unglazed porcelain strips are resistant to thermal shock, and because of their good wetting properties collect the mist particles in a very even

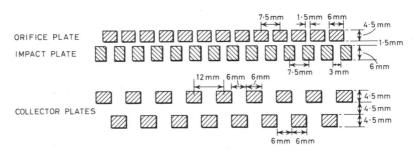

Figure 15.7 Proposed design for Calder–Fox scrubber plates fabricated with 4·5 × 6 mm ceramic strips

film. This factor is important when re-entrainment is considered (Section 15.4.2). If the gas loading is likely to vary over well-defined limits the scrubber should be designed for the highest gas rate—when operated at lower gas rates the free space of the orifice plate can be reduced with a blanket plate to maintain the same gas velocity whatever the gas volume handled. This plate is clamped on the upstream face of the orifice plate.

Luted sumps are fitted upstream and downstream of the plate assemblies for disposal of the collected mist, and pressure points are provided before and after the scrubber. If the gases contain solids likely to block the plates, spray nozzles are fitted upstream of the main plate assembly to flush it periodically.

15.4.2 Design Equations

The performance of Calder–Fox scrubbers has been studied mathematically by Tanner et al.[7] and Fairs[1]. The basic design equations given below are substantially the same as those given in the latter reference.

$$\Delta p = 2.5 \times 10^{-3} \rho V^2 \tag{15.1}$$

$$d = 11.2 \times 10^6 \left(\frac{D\eta}{V\sigma}\right)^{1/2} \tag{15.2}$$

$$d = 99 \times 10^3 \left(\frac{D\eta}{\sigma}\right)^{1/2} \left(\frac{\rho}{\Delta p}\right)^{1/4} \tag{15.3}$$

$$V_R = 0.7 \left(\frac{\gamma}{\sigma}\right)^{3/7} \left(\frac{\sigma^2}{h\eta_1 ma}\right)^{1/7} \tag{15.4}$$

where
- a = proportion of mist removed by the main plate assembly at the re-entrainment velocity V_R
- D = width of slots in orifice plate   mm
- h = length of slots in orifice plate   mm
- m = concentration of mist in inlet gas   kg/m³
- V = jet velocity at exit of orifice plate slots   m/s
- V_R = jet velocity at which re-entrainment commences   m/s
- γ = surface tension of collected mist   N/m
- Δp = pressure drop across main plate assembly   N/m
- η = c.g.s. viscosity of gas   Ns/m³
- n_1 = c.g.s. viscosity of collected mist   Ns/m³
- ρ = gas density   kg/m³
- σ = density of collected mist   kg/m³

The constant in equation (15.1) was determined experimentally for air in a wind tunnel and was found to be unaffected for plate thicknesses up to four times the orifice plate slot width. It has been observed, however, that this constant is not independent of gas density. The actual relationship has not yet been established although it seems that the pressure drop can be 50–100 per cent greater than the calculated figure for gases whose density is approximately three times that of air at n.t.p. For gases whose densities are close to that of air the deviation will not be significant. Equation (15.3) is shown graphically in Figure 15.8 for the separation of water droplets from air at n.t.p., and demonstrates that there is little improvement in the cut at pressure drops greater than 12 mb and that conversely the limiting cut is about 2.5–3 μm.

It should be noted when considering equations (15.2) and (15.3) that the diameter of the 'cut' particle is that of the particle separated with 100 per cent efficiency and not that at which there is an equal chance of capture or escape, as in certain other contexts.

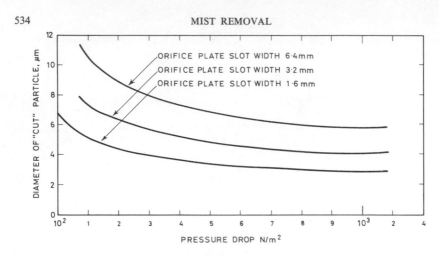

Figure 15.8 Relationship of size of 'cut' particle with pressure drop across Calder–Fox scrubbers

Equation (15.4) gives the critical velocity in the orifice plate slots above which the gas entering the impact plate slots may be expected to shear droplets from the film of liquid running down the impact plate, as is illustrated in Figure 15.9. It will be appreciated that this critical velocity is lowered

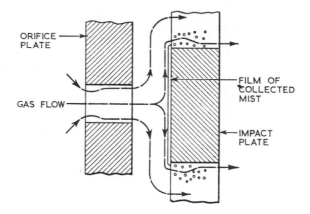

Figure 15.9 Mechanism of re-entrainment in Calder–Fox scrubbers

as the film thickness increases, and any tendency to uneven flow down the impact plate, because of poor wetting properties, will increase the risk of re-entrainment. Where plates are fabricated from plastics sheet therefore, it is desirable to roughen or etch the surface to promote wetting if the scrubber is likely to be operating near the re-entrainment velocity. Wherever the exit velocity of the orifice plate slots reaches 80 per cent of the critical re-entrainment velocity collector plates should be fitted to trap entrained droplets.

The critical re-entrainment velocity is also affected by the density of the dispersing gas and as will be seen from Figure 15.10 is considerably reduced in the case of gases under pressure. Similarly when dealing with low density gases the critical velocity is correspondingly high. In such cases better cuts

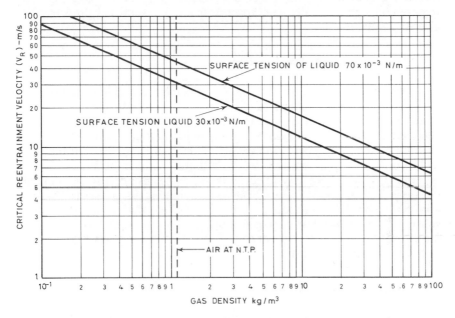

Figure 15.10 Relationship between gas density and critical re-entrainment velocity

can be achieved than when dealing with air at atmospheric pressure since much higher velocities can be tolerated and the pressure drops are correspondingly low. Both these effects have been confirmed in practice.

15.4.3 Erection and Operation

Calder–Fox scrubbers are simple to erect and operate so long as care is taken to ensure that the plates are inserted into the scrubber body with the slots vertical and that the plates make a gas-tight seal with the body. Small leaks will allow considerable quantities of gas to by-pass the scrubber untreated. It is also important to check that the plates have been installed the right way round, and to repeat this check each time the plates are removed for servicing. During operation all that is required is to ensure that the pressure drop across the scrubber remains at the correct value, abnormally high values indicate partial blocking of the slots and low values suggest distortion of the plates or leakage past the slot system. Periodical measurement (Section 15.2.3) of inlet and outlet mist concentrations will give an additional check on performance. Regular examination of the lutes should also be made to ensure that they are running freely. The behaviour of the scrubber in the light of the above tests will determine when it needs to be opened up for examination and servicing.

15.4.4 Range of Applicability

Calder–Fox scrubbers afford a relatively cheap and simple method of mist removal provided that the particle size is largely above 2·5–3 μm. They require no ancillary equipment, apart from a fan, if sufficient pressure is not already available.

15.5 Electrostatic Precipitators

It is not necessary to discuss the general principles underlying the operation of electrostatic precipitators, as this has been very adequately dealt with elsewhere[8]. It is only necessary to deal with those aspects that particularly affect the precipitation of acid mists. There is not a great deal of published information about the performance of acid mist precipitators but they seem to be confined almost entirely to the sulphuric acid industry, presumably because this mist is not easy to scrub by other means because of its fineness (Sections 15.1.3 and 15.1.4). Electrostatic precipitators have two main applications in this connection, (a) to scrub tail gas before passing to atmosphere and (b) in the case of pyrites-burning contact plants, to remove acid mist, together with dissolved arsenic from the burner gases thus avoiding poisoning of the catalyst mass.

15.5.1 Details of Design

Mist precipitators in the U.K. and the Commonwealth are generally of the wire-in-tube type though the wire-and-plate design is common in Europe.

A wire-in-tube precipitator for dilute sulphuric acid mist is shown in Figure 15.11. Lead alloy tubes are mounted between lead-covered tube plates. The ionizing electrodes consist of lead-covered steel cable in which the sheath is, in cross-section, in the form of a six-pointed star to give sharp edges to assist in producing a good corona discharge. These electrodes are suspended from regulus metal bars attached to lead-covered cross-pieces supported by the heavy high-tension leads. The lower ends are centred by attachment to a lead grid whose weight keeps them taut and helps to prevent swinging. Means are provided for draining collected mist from the bottom of the precipitator.

The sealing of the high tension leads is always a matter of some difficulty in acid mist precipitators. In certain cases this is achieved by means of oil seals, though these are not very satisfactory because of the risk of fire and where oil seals are fitted, therefore, it is desirable to install an automatic fire extinguisher. In many plants oil seals have been superseded by a closed chamber at the top of the precipitator which houses the insulators carrying the lead-in wire and electrode connection. A supply of dried and purified gas is fed into this chamber which helps to prevent condensation of moisture on the surface of the insulators, which is a not infrequent cause of breakdown in mist precipitators. Alternatively steam coils, whose surface may be covered with a water-repellant silicone film, are fitted round the insulators for a similar purpose.

The time of passage and the high tension voltage and current depend upon the fineness of the mist and the scrubbing efficiency required. Average gas velocities are about 0·6–1·0 m/s giving contact times of 3–4·5 s. The applied potential depends upon the diameter of the collecting electrode and is about 30–40 kV for 150 mm diameter tubes.

Some mist precipitators have two or even three passes in series in order to achieve a good precipitation efficiency. This is generally because of an

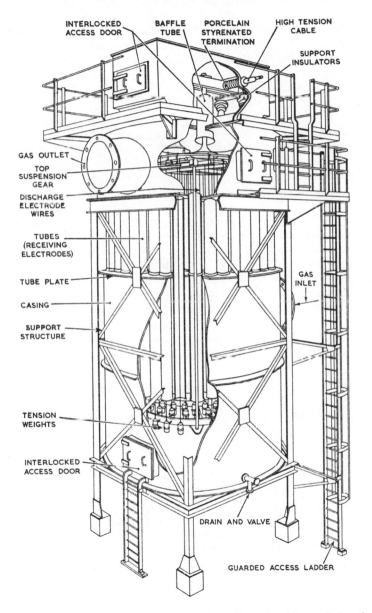

INTERLOCKED ACCESS DOOR
BAFFLE TUBE
PORCELAIN STYRENATED TERMINATION
HIGH TENSION CABLE
SUPPORT INSULATORS
GAS OUTLET
TOP SUSPENSION GEAR
DISCHARGE ELECTRODE WIRES
TUBES (RECEIVING ELECTRODES)
TUBE PLATE
CASING
SUPPORT STRUCTURE
GAS INLET
TENSION WEIGHTS
INTERLOCKED ACCESS DOOR
DRAIN AND VALVE
GUARDED ACCESS LADDER

Figure 15.11 Wire-in-the-tube mist precipitator. (Reproduced by permission of Sim-Chem Ltd.)

initially high concentration of small droplets which causes a partial quenching of the corona in the first pass with a consequent lowering of the precipitation efficiency[8,9]. In such cases it is advantageous to have a separate h.t. unit for each pass so that each can be operated at the optimum voltage.

15.5.2 Factors Influencing the Performance of Mist Precipitators

The main factors influencing performance have been fully covered theoretically[8] and need only be briefly mentioned. They are primarily too high concentration of mist resulting in corona quenching, particle size, and the effect of composition and temperature of suspending gas. In view of the number of factors involved and the lack of precise practical data upon particle mobilities, any attempt to design mist precipitators from fundamental principles would be hazardous. It must be accepted that design is an art demanding considerable experience, and manufacturers of electrostatic precipitators rightly ask for the fullest possible information on the mists and gases to be handled before quoting.

In cases where the mist is already available it is helpful to arrange for a pilot scale test. Suitable apparatus can usually be provided by the manufacturers. Nevertheless very small pilot trials, while giving valuable information on the conditions necessary for efficient precipitation, require very careful scaling up. In the case of large-scale installations, therefore, particularly on new plant, it is preferable to erect a single complete unit of the projected plant for preliminary trial. The experience of the precipitator manufacturer is invaluable, particularly where similar problems have been previously handled; but there is no certainty that the size distributions of mists from plants of like design and size will be similar.

The use of a 'factor of merit' as discussed in the following section will give some idea of the order of scrubbing efficiency achievable with different times of exposure to corona.

15.5.3 Assessment of Performance of Electrostatic Precipitators

In the case of wire-in-tube precipitators the efficiency of precipitation may be expressed by the well-known Deutsch equation:

$$S = 1 - e^{-2vt/b} \qquad (15.5)$$

where S = ratio of inlet and outlet mist concentrations
v = average migration velocity
t = time of passage through the precipitator
b = radius of precipitator tube in consistent units

In the case of wire-in-tube precipitators the ratio of precipitating surface to swept volume is $2/b$ and the corresponding figure for a wire-and-plate precipitator (where the wires are distance b from the plates) is $1/b$. For these precipitators

$$S = 1 - e^{-vt/b} \qquad (15.6)$$

Equation (15.6) is only approximate since it assumes that the field is uniform over the whole collecting surface, which is not strictly true.

Because of the uncertainties in determining v the above equations are difficult to apply and it has been suggested that in assessing overall performance of precipitators under actual working conditions no attempt should be made to ascribe the degree of performance to any particular factor.

In equations (15.5) and (15.6) the quantity $e^{-v/b}$ may be expressed as 'f'—a term embodying all factors involved in precipitation efficiency except time—thus including electrical conditions, the geometry of the electrodes and the nature of the mist to be scrubbed.

Therefore for a wire-in-tube precipitator

$$S = 1 - f^{2t} \tag{15.7}$$

and for a wire-and-plate type

$$S = 1 - f^t \tag{15.8}$$

It may be pointed out that the precipitation achieved in unit time $(1-f)$, is a convenient 'factor of merit' for comparing the performance of various

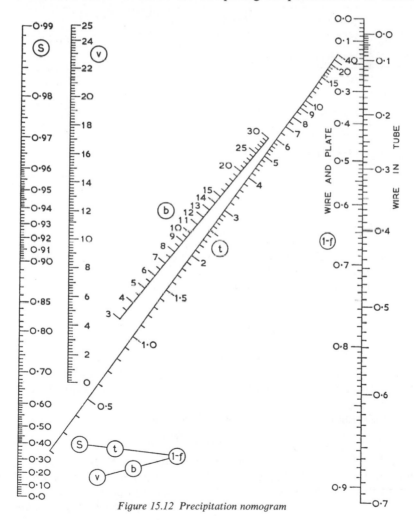

Figure 15.12 Precipitation nomogram

precipitators. This gives an estimate of the overall performance actually achieved in practice, under conditions which are in any case only known imperfectly. It does not give an indication of performance under ideal conditions. A nomogram is provided in Figure 15.12 by means of which this factor of merit may be determined from the precipitation efficiency and the time of passage through the precipitator. Means are also provided for determining the velocity of transfer although this quantity must be to some extent fictitious.

Periodic determinations of the factor of merit provide a useful check upon performance of individual precipitators and indicate clearly if there is any deterioration due to corrosion of electrodes or other causes. Typical factors are given in Table 15.5.

Table 15.5 FACTORS OF MERIT FOR PERFORMANCE OF VARIOUS WIRE-AND-TUBE MIST PRECIPITATORS ON SULPHURIC ACID PLANTS

Type of plant	Efficiency of precipitation, S %	Time of passage, t s	Factor of merit, $1-f$
Pyrites 'contact'	99·3	1·9	0·58
Plant no. 1,	85·3	1·4	0·49
Burner gas	98·7	2·8	0·54
Pyrites 'contact' Plant no. 2, Burner gas	99·0	2·8	0·50
Gaillard concentrator no. 1, tail gas	91·0	2·25	0·41
Gaillard concentrator no. 2, tail gas	94·7	1·75	0·56

It will be seen from these figures that an average factor of merit for an efficient mist precipitator is about 0·5 and this would be a reasonable figure to assume when making preliminary estimates of the scrubbing efficiencies likely to be attained for various times of exposure to the corona.

15.5.4 Efficiency of Precipitation

The desired efficiency of precipitation has an important bearing on the design of the precipitator, not only in relation to the applied voltage and current but also to the time of treatment and consequently the size of plant required.

Considering the exponential Deutsch equation (15.5)

$$1 - S = e^{-2vt/b}$$

it will be seen that each time the exit concentration $1-S$ is halved $-2vt/b$ and therefore t the time of passage will be increased in equal steps. The above relationship only holds strictly for mists of uniform particle size and, where mists of wide size range are involved and a high scrubbing efficiency is required, a proportionate increase in plant size will have to be made to compensate for the lower migration velocities of the smallest particles.

15.5.5 Maintenance and Operation

One of the most important factors in successful operation of electrostatic precipitators is the correct centring of the ionizing electrodes in relation to the collecting surfaces, particularly in the case of wire-in-tube precipitators. Any misalignment of one or more of these electrodes will tend to divert current to them and to starve the remainder. In extreme cases a fault on one tube may monopolize all the current in one unit and completely upset its performance. The centring of the ionizing electrodes should always be checked after cleaning and internal repairs. As slight deviations from the vertical in the collecting tubes will seriously upset the centring of the ionizing electrodes, the provision of adequate foundations is of the utmost importance in view of the great weight of lead precipitators.

Corrosion and sludge deposition on the electrodes will tend to impair performance and if allowed to persist will lower the critical potential for arcing and enforce operation at a lower applied voltage than the design figure. Regular washing of the electrodes, possibly once every six to twelve months, will usually prevent this trouble. The collecting tubes are now sometimes made of plastics to reduce corrosion, relying on the film of precipitated acid to provide the conducting surface.

Periodic inspection and cleaning of the h.t. insulators is required on a scheduled maintenance basis to prevent arcing at these points; oil seals and insulator heaters also require periodic inspection.

The particular risks of spark-over make the provision of an automatic voltage control and reclosing device[8] very desirable as this allows the h.t. voltage to be kept at as high a figure as possible even under fluctuating mist and gas conditions, thus ensuring maximum precipitation efficiency.

15.5.6 Range of Applicability

The range of applicability of the electrostatic precipitator is not restricted by a lower limit of particle size as is the Calder–Fox scrubber. Theoretically the mobility of particles in an electric field is dependent upon particle size but the factors determining the strength of the field are very complex and all that can be said is that it would seem that while larger particles—greater than about 10 μm—are scrubbed with equal ease, very fine particles—less than about 5 μm—will require strong electric fields and relatively long times of passage to precipitate them effectively. Thus although the pressure drop across the precipitator tubes is only about 0·6–1·0 mb, the power used in creating the corona discharge may be equivalent to that required for a fan overcoming a pressure of 30 mb. But because of the low pressure drop, even distribution of the gas across the precipitator must be ensured either by a perforated lower tube plate (see Figure 15.11) or by means of correctly designed gas splitter baffles. Hence before commissioning a plant it is desirable to make a pitot survey to check gas distribution. Similarly, gas distribution is always one of the items that should be checked when the performance of a plant is below the expected value.

Electrostatic precipitators are designed for a fixed efficiency and the exit mist concentrations achieved will therefore vary with the inlet concentrations. If a limiting exit concentration is stipulated for a plant whose inlet mist concentrations fluctuate, the precipitator will have to be designed on the basis of the worst conditions likely to occur.

15.6 Hydrophobic Fibre Filters

It is well known that compressed beds of fibres are exceedingly efficient filters for fine particles, provided that the fibre diameters are sufficiently small. The mechanism of filtration has been worked out by Bosanquet[10]; his treatment postulated filtration partly by impingement and partly by diffusion, the diffusional effect becoming predominant for particles below 2 μm. In either case the general effect is the same—the finer the fibres, the smaller the particles which they can remove.

Hitherto such filters, when used with fine mists, have not attained the theoretical efficiencies predicted by the Bosanquet equations, and moreover they tend to log with collected liquor. Fairs[11] discovered that highly efficient filters of this nature can be produced provided that the fibres collect the mist dropwise rather than filmwise. While this effect cannot

Figure 15.13(a) Hydrophilic glass fibre, filmwise collection

Figure 15.13(b) Hydrophilic silicone-treated glass fibre. Dropwise collection

always be related to any particular physical property, such as a high contact angle between droplet and fibre it is convenient to refer to fibres which collect mists dropwise as 'hydrophobic'. Such filters do not log and the theoretically predicted scrubbing efficiencies are achieved in practice.

Silicone-treated fibres used in the original research were highly efficient but the hydrophobic surface was found to be attacked by alkaline mists and

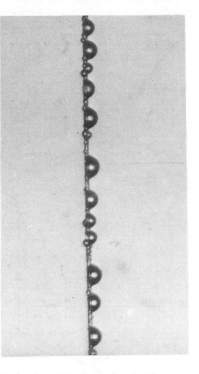

Figure 15.13(c) Hydropholic Terylene polyester fibre. Dropwise collection

by mists of strong acids of concentration over 20 per cent. Synthetic hydrophobic fibres resist these solutions. Fibres of Terylene polyester, polypropylene and nylon are particularly useful and cover a wide range of temperature as well as acid and alkaline conditions. Photomicrographs of these two types of fibre after exposure to acid mist are shown in Figure 15.13 compared with (hydrophilic) untreated glass fibres.

15.6.1 Details of Design

Since the packing density of the filter medium is 130–160 kg/m^3 compared with a bulk density of 30–50 kg/m^3 for the loose fibres, considerable pressure is required to produce the filter bed. If acid mist filters are prepared by compressing the loose fibres between gauzes, stress corrosion of the restraining bolts is likely to occur and expansion of the bed results. However, it has been found[10] that if the fibres are compressed in a canister to the required density they can be suitably heat-treated to relieve compression stresses. After cooling the compact filter element can be removed from the canister without expansion and inserted in the filter with suitable packing at the periphery.

These elements can be either in disc or candle form, the latter being generally preferred since the flow rate at any given pressure-drop is rather higher and a greater filter area can be accommodated in a given volume of plant. A schematic arrangement of the candle type unit is shown in Figure 15.14.

It is essential when scrubbing condensation mists to use as fine fibres as possible, consistent with mechanical strength, and highly successful elements

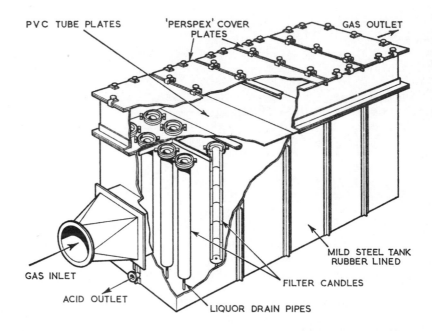

Figure 15.14 Arrangement of hydrophobic filter unit. (Reproduced by permission of Mancuna Engineering Ltd.)

have been developed which will give complete removal of the very fine sulphuric acid mist shown in column 5 of Table 15.4, an extremely difficult duty. The stack discharge from such a plant is invisible. A hydrophilic fibre filter, fabricated from untreated glass of the same fibre diameter, gave an 'escape' of over 10 per cent under exactly similar conditions. The filter life of silicone-treated glass fibre was about six months, but with Terylene polyester there was no deterioration whatever after three years' continuous running.

The voidage of the elements is 85–98 per cent depending on the packing density, and the filter is self-draining and self-cleaning. Gas flow may be outwards or inwards in the case of candle-type filters, but *must* be downwards in disc-type filters otherwise logging will occur. Drainage commences as soon as an equilibrium hold-up of liquid has built up in the filter, about 80 per cent of the total pressure drop across the unit is due to this liquor hold-up.

The pressure drop across non-irrigated candle filters, compressed to a density of 160 kg/m^3, is about 25 mb for a face velocity of 0·15 m/s (i.e. a gas volume rate of 0·15 m^3/s per m^2 filter area). For water-irrigated filters (packing density 130 kg/m^3, Section 15.6.3) the corresponding pressure drop is about 38 mb. Since the liquid draining from the filter bed does not re-entrain in the gas stream, spray arrestors are not required.

15.6.2 Erection and Operation

No particular difficulties are experienced in erecting and operating plant of this type. Care must, however, be taken, when replacing filter elements, to ensure that the seal is gas-tight. One way in which this can be achieved is by stemming the elements into position with 'Superfine' glass wool (Section 15.2.3) which becomes rapidly liquor-logged in use.

A flowmeter should be fitted as well as a manometer since any increase of resistance to gas flow will tend to show as a decrease in gas rate rather than an increase in pressure-drop. Filtration efficiency should be checked periodically by measuring inlet and outlet mist concentrations (Section 15.2.3).

In certain gases, where the mists contain dissolved salts, a hydrophilic layer may gradually be deposited on the surface of the fibres thereby lowering the filtration efficiency. This can be cured by flooding the elements with water for about $\frac{1}{4}$ h to dissolve the hydrophilic film. The frequency of washing will vary according to plant conditions but in the experience of the author, may be necessary every 3–20 weeks. It is also desirable to soak new filter elements with water before inserting into the supports, as otherwise they will not reach their full efficiency until they become saturated with collected mist, possibly not until 24 h later.

The main servicing cost will be filter element replacement, but as has already been mentioned the life of Terylene polyester elements has not yet been established, being at least three years and may well be much longer. Patent protection has been obtained in the case of these filters and their mode of fabrication. Commercial units are now being produced in the U.K. and full-scale units have been installed here and abroad.

15.6.3 Range of Application

Hydrophobic fibre filters are capable of completely removing the finest mists likely to be encountered over a wide range of inlet concentrations. A range of 2–100 g/m^3 H$_2$SO$_4$ has been dealt with effectively.

The main limitation in operation is the acid concentration which can be tolerated without attacking the fibres. The silicone surface on glass fibres is destroyed by exposure to mineral acids at concentrations above 20 per cent; Terylene polyester fibres are similarly attacked by concentrations above 70 per cent. Later work, however, indicates that concentrated sulphuric acid mist can be sufficiently diluted in the filter medium by continuous irrigation with a water spray. Alternatively the misty gases may be passed through a prehumidification chamber. The use of irrigated filters may well be desirable for treatment of acid mists below 70 per cent strength as the degradation of the fibres when handling acids of moderate strength will be more rapid than in the case of dilute mists. Where it is desirable to retain the collected acid in concentrated form the candles may be fabricated from untreated (hydrophilic) glass fibres. To compensate for the inevitable loss of filtration efficiency a finer grade (2–5 μm) of fibre is used than would be necessary if the fibres were hydrophobic. The pressure drop is then appreciably greater.

Hydrophobic fibre filters provide a satisfactory alternative to electrostatic precipitators for the complete removal of fine mists. Recent experience is that the capital cost of these filters is appreciably lower than that of the extra large electrostatic precipitators required to produce an invisible discharge to atmosphere, the running and maintenance costs being approximately the same for both.

15.7 Miscellaneous Types

A few other types of mist removal equipment have been described in the literature. Unfortunately performance data given in these references are usually scanty, particularly in regard to the size distributions of the mists handled, although some idea of their fineness can occasionally be inferred. They can therefore only be discussed briefly in the light of available information. All the methods described in this section primarily coagulate fine mist particles, rendering them easily removable by a simple spray arrestor.

15.7.1 Ceramic Candle Filter

This scrubber was originally developed by Lurgi, A.G. in Germany and as the name implies consists of a number of ceramic candles in parallel through which the misty gas is passed. The mist particles are coagulated in the pores of the candles and are blown on to the downstream surface. Since the gas velocity in the pores is relatively high there is a tendency for the collected liquid to be re-entrained in the gas stream in the form of coarse droplets and a spray arrestor is therefore necessary downstream of the filter.

Ceramic candle filters have been installed to treat tail gases from a few sulphuric acid plants in the U.K. A unit handling tail gas mist from a Kachkaroff plant has been described[12], which operated at pressure drops up to 33 mb and gas flow rates in excess of 0·3 m³/s per m² candle area, giving escapes of 0·5–2 per cent. No information is available about the fineness of the mist, except that it tended to 'fall down'. This observation has been supported by statements[13] which indicate that Kachkaroff mists fall rapidly to ground level. This indicates that such mists are rather coarser than normal 'condensation' mists and suggests that they are due in part at any rate to carry-over from the tower system.

On the other hand the Annual Reports of H.M. Chief Alkali Inspector for 1956–8[14] (referring to a unit treating the tail gases from an anhydrite contact plant) were not very encouraging and, in particular, doubted the ability of the ceramic candle filter to operate effectively under varying plant conditions. It is likely, as will be seen from the size analyses given in column 4 of Table 15.4 (Section 15.2.2), that this mist is much finer than that from a Kachkaroff plant.

Massey[15] gives some operational data for a ceramic filter unit treating 1·65 m³/s tail gas from a sulphur burning contact plant in America. Again the fineness of the mist is not stated but it seems clear from the description that it is coarser than the normal condensation mist and is due in part to 'carry-over'. Escapes of 9·5–1·4 per cent were observed for pressure drops of 25 mb and a face velocity of 1·5 m/s relative to the candle surface. The escape, however, increased to 25–28 per cent when the pressure drop was reduced to 20 mb. It seems, on the available evidence, that ceramic candle filters will handle relatively coarse mists effectively, although at a fairly high pressure-drop, but may not be able to deal with condensation mists unless candles of a smaller pore size are used, in which case the operating pressure-drop would be much higher.

15.7.2 Venturi Scrubbers

A description of the venturi scrubber for dusts has already been given in Chapter 12 and need not therefore be repeated. It should be more easily applied to mist removal since the problem of effectively wetting the particles does not arise. It does not appear to have been used in the U.K. for treating acid mists, although there have been a number of applications abroad, particularly in America and Russia.

The scrubbing action is produced by passing the mist-laden gas through a dense water spray in a zone of intense turbulence in a venturi throat, whereby the mist particles are enveloped in the spray droplets, which are then trapped in a spray arrestor. The finer the particles to be removed the higher will be the throat velocity and spray density needed; the condensation mists considered in this chapter may well require throat velocities of 100 m/s and spray densities greater than 0·5 m³/1000 m³ of gas treated. Such conditions might possibly require pressure drops in excess of 50 mb.

There are few published performance data on the removal of mists by venturi scrubbers. Eckman and Johnstone[16] refer to applications on sulphuric, chlorosulphonic and phosphoric acid plants and in particular discuss the influence of water/gas ratio, pressure-drop and throat velocity on the removal of sulphuric acid mist of unknown particle size. In this case a 2 per cent escape occurred at a pressure drop of 50 mb, with throat velocities of 91 m/s and a water/gas ratio of 0·8 m³/1000 m³. Performance on P_2O_5 fume is given in Section 15.10.2. It is evident that although exit mist concentrations can be achieved as low as those with electrostatic precipitators they can be produced only at the expense of very high pressure drops. Venturi scrubbers do not seem to attain the almost complete removal of very fine mists achieved by hydrophobic fibre filters.

15.7.3 Sonic Agglomeration

Although agglomeration by means of an air siren has been described in the literature it does not seem to have been applied to any great extent to mist removal on an industrial scale. Danser and Neumann[18] describe a plant for treating mist in 40 000 m³/h sulphuric acid tail gas 'believed to be from 0·5 to 5 μ' in a tower 2·4 m diameter × 10·6 m high, i.e. for a contact time of 4 s. Ten per cent escape occurred for a sound pressure field of 150 dB. Since agglomeration is achieved by collision between mist particles and not between mist particles and spray droplets, as for the venturi scrubber, there must be an adequate initial concentration of mist droplets, otherwise satisfactory agglomeration will not take place. Green and Lane[19] have suggested that the concentration be about 2 g/m³ for 1–10 μ particles, i.e. about 10^8 to 10^{12} particles/m³ but Soderberg[21] quotes concentrations for 'scale furnace black' as high as 14 g/m³. Thus sonic agglomerators are only applicable to relatively high concentrations of mists, there are also objections to their use on a commercial scale unless very effectively sound-insulated. They are likely to be less efficient and to require more power than venturi scrubbers.

A comprehensive review of the theory of sonic agglomeration and of the few recorded industrial applications in France, Japan, U.S.A. and U.S.S.R. has been given by Mednikov[17]. Poor results were ascribed to not using optimum frequency for the range of aerosol sizes and not adjusting the coagulation chamber to resonance.

15.8 Operating Costs

It is impossible to generalize on capital costs of mist removal plant since choice will depend on the size distribution of the mist to be handled, the efficiency of scrubbing required, the volume of gas to be treated and the materials of construction. Any attempt to give comparative orders of cost would be most misleading.

As far as running costs are concerned the main item is power, in the case of electrostatic precipitators to produce the corona discharge, for sonic agglomerators to operate the siren and in the case of the remainder to overcome the pressure drop across the scrubber.

Since there are no relative performance data on identical mists strict comparisons cannot be made: however, with this limitation orders of power requirements for the various types of scrubber that have been discussed are given in Table 15.6.

Apparently, therefore, no modern method of scrubbing very fine condensation mists achieves any marked reduction in power used, nor does it appear likely that one will be discovered in the near future. Initial capital costs and maintenance charges will therefore be important factors when selecting scrubbing equipment for such duties. Where, however, the mists are rather coarser, i.e. with a substantial weight percentage of the particles greater than 3 μm, simpler scrubbers such as the Calder–Fox scrubber would be adequate and the running costs would be lower.

Table 15.6 ORDERS OF POWER REQUIRED TO OPERATE MIST SCRUBBERS (FAN EFFICIENCIES ASSUMED TO BE 70 PER CENT)

Type of scrubber	Escape %	Power used kW per 100 m³/s at n.t.p.	Remarks
Calder–Fox scrubber	—	210	Operating at 15 mb on fairly fine mist. Cut 2·5 μm
	—	75	Operating at 5 mb on coarser mist. Cut 5 μm
Electrostatic precipitator	0·01	310	Operating on moderately fine mist before converters of contact plant[8]
	0·6	290	Acid mist from sulphur burning furnace[8]
	0·5	540	Operating on very fine mist in contact plant tail gas
	0·4	130	Operating on rather coarser mist from sulphuric acid concentrator
Hydrophobic fibre filter	nil	425	Operating on very fine mist in contact plant tail gas. 30 mb pressure drop
Irrigated hydrophobic fibre filter	0·2	585	Operating on a very fine H_2SO_4 mist with simultaneous dilution. Pressure drop 42 mb[11]
Ceramic candle filter	1·4	360	Operating at 25 mb on relatively coarse mist[15]
Venturi scrubber	1–2	640	Operating at m/s throat velocity and water/gas ratio 1 m³/100 m³. Pressure drop 43 mb (including spray arrestor)
		850	Operating at 90 m/s throat velocity and water/gas ratio 0·5/1000 m³. Pressure drop 60 mb (including spray arrestor)
Sonic agglomerator	10	235–715	Reference 18
		530	Reference 21

PART B REMOVAL OF PHOSPHORIC ACID MISTS

J. A. BRINK, Jr.

15.9 Formation

In any process where phosphorus comes in contact with air or even gases containing a small percentage of oxygen, P_4O_{10} is formed which, in the presence of moisture, forms phosphoric acid mist often referred to as P_2O_5 mists. The most common occurrence of phosphoric acid mist is in the manufacture of phosphoric acid from elemental phosphorus. In this process phosphorus is burned with air and the resulting gases cooled and hydrated by water or acid sprays.

The concentration of the acid in the mist particles is a function of the gas humidity. In general, the mist particles tend to be in equilibrium with the gas, and their concentration can be predicted from vapour pressure relationships[22,23]. In phosphoric acid manufacture the mist particles consist usually of orthophosphoric acid when large quantities of water vapour are present. In other processes where the gas humidity is low, condensed acids such as metaphosphoric acid can be expected. The chemical reactions which take place are as follows:

$$P_4 + 5O_2 \rightarrow P_4O_{10} \text{ (phosphorus pentoxide)}$$

$$P_4O_{10} + 6H_2O \rightarrow 4H_3PO_4 \text{ (orthophosphoric acid, commonly called}$$
$$\text{phosphoric acid)}$$

$$P_4O_{10} + 2H_2O \rightarrow 4HPO_3 \text{ (metaphosphoric acid)}$$

Complete physical and chemical data on phosphorus pentoxide and phosphoric acid which have been published[24] are useful in predicting the quality and species of P_2O_5 mist present in any particular industrial process gas.

15.9.1 Particle Concentration and Size

The particle size distribution of P_2O_5 mist in a phosphoric acid plant is shown in Figure 15.15. An appreciable percentage of the acid particles is less than 1 μm in diameter. The particles entering the venturi scrub-

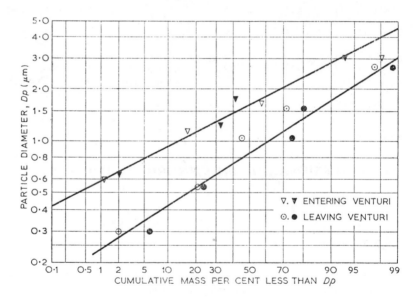

Figure 15.15 Particle size distribution and mist loading of P_2O_5 entering and leaving venturi scrubber in a phosphoric acid plant[39]

	mg P_2O_5/g/m³, n.t.p.	
	0·1–5 μm loading	total loading
Entering	20	52
Leaving	0·30	0·75

ber were larger in diameter than the particles leaving the venturi scrubber. Similar types of particle size distributions for phosphoric acid mist are present in most acid plants. Extensive experimental work has shown that particles in this general size range are obtained over a wide range of gas humidities[22,23,25,26].

Special instruments, such as cascade impactors[27-38], and techniques are used for the determination of the particle size distribution of P_2O_5 mist. This mist usually occurs in gases containing an appreciable humidity. Process gases in phosphoric acid plants are usually saturated with 5–40 per cent water vapour, depending on the process design and operation, and the particle size distribution should be determined under adiabatic sampling conditions[27].

In addition to fine mist particles with diameters under 5 μm, industrial gases usually contain appreciable quantities of spray droplets and other entrained particles, which may be as large as 500 μm in diameter. Such gases should be sampled in such a way that entrained droplets are separated from the fine mist particles by the use of a cyclone or other entrainment separator in conjunction with equipment suitable for collecting the fine mist particles [22,23,38]. If the particles are mixed together, confusing results are obtained.

The occurrence of extremely high loadings of P_2O_5 mist is quite common. Within processes, loadings of 52 g/m³ dry gas n.t.p. have been reported[39]. It is not uncommon for as much as one-half of the P_2O_5 in an industrial process to be tied up as liquid particles suspended in the gas stream. In a phosphoric acid plant operated by the Tennessee Valley Authority, as much as 60 per cent of the P_2O_5 produced in the process was collected from the electrostatic precipitator and only 40 per cent of the acid collected from the hydrator[40]. High mist loadings of this type do not usually occur in industrial processes in which SO_3 mist is present.

15.10 Equipment for Collection of Phosphoric Acid Mists

Four types of mist collection equipment are being used in the chemical industry: (i) packed towers; (ii) venturi scrubbers; (iii) electrostatic precipitators; and (iv) fibre mist eliminators.

There are many factors which must be considered in the selection of the most suitable type of equipment for any particular industrial application. Different types of equipment give different mist collection efficiencies, have different pressure-drop requirements, differ in their ability to handle any solids which may be present in the gases, and may be constructed of different materials which may or may not be suitable from the standpoint of corrosion. Also, the capital cost and operating cost requirements vary greatly from one type of equipment to another. Best selection as to equipment type can be made only after such factors are considered.

In his 102nd Annual Report (for 1965) the Alkali Inspector for England states that in his experience the emission of P_2O_5 fume should be reduced below 0·048 g/m³ n.t.p. and preferably below 0·024 g/m³ to be acceptable to the public; this difficult requirement was being achieved at some works. U.S.A. requirements in some States are as stringent.

15.10.1 Packed Towers

Towers packed with Raschig rings or coke have been used for many years for the collection of P_2O_5 mist [41,42]. Extensive work has been reported by the Tennessee Valley Authority (T.V.A.) on mist collection with packed towers[40,43,44]. Typical data are given in Figure 15.16. The acid recovery reported as a percentage along the ordinate represents the total collection

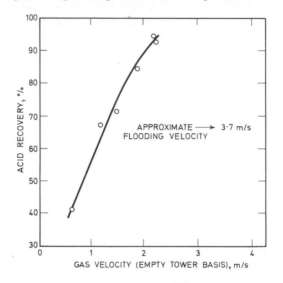

Figure 15.16 Collection of P_2O_5 mist in packed tower[43]. Tower packing 5·5 m of 25 mm carbon Raschig rings. Acid concentration 81–87 per cent H_3PO_4. Inlet gas temperature 225–290°C; P_2O_5 content of gas 32–40 g/m^3

of the packed tower and includes collection of large particles as well as collection of fine mist particles. These data were obtained on equipment consisting of a burner in which phosphorus was burned with atmospheric air and passed downward through an air-atomized water spray. Some acid was collected at the bottom of the combustion chamber. The gases then were passed up through the packed tower which was irrigated with either water or dilute acid at the top of the packing. The acid recovered from the bottom of the tower contained about 80 per cent H_3PO_4. The efficiencies of 90 per cent shown in Figure 15.16 were obtained only by utilizing high gas velocities through the packed tower thus giving high pressure drops.

T.V.A. recovered mist in packed towers where the mist was highly concentrated phosphoric acid[44-47]. Typical data on highly concentrated acid are given in Table 15.7.

These data were determined on a carbon tower, 3 m high, packed with 13 mm carbon Raschig rings. The efficiency shown in Table 15.7 as P_2O_5 per cent recovery represents an overall efficiency for the collection of both entrainment and mist. The efficiency of the packed tower for mist alone where mist is considered to be particles below 5 μm in diameter, would be lower.

Further work by T.V.A. showed that a two-fold increase in packing depth produces practically no increase in recovery when acid containing more than 82 per cent P_2O_5 was collected.

Packed towers are used when lower mist collection efficiencies are acceptable since they have some advantages over more complicated collection equipment. They can be constructed from conventional materials of construction which are readily available. Packed towers can be operated counter-currently and utilized as gas–liquid contacting devices for hydration of acid mists as well as for mist collection.

Table 15.7 RECOVERY OF STRONG P_2O_5 ENTRAINMENT
AND MIST IN PACKED TOWERS*

Gas velocity m/s†	Acid concentration % P_2O_5	P_2O_5 recovery %
2·6	88·5	86·0
3·0	88·5	72·3
2·3	87·6	80·2
1·7	83 7	57 9
2·4	73·6	51·4

*Abstracted from Striplin, M. M., *Chemical Engineering Report No. 2 Tennessee Valley Authority*, 1948, page 111 (Superintendent of Documents, U.S. Government Printing Office, Washington 25, D.C.).
†Calculated on basis of empty tower.

15.10.2 Venturi Scrubbers

Venturi scrubbers have been described previously in Chapter 12 and in this chapter, and in the literature since the first industrial-scale installation in 1947[48–52]. When applied to the collection of P_2O_5 mist, the venturi

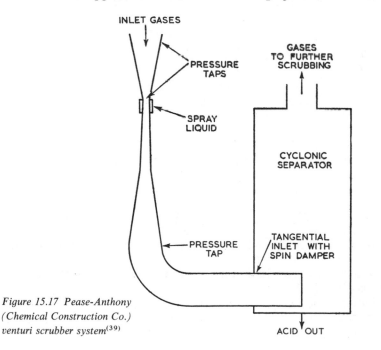

INLET GASES

PRESSURE TAPS

GASES TO FURTHER SCRUBBING

SPRAY LIQUID

CYCLONIC SEPARATOR

PRESSURE TAP

TANGENTIAL INLET WITH SPIN DAMPER

Figure 15.17 Pease-Anthony (Chemical Construction Co.) venturi scrubber system[39]

ACID OUT

scrubber can be utilized as depicted in Figure 15.17. A spray liquid is intro-duced into the gas stream at the venturi throat where it is atomized by the high-velocity gas stream. Mist particles are impacted on the atomized spray which is then separated from the gas with a cyclonic separator. In this type of application, the spray liquid is usually phosphoric acid which can be recycled and recovered in the process.

Extensive performance data were taken on an industrial venturi scrubber installed in a phosphoric acid plant by Brink and Contant[39]. The venturi throat had a rectangular cross-section. The angle of the convergent section was 25°; the divergent section had an angle of 2·2° following the venturi throat, and then an angle of 15°. The inlet gas mist loading was held at 50 g P_2O_5/m^3 n.t.p. by careful control of the process. The inlet mist averaged 80 per cent phosphoric acid (H_3PO_4) in composition, and the spray acid to the venturi throat averaged 30 per cent. The particle size distribution of the mist entering the venturi and leaving the venturi is given in Figure 15.15.

When the venturi was operated with forty-five spray jets, a liquid injection velocity of 6 m/s, a liquid rate of 1·26 m^3/s and a gas velocity of 6·6 m/s, the lower curve in Figure 15.15 was obtained. From the data presented in this figure, the collection efficiency of the scrubber for various particle sizes can be calculated. The results of these calculations (Figure 15.18) show that the collection efficiency was dependent on mist particle size. These results

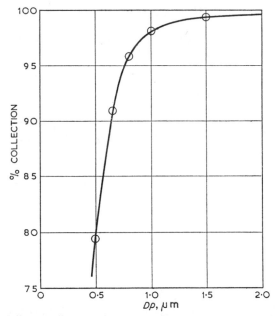

Figure 15.18 Collection efficiency of venturi scrubber as a function of P_2O_5 *mist particle size*[39]

confirmed previous data taken on aerosols with different size distri-butions[53-56].

Venturi scrubbers on P_2O_5 mist have been operated over wide ranges of gas velocity, liquid to gas ratios, and liquid injection velocities[39]. At pressure drops of 100 mb of water, overall collection efficiencies of 98 per

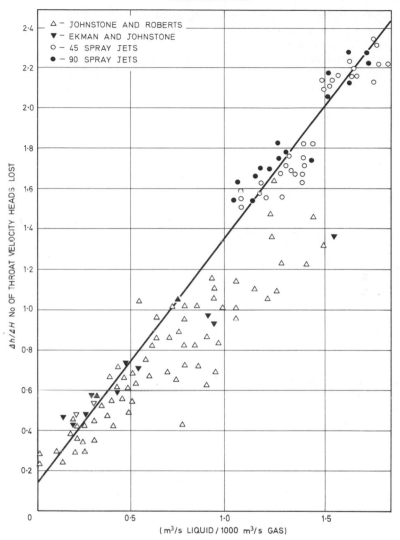

Figure 15.19 Pressure drop across venturi scrubbers[(39)]

Δh = overall pressure drop
ΔH = pressure drop across convergent section
L = liquid to gas ratio

cent have been reported. At lower pressure drops, lower efficiencies are experienced. In the design of venturi scrubbers, the pressure-drop requirements are an important item in design. The ratio of overall pressure drop to the drop across the convergent section of the venturi is essentially linear with the liquid-to-gas ratio[(39,53,55)]. This relationship is shown in Figure 15.19.

Venturi scrubbers find application when their efficiency is high enough to meet the requirements of the particular application. Since efficiencies are low on particles below 0·7 μm, the appearance and rate of dissipation of the chimney plume may be poor for venturi scrubbers when large numbers of small particles are present.

In those applications where the venturi scrubber meets the efficiency requirements and pressure drops in the order of 500–1000 mm of water are not considered excessive, it is often found that the maintenance cost on venturi scrubbers is quite reasonable. Generally, the operation of venturi scrubbers on phosphoric acid is rather smooth, and operational troubles are infrequent as long as the gas flow variations remain small. When the gas flow varies widely, both the pressure drop and efficiency vary widely.

Venturi scrubbers can be constructed out of almost any material of construction. When extremely corrosive acid mist must be handled, the venturi scrubber may be the only suitable equipment available.

15.10.3 Electrostatic Precipitators

Electrostatic precipitators have been described previously in Chapter 12 and Part A of this chapter. Much of the information which has been included there is also applicable to the collection of P_2O_5 mist, but there are some areas of differences.

An electrostatic precipitator was first applied to the collection of P_2O_5 mist in 1915 by the United States Department of Agriculture[57], and used during World War I for the production of high-grade phosphoric acid[58]. Since then precipitators have been applied extensively in this service[59] as well as on many other mists[60].

The construction details of a large electrostatic precipitator operated by the T.V.A. for P_2O_5 mist removal are shown in Figure 15.20[61]. All stainless steel used on the T.V.A. unit was American Iron and Steel Institute Type 316. Electric current was supplied from a half-wave rectifier by electrical leads entering the precipitator through lead-lined oil seals which contained insulators. 9·4 m^3/s of gases at 106°C were pulled through the three parallel sections of the precipitator by a 1170 rev/min stainless steel fan. The gases entered the precipitator at about 121°C; 1180 kg/h of 80 per cent H_3PO_4 mist and entrainment were collected by the unit and the losses were about 180 kg of P_2O_5 per day. The overall efficiency of this precipitator on entrainment and fine mist was about 99 per cent, which was sufficient recovery from the standpoint of economics; however, the recovery was inadequate from the standpoint of air pollution control. The T.V.A. treated the gases from the precipitator with a water scrubber and then discharged the scrubbed gases to the atmosphere with a 61 m high concrete stack which was lined with acid-proof brick.

Since high concentrations of P_2O_5 mist are often present in process streams and since the particle size of the mist is low, large electrostatic precipitators are usually required. It is not uncommon to have two electrostatic precipitators in series to meet the high efficiency requirements rather than single sections as depicted in Figure 15.20.

Since precipitators tend to be large and relatively expensive materials of construction are required, the installation cost of electrostatic precipitators for P_2O_5 mist runs considerably higher than for dust or for sulphuric acid mist. The T.V.A. estimated the cost of the precipitator shown in Figure 15.19 to be $100 000 in 1948[62]. A precipitator installation consisting of two such units in series, as would be required to meet present-day air pollution requirements, would cost many times this figure at present-day prices. The electrostatic precipitator shown in Figure 15.20 was the most expensive single equipment item in the T.V.A. phosphoric acid plants[62].

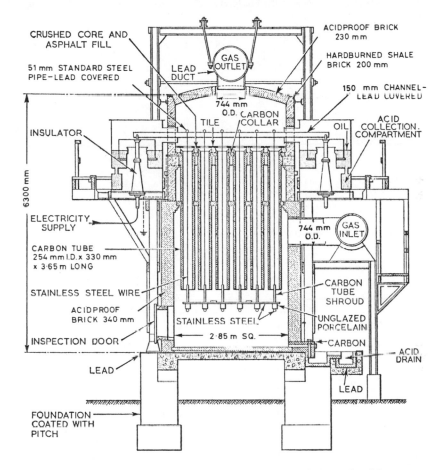

Figure 15.20 Electrostatic precipitator used for P_2O_5 mist removal. (Reproduced by permission of Tennessee Valley Authority)

The operating characteristics of six electrostatic precipitator installations collecting phosphoric acid mist have been reported[62]. The gas flow rates for these installations ranged from 1·67 to 6·65 m^3/s n.t.p. with collection efficiencies ranging from 96·3 to 99·9 per cent.

The P_2O_5 losses from an electrostatic precipitator are affected only slightly by the rate of gas flow or by temperature as long as the gas flow is below design rate. P_2O_5 mist losses are affected materially by the cleanliness of the equipment and by the electrical conditions employed in its operation.

15.10.4 Fibre Mist Eliminators—High Efficiency Types

Fibre mist eliminators[63,64] are a recent development in the mist collection area: the design described below is different from that described in Section 15.6. The general construction of this equipment is depicted in Figures 15.21 and 15.22. As shown in Figure 15.21 an element of a fibre mist eliminator consists of two concentric wire mesh screens between which a fibre is packed.

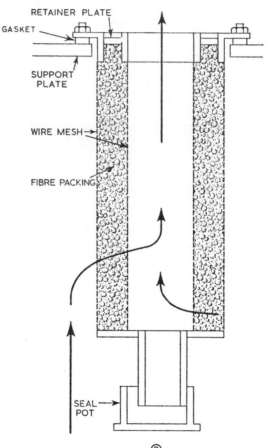

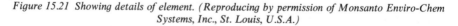

HIGH EFFICIENCY BRINK ® MIST ELIMINATOR

Figure 15.21 Showing details of element. (Reproducing by permission of Monsanto Enviro-Chem Systems, Inc., St. Louis, U.S.A.)

One or more elements are installed on a support plate as shown in Figure 15.22.

Small particles can be collected on fibres at high efficiencies by several different mechanisms[65-78]. As a gas containing mist particles moves towards a fibre, the gas streamlines around the fibre. Particles greater than about 0·5 μm in diameter will not conform to the streamline flow and some will touch the fibre in passing or will be directly intercepted by the fibre in its path. Particles collected in this manner are collected by the mechanism of interial impaction.

Smaller particles, particularly those below 0·3 μm in diameter, exhibit considerable Brownian movement and do not move uniformly along the

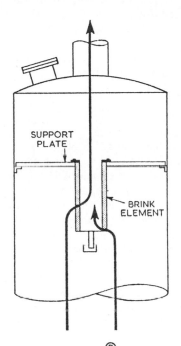

HIGH EFFICIENCY BRINK ® MIST ELIMINATOR

Figure 15.21 Showing details of element. (Reproduced by permission of Monsanto Enviro-Chem Systems, Inc., St. Louis, U.S.A.)

gas streamline. These particles diffuse from the gas to the surface of the fibre and are collected.

Particles may also be collected by direct interception. The particle may follow a gas streamline and be collected without inertial impaction or Brownian diffusion if the streamline is fairly close to the fibre. If a particle 1·0 μm in diameter follows a streamline which passes within 0·5 μm of the fibre, the particle will touch the fibre and will be collected.

Any mist particle passing through a fibre bed may be subjected to the combined effects of these three mechanisms. The mathematics of the various mechanisms, the combinations of the mechanisms and the complications of interference of each fibre with its neighbouring fibres becomes quite complex. A mathematical treatment based on the various mechanisms has been published by Chen[79] (see also Section 15.6).

For continuous steady-state operation, fibre mist eliminators are designed and operated so that the liquid drains from the fibres at the same rate as it is collected. For the design shown in Figure 15.21 the gas enters the element from the outside and passes on into the inner core and on up and out of the element. Gravity tends to make the liquid which is collected on the surface of the fibres move to the bottom of the element while the flowing gas tends to move it horizontally through the bed. When these two forces are of the same order of magnitude, the liquid moves downward through the bed at approximately 45°. Liquid at the downstream side of the fibre bed drains down the screen and collects at the bottom in the seal pot where it overflows back into the process.

At constant gas flow and mist loading, the pressure drop across the element will remain constant as long as the fibre bed is mechanically and chemically stable. A new dry bed of fibres reaches steady-state operation within a few days of start-up.

Fibre mist eliminators differ from the hydrophobic fibre filters described previously in this chapter in several respects. The fibres utilized in fibre mist eliminators are neither limited to glass fibres given special treatments to make them hydrophobic nor to fibres which are intrinsically hydrophobic. Fibre mist eliminators have been developed and are used extensively for the collection of P_2O_5 mist and other highly concentrated mists, such as 98 per cent sulphuric acid mist and oleum mists[64]. Unlike the hydrophobic fibre filters described previously in this chapter, dilution of the mist by the introduction of water into the process gas stream is not required for fibre mist eliminators, since these are designed to withstand the corrosive action of strong acids.

Fibre mist eliminators can recover up to 99·98 per cent (depending on design) of fine P_2O_5 mist particles that are 3 μm and less in diameter, and 100 per cent of the particles that are greater than 3 μm in diameter. Pressure drop across this type of equipment is relatively low, usually between 5 and 25 mb. Varying production rates of any magnitude, as long as the rate is not appreciably higher than the design rate, do not affect its efficiency.

Extensive experience on fibre mist eliminators has been obtained on plant installations which have operated over considerable periods of time[64]. For example, at one plant, a new installation, the stack plume was highly persistent and visible for several miles. The high visibility of the plume was caused by high loadings of below 3 μm phosphoric and sulphuric mists. A fibre mist eliminator was installed in December 1958, and has operated continuously since that time with a collection efficiency of 99 per cent on particles below 3 μm in diameter. The mist entering this fibre mist eliminator had 2·8 and 7 g P_2O_5/m^3 n.t.p. (dry basis) of phosphoric acid mist particles and 1 g H_2SO_4/m^3 n.t.p. of sulphuric acid mist particles which were below 3 μm in diameter plus varying amounts of acid particles with diameters greater than 3 μm. The stack gases from the fibre mist eliminator contained 30 to 74 mg/m^3 (dry basis) of phosphoric acid mist particles and 10 mg/m^3 of sulphuric acid mist particles with diameters less than 3 μm. Since no particles greater than 3 μm in diameter have been found in the stack gases, the efficiency on large particles has been 100 per cent. The present stack plume, which contains about 15 per cent by volume of water vapour, disappears within 12–15 m of the stack on dry days and 50 m on wet foggy days when the humidity is high. The cost of this fibre system was a fraction of the cost of an electrostatic precipitator.

In another case, a phosphoric acid plant, two electrostatic precipitators were in service which were not performing satisfactorily. Maintenance costs on these units were excessive. In the summer of 1959, the precipitators were removed and replaced by a fibre mist eliminator. The total inlet loading to the fibre mist eliminator was 41 g P_2O_5/m^3 (dry basis) of phosphoric acid mist particles of which 9 per cent was below 3 μm in diameter. The stack gases from this fibre mist eliminator contained 0·7 mg P_2O_5/m^3 of phosphoric acid mist particles with diameters less than 3 μm and no larger particles. The mist eliminator delivered 99·98 per cent efficiency on particles less than 3 μm in diameter and 100 per cent on larger particles for an overall efficiency of 99·998 per cent. The stack gases were completely invisible—it was not possible to tell from the appearance of the stack whether or not the unit was operating.

Fibre mist eliminators are the most economical equipment available for the collection of P_2O_5 mist when high efficiencies are required. They have been installed with capacities ranging up to 55 m³/s at costs ranging up to about $100000 for high efficiency elements of special glass fibre and 316 stainless steel. By 1970, these high efficiency type elements had been supplied to over 1000 plant installations in the free world. The widespread application of these units has included many processes in addition to phosphoric acid[80,81].

15.10.5 Fibre Mist Eliminators—High Velocity Types

The design superficial gas velocity through the fibres in the high efficiency type units described in Section 15.10.4 is usually in the range of 30 to 160 mm/s. Extensive testing led to the development of fibre mist eliminators which operate at gas velocities in the range of 0·16 to 4 m/s[82,83]. The high velocity type units are smaller and less expensive than previous designs.

At high gas velocities the controlling mechanism for collecting mist particles on the fibres is impaction. The collection efficiency increases as the gas flow is increased. Efficiencies of essentially 100 per cent on acid particles greater than 3 μm in diameter and 90 to 98 per cent on particles 3 μm and smaller, depending on the particle size distribution and gas velocity, have been reported[83]. Typical pressure drops are in the range of 15 to 20 mb for superficial gas velocities of 2 to 2·5 m/s.

High-velocity type elements consist of fibres packed between two flat parallel screens as shown in Figure 15.23. Two sizes of elements, 470 × 660 mm and 470 × 1345 mm have been used in acid plants. For a typical plant installation, depending on the gas flow and element size, from ten to eighty elements are mounted in a polygon framework closed at the bottom by a conical drain plan. The top of the polygon is surrounded by a circular ring which is welded to the inside of the tower head as shown in Figure 15.24. For large high velocity towers, recent designs have been double polygons (one inside the other) so that more fibre bed area is achieved in a given tower cross-section. The gas flow is horizontal through the fibre bed and then upward. The liquid drains downward across the pan to the seal pot and back into the tower.

High velocity units have been installed to handle gas flows up to 60 m³/s

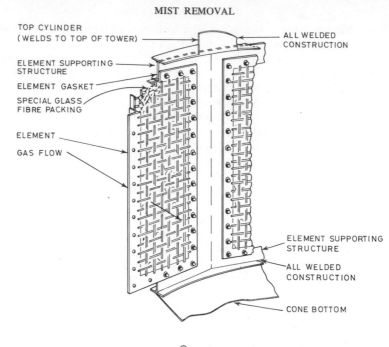

TOP CYLINDER
(WELDS TO TOP OF TOWER)

ALL WELDED
CONSTRUCTION

ELEMENT SUPPORTING
STRUCTURE

ELEMENT GASKET

SPECIAL GLASS
FIBRE PACKING

ELEMENT

GAS FLOW

ELEMENT SUPPORTING
STRUCTURE

ALL WELDED
CONSTRUCTION

CONE BOTTOM

HIGH VELOCITY BRINK ® MIST ELIMINATOR ELEMENT

Figure 15.23 Sectional view

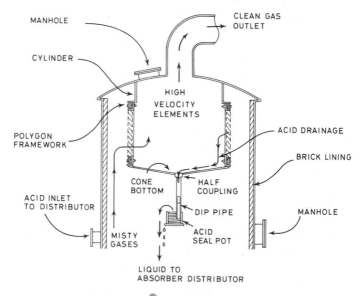

MANHOLE

CLEAN GAS
OUTLET

CYLINDER

HIGH
VELOCITY
ELEMENTS

POLYGON
FRAMEWORK

ACID DRAINAGE

BRICK LINING

CONE
BOTTOM

HALF
COUPLING

ACID INLET
TO DISTRIBUTOR

DIP PIPE

MANHOLE

MISTY
GASES

ACID
SEAL POT

LIQUID TO
ABSORBER DISTRIBUTOR

HIGH VELOCITY BRINK ® MIST ELIMINATOR ELEMENT

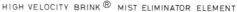

Figure 15.24 Sectional arrangement
(Reproduced by permission of Monsanto Enviro-Chem Systems, Inc., St. Louis, U.S.A.)

and have been designed for even higher flows. Costs for internals, based on special glass fibre and 316 stainless steel construction of elements and polygons, range from about $5000 for 4·2 m^3/s to $45000 for 51 m^3/s. By 1970, thousands of high velocity elements had been installed in many countries.

16

Spray Elimination

F. STEARMAN AND G. J. WILLIAMSON

16.1 Introduction

In many industrial processes it is necessary to remove spray droplets from gas streams in order (i) to purify the gas and remove liquid which would contaminate a subsequent process, damage machinery, or constitute an undesirable atmospheric effluent; or, (ii) to recover a useful liquid product of the process.

The types of separator discussed are suitable for the removal of most mechanically-formed spray droplets which usually have a size range of from 10 to 1000 μm, most being greater than 50 μm. Because of their size it is comparatively easy to remove them from the entraining gas streams, in contrast to the removal of fume or condensation mists which are often 1 μm or less in diameter (this latter range of particle size is dealt with in Chapter 15). Figure 16.1 shows the size range of various commonly-encountered aerosols and indicates the range which is dealt with in this chapter.

16.2 Methods of Spray Formation

Many of the problems of spray removal concern droplets formed by splash-type liquid distributors in packed absorbers and cooling towers of various types, and even with essentially non-splash (trough and gutter type) distributors as used in some water-cooling towers, droplets are thrown off by the liquid streams in flowing on to the packing. Those droplets whose free-falling speed in the gas is less than the upward velocity of the gas are thus carried out with the gas and may need to be arrested by some form of spray eliminator. The size grading of droplets from splash-type distributors has been determined by Chilton[1], and the drops are shown to be mostly in the range 100–500 μm.

Spray is also produced by the bursting of gas bubbles at a liquid surface which may occur in bubble trays or other gas/liquid tray-contacting devices. In this case also, the smaller droplets will be carried away by the gas stream. Newitt, Dombrowski and Knelman[2] show that when a bubble bursts droplets of from 20 to 1400 μm are formed. These group themselves into two ranges 20–80 μm (peak frequency at 50 μm) and 600–1200 μm (peak frequency at 1000 μm). Although the smaller range constitutes only about 1 per cent by weight of the total spray formed, it may constitute the larger number of particles in the actual amount carried over.

A further source of spray is the stripping of liquid by gas streams passing at high velocity over wetted surfaces. This commonly occurs in pipelines and may occur in centrifugal mist collectors, generally producing droplets of about 50 μm or larger.

The free-falling speed of droplets may be calculated from Stokes' equation or the modification of Stokes' equation required above the streamline

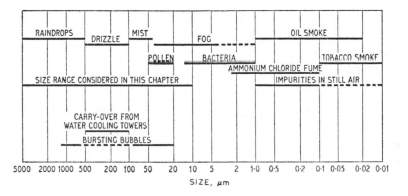

Figure 16.1 Size range of common aerosols

region; Table 14.10 (Chapter 14, p. 501) gives the free-falling speed of particles of various sizes and densities in air at room temperature and pressure. The size grading of spray droplets can be found by the method described in Chapter 15 (p. 523). Other methods which can often be applied to larger sizes of droplet, e.g. precipitation from cooling towers, etc., are based on the use of photographic film or slides coated with magnesium oxide which are marked by the droplets falling on them. The methods are described by Jackson and Waple[3] and by May[4].

16.3 Types of Spray Separator

The types of separator dealt with fall into three classes.

(i) Simple disengagement vessels which remove massive liquid by allowing the liquid to fall to the bottom of the vessel while the gas is taken off at the top.

(ii) Those in which the spray is collected by impingement on an obstacle placed in the gas stream. The gas flows round the obstacle, whereas the droplet, due to its inertia, is unable to do so and impinges on the obstacle.

(iii) Centrifugal types in which the gas is caused to spin and the drops of liquid are thrown to the walls of the vessel by the centrifugal forces.

The type of separator favoured for a particular duty depends on the amount and nature of the liquid phase and to some extent the density and viscosity of the gas. It also depends on the degree of separation required, the permissible pressure-loss across the device, and on the extent to which solids or sticky liquids are present. These might cause chokage of some types of separator. If fine droplets or mists are present the separators discussed in this chapter may be regarded as first-stage separators to be followed by one of the more efficient types described in Chapter 15. The factors to be considered in the selection of a suitable type of separator are discussed in more detail later.

It is essential in all designs to ensure that liquid once collected is not stripped from the wetted surfaces and re-entrained by the gas flow. The re-entrainment effect can be roughly measured in terms of a parameter expressing the shear forces exerted by the gas on the liquid surface (equivalent to the rate of destruction of momentum when the gas is brought to rest). It is usually expressed as ρv^2 where ρ = actual density of the gas (kg/m^3), and v = actual gas velocity (m/s). This expression has various values at different points in the separators, and when the gas density is known, the maximum permissible velocities at the various points may be calculated. Thus the necessary sizes of the gas passages are obtained.

16.4 Design of Spray Separators

16.4.1 Louvre Type

A simple type of impingement collector consists of narrow slats arranged in the form of a venetian blind across the gas stream, as shown in Figure 16.2. Chilton[1] reports the results of tests on a great many different arrangements of the slats for collecting the carry-over from water-cooling towers.

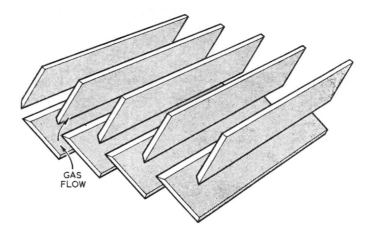

GAS
FLOW

Figure 16.2 *Arrange of louvre-type spray eliminator (a more specific arrangement with dimensions is shown in Figure 16.3)*

These louvre-type arrestors when arranged to best advantage are highly efficient, and will remove from 95 to 100 per cent of droplets similar in size to those carried over from splash-type distributors in water-cooling towers. The pressure loss can be extremely small; for instance, an efficiency of 98 per cent is obtained at less than 0·1 mb. A satisfactory arrangement for operation at atmospheric pressure is shown in Figure 16.3. The gas velocity approaching the louvres should be in the range of 2 to 3 m/s for optimum performance; below 2 m/s the impingement efficiency falls away and above 3 m/s the water film is re-entrained.

This type of arrestor has been found to be satisfactory for the difficult duty of reducing the emission of grit and spray from coke quenching towers.

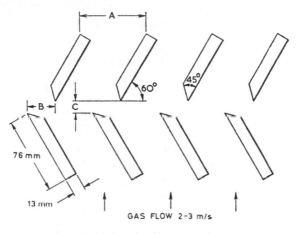

Figure 16.3 Details of louvre spacing

	Size, mm	
Dimensions	Type I	Type II
A	70	57
B	25	19
C	13	13

Jackson and Waple[3] show that a reduction per cent in the deposition of grit of more than 90 per cent can be achieved. The slats tend to be self-cleaning with only occasional hosing down needed to maintain efficiency and low pressure drop.

16.4.2 The Simple Fall-out Vessel

A simple gravity separation vessel, or a development of it, is always required where heavy liquid loadings (say greater than 1 kg/m^3 of gas) are to be removed. This is designed to trap liquid flowing along the pipe walls and to remove all drops with a free-falling speed greater than the upward velocity of the gas in the vessel. It has the disadvantage that the incoming gas imping-ing on the collected liquid may induce a spray, unless a disc is installed opposite the end of the gas inlet pipe as shown in Figure 16.4. In addition, much of the airborne spray which impinges on the disc is borne sideways to the wall and drains to the base of the vessel.

The first step in design is to calculate the diameter d of the inlet pipe, making the value of ρv^2 (ρ in kg/m^3 and v in m/s) not more than 200. Strictly the value of ρ should be taken as the average density of the gas–liquid mixture; normally the liquid loadings are small and the actual gas density may be used. The diameter D of the vessel is then calculated to make the rising velocity of the gas in the vessel equal to the free-falling speed of the smallest droplet to be removed. To avoid extremely large diameter vessels

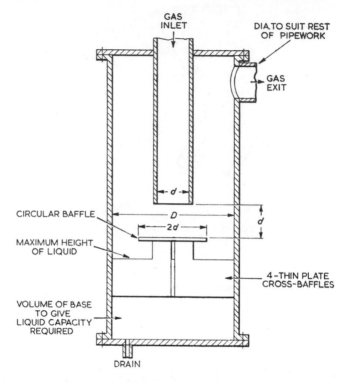

Figure 16.4 Fall-out vessel with impingement disc

it is usual to make this rising velocity about 0·3 m/s (i.e. the free-falling speed in air at 20°C and 1 bar abs. pressure of a water droplet 110 μm in diameter). The remainder of the dimensions should approximate to the proportions given in Figure 16.4.

16.4.3 Knitted Wire-mesh Arrestor

The fall-out vessel is usually followed by a separator of a more efficient type. One which can be conveniently fitted inside the fall-out vessel itself is the knitted wire-mesh separator, which collects the drops by impingement on the wires. A full analysis of the mechanism of collection of particles by impingement on spherical and cylindrical obstacles has been made by Stairmand[5]. This includes a method of calculating the collection efficiency which can be virtually 100 per cent on drops of 10 μm and larger (see Appendix to this chapter). Such a knitted wire-mesh arrestor is shown in Figure 16.5; the mesh pads can be obtained from various suppliers. These pads are formed by knitting fine wire, usually of 32 swg (0·27 mm) into a mesh of about

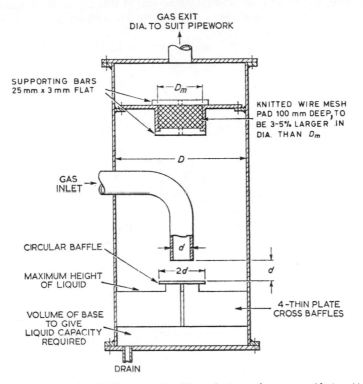

Figure 16.5 Combined fall-out vessel and knitted wire-mesh separator (design A)

4 mm aperature (Figure 16.7(a)), which is then crimped into corrugations of about 4 mm depth. Layers of this mesh are then built up to give a pad of the required thickness (Figure 16.7(b)). The voidage is usually high, about 97·5 per cent, so that high actual internal gas velocities are avoided. For a typical installation the pad thickness is 100 mm. The main reason for its effectiveness is that the collected liquid forms large drops on the loops formed by the knitting process, and these drops then drain back against the upward gas flow and fall to the bottom of the vessel.

The first step in the design is to determine the cross-sectional area of mesh pad necessary. The velocity of the gas through the mesh for the type described should be such that ρv^2 does not exceed 11 (ρ in kg/m^3 and v in m/s). This is a maximum value, with virtually no safety factor. It is generally recommended that the actual operating velocities should be about 75 per cent of the maximum. Since the collection efficiency increases with gas velocity, it is desirable to use the highest possible value. A velocity of about 0·8 m/s is normally considered to be the minumum for effective performance, although in certain applications where other types of separator were impracticable, velocities as low as 0·25 m/s have been used satisfactorily.

It is most important that the mesh should be a close fit in its holder and flanges must be provided around the periphery of the pad to prevent liquid from by-passing the mesh. The supports should cause the minimum possible obstruction to gas flow, so that collected liquid will drain off. A simple grid of flat strips, say 25×3 mm edge-on to the gas flow and spaced about 150 mm apart will usually be satisfactory.

A typical use of the knitted-mesh separator inside a vessel is to remove water mist from the gas leaving the interstage cooler of a gas compressor.

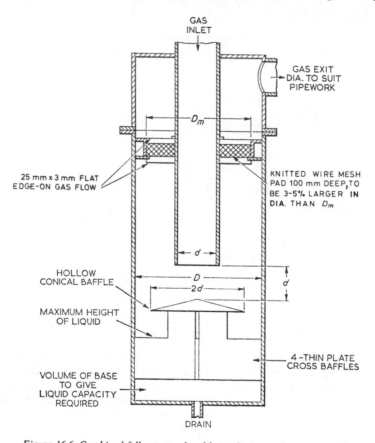

GAS
INLET

GAS EXIT
DIA. TO SUIT
PIPEWORK

D_m

25 mm x 3 mm FLAT
EDGE-ON GAS FLOW

KNITTED WIRE MESH
PAD 100 mm DEEP, TO
BE 3-5% LARGER IN
DIA. THAN D_m

d

HOLLOW
CONICAL BAFFLE

D

$2d$

d

MAXIMUM HEIGHT
OF LIQUID

4 -THIN PLATE
CROSS BAFFLES

VOLUME OF BASE
TO GIVE
LIQUID CAPACITY
REQUIRED

DRAIN

Figure 16.6 Combined fall-out vessel and knitted wire mesh separator (design B)

Mesh only is commonly used in the top of absorption towers or evaporators to prevent carry-over of liquid droplets, or in cases where the liquid loading does not exceed 100 g/m^3. An advantage of the mesh type of separator is its low pressure drop, 1·2 to 2·5 mb. Its main disadvantage is the risk of chokage if the gas contains solid or sticky particles.

Because of the large size of vessels resulting from designs having a low rising speed of gas in the vessel to allow droplets to fall out, it is usual to rely on the mesh to remove the spray which is not collected on the impingement plate. The vessel diameter is then determined by the diameter of mesh

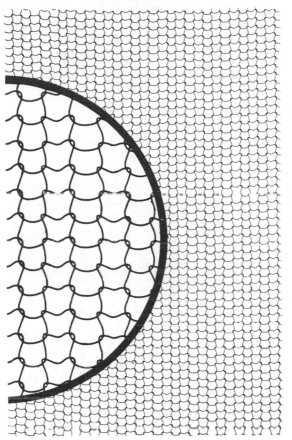

Figure 16.7(a) Single layer of knitted wire mesh. This illustration shows the stitches both actual size and enlarged. (Courtesy of Begg, Cousland & Co. Ltd.)

Figure 16.7(b) Pad of knitted wire mesh. (Courtesy of Begg, Cousland & Co. Ltd.)

required, and by the diameter of the impingement plate, which is made in
the form of a shallow cone so that the liquid is directed downward and is not
carried up the walls by the gas flow. A typical design is shown in Figure
16.6 and is approximately to scale. Large vessels over about 1 m diameter,
may, however, be made rather more squat in shape.

16.5 Centrifugal Separators

These separators can take many forms, but the principle of operation is the
same as that of the cyclones used to remove dust and grit from gases. The
design of such cyclones has been dealt with in Chapter 12, which shows how
the pressure-drop and 'cut' size of particle may be calculated. The mist
cyclone has the advantage that once the droplets are collected on the walls
they are not re-entrained so long as the cyclone is correctly designed; in the

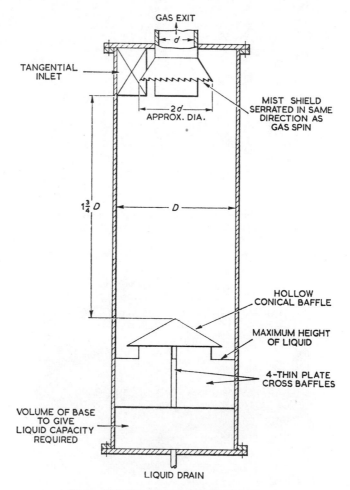

Figure 16.8 Top-gas-exit centrifugal separator

dust cyclone, particularly near the apex of the cone some re-entrainment is inevitable. To be correctly designed the spinning speed of the gas at the cyclone walls must not exceed a certain critical value, otherwise the film of collected liquid will be torn away and re-entrained in the gas flow.

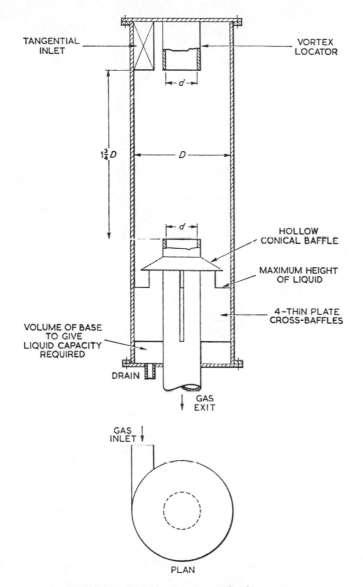

Figure 16.9 Bottom-gas-exit centrifugal separator

A conical base is not necessary in the case of a mist cyclone, and usually a cylindrical vessel is used. The arrangement of inlet and exit ducts may vary considerably, the simplest arrangement being that commonly used for dust cyclones, viz. an inlet arranged tangentially at the top with the exit pipe

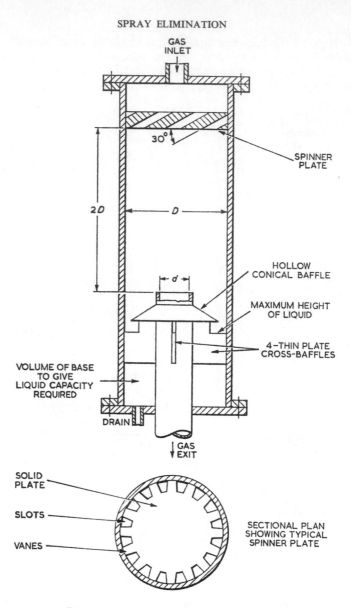

GAS
INLET

30°

SPINNER
PLATE

2D

D

HOLLOW
CONICAL BAFFLE

d

MAXIMUM HEIGHT
OF LIQUID

4–THIN PLATE
CROSS-BAFFLES

VOLUME OF BASE
TO GIVE
LIQUID CAPACITY
REQUIRED

DRAIN

GAS
EXIT

SOLID
PLATE

SLOTS

VANES

SECTIONAL PLAN
SHOWING TYPICAL
SPINNER PLATE

Figure 16.10 Vane inlet centrifugal separator

placed axially at the top. However, if it is found to be more convenient, e.g. in a high pressure forging, a vane-type axial inlet may be used or the exit may be at the bottom.

To prevent re-entrainment of the collected liquid film, ρv^2 at the walls of the vessel must not exceed a certain value. Stairmand[6] originally gave a figure of 1860 but to give a factor of safety in practical application it is now considered that the value of 1300 should be taken as a maximum. The velocity of the gas at the inlet to the cyclone should be the value given by the above limit, or 15 m/s whichever is the smaller. (For simplicity it is assumed that the spinning speed at the walls is equal to the gas velocity at the inlet; this is very nearly so for a well-designed cyclone.) The area a of the gas inlet can then be calculated when the gas rate is known.

$$a = 278 \, R/v.$$

where a = area of inlet required, mm^2

R = actual gas rate, m^3/h

v = gas velocity, m/s.

The diameter D of the body is calculated from a formula based on dust-cyclone practice.

$$D = 55\sqrt{R/v} \, \text{mm}$$

The remaining details should be as shown on Figures 16.8–16.10 which give roughly the proportions of three different arrangements.

In the top gas exit designs an exit shield serrated in the direction of gas spin must be fitted round the exit pipe as shown in Figure 16.8. The film of liquid which, under the influence of precession currents, creeps across the top of the vessel and down the outside of the exit pipe is thus prevented from being drawn into the exit pipe. The cross-baffle surmounted by a conical baffle fitted at the bottom of the vessel limits the region in which the gas spins, and prevents the collected liquid from rotating and so creeping up the cyclone walls. When a bottom exit pipe is used with a tangential inlet a dummy top exit pipe is necessary to stabilize the central vortex as shown in Figure 16.9.

16.6 Factors Affecting the Choice of a Separator

In many cases, a primary consideration is the pressure loss which can be tolerated. Where extremely small pressure drops, say less than 0·2 mb, are essential (for example, in water cooling towers) the louvre type is the best choice, and is effective on droplets down to 150 μm in size.

When drops of smaller size (down to 10 μm) are to be collected, knitted wire mesh, with a pressure drop of about 2 mb may be used. The louvre and mesh types can often be fitted directly to the top of the tower or vessel.

Centrifugal separators usually have a higher pressure drop, up to about 15 mb when treating air at room temperature and pressure but may have to be used when high collection efficiencies are required in the removal of spray droplets from gas streams at high pressures and therefore high densities. This is because the permissible velocity of the gas through knitted mesh is too low for effective removal of the mist if carry-over is to be avoided. Under these conditions the cyclone will usually give superior performance. Several cyclones may be used in parallel in order to take advantage of the better performance of small diameter vessels.

Where very heavy liquid loadings are to be removed from pipelines a fall-out vessel is always needed. It is easy to fit mesh as a secondary separator if its performance is satisfactory; otherwise, though this is unusual, a fall-out vessel followed by a cyclone may be required.

When the gas contains solid or sticky particles, the risk of chokage must be considered before deciding to use mesh. This is less likely with cyclones;

louvre types are unlikely to be affected by solid concentrations. Table 16.1 gives approximate figures for the performance of the various types of separator, and typical applications.

Table 16.1 PERFORMANCE AND APPLICATION OF VARIOUS TYPES OF SEPARATOR

Type	Size range of drops to which applicable μm	Efficiency %	Approximate pressure drop* mb	Liquid loading g/m³	Application
Louvre Type 1	> 150	98% on 150 μm	0·08–0·15	No practical limit	Emission from water cooling towers, and coke quenching towers.
Type 2	> 150	99% on 150 μm	0·09–0·17	No practical limit	Spray from wet dedusters.
Fall-out vessel	> 100	99% on 100 μm	1·5	No practical limit	Condensate after gas coolers.
Mesh only	> 10	99% on 10 μm	2	100	Carry-over from absorption towers and evaporators.
Mesh in fall-out vessel	> 10	99% on 10 μm	4	No practical limit	Condensate from gas after interstage coolers on compression plant.
Cyclones	> 20	50% on 5 μm 99% on 20 μm	15	1000	Condensate between stages of high-pressure gas compression plant.

*These pressure drops refer to air at 1 bar abs., and 20°C. For other conditions the pressure drop is proportional to the value of ρv^2 in the separator.

APPENDIX

Performance of knitted wire mesh (standard 100 mm deep pad of 32 s.w.g. wire, bulk density 190 kg/m³).

Overall efficiency $= 100\{1 \times (1 - \eta_T)^s\}$ (Stairmand[5])

where
$\qquad \eta_T$ = target efficiency
$\qquad s$ = number of treatments
Assume density of stainless steel to be 7900 kg/m³
density of wire mesh pad is $\qquad\qquad$ 190 kg/m³

therefore
$\qquad$ voidage $\qquad\qquad\qquad\qquad$ = 97·6 per cent
$\qquad$ diameter of wire (32 s.w.g.) $\qquad$ = 0·274 mm

therefore

volume per metre run $\qquad = 5{\cdot}9 \times 10^{-8}\ m^3$

therefore

length of wire in 1 m^3 of mesh $\qquad = 408\,000\ m$

therefore

projected area of wire in 1 m^3 of mesh $\qquad = 112\ m^2$

therefore

projected area of wire in 100 mm deep pad
1 metre square $\qquad = 11{\cdot}2\ m^2$

Thus we can assume 11 'treatments' (using the concept of impingement theory).

Example

To calculate the cut size of water droplet which will be removed by a standard 100 mm deep pad of knitted wire mesh from nitrogen at 4·2 bar abs. and 40°C at 99·9 per cent efficiency.

For an overall efficiency of 99·9 per cent

$$\eta_T = 100\{1-(0{\cdot}001)^{1/11}\}$$
$$= 46{\cdot}6\ \text{per cent}$$

hence from a graph given by Stairmand[5], $\dfrac{Dg}{vf} = 1{\cdot}5$

where D = diameter of obstacle

g = acceleration due to gravity

v = velocity of gas

f = free-falling speed of droplets

in any self-consistent units

therefore

$$f = \frac{0{\cdot}274 \times 10^{-3} \times 9{\cdot}81}{1{\cdot}5\,v}$$

$$-\frac{0{\cdot}001\,79}{v}\ \text{for the standard 100 mm deep pad.}$$

Actual density of gas at 4·2 bar abs. and 40°C

$$= 4{\cdot}5\ kg/m^3$$

$$v = \sqrt{\frac{11}{4{\cdot}5}} = 1{\cdot}56\ m/s\ (\rho v^2\ \text{not to exceed 11, see Section 16.4})$$

therefore $f = \dfrac{0{\cdot}001\,79}{1{\cdot}56} = 0{\cdot}001\,15\ m/s.$

The diameter of a water droplet having this free-falling speed can be determined using Stokes' law, and is found to be approximately 6 μm (cf. also Chapter 14, Part B).

17

Air Purification

PART A AIR PURIFICATION FOR BUILDINGS

N. R. WAY

I AIR PURIFICATION FOR OFFICES AND ASSEMBLY HALLS

17.1 Introduction

Pollution in atmospheric air consists of combustible matter such as soots, tars, vegetable debris and pollens, together with non-combustible matter such as silica from soil erosion and building debris, flue dusts containing aluminas and metallic oxides, and contamination from various industrial processes.

The amount of contamination in one cubic metre of air varies from the order of 0·03 mg in clean rural areas up to 4 mg in industrial areas. A typical size distribution of the particles in the air in a British industrial town showed that each cubic metre of air containing 8 mg had tens of millions of particles in the 1–5 μm range, hundreds of thousands in the 5–10 μm range, tens of thousands in the 10–20 μm range, and a few hundred above this size.

Particles larger than 10 μm are a nuisance rather than a hazard (assuming they are not toxic) as they rapidly settle out, contaminating equipment, etc. Particles between 1 and 10 μm are accepted to cause the principal health hazard, as are particles smaller than this if in sufficient concentration, e.g. smog[1,2].

17.2 Types of Filter

Any filter giving a purely sieve action against atmospheric pollution would have to contain extremely fine holes, and its proportion of open area would be so small that it would clog very rapidly. The most commonly used method employed to remove impurities from the air is to cause the air to pass through a medium where the holes are large compared with the particles to be filtered, but so randomly arranged that the particles come into contact with the fibres due to impingement within the tortuous passages through the medium (centrifugal force), or possibly by electrostatic attraction. The particles are retained by the medium due to wedging in the fibre intersections, electrostatic attraction, or by a tacky coating (such as oil) on the medium.

17.2.1 Dry Filters

(i) Fabric. Fabric filters employ felts, woven materials, papers (generally resin-impregnated to improve strength and water resistance), animal and vegetable fibre laps, e.g. acetate and glass.

The felts, woven materials and paper filters are normally manufactured in a crimped V-formation so that a large area of lower porosity medium can be used. This gives higher dust-retaining efficiency and dust-holding capacity than if a flat sheet of similar medium were employed, as this would have to be more porous to give the same resistance to air flow at the higher media velocity.

The lap materials can be employed as described above, or can be used in a deep mat form to give depth of filtration. In this form a more open mat would be employed to give a less tortuous path for a greater distance and efficiencies and dust-holding capacities can be obtained similar to the crimped filter.

The dry filter is not always cleanable owing to the tenacious nature of tarry sooty material present in the atmosphere of this country. The felt and some of the paper filters can be vacuum-cleaned, or cleaned in an organic solvent (or the dirt may be blown off with compressed air), but there is a limit to the number of effective cleanings.

(ii) Electrostatic precipitators. The electrostatic precipitator filter removes dust from the air by charging the particles and then collecting them by virtue of their charge. The air is passed between wires, to which some 10000 or more volts have been applied, and earthed plates; the strong electrostatic field causes each particle of dust to acquire a surface charge which is then attracted to the earthed collector plates. It is usual to have a positively charged ionizer, as oxygen is not so readily converted to ozone as when the ionizer is negatively charged, ozone being toxic, and undesirable in photographic film manufacture.

The charge acquired by a particle is approximately equivalent to its surface area; therefore small particles acquire greater charges than large particles relative to their mass. Thus a well-designed electrostatic precipitator can give a good performance over a wide range of particle size, including those in the smoke range. The construction, being of metal with ceramic insulators, permits operation at elevated temperatures. As there is a possibility of re-entrainment, particularly of large particles, the collector plates are often coated with oil to retain the attracted particles.

Maintenance of the precipitator includes hosing the collector plates with water, or, if oiled, by a solvent followed by re-oiling. If this maintenance is not carried out regularly the build-up of dust will cause flash-overs with consequently re-entrainment of agglomerates; it is frequently recommended that gauzes or fabric filters be placed downstream of the precipitator to collect these agglomerates. As would be expected, the efficiency of a precipitator decreases as the air velocity through it increases. A velocity of 0·5–1·5 m/s is normal.

Performance of precipitators in submarines is described in Part 17C.

17.2.2 Viscous Filters

Type A. This type of filter is generally of a more open nature than the dry type, relying on direct impingement of the particles and changes in direction of the air-flow to throw the dust on to the oil-wetted surface. It is not generally used in this country owing to the fine nature of the particles in the air, but is employed overseas where high concentrations of dust from soil erosion are encountered.

These filters often employ either wire mesh in various formations, such as herringbone crimp, Figure 17.1, or a knit, or layers of wire or cotton gauze in crimped form; they are oil-wetted by a spraying or dipping process. The type of oil and amount used are of considerable importance in this type of filter, as it relies on the tacky medium to retain the dust. A dry filter of this type has an extremely low efficiency.

They can be efficiently cleaned by solvent dip and can be re-oiled and re-used until normal wear and tear of the material causes the end of their useful life.

Type B. Another form of viscous filter comprises any of the dry types previously mentioned, lightly oiled by spraying or dipping in a solution of oil in a volatile solvent. This treatment can, under some conditions, increase the dust load capacity of a dry filter by assisting in the formation of a more porous film of dust, and it can also enable the filter to be cleaned more effectively.

Oil wetting will improve the efficiency of the fibre laps by assisting retention of the dust collected; thus some types of filters, such as coarse hair or coarse glass fibre laps in open form, which would be virtually useless in the dry state, are very effective in the oil-wetted condition. The oil used is normally of SAE 10 viscosity with good wetting characteristics.

17.3 General Characteristics of the Dry and Viscous Filters

The general relation between the efficiency and dust loading characteristics of the various types of filters is given in Figure 17.2. As the dust load (weight of dust on filter) increases, the felts and papers generally show a gradual improvement in dust-retaining efficiency due to blockage of the pores, which also causes the pressure drop to increase gradually at first, followed by a rapidly increasing gradient. The oil-wetted crimped wire/cotton mesh filters have similar characteristics.

The dry and oil-wetted lap filters being of greater depth but of a more open nature again show a gradual rise in dust-retaining efficiency. A level can be reached due to bad maintenance where the filter becomes so heavily loaded that it becomes unstable and the efficiency begins to fall. The increase of pressure-drop with dust load is generally more gradual than with felt and paper filters.

The open-mesh viscous filter has its highest dust-retaining efficiency initially; this remains fairly constant for a time, depending mainly on the amount of oil on the filter. When a certain quantity of dust has been retained and absorbed by the oil the efficiency fails, due to insufficient wetting of

Figure 17.1 Herringbone crimp filter fabric

subsequent dust. The increase in pressure drop with dust loading is very gradual.

It is possible, therefore, to determine the useful life of the felt, paper and lap-type filters by pressure-drop data, but with the open-mesh viscous filter it is necessary to establish its operating period by experiment. The

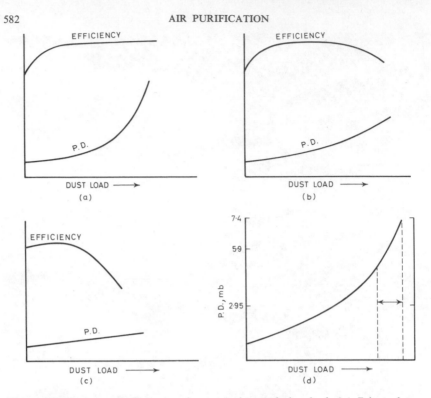

Figure 17.2 Variation of efficiency and pressure drop with dust load. (a) Felts and papers; (b) laps; (c) viscous (open mesh); (d) increase in pressure drop as dust is collected

efficiency of an electrostatic precipitator is fairly constant unless flash-over occurs; this must be avoided or large quantities of dust may be re-entrained.

17.4 Form of Filters

All the filters for air conditioning are generally available in single panels of fairly standard dimensions; typical dimensions are $50 \times 50 \times 5$ cm deep, and take the following forms:

17.4.1 Throwaway Filters

Throwaway filters are scrapped after service. They are generally made from a lap in crimped or flat panel form, or paper in crimped form. The filter frames are generally constructed of cardboard for cheapness and ease of disposal.

17.4.2 Replaceable Media Filters

Filters with replaceable media are also of crimped or flat form usually employing the lap medium, but the frames and filter medium supports are of metal. The replacement medium can be bought in roll form and maintenance is made relatively easy.

17.4.3 Cleanable Filters

Cleanable filters are the oil-wetted impingement type which are cleaned by solvent dip and wash followed by re-oiling.

The filter panels are removed to a workshop and soaked for a short period (from 2 to 5 min) in a suitable solvent which is miscible with both oil and water. The dirt is then removed by pressure-hosing with cold water or agitation in a tank of hot water. The water is removed by centrifuging or compressed-air blowing. The filters are then re-oiled by dipping in the wetting oil and removing the excess oil by draining or use of the centrifuge.

Solvents are recommended by the filter manufacturers; they should be non-inflammable and non-toxic, and must not attack the components of the filter. Wetting oils used range from gel oils, which contain a small percentage of a low melting point wax-like additive to allow greater weights of oil to be retained by the filter, to oils with a tacky additive. The oil recommended for the type of filter in service should be used.

17.4.4 Automatic Filters

Type A. Employing lap filter medium. Filters employing lap media are generally of the form shown in Figure 17.3(a) and consist of a fibrous lap medium (dry or oil-wetted) backed with a muslin for strength. The medium is contained on a spool at the top of the filter and passes across the air flow aperture on to a take-up spool at the base of the filter. As the material becomes dust laden, a pressure differential or time switch causes a motor to

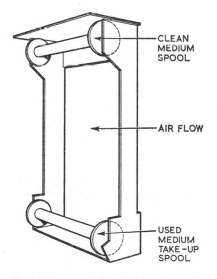

Figure 17.3(a) Automatic filter (fibrous lap medium)

operate the take-up spool, and a given length of fresh medium is exposed. This type of filter reduces maintenance to disposal of the used spool and its replacement. It is obtainable in a wide range of heights and widths.

Type B. Self-cleaning filters. Self-cleaning filters are generally of the viscous open-structure impingement type, a typical design being shown in Figure 17.3(b). A continuous band of filter panels is fixed to a pair of endless chains and is caused to rotate a certain distance at fixed time intervals. The oil sump at the base contains a simple device by which the filters are cleaned as they pass through.

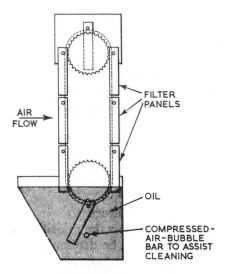

Figure 17.3(b) Automatic self-cleaning filter

The characteristics of this filter are similar to those previously described, but the time taken for the filters to rotate is so arranged that the filter is always operating at the maximum efficiency. It must also be noted that the downstream chain of filters is also in operation giving double filtration.

The only servicing necessary is occasional scraping of sludge which settles at the base of the sump (automatic equipment is also available for this operation) and topping up or changing oil.

This type of filter is also available in a wide range of sizes. It is useful for operation in heavy dust concentrations but is not normally used for air conditioning in the U.K.

17.5 Information Required for Designing a Filter Plant

(a) Air flow required—m^3/s
(b) Available space for filters (floor area and height)
(c) Maximum permissible pressure drop across the filters.
(d) Concentration of particulate matter in dirty air.
(e) Type and size distribution of particles in dirty air.

(f) Degree of pollution permissible in filtered air.

(g) Temperature variation of air, and relative humidity in dirty air.

(h) Permissible range of temperature and humidity in purified air.

The method of obtaining and applying this information is as follows:

17.5.1 Air Flow Required

This depends on the size of room and in some ways on protection required. The number of air changes required can vary from 6 to 30 per hour in offices and assembly rooms.

17.5.2 Available Space for Filters

Having determined the air flow, the velocity through the aperture available for the filters can be determined by

$$\text{Velocity in metres per second} = \frac{\text{Air volume in cubic metres per second}}{\text{Area of aperture (square metres)}}$$

Filters for office and assembly room filtration are generally designed to operate at some definite face velocity between 1·5 and 3 m/s; this variation in velocity is dependent on many factors. As the depth of a crimped filter increases the area of media increases; therefore, the velocity at the face of the filter can be higher. Also, some oil-wetted impingement filters give improved dust-retaining efficiency at velocities of about 2·5 m/s. If the determined velocity is less than or equal to the design velocity for the filters, there is no problem, and the filters can be arranged in line across the aperture. Under-rating a filter (within limits) often improves the efficiency (not of open mesh viscous types) and always increases its life; for instance, employing a filter at 50 per cent of its air flow rating can increase its useful life 3–4 times normal.

If the space available for the filters is insufficient to allow the filter panels to be arranged in one plane, they can be arranged in V- or square formation; thus:

The V-formation is to be preferred and the included angle of the filters should be kept to a maximum to prevent uneven air distribution. More complicated arrangements usually give such bad air distribution that the advantages of increased filter area are lost.

Generally the air flow through a filter should not be increased by more than 10 per cent of its recommended rating. Should the space available be such that the filters must be used above their normal rating, the advice of the manufacturers should be obtained.

17.5.3 Maximum Permissible Pressure Drop across the Filters

The permissible pressure drop depends on the fan characteristics and the constant losses due to heaters, humidifiers and duct work. If, for instance, the maximum pressure drop to be allowed across the filters is 1·8 mb this is the figure at which the filters must be replaced or serviced. The pressure drop across ventilation filters in the clean state is usually from 0·2 to 0·5 mb, but this is of little importance as the criterion is the life of the filter before a pressure drop of 1·8 mb is reached.

The pressure drop–dust load characteristics of the filter must also be considered; for instance, if the characteristics are as shown in Figure 17.2(d) then the advantage in having a fan capable of allowing a 2·5 mb instead of 1·8 mb pressure drop is only some few per cent increase in life. The cost of increased fan power against that saved in replacement filters must also be considered.

17.5.4 Dust Concentration

Dust concentration together with the size and nature of the dust determines the life of any filter. A useful guide[3] of the suspended matter in the air in the larger towns can be obtained from atmospheric pollution records made by the Local Authority, but this will not always be accurate for the particular installation as the variation of emission from nearby chimneys has to be taken into consideration with all frequent wind directions; measurements taken during the most frequent or prevailing wind directions are insufficient. There is no empirical formula available to give even an approximate estimate of life from the data and the experience of the filter manufacturer must be relied upon. Filters known to have a service life of several months in industrial areas have been known to clog in a few days in supposedly similar installations because the contamination presented to them is mainly tarry products from a nearby chimney.

A standard method of determining fine dust (smoke) concentration, known as the blackness test, is to filter a known quantity of air through a given area of standard filter paper[4]. The grey stain obtained is then compared visually with standard stains calibrated in mg/m^3. The result obtained is approximate as the shade of stain is affected by the size and colour of particle collected, but an indication is given of the concentration of dust which will soil furnishings, etc.

If it is required to determine the dust concentration by direct weighing, there are cellulose acetate membranes available which have extremely high collection efficiency (a suitable membrane is 'aerosol assay' or AA millipore). The membrane is weighed (approx. 50 g/m^2) to constant weight after drying at 100°C (a static eliminator must be used in the balance); a known volume of air is drawn through the membrane which is then dried and weighed. The results are not always comparable with the blackness test, as the latter method is not sensitive to larger particles; for instance, one 10 μm particle is the same weight as 1000 1 μm particles of the same specific gravity. The membrane can be made transparent by the use of oil for microscope examination of the particles.

17.5.5 Type and Particle Size Distribution of Dust

The type of dust is obtained by quantitative chemical analysis. The sample can be obtained by collection on a filter paper which can easily be dissolved or ashed away. Suitable cellulose acetate membranes of various pore size are available. The essential components of the dust are determined as follows:

    (i) Oils and tars—by Soxhlet extraction using *n*-heptane;

    (ii) Carbonaceous and vegetable debris—by ashing the residue from (i);

    (iii) Metals and mineral matter—it is not usually required to analyse these constituents other than to determine the proportions of acid solubles and insolubles.

It is also essential to determine the degree of acidity or alkalinity of the dust, if any. This will determine if any special protection of the metal parts is required, and the type of media which can be used (e.g. sulphuric acid can rapidly disintegrate cotton fabrics and caustic can reduce wool to a slime).

The determination of particle size distribution of the dust is a difficult problem owing to its fineness and tendency for agglomeration to occur under examination. The most satisfactory method is by standard microscope techniques, carrying out the analysis on a count basis[5].

The collection of samples is fully discussed by Green[2]. Collection can be made directly on to a microscope slide by a thermal precipitator[2], or by a cascade impactor[6]. The thermal precipitator causes the air to pass over a hot wire which has a cover glass on either side of it. Dust particles are brought by convection to the cover glasses. This apparatus is efficient in collecting particles smaller than 5 μm[2]. The cascade impactor (Figure 17.4) has the advantage that it partially grades the dust on to four microscope slides by

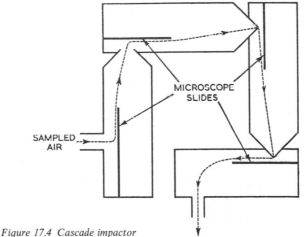

Figure 17.4 Cascade impactor

varying the impingement velocity on each slide. The slide can be made tacky by treating it with a thin film of petroleum jelly diluted with *n*-heptane; the deposits on each slide are concentrated in a rectangle.

The results are usually quoted in number of particles in a given size range per cubic metre by sampling a known volume of air. The collection of the sample and analysis is a specialized technique and requires extreme cleanliness of working. The limits of the method are determined by the resolution of the microscope used[5], the collection efficiency of the apparatus used, and the cleanliness of the technique.

17.5.6 Degree of Pollution Permissible in the Filtered Air

The specification necessary for the purified air can only be determined from a knowledge of the process and the type of contamination which it is required to remove. If protection of objects from visible dirt is required, then it can generally be accepted that, if a 'blackness' test indicates an 80 per cent efficiency of a filter, then it will take at least five times longer to obtain the same degree of dirtiness than if filters were not permitted, but if it were paintings that were being protected, then it would be very important to know, also, the sulphur dioxide and trioxide content of the air which could be tolerated. The worst conditions (e.g. smog) must always be considered as the efficiency of a filter does not increase in proportion to the dust concentration. The SO_2 content of the air can rise to more than 1000 $\mu g/m^3$ in a London smog. A high proportion of this is adsorbed on the fine smoke particles and is, therefore, reduced as these particles are filtered out. The most efficient filters for reducing this level are the absolute filters (see Section 17.12) which should have pre-filters to extend their life. If this type of filter is too expensive, then a reasonable degree of protection can be obtained with a good quality dense fibre lap filter at relatively low media velocities (0·1 to 0·15 m/s).

'Small scale tests' as described under Section 17.6.4 can be helpful in determining the permissible degree of pollution by solids and whether the best filtration economically possible overcomes the problem.

17.5.7 Temperature and Relative Humidity Variation

These data should always be made available as they can affect the range of filter materials suitable.

17.5.8 Adjustment of Humidity

It is usually necessary to adjust the moisture content of the air, this being carried out by means of a de-humidifier situated after the filter. The air is passed through fine water sprays followed by scrubber plates to remove the free moisture. The spray regulates the amount of moisture in the air by saturating it at approximately the temperature of the water; thus the air leaving the washer is always at its dew-point. In winter when the air is cold and dry the water is warmed before spraying and in summer when cooling is required the water is supplied cooled. After leaving the washer the air is heated to the required temperature, normally 13°–18°C. For further information see Faber and Kell[7].

17.6 Choice of Suitable Filters

The information obtained in Section 17.5 will enable the filter manufacturers to recommend the filters capable of meeting the requirements and the choice would be made from the following considerations.

17.6.1 Preliminary Purification or Washing

In some instances it is advantageous to give the air a preliminary cleaning by washing with a water spray. This is useful when the air inlet is adjacent to the outlet from a very dusty operation such as sand grinding or sieving where gross contamination is expected. The optimum size for removal by this method is 1 mm particles; these will collide with some particles in their path as they fall, but the majority of particles smaller than 5 μm are displaced sideways by the air movement set up by the drops[2].

17.6.2 Dry or Oil-wetted Media

Oil-wetted filters are generally free from oil carry-over but there may be reasons why they cannot be considered, such as the filters being located where people may brush against them. If both dry and oil-wetted media can be used, the choice will depend mainly on costs.

17.6.3 Space Required by Filters

The rating of various types of filters of the same size will vary and some will be eliminated due to insufficient space being available.

17.6.4 Comparison of Life and Efficiency of Proposed Filters

(i) Pilot scale tests. An extraction efficiency determination can only be accurately carried out by tests using scale models of the proposed filters in pilot investigations at the site of a new plant (Figure 17.5 gives a typical lay-out).

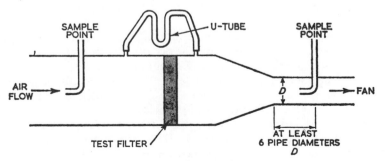

Figure 17.5 Apparatus for pilot scale tests

Scale tests must be carried out taking precautions to ensure that the model is placed at the location of the installation inlet with its inlet facing in the correct direction and with no abnormal shielding from adjacent structures. The model filter should be at least 50 cm square, but should preferably be a unit filter of the size to be used (e.g. $50 \times 50 \times 5$ cm deep) rated in proportion to that of the installation. If one of the automatic filters is to be tested, then a sample of the medium, or one of the panels, can be used.

Samples of inlet and filtered air can be taken to determine the efficiency by the blackness test. This test is carried out by sampling isokinetically and measuring the volumes of air through a filter paper to give the same density of stain upstream and downstream of the filter. The efficiency (per cent) is given by:

$$100\left(1 - \frac{\text{upstream volume}}{\text{downstream volume to give same stain density}}\right)$$

Cascade impactor samples can also be taken for determination of particle size distribution and intrinsic efficiencies.

A plot of filter pressure drop against days in operation is obtained and the life of the filter determined. The filter can be weighed at intervals but, as humidity changes can cause the weight of a fabric filter to vary by ± 10 per cent, the weighings must be carried out under carefully controlled conditions.

This method of test gives valuable comparisons between filters if the data are examined critically. It is best to test several filters at the same time and using one type of filter as a control for each group of tests.

Filter manufacturers are usually well equipped to carry out these pilot tests. Although highly desirable, it is not always practicable or convenient to conduct them.

(ii) British Standards method of test for filter media. Comparison of actual filter media can be made by laboratory tests to British Standard 2831, *Air Filters for Air Conditioning and General Ventilation*[8]. Results of these tests can be obtained from the filter manufacturer. It should be insisted that a report giving results of laboratory tests to this standard is submitted for each type of filter recommended. B.S. 2831 is the standard applicable in this country as British conditions are different from those in the United States and Europe due to the greater amount of domestic coal smoke.

This method of test determines the dust-retaining efficiency and life of the filter when dealing with three dusts described below in order of decreasing size.

Test dust No. 3; Aloxite optical powder 225. This is a fused alumina powder containing approximately 60–80 per cent by weight of particles in the 15–25 μm band (Figure 17.6). It is a smooth penetrating dust which represents the coarser fraction of particles present in atmospheric pollution.

Test dust No. 2; Aloxite optical powder 50. This is a fused alumina powder containing 60–80 per cent by weight of particles in the 3·5–7 μm band. This represents the dust in the air which constitutes the greatest health hazard.

Test dust No. 1; methylene blue smoke. This is produced by atomizing a 1 per cent solution of methylene blue dye into the air stream to the filter. The water evaporates from this spray leaving particles which vary in size

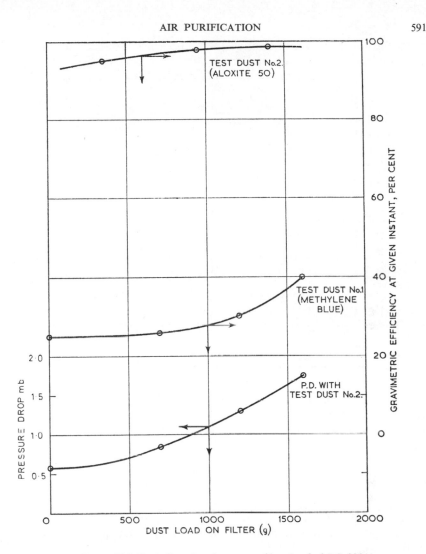

Figure 17.6 Typical results of tests on a filter (method B.S. 2831)

from 1 μm to less than 0·1 μm and has a mean size by weight of 0·5 μm. This represents the smoke and smog of the atmosphere. It is a very useful dust as it can be produced consistently to size and the efficiency of a filter can be determined accurately by the stain technique described in B.S. 2831.

The tests are carried out with dusts 2 and 3 separately, determining efficiencies against methylene blue at various stages of dust loading in each test. The efficiencies against dusts 2 and 3 are determined by gravimetric means, and the pressure drop across the filter is recorded against dust load. Figure 17.7 shows graphically the general type of results obtained. Although it is not part of the above specification, the efficiency and dust loading characteristics of a filter against a carbon black dust gives useful information. Filters generally take a far greater dust load of the two aloxite powders than would be obtained against atmospheric pollution and carbon black gives a more realistic figure. Unfortunately it is a dust which is difficult to disperse in air and efficiencies determined are sometimes high due to agglomeration.

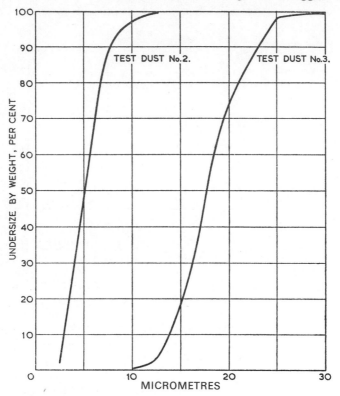

Figure 17.7 Particle size distribution of B.S. 2831 test dusts No. 2 and No. 3. Typical analysis by Andreason pipette method

It must be remembered when interpreting these results that the tests are carried out over a few days using dust concentrations many times greater than would be encountered in practice and the tests are for comparison purposes only.

17.6.5 Costing

The costing of the system on the basis of the complete filter installation must take into account the following:

(i) Initial expenditure
    (a) cost of filter-locating frames;
    (b) cost of filters;
    (c) cost of any auxiliary equipment to the filters such as electrical connections, compressed air;
    (d) cost of cleaning equipment;
    (e) cost of re-oiling equipment; and
    (f) labour costs of erection.

(ii) Operating costs. Operating costs should be considered on a yearly basis and assumptions will have to be made regarding life of filters.

(a) Cost of replacement filters or replacement media refills if filters are of throwaway type. Labour costs in replacing.

(b) Cost of servicing filters if applicable. This includes cost of operating cleaning equipment, cost of cleaning solvents used, oil for re-oiling, labour involved in removing, servicing and replacing filters. If an automatic self-cleaning filter is used, the cost of de-sludging, oil for topping up and oil replacement must be considered.

(c) Even if the filter is of the completely cleanable type allowance must be made for depreciation by assuming the time at which the filter would have to be replaced due to normal wear and tear.

17.7 Design of Installation

A typical layout of a filter installation is shown diagrammatically in Figure 17.8.

The filters are normally placed on the suction side of the fan as this often reduces the cost of ductwork, protects the fan from dirt and assists in obtaining

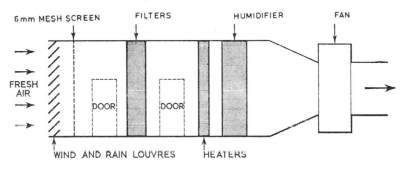

Figure 17.8 Layout of air-conditioning system

even air distribution. Advantages in placing the filters on the pressure side of the fan are:

   (i) any leakage on the clean side of the filters is outwards, permitting clean air leaks rather than ingress of dirty air;

  (ii) dust from corrosion and scaling in the fan and duct is filtered;

 (iii) the filter has a silencing effect on air and fan noises.

Placing the air intake as high above ground level as possible will reduce the inlet concentration of larger particles and dust disturbed from ground level. It must also be placed so that the inlet is not in direct line with contamination from nearby chimneys or other sources of air pollution. Louvres should be placed at the inlet to prevent rain from entering, and shield it from wind. Wire mesh should be fitted to the inlet to prevent birds and mice entering; filter breakdowns due to media being removed by mice or punctured by birds eating the insects collected are not unusual. Heaters should not be placed too near to the filter interlock as damage can be caused if the fan is shut down and the heaters are left operating when there is no interlock.

Precautions must be taken to ensure efficient sealing at all points, employing cork, rubber or other suitable jointing materials at all connections and access doors, all of which should be placed on the pressure side of the duct wall to assist sealing. The header surface to which the filters seal should be flat and of sufficient strength with welds filled level. If double skin ducting with insulating material is used, checks must be made that the insulant cannot leak into the air stream. Filters should be in a vertical place with fins vertical, as vibration can cause sieving of collected dust through the medium if they are placed in a horizontal place.

All ductwork must be protected from corrosion and from flaking as the object of filters is defeated if dust is emitted from ductwork downstream of the filter.

If the filters are not placed in line with the inlet, they should be placed as far from any bends as possible, as uneven air distribution will cause over-rating of some filters, lowering the efficiency of the installation. Baffles or vanes to make the air flow uniform may be required. Recirculation of the air is often permissible and this can increase filter life; it is often possible to re-circulate 50 per cent of the air[8]. It is important to allow sufficient space and illumination in front and behind the filters for inspection and removal. A pressure differential gauge should be fitted in order that the time to service the filters is indicated. Warning devices are available which are operated at a given pressure loss across the filters.

If the air has to pass through long lengths of duct before being discharged into the room, agglomeration of the fine particles passing the filter can occur. It is an advantage, though it may not be considered economical, to fit secondary filters at the outlets in place of the normal grill. These filters should give long service as they are only dealing with contamination which has passed the inlet filters together with that emenating from the duct.

A proportion of the extract air from offices and workshops can often be re-circulated provided that this air does not contain any toxic contamination from the processes which could harm the occupants or poison the process; for instance, in drug manufacture or mushroom cultivation. The recirculated air must be discharged into the ducting before the filters where it will mix with the fresh air intake. The air for recirculation should be taken from the cleaner parts of the workshop.

Recirculation will save filter costs by increasing filter life in dirty industrial districts and will also save heating and humidity control costs. The amount of air which can be recirculated varies with different applications and local regulations often apply. An approximate figure is that there should be 17–21 m^3 of fresh air per hour for each occupant.

17.8 Supervision During Plant Construction

Careful supervision is required during erection of the plant to ensure cleanliness of flues and tight joints as mentioned in the previous section. It is not uncommon for filters to be fitted before the ductwork has been completed and cleaned with the result that they become clogged with builder's debris, etc., and damaged before any air has been drawn through them.

Special supervision during the fitting of the filters is essential. All filters should fit comfortably into their locating frames and should be visually checked for badly fitting seals.

17.9 Advice on Operating Plant

17.9.1 Initial Checks

Before the plant is commissioned check tests should be carried out as follows:

(i) Tests for even air distribution should be made over the whole filter surface with an anemometer. If any points of high velocity are found, the filter manufacturers should be consulted to ascertain whether the over-rating can be tolerated; if not, air distribution baffles must be fitted.

(ii) Some efficiency check should be made. The simplest method is to employ the blackness test previously described. Samples should be taken isokinetically on the upstream side of the filters near the centre of the duct, also immediately downstream of the filters and near the outlet grills.

Samples can also be taken on sticky plates in the same positions for microscope examination if required.

(iii) If there is any doubt about the effectiveness of the installation the seals should be re-checked for compression. Leaks can often be detected by means of a pencil beam of light directed at right-angles to the surface. If one filter is suspect, seal off the face of each of the eight surrounding filters and detect leaks with suitable smoke.

17.9.2 Routine Checks

The pressure drop across the filters should be checked daily at least for the first month and thereafter weekly so that if any unusual rise in pressure loss is recorded an attempt to locate the cause can be made immediately. Inspection of the installation should also be made and, if required, further blackness tests can be carried out as the filters become dust-laden.

When the filters require replacing, or servicing, it is recommended that this is carried out *en bloc* if possible. The system of changing only a proportion of the installation at one time is not to be recommended since uneven air distribution is thereby obtained. If the filters are of the cleanable type they should be examined for damage to the media and seals.

17.10 Troubles Encountered in Operation

The causes of troubles, e.g. apparent loss of efficiency or rapid clogging of the filters, are sometimes difficult to trace, and the following advice can be offered only as a guide.

17.10.1 Apparent Loss of Efficiency

(i) Examine filters and seals *in situ* to determine if any signs of damage are visible. This should also be carried out from the clean side, as signs of excessive leakage are sometimes shown by dust deposits at leakage points.

(ii) Remove some filters for closer examination especially round the filter frames, i.e. ends of fins. Rubber seals can harden and even disintegrate under certain conditions; for example, ozone will accelerate breakdown as will excessive heat.

(iii) If the filters appear satisfactory examine equipment and ductwork downstream of filters for signs of flaking. Dust which normally passes the filters can collect on duct walls or heaters and then shed in larger pieces.

(iv) Excessive vibration, due to wear of fan bearings, can cause lowering of filter efficiency and this vibration has been known to fatigue supporting wire which can puncture or tear filter media.

(v) Examine ductwork and joints for leakage.

(vi) Check air velocity distribution over filter face with pitot tube or anemometer.

(vii) Carry out efficiency checks as shown in Section 17.6.4. If the efficiency checks with that found on commissioning the plant, it may be that higher dust concentrations are being presented to the filter due to additional factories in the vicinity. Although the filter efficiency may be up to standard, if double the normal dust concentration is present upstream, then an increased dust concentration would be expected downstream.

17.10.2 Rapid Clogging of Filters

Clogging of filters may be caused by:

(i) a small increase in the concentration of tarry particles (which need not be much) or might arise, for instance, from a new process which emitted tarry by-products into the airstream;

(ii) high humidity conditions due to inefficient rain louvres, or a breakdown of a humidifier placed before the filter. These changes in conditions can cause a rapid rise in pressure drop; or

(iii) chemical reaction of acidic components of the dirty air on some parts of the dust with other collected dust; this also can cause rapid blockage.

In factories where there are no facilities for examination of the filters, a few sections should be sent to the manufacturer of the filter plant. They should be carefully packed in plastics bags to ensure that the dust is disturbed as little as possible. Physical and chemical analysis of the dust deposits can often reveal causes of failure. If no explanation is discovered, fitting of replacement or serviced filters will determine if the failure was an isolated case.

II AIR PURIFICATION FOR FACTORIES WHERE ABSENCE OF DUST IS ESSENTIAL

17.11 Introduction

There is an increasing number of factory operations in which complete freedom from dust and often from bacteria is required. Examples are assembly of fine engineering or electrical components, processing of beryllium metal, and the manufacture of photographic film, and biological products such as penicillin.

The production of such clean air is not easy and to obtain near absolute filtration of the air and maintain it in that condition requires most careful installation and operation. The method of obtaining these conditions is discussed in the following sections and the requirements of the user must be considered in deciding the extent to which these recommendations must be employed.

17.12 Types of Filter

The filters developed for these applications depend for their efficiency on the use of fine fibres. Asbestos is a material which can be split longitudinally a very considerable number of times to produce fibres with diameters of a few microns. Filters of the absolute type were originally made by mixing asbestos fibre with wool or cotton in pack form to give depth filtration. Wool coated with frictionally electrified resin particles has also been used; the electrical charges by friction with the air stream are claimed to assist filtration[2].

The filters described above were very large compared with their air-flow capacities and have generally been replaced by special papers manufactured from fine fibres. These papers are manufactured from asbestos fibres mixed with cotton to give an open network of fine fibres and improve the strength of the paper. There are also available papers made of specially prepared fine glass fibres which may have diameters even less than one micron; these fine fibres are mixed with coarser glass fibres for strength. Such filters are made up in crimped V-form to give increased filtration area. Filters 30 cm deep are generally rated at an air velocity of 1·2 m/s and have a pressure drop of about 2·5 mb. For detailed design, see Reference 12.27. The type of asbestos used must not cause lung damage.

17.13 Design of Installations for Fine Filtration

The design of an installation to maintain a room as free as possible from atmospheric pollution requires not only the most efficient filters available, but precautions to prevent contamination being carried into the room by personnel or materials.

17.13.1 Choice of Filter

The filters available for this application must be manufactured to a special high standard and this standard must be proved for each individual filter. The filter medium is usually sealed into its frame by an adhesive, and for effectiveness this sealing must be leakproof as must that of the seals (sponge rubber) of the filter frame to the header plate (Figure 17.9). The method of proof is to test the filters against a methylene-blue cloud as previously described, or by a sodium chloride test cloud[11] Both clouds have a mean particle size of approximately 0·5 μm, and a given filter shows similar efficiency whichever test is used. Filters are available which give penetrations of 0·01 per cent and less of such particles.

When ordering these filters it should be insisted that these proving tests are carried out on every filter in a *closed* duct so that any leakage at the rubber seal is detected. It must also be specified that the filter medium must not shed its fibres.

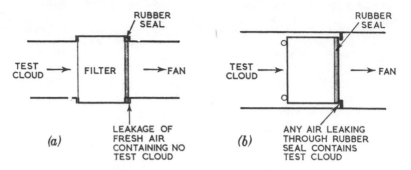

Figure 17.9 Superiority of closed duct method of testing filter units. (a) Open duct; (b) closed duct

Obviously these filters are expensive and since they are not cleanable, their life is prolonged by addition of a pre-filter to take the bulk of the dust load. Any of the range described previously can be used—a good quality felt or cotton wadding filter is suitable.

17.13.2 Layout

A typical arrangement for a filter installation protecting a room used for assembling engineering components under clean conditions is shown in Figure 17.10. The important points in the arrangement are:

(i) The filter must be placed on the pressure side of the fan and the room must be maintained under a slight pressure to prevent leakage of uncleaned air into the room.

(ii) The filters should be placed at the air entry grills to the room. It is useless to filter the air immediately downstream of the fan and allow the clean air to pass through heaters, humidifiers and ductwork, which can erode and contaminate the air with large particles.

(iii) The filter housings must be designed so that the filters may be easily inserted without damaging the filter medium or sealing rubber. The method of compressing the rubber seals to the housing header plates must be positive to eliminate leaks, but the compression must not be too high, or filter distortion can crack the adhesive, giving rise to leakage. The filters must be handled with great care as the filter medium is easily damaged.

(iv) The air-lock between the changing room and the clean room must also be pressurized by air of the same standard of cleanliness as in the clean room, so that, on opening the door to the changing room clean air is blown out, and on opening the door to the clean room air goes from the clean room to the air-lock. A delay period must be allowed after entering the air-lock from the changing room before opening the door to the clean room.

(v) If any hatches for transfer of components into and out of the room have to be provided, an air-lock should be included.

(vi) The life of the filters is increased by recirculating part of the air back through the filters together with a make-up of fresh air. The amount of make-up air should be 15–20 per cent of the total air flow in order to maintain air freshness and the pressure in the system (see Section 17.7).

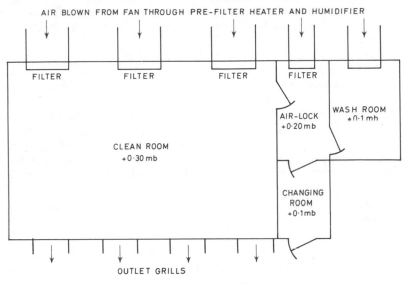

Figure 17.10 Clean-room layout

(vii) To carry away dust build-up in the room, the number of air changes per hour should be high; at least thirty is recommended.

(viii) To maintain the high standard of cleanliness provided by the filters all precuations must be taken to prevent contamination of the air by the workers. Clothing outfits that include complete coverage of the hair and shoes should be put on in the changing room. Clothes should be made of nylon, Terylene or similar material to keep fibre emission to a minimum. After dressing the clothes should be vacuum-cleaned; face powders must not be used; toilets should be provided adjacent to the changing room.

17.14 Installation and Operation of the Plant

All ductwork must be thoroughly cleaned before the installation of the filters, and the rooms vacuum cleaned. The plant should be operated for several days to flush the system. A check should then be carried out, before the room is put into use, to determine the level of contamination in the room.

The dust concentration immediately downstream of the filters should be determined by means of a cascade impactor or thermal precipitator, sampling near all the inlet grills. All slides must be carefully cleaned beforehand, cleaned again in the clean room, and examined under the microscope to ensure they are not contaminated. The sampling equipment must be perfectly clean. As there should be very little contamination in the air, sampling will have to be carried out over an extended period; at least 500 litres of air should be sampled. The slides must be carefully covered immediately after collection of the sample and put in sealed containers. Care must also be taken that there is no contamination during counting; this should preferably be carried out in the clean room.

Further samples should be taken at various positions in the room, and results compared in order to determine if the dust concentration at bench level or in assembly cabinets is increased due to any sources of contamination within the room.

To determine the amount of dust which can settle on the working surface, perfectly clean settling trays, such as Petri dishes, should be placed to collect any contamination. They should be left in position for several days for an accurate determination.

The above tests should then be carried out under production conditions to determine the contamination which is not caused by penetration through the filters. Generation of dust will probably be the cause of the greatest contamination, particularly of large particles, and a high velocity of the air through the assembly cabinets will have to be used to prevent these particles from settling on to the components.

17.15 Routine Checks

Settling trays should be maintained in position at assembly points at all times and should be frequently examined under the microscope. Samples of the air in the workroom can be taken quickly by means of the cascade impactor and examined for particles above the critical size. Materials passed into the room should be examined to ensure that they have been properly cleaned.

The above installation has been described primarily for providing clean air for assembly of components. Operations which may produce dust should be carried out under very high velocity hoods.

17.16 Procedure When Sterile Conditions are Necessary

The filters recommended for the above processes are highly efficient against bacteria, and should this be the requirement, sampling techniques can be adapted and determinations of the efficiency of the installation made by cultivation of the bacteria in the samples.

PART B GAS ABSORBENTS FOR BREATHING APPARATUS AND RESPIRATORS

P. E. LOVERING

17.17 Introduction

Attempts to protect the individual by the prevention of inhalation of toxic gases probably originated when men were first called upon to control outbreaks of fire. Little real progress was made until the latter half of the eighteenth century, and even then development was slow until industrial progress in the nineteenth century made many protective devices essential. By the end of the nineteenth century the gas absorbents in use were, in principle, very similar to those in use today.

Early respirators were simply mechanical filters, capable of removing solids and liquids (dust and mists) from the atmosphere being breathed, providing no protection against gases and vapours. By 1825 the first attempt at chemical absorption had been recorded, when Robertson used a sponge impregnated with an alkaline solution for protection against acid gases. The use of charcoal as an adsorbent was reported in the 1850s by several workers, and of course activated charcoal is still one of the principal components in canister respirator filters.

Prior to World War I, respirators were mostly used for fire-fighting and rescue work. In these fields composition and concentration of toxic gases were usually unknown, so the emphasis was on self-contained or supplied-air breathing apparatus. The introduction of gas warfare in World War I necessitated the provision of an efficient, yet light and simple, respirator for the protection of troops. The result was the forerunner of the modern filter box, or canister, respirator used today. The respirator provided both eye and respiratory protection against all the toxic gases which were at that time used in warfare.

The success of the canister respirator in war led to its widespread use in industry in subsequent years. It was soon possible to provide protection against low but highly toxic concentrations of almost any poisonous gas, vapour, particulate smoke or dust likely to occur in a factory atmosphere. Because of its versatility, users often over-estimate the capabilities of the canister respirator, and tend to overlook its limitations. For example, the canister respirator is often considered suitable for emergency fire-fighting where the hazards are often unknown, gas and vapour concentrations can be high, and the oxygen content of the atmosphere may fall to a dangerously low level. These respirators should not be used if the gas concentration is likely to exceed 1 per cent by volume, since the service life will be short. The presence of such a concentration often indicates inadequate ventilation with the consequent possibility of a shortage of oxygen in the atmosphere. Testing authorities universally require a clear notice regarding these limitations to be fixed to every canister, for example canisters approved by the Department of Employment in the United Kingdom[9] carry the following notice:

'Suitable for use in the following gases in air . . . BUT ONLY IN LOW CONCENTRATIONS.
This respirator must *not* be used in any other gas, in any place where there may be a shortage of oxygen, or in stills, tanks, or other enclosed spaces.'

'When in doubt, do not use a canister' should be a maxim for all respirator users. Fire brigades, mines and other rescue teams always use self-contained or supplied-air breathing apparatus.

17.18 General Requirements

The essential requirement for an absorbent used in a respirator canister is that it should completely remove toxic material from the air passing through it for as long as possible. In order that the men wearing the respirator can carry on their work unimpaired, dimensions and weight must be kept as small as possible, and the respiratory effort required to breathe through the canister must be negligible. This necessitates the use of absorbents of high activity, capacity, and retentivity, produced in such a form that the pressure drop (resistance) across the canister is as low as possible.

Different testing authorities throughout the world have different requirements for the absorption capacity and breathing resistance of respirator assemblies, but the following British requirements may be taken as typical (B.S. 2091):[10]

Canister (i) The filled canister shall be tested under water to withstand an internal air pressure of 140 mb.

(ii) Every canister shall be capable of passing an absorption test as specified. The test gas, when present in the specified volume concentration in air (usually 1 per cent), shall be completely absorbed during the period of time laid down (usually 30 min), with a continuous aspiration of 16 litres/min.

(iii) Canisters containing particulate filters shall be capable of passing a particulate penetration test. When submitted to either the Sodium Chloride Particulate Test described in B.S. 4400:1969[11] or the Methylene Blue Particulate Test described in B.S. 2577:1955[12] the penetration shall not exceed 0·25 per cent.

Assembled Respirator. The assembled respirator shall have a resistance to inhalation not exceeding 10 mb at an air flow of 85 litres/min.

By using carefully size-graded granular absorbents, the resistance requirement was fairly easily achieved, and the principal problem was to develop materials with the necessary absorption properties which were mechanically strong so that they do not break up or dust either in use or transport.

Although the test concentration for most canisters is 1 per cent by volume, such a concentration is rarely encountered in practice. Usually the service life of a canister is well over 30 min (a rough estimate can be obtained by relating the average gas concentration expected with the test life of 30 min in a volume concentration of 1 per cent), and this raises the question of detection of approaching failure. Most toxic gases and vapours are readily detected by odour and as the initial leakage when a respirator canister is saturated is very small, little risk is involved in relying on this method of deciding when a canister is exhausted. There are, however, several important exceptions, for example, hydrogen sulphide and hydrogen cyanide. Although both have characteristic odours, the sensory response is not proportional to concentration, making subjective evaluation dangerous. Windows may be fitted to absorbent canisters for these gases through which a layer of indicator material is visible. Distinctive colour changes occur when the gas front reaches the indicator, which is usually placed about two-thirds of the way up the canister, so giving the user an ample safety margin. In addition to the two gases discussed 'indicator' canisters have been made for acid gases generally and for carbon monoxide. The latter will be discussed in more detail in the section dealing with carbon monoxide absorption.

The particle size of dust clouds occurring in industrial atmospheres varies considerably with local conditions, but it has been established that unless particles are less than 10 μm diameter they are not dangerous and are called 'nuisance dusts', for which simple filters, such as cotton wool and gauze pads, are adequate protection. Particles less than 10 μm diameter are inhalable, but few above 5 μm reach the alveoli of the lungs. Maximal deposition of particles between 0·8 and 1·6 μm diameter occurs in the fine bronchioles and alveoli, and these are the most dangerous. About 80 per cent of particles 0·2–0·3 μm diameter are exhaled again[2]. The sodium chloride[11] and methylene blue[12] tests were, therefore, designed so that the particles used were in the dangerous particle size range. They have a mass median diameter of about 0·5 μm; all are less than 1·5 μm diameter.

17.19 Types of Absorbent

The absorptive materials may be divided into two main groups: (a) *adsorbents*, in which the toxic gas or vapour is physically held on the surfaces of, or condensed in, the ultramicroscopic capillaries characteristic of this type of material, and (b) *chemical absorbents*, with which the toxic material reacts, producing a stable non-volatile compound which is permanently held in the absorbent bed.

In the special case of carbon monoxide neither of the above methods are commonly used, although chemical absorbents for the gas are well known, the usual practice being to oxidize carbon monoxide to relatively harmless carbon dioxide catalytically.

17.19.1 Physical Adsorbents

Charcoal was one of the earliest adsorbents used, and in a highly activated form is still the most widely used material for respirator canisters. Vegetable charcoal was first used for chemical purification work, but for many purposes it was superseded by bone charcoal in the early nineteenth century. Bone charcoal has a relatively low adsorptive capacity for gases, and investigations as long as a century ago showed that the better sources of vegetable charcoal for gas purification were the hard woods, and that nutshell charcoal was the best. The coconut shell is still widely used as a source of respirator charcoal, though a number of alternative sources have been developed (see also Chapter 9).

Commercial activated charcoals may vary widely in porosity, density, hardness, strength, and adsorbing ability. Table 17.1 gives an indication of the variation which occurs with different woods[13].

With the greatly increased demand for respiratory protection in more recent years, much work has been carried out in the development of alternative sources of activated charcoal and the following raw materials have been used[14]:

Bituminous coal   Coconut fines–coal mixtures
Compressed wood briquettes   Coal–nutshell–sawdust
Apricot stones   Pecan shells
Walnut shells   Wood charcoal
Coconut shells

Table 17.1 ADSORPTION OF GASES BY
CHARCOAL FROM DIFFERENT WOODS

Wood	Volumes of gas per volume of charcoal		
	NH_3	CO_2	$(CN)_2$
Ebony	107	47	90
Boxwood	86	31	29
Beech	58		
Vegetable ivory		50	57
Coconut shell	176	71	114

For modern respirator charcoals steam activation is usually adopted, though chemical activation has been used[15]. The steps of manufacture are:
(a) Preliminary crushing and sizing.
(b) Intermediate temperature devolatilization and carbonization in a closed retort at about 600°C.
(c) High temperature activation in steam at 800°–1000°C.
(d) Final screening.
British respirator charcoals are produced either from coal or coconut shells. The initial stages with the former are pulverizing to pass 75 μm B.S. sieve followed by briquetting and granulation, while with the latter only preliminary crushing and sizing are necessary. A common method in Germany is to use beech charcoal, produced by destructive distillation, followed by pulverization to pass 75 μm B.S. sieve, mixing with tar (obtained during the destructive distillation), and extrusion into spaghetti-like rods. The rods are then carbonized, activated and cut up into short lengths to give what is effectively a granular product.

The above production methods aim at the ideal respirator charcoal which should have maximum adsorption capacity per unit volume, rather than per unit weight[16]. This means that the largest mass of active charcoal must be contained in unit space consistent with free access or passageway to all the particles in the mass. In other words, the charcoal must not be too dense or its permeability is destroyed, and it must not be porous to the extent of needlessly sacrificing adsorbent material. If the density falls below a critical value, the charcoal begins to lose its absorbent capacity per unit volume. The best gas adsorbent charcoal is relatively dense, for instance a good coconut shell charcoal has an apparent density of about 660 kg/m³. Adsorptive efficiency has often been determined in terms of vapour pressure, obtained by dynamic methods of measurement, but for respirator charcoals empirical methods have been developed. A British method commonly used involves the passage of a standard concentration of carbon tetrachloride vapour through a bed of charcoal at a fixed velocity. The test is continued until the first detectable leak of vapour through the charcoal occurs, and the 'volume activity' of the charcoal is calculated in terms of the weight of vapour adsorbed per unit volume of adsorbent.

Theoretically the ideal respirator charcoal should be dry to achieve maximum adsorptive capacity, but in practice it is found advantageous to have a fairly high moisture content. Activated charcoal does not selectively adsorb water vapour, the tendency being for many organic vapours to displace adsorbed moisture. This minimizes the effects of heat of adsorption, since they are about equal to the heat required to vaporize the water previously adsorbed.

Low volatility gases and vapours are adequately adsorbed by charcoal as activated, indeed it has been stated that it will effectively adsorb all gases of molecular weight above 50. There are, however, some exceptions, including the low boiling-point halogenated hydrocarbons, and cyanogen chloride. Impregnation with piperidine, pyridine, or hexamethylene tetramine (hexamine) brought about a considerable improvement in these cases. (The use of impregnated charcoals is increasing; other impregnants will be discussed in the following section on chemical absorbents.)

Although charcoal apparently has a high adsorptive capacity for ammonia, respirator charcoals are not very effective, and for many years chemical absorbents were used for this gas. Improvements in the quality of silica gel led to its use for adsorption of ammonia in respirator canisters. Silica gel selectively adsorbs water vapour, which assists in the retention of ammonia, because after initial adsorption the ammonia dissolves in the water already present in the capillaries of the gel. With charcoal, where desorption of water vapour occurs, some ammonia is probably carried into the effluent gas stream by desorbed moisture, so explaining its inefficiency as a 'dynamic' adsorbent.

Impregnation with a copper salt enhances the efficiency of the silica gel, assisting retentivity by the formation of complexes, which is the principle underlying some chemical absorbents for ammonia.

17.19.2 Chemical Absorbents

A variety of alkaline materials are used for the removal of acidic gases from the atmosphere, and these are widely used in both canister respirators and self-contained breathing apparatus. Although activated charcoal adsorbents are effective, in several cases complete removal of the toxic gas is not possible and a common solution is to use a canister filled with a mixture of activated charcoal and alkaline granules.

Caustic alkalis in pea or stick form have been used, particularly for the removal of carbon dioxide from the gases in a closed circuit self-contained breathing apparatus, and indeed are still used by some manufacturers. The majority of breathing apparatus in use today uses a non-hygroscopic alkaline absorbent of the soda-lime type for carbon dioxide removal. Hydrated lime is usually the basic ingredient, to which is added caustic alkali (soda-lime) barium hydroxide ('Baralyme') and Portland cement in appropriate proportions. The last named type has proved most useful for canister respirators because of its stability, being active at the equilibrium moisture content and virtually unaffected by contact with the air. Both soda-lime and baryta-lime are active only if the moisture content is carefully controlled at a level above the equilibrium figure, so canisters filled with these materials must be kept sealed when not in use. Baryta-lime also carbonates readily in moist air, tending to powder, which may cause clogging of the filter and consequently loss of efficiency by increasing breathing resistance.

The addition of Portland cement to hydrated lime provides an effective binding agent to give it mechanical strength, provides a porous structure, and on setting releases more calcium hydroxide which enhances the alkalinity. Activated charcoal is often added in powder form further to increase porosity and hence activity.

Some acid gases, notably nitrous fumes, are not removed effectively by adsorption or by conventional alkaline absorbents, but the addition of an oxidizing agent such as potassium permanganate considerably improves performance.

Hydrogen cyanide is not efficiently absorbed by the lime–cement type of granular material, and the usual practice is to use either soda-lime or baryta-lime. Recently activated charcoal impregnated with copper as oxide or sulphide has been used for the absorption of hydrogen cyanide[14], but the general practice is still to use the well-tried alkaline materials. Impregnation of charcoal with zinc salts has also been reported as being effective.

Chemical oxidation has been used for the removal of carbon monoxide by canister respirators, the well-known iodine pentoxide oleum reagent ('Hoolamite') being used, but the obvious disadvantages of its cost, corrosive nature, and the need to adsorb the released iodine prevented its commercial development. Some attempts have been made to use non-corrosive chemical oxidants for carbon monoxide. Higher silver oxides, supported on an inert material like asbestos[17] and silver permanganate, supported on inert oxide mixtures[18,19] have been used. These are effective, but suffer commercially because of their high cost.

17.19.3 Catalysts

Some impregnated activated charcoals catalytically assist the absorption of arsine, the impregnant being either a zinc or silver salt (the latter is preferred in the United Kingdom).

Carbon monoxide is one of the commonest toxic gases, and consequently one of the most dangerous, but until the discovery during World War I of the oxide mixtures which catalyse its oxidation to carbon dioxide at ordinary temperatures, satisfactory canister respirator absorbents were not available commercially.

These oxide mixtures are known by the general name of 'Hopcalite', the original preparation being:

manganese dioxide (MnO_2)	50%
copper oxide (CuO)	30%
cobalt oxide (Co_2O_3)	15%
silver oxide (Ag_2O)	5%

Various compositions have since been used, the most widely known being MnO_2 60 per cent, CuO 40 per cent, with small additions of cobalt or silver oxides. Methods of manufacture vary considerably with the source.

All Hopcalites suffer from the defect common to catalysts in that they are readily poisoned, particularly by water vapour, which is always present in the air to a greater or lesser extent. This necessitates the provision of an efficient drying agent in the canister to protect the Hopcalite catalyst. Many organic vapours, acid gases, and ammonia also tend to poison Hopcalite so the usual practice is to produce an 'all service' canister which contains absorbents to remove these contaminants as well as water vapour.

It is generally accepted that respirator canisters for carbon monoxide should not be expected to remove more than 1 per cent by volume of the gas. As is well known, the oxidation product is carbon dioxide, and while this gas is relatively harmless, toxic effects occur if high concentrations are breathed for long periods; even 1 per cent is likely to produce a headache after two hours, the rated life of a British 'all service' canister. It must be remembered that the protection afforded against carbon monoxide is controlled not by the concentration of gas, but by the 'life' of the drying agent. In high humidity conditions, this will become exhausted in 2 or 3 h, hence the instruction to discard such canisters after 2 h total usage, whatever the atmospheric conditions. Approaching failure may be detected by the incorporation of a small window through which a humidity indicator can be seen (a cobalt salt on silica gel may be used), the colour change occurring as the drying agent becomes exhausted. Other methods used include the incorporation of a compound which produces a distinctive odour on contact with water, e.g. calcium carbide, breath-counting devices and timers.

PART C PURIFICATION OF THE ATMOSPHERE IN NUCLEAR-POWERED SUBMARINES

G. NONHEBEL

17.20 Introduction

To secure conditions of habitability during a prolonged underwater cruise of a nuclear-powered submarine is a problem of air purification which was demonstrably solved by the 60-day cruise of U.S.S. *Seawolf* in 1959. It is now required to keep the air sweet for up to a year. Some make-up of oxygen from cylinders or electrolytic generators is necessary to replace oxygen converted to water vapour by the human body. An excellent account of the chemical engineering research involved was published in 1952[20]. In the following description of the types of plant installed, it will be found that use has been made of many of the processes described in this book. It will be seen that considerable chemical engineering skill is required to maintain the purification systems in the perfect conditions required for long underwater journeys.

There are two important considerations in the design of the air purification plant:

(i) Space is very limited, though ample power is available.

(ii) Since not all the air can be purified instantaneously, the limiting concentration of undesirable compounds will depend on both the rates of production and removal and on the distribution throughout the ship between the production and removal points. The limits of concentration that can be lived with and the limits of air purification required are problems which have to be solved by experiment and, in the last resort, the submarine itself is the best laboratory for proving the success of the techniques.

17.21 Impurities in Submarine Atmospheres

The removal of carbon dioxide arising from human exhalation is relatively simple. It is required to maintain its concentration below 1 per cent though it is possible to operate for short periods with concentrations as high as 5 per cent. Smoking must be allowed and hence both carbon monoxide and particulate matter must be removed. The space is confined and there may be 100 men in an air volume of only 2400 m^3. Other serious contaminants are trace quantities of organic compounds from cooking, from the body odours, from the breakdown of lubricants, from paints and cleaning solvents.

Table 17.2 given a list of compounds which have been quantitatively identified in submarine atmospheres using the techniques of gas chromatography and infra-red and mass spectroscopy to back specific chemical

Table 17.2 COMPOUNDS QUANTITATIVELY IDENTIFIED IN SUBMARINE ATMOSPHERES

Material	Chemical formula	Type of submarine (F = fleet; N = nuclear)	Highest concentration normally found	Maximum acceptable volume concentration in p.p.m. (ACGIH)*
Acetylene	C_2H_2	N	0·5 p.p.m.	—
Ammonia	NH_3	N	>1 p.p.m.	100
Carbon dioxide	CO_2	F,N	1·1%	5000
Carbon monoxide	CO	F,N	38 p.p.m.	100
Chlorine	Cl_2	F,N	1 p.p.m.	1
Freon-12	CCl_2F_2	F,N	70 p.p.m.	1000
'Hydrocarbons' (other than CH_4)	'HC'	F,N	25 p.p.m.	—
Hydrogen fluoride	HF	N	0·3 p.p.m.	3
Hydrogen	H_2	F,N	1·75%	—
Methane	CH_4	F,N	118 p.p.m.	—
Methyl alcohol	CH_3OH	N	6 p.p.m.	200
Monoethanolamine	$HOCH_2$ CH_2NH_2	N	<1 p.p.m.	—
Nitrogen	N_2	F,N	80%	—
Nitrogen dioxide	NO_2	N	0·1 p.p.m.	5
Nitrous oxide	N_2O	N	27 p.p.m.	—
Oxygen	O_2	F,N	20%	—
Stibine	SbH_3	F,N	1 p.p.m.	0·1
Water vapour	H_2O	F,N	60% R.H.	—
'Cigarette smoke'	—	F,N	0·4 μg/l	—

*MAC either not applicable or not established for materials listed with a dash in this column. ACGHI = American Conference of Government Industrial Hygienists.

tests. Monitoring instruments for specific types of chemicals are, however, less sensitive to a few compounds than human eyes, noses, etc.

The atmosphere is maintained at 21°C and 50 per cent relative humidity. Aromatic compounds, which are more toxic than aliphatic, amount to about 50 per cent of the hydrocarbons. One source is mineral cleaning fluids, but during early cruises the largest source was traced to oil-based paints which were found to give off traces of hydrocarbons for many weeks after application. This trouble was eliminated by use of water-based PVA paints; these lose 95 per cent of their volatile components one hour after application. It is of interest to note that, for psychological reasons, these submarines are redecorated internally after every voyage.

Investigation under operating conditions quickly showed that minute traces of very objectionable compounds were formed as a result of incomplete combustion of some of the main air contaminants when they were passed through the catalytic burner designed primarily to remove carbon monoxide. These organic nitrogen compounds, and ammonia derived from decomposition of monoethanolamine, give traces of toxic oxides of nitrogen. Freon, from small leaks from refrigeration systems, gave traces of hydrogen fluoride and hydrogen chloride (which, however, were reduced by incorporating lithium hydroxide or marble chips in the catalyst bed). A special Freon leak detector had, however, to be designed. Methanol, derived from fluids used in duplicating machines, gave traces of formaldehyde sufficient in concentration to be lachrymatory; replacement of methanol by ethanol was indicated. Triaryl phosphates present in hydraulic fluids at 275 bar are a potential danger because of their extreme toxicity. The maximum allowable concentration is 0·06 p.p.m. for 90 days exposure.

The equilibrium concentration of cigarette smoke, namely 0·4 μg/l, maintained by the electrostatic precipitator, is about 75 per cent of the total aerosol content of the atmosphere.

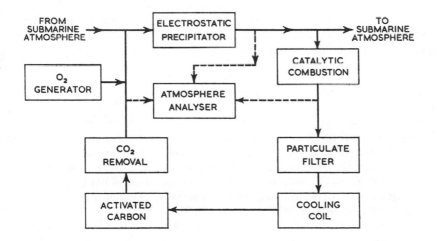

Figure 17.11 An integrated atmospheric system. (Reproduced by permission of the U.S. Naval Research Laboratory)

17.22 The Purification Chain

Figure 17.11 shows a possible arrangement of the component parts of an air purification train. From the published description of equipment that has been used it is not, however, clear whether a completely integrated system is yet in service. All that has been stated is that the total air flow through a number of small recirculating systems is 24 m³/s, and that the volume of air in the submarine is 2400 m³.

The following sections describe the salient points of design of the specially developed components of the system.

17.23 Carbon Dioxide Removal Systems

17.23.1 General

The production of CO_2 from a crew of 120 is 2·5 m³/h (5 kg/h).

A removal system employing regenerable solutions or solids is necessary with expulsion to sea of regenerated carbon dioxide. An important difference from normal chemical factory plant is that the total height of absorption and regeneration towers must be less than about 3 metres.

17.23.2 Monoethanolamine Removal System

The first submarines used the well-developed monoethanolamine system described in Chapter 7. Two units (1 working, 1 spare) were installed, each having a throughput of 120 litres/s of air and designed to remove 6 kg/h of carbon dioxide from air containing 1 per cent carbon dioxide. To reduce headroom, absorption was in two towers side by side, the first employing co-current and the second counter-current flow. The absorbent solution is 4·5 N MEA. As MEA is slightly volatile and, as the upper limit of MEA in the atmosphere must not exceed 1 p.p.m., the air leaving the scrubber is passed through a purifier (details not specified). Another disadvantage of MEA is its poor oxidation stability.

17.23.3 Advantages of Alkazid as Absorbent

Solutions of alkali salts of N-substituted amino acids have been used by the Germans for carbon dioxide and hydrogen sulphide removal for about 30 years. As the solutions were more expensive and more corrosive than ethanolamines, they had not received much attention in the U.S.A., although non-volatile. For CO_2 removal, the particular compound used is the potassium salt of N-methyl aminoacetic acid known as Alkazid M. The relative merits of Alkazid M and MEA are given in Table 17.3.

Examination of commercial Alkazid M showed that it contained traces of an odorous impurity. This can be substantially removed by extraction with cyclohexane. At the time of the report[20], sea trials of this promising absorbent were held up pending determination of biological hazards.

Table 17.3 SUMMARY OF RELATIVE-MERITS OF ALKAZID M AND MEA

Property	Result of examination
Ease of handling	Alkazid M slightly superior to MEA though concentration of former is fixed
Vapour pressure (atmospheric contamination)	Alkazid M greatly superior to MEA
Viscosity	MEA considerably less viscous
Oxidation resistance	Alkazid M much superior
CO_2 absorption rate	Not much difference; MEA very slightly superior
CO_2 absorption capacity	MEA has greater capacity when compared with Alkazid M
Stripping rate	MEA slightly superior
Toxicity	Alkazid M comparatively non-toxic, except in sense that any fairly corrosive alkaline material is toxic
Corrosion	MEA less corrosive

17.23.4 Solid Regenerable Absorbents

The only solid absorbent for carbon dioxide which merited examination was an alkali metal alumino-silicate used as a molecular sieve. This would remove water vapour and organic materials in a primary absorber and carbon dioxide in a secondary absorber. Both vacuum and heat are necessary for regeneration.

Trial indicated that the necessary equipment would be too bulky to install.

17.24 Dual System for Carbon Dioxide Removal and Oxygen Generation

The principle of this attractive system, illustrated in Figure 17.12, is to produce, in a diaphragm electrolytic cell containing about 15 per cent sodium sulphate solution:

(i) hydrogen (which is discharged to sea) and sodium sulphate solution containing caustic soda; and

(ii) oxygen and sodium sulphate solution containing sulphuric acid.

Solution (i) is used for absorption of carbon dioxide from the air. As there is negligible back-pressure of carbon dioxide over the carbonated caustic/sulphate solution, it is possible to use co-current flows of gas and liquor; this enables higher gas and liquor rates to be used in the absorption tower without flooding of the packing, though power requirements are somewhat increased. It was found that the gas film coefficient of absorption of carbon dioxide by 1 N sodium hydroxide was substantially diminished as the concentration of sodium sulphate was increased.

The carbon dioxide in the liquor leaving the absorption tower is expelled by neutralization of the $Na_2CO_3/NaOH/Na_2SO_4$ solution with the acid sodium sulphate solution (ii).

It is not known, at present, whether an operational design of this system has proved satisfactory in service.

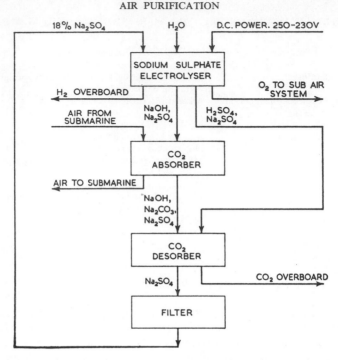

Figure 17.12 Flow sheet for sulphate cycle. (Reproduced by permission of the U.S. Naval Research Laboratory)

17.25 Elimination of Oxidizable Components

The catalytic combustion system known as the Desomatic burner, Figure 17.13 (developed and manufactured by Desomatic Products, Division of Atlantic Research Corporation, U.S.A.), has a capacity of 120 litres/s. Operation is within the range 315°–345°C, using Hopcalite as catalyst. A rotary heat exchanger is installed for compactness. To prevent chokage by fine dust, it is preceded by a paper filter assembly. An activated carbon pre-absorber before the burner was discarded because of the frequent regeneration required and because of the high efficiency of the catalyst. Thus it is reported that the burner is 100 per cent efficient with CH_3OH, CH_2O, C_4H_8, C_4H_{10}, C_3H_8, C_3H_6, C_2H_4, C_2H_2, CO and H_2. It oxidizes 90–95 per cent of benzene and toluene presented at a concentration of 100 p.p.m. but, even at 340°C, only 40 per cent of the methane is oxidized. Traces of NO are formed by oxidation of ammonia and organic nitrogen compounds. Difficulties through production of hydrogen fluoride and hydrogen chloride by decomposition of Freon were overcome by incorporating 10 per cent by volume of granular lithium hydroxide or marble chips in the catalyst.

The '1-1-1 catalyst' used in early cruises consisted of a few per cent of cobalt oxide and traces of platinum and palladium on an inert carrier. It was not sufficiently effective because, at its maximum operating temperature of 205°C, it did not destroy all hydrocarbons and its efficiency with carbon

monoxide was low in absence of hydrogen (which raised its surface temperature). Specially hard Hopcalite in 4–6 mesh grains has been found highly
efficient as indicated above. This catalyst, which is a co-precipitated mixture

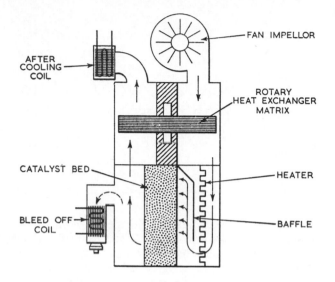

Figure 17.13 Air-flow diagram for Desomatic burner. (Reproduced by permission of the Department
of the Navy, Bureau of Ships, Washington, D.C.)

of equal amounts of oxides of manganese and copper, has been used for
years at low temperatures for oxidation of carbon monoxide, but below
120°C is affected by water vapour and is poisoned by hydrocarbons. Its use
at elevated temperatures is a new development. The life of a catalyst charge
is about 1000 h provided the hydrocarbon content of the air does not rise
excessively.

17.26 Aerosol Removal

It is required to keep the aerosol concentration below 0·1 μg/l. The capacity
of the first electrostatic precipitator was 550 litres/s. High duty compact
electrostatic precipitators since developed for this work have the specification:

Capacity	4500 litre/s
Linear velocity	1 m/s
Efficiency	Over 99·9 per cent (99·95 per cent has been obtained on test bench)
Ozone in outlet	< 0·1 p.p.m.
Volume	3·1 m^2

They operate at 25 kV and have a pressure drop of 2·5 mb.

18

Meteorological Factors Affecting Chimney Discharges

G. NONHEBEL

Much of this chapter has been taken (with permission) from the Recommended Guide for the Prediction of the Dispersion of Airborne Effluents prepared by eminent meteorologists for the American Society of Mechanical Engineers[1]. A more advanced book, which reviews current literature is *Meteorology and Atomic Energy*;[2] only two of the eight chapters in this book deal with the special problems of release of radioactive materials. The relations between meteorological conditions on air pollution are illustrated by over 100 photographs, many in colour, in Professor Scorer's book, *Air Pollution*[3].

In this chapter discharges from chimneys are referred to as smoke.

18.1 Introduction

Even when a chimney is sufficiently high for the discharge to be unaffected by air currents set up by the wind blowing past adjacent buildings (Chapter 19), some of the effluent gases will reach the ground by the process of eddy diffusion; fine fume and dust are carried along in the gas stream though grit falls to the ground nearer the chimney. Mathematical formulae have been developed by means of which it is possible to calculate the concentrations at ground level of gases discharged from a high chimney. The use and limitations of these formulae are discussed in Chapter 19.

Because of the importance of the dispersal of gases when discharged from a chimney, it is necessary to have some knowledge of air movements under various weather conditions.

A casual observation of smoke discharged from a chimney will reveal that although it is carried along by the prevailing wind, it is rapidly dispersed and diluted within the directional wind movement. Major meteorological factors which affect the adequate dispersal of flue gases are:

  (i) the force and direction of the wind for overall directional movement;
  (ii) the internal movement within the overall wind flow, known as eddy diffusion, which accounts for the dilution and dispersion of the gases

within the wind (molecular diffusion is so slow by comparison that it may be ignored);

(iii) the vertical temperature gradient in the atmosphere above the 'smoke' trail.

18.2 Wind

The general wind flow over the earth is induced by the large-scale pressure variations commonly depicted on the synoptic meteorological charts. The intensity of these pressure systems and their normal positions or trajectories determine the general distribution of winds in a given area. Within this large-scale framework there are many factors that influence the details of the air movement in both the vertical and the horizontal, and for most air pollution problems it is some combination of broad and detailed patterns that is important.

Frequency Records. The ten-year average frequency of wind directions and velocities for a new site should be obtained for the nearest representative meteorological station which takes 24-hour records (preferably by automatic recording charts). Whilst the standard height of instruments is 10 m, the height should nevertheless be checked. Table 18.1 shows the records in sectors of 30° for a sea-level airport in Great Britain with steep hills to the north and south. Figure 18.1 is the wind-rose pictorial representation. Meteorologists define wind direction as degrees from north from which the wind is blowing whereas the bearing of a place in respect of a chimney is

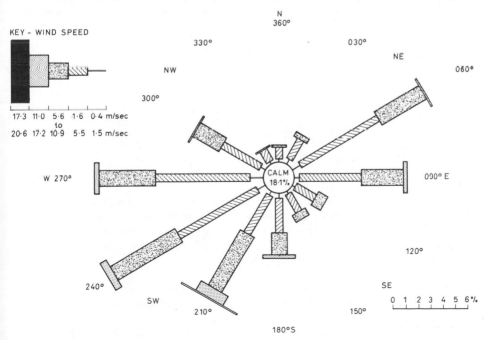

Figure 18.1 Wind-rose from data in Table 18.1

given as degrees from north of the place. To obtain the wind direction from the chimney to the place add 180° to the bearing and subtract 360° if the sum is more than 360°.

Table 18.1 ANNUAL PERCENTAGE FREQUENCY OF WIND DIRECTION AND VELOCITY AT RENFREW AIRPORT FOR TEN YEARS 1956-65

Mean wind speed at 10 m height miles/h	N 350 −010	020 −040	E 050 −070	080 −100	110 −130	140 −160	S 170 −190	200 −220	230 −250	W 260 −280	290 −310	320 −340	All directions
0	—	—	—	—	—	—	—	—	—	—	—	—	18·1
1–3	0·2	0·4	0·7	0·4	0·2	0·2	0·3	0·3	0·7	1·0	0·4	0·2	5·0
4–7	0·4	1·0	3·0	2·0	0·9	0·8	1·2	1·2	2·7	3·6	1·4	0·5	18·7
8–12	0·5	0·8	4·3	3·0	1·0	0·9	1·6	2·4	4·4	4·0	2·1	0·5	25·5
13–18	0·2	0·4	3·6	2·8	0·8	0·6	1·5	3·7	4·6	3·7	2·0	0·2	24·1
19–24	0+	0+	0·5	0·6	0·1	0·1	0·3	1·5	1·4	0·9	0·4	0+	5·8
25–31		0+	0·1	0·2	0+	0+	0·2	0·7	0·5	0·3	0·1	0+	2·1
32–38			0+	0·1	0+	0+	0·1	0·2	0·1	0·1	0+	0+	0·6
39–46			0+	0+	0+	0+	0·1	0+	0+	0+	0+		0·1
47–54							0+	0+	0+				0+
55–63								0+					
Total	1·3	2·6	12·2	9·1	3·0	2·6	5·2	10·1	14·4	13·6	6·4	1·4	100·0

Note on wind speeds

Mean wind speed at 10 m miles/h	Beaufort Scale Force	Description	Mean wind speed at 10 m m/s
0		Calm	0
1–3	1	Light	0·4–1·3
4–7	2	Light	1·8–3·1
8–12	3	Light	3·6–5·4
13–18	4	Moderate	5·8–8·0
19–24	5	Fresh	8·5–10·7
25–31	6	Strong	11–14
32–38	7	Strong	14–17
39–46	8	Gale	18–21

The predominant direction in a wind rose is usually called the 'prevailing wind'. The term is often misconstrued as meaning virtually the only wind direction observed at a locality, but it merely denotes the most frequently observed direction from a 45° sector, e.g. SW, which in Table 18.1 is seen to be for about 25 per cent of the year.

Persistence. There are instances in which the wind direction is quite constant over a period of time, and these cases may be particularly important in relation to air pollution episodes or accidents.

The most common representation is the persistence table (Table 18.2) which shows the number of instances during which the wind remains within a given direction sector for a specified number of hours. In the example shown, there were very few cases where the wind remained invariant for more than 36 hours, and these few were associated with south-east and south-west winds.

Table 18.2 PERSISTANCE OF WIND DIRECTION

Hours	N	NE	E	SE	S	SW	W	NW
6–12	24	26	5	47	54	78	79	38
13–24	1	5	0	16	16	24	28	11
25–36	0	2	0	0	3	0	6	1
37–42	0	0	0	2	0	1	0	0

Note. The data indicates the number of separate instances in a single year during which the wind remained within the 45 degree sector indicated.

Another expression of persistence is a statistical quantity known as 'constancy' or 'steadiness'. This expression utilizes the ratio of the vector and scalar winds, giving a value of 1 for invariant wind directions and 0 for completely uniform distributions. Unlike persistence, it is little affected by brief deviations interrupting otherwise consecutive periods of invariant directions.

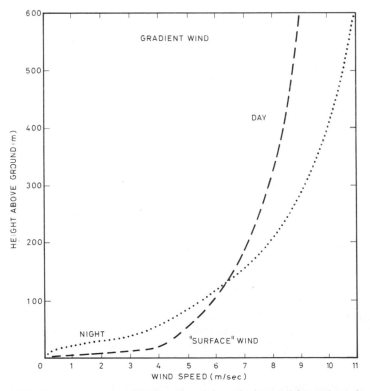

Figure 18.2 Change of wind speed profile with stability. The frictional drag reduces the wind speed close to the ground below that found at the gradient level. The profile at night when the air is stable is usually steeper than that found during the day

Wind Shear. The variation of the horizontal wind speed and direction with height is important in evaluating diffusion from stacks. At some height above the ground (usually 500–750 m) the wind flow is nearly parallel to the lines of equal barometric pressure at a speed dictated primarily by the horizontal pressure gradient, and it is therefore called the 'gradient level wind'. Closer to the ground the effects of friction retard the wind flow and cause it to change direction as well.

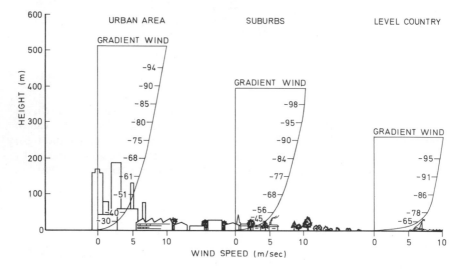

Figure 18.3 Effect of terrain roughness on the wind speed profile. With decreasing roughness, the depth of the affected layer becomes shallower and the profile steeper

As shown in Figures 18.2 and 18.3 the vertical wind speed profile is affected by changes in the underlying terrain and the thermal stability of the atmosphere. A good first approximation is given by:

$$\bar{u}_h = \bar{u}_1 (z/z_1)^p \tag{18.1}$$

where $\bar{u}_h$ = wind at some upper elevation, z, and $\bar{u}_1$ = wind at reference height, z_1. The exponent p is not constant, but varies from approximately 0·16 over sea, 0·17 over open flat fields, 0·28 over woodland to about 0·4 over large cities with high buildings[4].

The change in wind direction with height over uncomplicated terrain normally amounts to a clockwise turning with increasing elevation of approximately 15–30 degrees between ground level and the gradient level, as illustrated in Figure 18.4. The change in direction may sometimes be much greater and more complicated in irregular terrain during stable conditions where the low-level flow pattern is completely divorced from the pattern aloft.

Local Circulation. In open country the horizontal change in the wind flow is normally gradual and of little significance unless one is concerned about dispersion many kilometres from the source. In irregular terrain or in areas

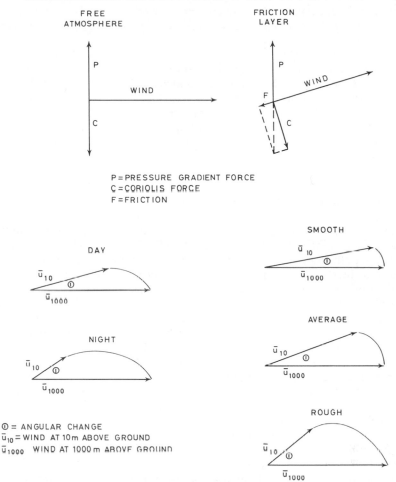

Figure 18.4 Change of wind direction with height. Not only the wind speed, but the direction changes with height as a result of frictional forces. The angular change is usually less during the day that at night, and less over smooth surfaces than over rough

where there are significant changes in surface temperature, the horizontal direction and speed may change over a short distance.

Drainage Winds. Where there is a marked slope to the land surface, a 'drainage' or 'katabatic' wind develops close to the surface. This is a simple gravity flow in which air cooled by radiation at night flows downhill. This wind may be markedly different from the gradient wind aloft; it is usually shallow. Pools of cold air in valley bottoms are a common cause of accumulation of pollution for long periods.

Valley Winds. In well-defined valleys, complex flow patterns are usually encountered. At night, a thin layer of drainage wind is usually found flowing down the valley sides towards the centre. Over the centre, one normally finds a well developed flow towards the lower end of the valley. During daytime hours there is a tendency towards a poorly defined flow up the centre of the valley.

Land and Sea Breezes. The disparity between temperatures of adjacent land and sea surfaces will often cause a localized flow to develop, affecting a region extending from a few miles out to sea to five or ten miles inland. During the day the air over the land becomes warm relative to that over the sea and an onshore circulation develops. During the night the reverse temperature structure develops and there is a tendency for a flow from the land towards the sea.

18.3 Turbulent Eddy Diffusion

Turbulence is another aspect of the variation of wind, deserving treatment as a separate subject because of its direct influence on local dispersion. For most air pollution problems turbulence includes those fluctuations in the wind flow having a frequency more than 2 cycles/h, and the most important fluctuations are usually those in the 1 to 0·01 cycle/s range. All definitions of 'mean' and 'turbulent' quantities are somewhat arbitrary since they depend on the overall time and space scales of the specific problem.

It is important to understand the generation of turbulence and the expressions used in meteorological literature to define it.

The primary factors creating atmospheric turbulence are the flow of air over roughness elements on or of the ground surface, and convection associated with a disparity between the surface and ambient air temperatures. In general, an increase in the gradient wind flow or an increase in the air temperature close to the earth's surface compared to that aloft creates a corresponding increase in turbulence.

The momentum of the wind near the ground is continually dissipated by the friction at the earth's surface, and surface winds would rapidly die away if they were not reinforced by masses of fast-moving air descending from the strong winds which blow in the middle atmosphere. The mechanism which brings about this interchange of mass (and so momentum) is known as 'turbulent eddy diffusion'. 'Turbulence' means, roughly, the random movements of air which are superimposed upon the mean wind speed. An individual movement is called a 'turbulent eddy'; it may move in any direction and at any speed and its diameter may vary from less than 25 mm to over a thousand miles. Large eddies are the depressions and anticyclones seen in weather maps. The smallest eddies are responsible for dilution of a plume as it leaves a chimney whilst larger eddies cause the plume to move up, down and sideways.

Near the ground additional turbulence or eddy motion is also set up by the obstacles presented to the direct flow of air by the surface and its irregularities. This form of turbulence is usually referred to as 'gustiness' and the greater the resistance offered by the obstacles, the more pronounced is the resulting gustiness. Where the surface is nearly flat, for example over a playing-field, the turbulence is less marked than where the air has to make its way over and around groups of buildings.

In average conditions and when the wind is blowing over a fairly smooth surface, it has been found that the range of the instantaneous variations of wind speed above and below the mean is about one-quarter of the mean, the average variation being about one-tenth of the mean wind speed.

It follows, therefore, that statistical methods must be employed in the development of mathematical formulae to describe the mean path and dilution of a chimney plume over a period of time. The most useful quantitative description of turbulence is the statistical standard (i.e. root mean square) deviation of the wind fluctuations taken over a period of approximately one hour. These standard deviations (σ values) can be converted into estimates of the vertical and horizontal parameters in the dispersion equations used in Chapter 19.

More detailed information on the behaviour of chimney plumes in normal and abnormal weather conditions will be found in References 3 and 4.

18.4 Stability

In its simplest terms, the stability of the atmosphere is its tendency to resist or enhance vertical motion, or alternatively to suppress or augment existing turbulence. Stability is related to both wind shear and temperature structure in the vertical, but it is generally the latter which is used as an indicator of the condition.

18.4.1 Adiabatic Lapse Rate

A mass of air rising in the atmosphere will cool, even when it loses no heat to its surroundings and does not mix with the surrounding air. It will cool

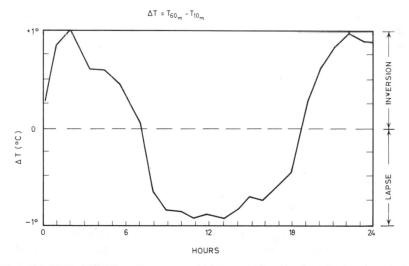

$$\Delta T = T_{60_m} - T_{10_m}$$

Figure 18.5 Diurnal variation of lapse rate, open country. The mean diurnal variation in the lapse rate between temperature sensors at 60 m and 10 m from a station in open country is shown. Typically, the temperature decreases with height during the daylight hours and increases with height during the night

because as it rises the pressure acting upon it is reduced, and hence it expands adiabatically. The rate at which a mass of dry air, rising adiabatically, cools is known as *the dry adiabatic lapse rate* and is about $-1°C$ per 100 m of altitude. If the rising air contains water vapour, the cooling due to adiabatic expansion will result in the relative humidity being increased and saturation may be reached. Further ascent would then lead to condensation of water vapour with the formation of cloud and the latent heat thus released would reduce the rate of cooling of the rising air.

At heights greater than say 300 m, the actual lapse rate is fairly steady at about two-thirds the dry adiabatic rate; only in the lowest layers is a diurnal variation of lapse rate observed. The range of this variation is greatest the first few metres above the ground and decreases with increasing height, see Figure 18.5. The modal rate near the ground is the dry adiabatic rate and, at the heights at which smoke from large industrial chimneys disperses (say, 100–500 m), the range on either side of the mode is not great. Consequently the assumption of an adiabatic or near-adiabatic lapse rate in calculations of the height of rise of a smoke plume (Chapter 19) is reasonable, at least, in the U.K.

18.4.2 Potential Temperature

If a parcel of dry air were brought adiabatically from its initial state to the arbitrarily selected standard pressure of 1000 mb, it would assume a new temperature, θ, known as the 'potential temperature'. The quantity is closely related to the dry adiabatic lapse rate, since an atmosphere having a decrease in ambient temperature with height of $-1°C/100$ m has a potential temperature that is constant with height. An increase of potential temperature with height implies stability and a decrease, instability, as explained in the following sections.

The *gradient of potential temperature* in the lowest layers of the atmosphere is the difference between the adiabatic lapse rate and the actual atmospheric lapse rate. This term is widely used in the literature. It is also expressed in $°C/km$.

18.5 Environmental Lapse Rate

The actual distribution of temperature in the vertical is known as the 'environmental lapse rate', and it seldom approximates the adiabatic lapse rate in the lowest 100 m over any extended time period. Examples of typical environmental lapse rates are shown in Figure 18.6.

18.5.6 Superadiabatic

On days when strong solar heating is occurring or when cold air is being transported over a much warmer surface, the rate of decrease of temperature with height usually exceeds $-1°C/100$ m, implying that any small volume displaced upward would become less dense than its surroundings and tend to continue its upward motion. A superadiabatic condition, as depicted in the top section of Figure 18.6, favours strong convection, instability, and

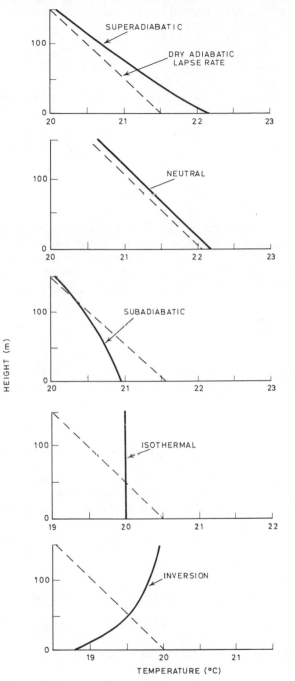

Figure 18.6 Typical environmental lapse rates. Typical examples of vertical temperature profiles are shown in comparison with the dry adiabatic lapse rate (− 1°C/100 m) which serves as a reference for distinguishing unstable from stable cases. The position of the dashed line representing the adiabatic lapse rate is not important; it is significant only as far as its slope is concerned

turbulence. Superadiabatic conditions are usually confined to the lowest 200 m of the atmosphere.

18.5.2 Neutral

A neutral condition, in which the lapse rate in the atmosphere is nearly identical to the dry adiabatic lapse rate, implies no tendency for a displaced parcel to gain or lose buoyancy. Neutral conditions are common in the U.K. since they are associated with overcast skies and moderate to strong wind speeds: they are much less frequent in the U.S.A.

18.5.3 Subadiabatic

An atmosphere in which the temperature decreases more gradually than $-1°C/100$ m (Section 2 of Figure 18.6) is actually slightly stable, since a small parcel displaced upward will become more dense than its surroundings and tend to descend to its original position, whereas a parcel displaced downward will become warmer and rise to the original level.

18.5.4 Isothermal

When the ambient temperature is constant with height, the layer is termed isothermal, and as in the subadiabatic case there is a slight tendency for a parcel to resist vertical motion.

18.5.5 Inversion

A stable atmospheric layer in which temperature increases with height strongly resists vertical motion and tends to suppress turbulence. It is therefore of particular interest in air pollution, since it allows very limited dispersion. There has also been much confusion over different types of temperature inversions, and clarification is therefore particularly in order.

Surface or Radiation Inversion. One form of inversion is shown in the bottom section of Figure 18.6 This structure is usually found at night with light winds and clear skies, when the loss of heat by long-wave radiation from the ground surface cools the surface and subsequently the air adjacent to it. The condition is the cause of mists in open country and of fogs and smogs in the U.K.

Elevated Inversions. In Figure 18.7 the temperature decreases with height up to 600 m and then is capped by an inversion layer. Above the inversion there is a normal decrease of temperature with height. Such inversions may be caused by:

    Subsidence. The gradual descent of air aloft, accompanied by adiabatic warming of the layer resulting from the increase in pressure.

    Sea Breeze. Introduction of a layer of cool air beneath a warmer air mass results in an elevated inversion.

Frontal. A meteorological front in the atmosphere is also a boundary between cold air below and warm air aloft, marked by an inversion in the temperature structure.

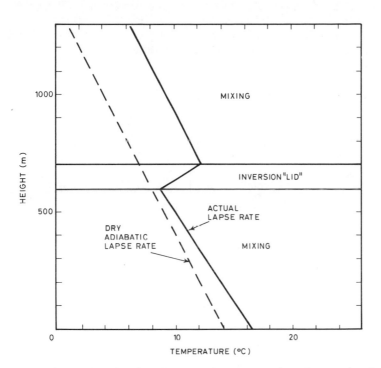

Figure 18.7 Elevated inversion. Sometimes an inversion exists above the ground surface, acting as a barrier between the mixed layer close to the surface and that aloft

The key factor to remember is that vertical motion is inhibited in the inversion layer. If it exists aloft, it tends to act as a 'lid'; if it develops near the ground it will inhibit upward dispersion of low-level pollutants but it will also prevent the downward movement of pollutants released above it.

Mixing Layers. Whenever the potential temperature between the surface and a capping inversion aloft decreases with height the layer can be considered a 'mixing layer'. In a sense the entire atmosphere below the tropopause (normally found at 10000 m) constitutes a mixing layer, since the tropopause is a virtually permanent inversion lid. Frequently, however, lower transient inversions confine the mixing to much shallower layers.

Variability in Time and Space. Stability in the lowest few hundred metres of the atmosphere usually exhibits marked diurnal variation, alternating between stable and unstable conditions according to the time of day. Figure 18.5 shows the typical diurnal variation in open country.

Elevated inversions, on the other hand, often persist for days or even weeks at a time. The Southern California coastal inversion, for example, is produced by a combination of subsidence and the cold ocean surface, and it is very persistent.

Table 18.3 gives measurements of the frequency and lapse rates of surface inversions at Cardington—flat country on the eastern side of England[6]. It will be seen that lapse rate decreases to less than 0·5°C above a height of 100 m. Hot flue gases issuing above a chimney of this height are therefore still likely to rise a considerable distance, as described in Chapter 19. The theory is described in Reference 13.

Table 18.3 AVERAGE NUMBER OF INVERSIONS IN SURFACE LAYERS OF DIFFERENT DEPTHS AT VARIOUS HOURS OF THE DAY IN WINTER (NOVEMBER–FEBRUARY) AT CARDINGTON

Position of layer above ground (ft)	Mean no. of occasions	Mean lapse (deg C) 100 ft)	6 a.m. No.	deg C	Midday No.	deg C	6 p.m. No.	deg C
0–50	41	2·3	36	2·0	9	2·3	38	2·2
50–100	40	1·3	32	1·2	9	1·1	40	1·2
100–250	38	0·9	31	0·6	8	0·5	38	0·6
250–500	36	0·4	31	0·4	9	0·3	32	0·3
500–750	35	0·3	31	0·3	9	0·2	32	0·2
750–1000	35	0·2	30	0·2	9	0·2	28	0·2
1000–1250	31	0·2	29	0·2	10	0·2	25	0·2
1250–1500	27	0·2	26	0·2	11	0·1	21	0·1

Multiply feet by 0·305 to convert to metres.

During anti-cyclonic weather in winter, and when there is little wind, surface inversions formed under clear skies may grow upwards to a substantial height and persist for several days, thus leading to the dense smogs found in cities in Britain before there was smoke control from domestic coal fires. The frequency of quiet anti-cyclonic conditions in 25 cities in Britain are given[7] in Table 18.4. The table gives the maximum number of days when fog might occur but whether a smog develops depends on many other variables including topography, humidity, and low level smoke emission per unit area; these are not essential factors as in an anti-cyclonic calm. Thus it must not be inferred that Birmingham experiences twice as many smogs as Glasgow.

18.6 The Importance of Chimney Height During Inversions

We have seen that, during surface inversions, the air at ground level is at a lower temperature than the air at some height above, though at a still greater height the air temperature again falls with increase in height. There can also be high-level inversions. The initial mixing of warm flue gases discharged from a chimney with the surrounding air is usually sufficiently rapid to cool them below the temperature of the air above the boundary of a surface

Table 18.4 DAYS OF QUIET, ANTICYCLONIC WEATHER IN FINE WINTERS (NOVEMBER–FEBRUARY)

Town	Total No. of days in 5 winters	Highest No. of days in any winter	Lowest No. of days in any winter	Sequences				
				2 Consecutive days	3 Consecutive days	4 Consecutive days	More than 4 consecutive days	Longest period of consecutive days
Glasgow	46	17	4	2	3	1	1	7
Edinburgh	49	17	6	2	1	1	1	7
Newcastle	70	32	8	9	6	3	—	4
Middlesbrough	67	32	7	7	6	3	—	5
Blackburn	75	35	7	8	6	4	1	5
Liverpool	77	34	7	6	6	4	2	5
Manchester	81	37	7	7	6	4	2	5
Leeds	74	36	7	7	6	4	1	5
Sheffield	81	37	6	7	6	4	2	5
Stoke-on-Trent	85	38	7	10	6	4	2	6
Hull	74	36	6	6	7	3	2	5
Nottingham	84	38	7	10	7	4	1	6
Birmingham	90	38	8	10	7	4	4	6
Swansea	73	31	6	10	5	2	2	5
Newport	83	36	7	11	7	2	2	6
Cardiff	80	35	7	13	5	2	2	6
Bristol	87	37	7	13	8	3	2	6
Plymouth	76	30	8	10	7	2	—	4
London Area	87	36	10	8	9	3	1	6
Portsmouth	83	35	8	8	7	3	1	6
Chatham	79	3	10	10	5	3	—	4

inversion and consequently they cannot rise further but are trapped somewhere below the boundary of the inversion layer as shown in Figure 18.8. This is the reason for the smoky atmosphere which develops in towns during still evenings. If the air near the ground cools sufficiently to develop fog, the ensuing mixture of smoke and fog is termed smog.

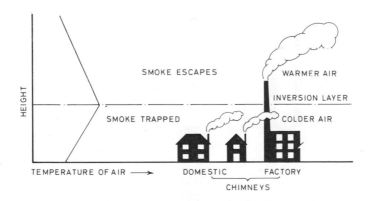

Figure 18.8 Effects of inversion layer

Figure 18.9 (*a*), (*b*) and (*c*) shows the effects of some typical inversion conditions on the flow of smoke from chimneys of three different heights. Full discussion of these examples has been given by Meade[8].

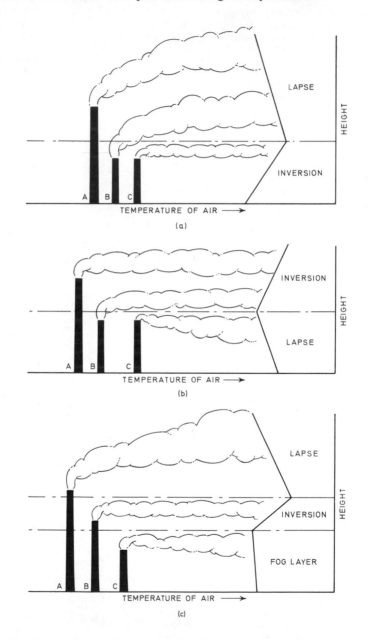

Figure 18.9 Effects of inversion layers on chimney discharges. (a) Inversion layer below, lapse condition above. Hot gas from B penetrates inversion. (b) Lapse conditions below, inversion layer above. Gas from C mixes with air below inversion. (c) Inversion layer with fog layer below, and lapse condition above. Gas from B will come to ground when inversion breaks

Since industrial chimneys are higher than those of houses, there are many occasions when the flue gases from them will rise above the relatively low inversion layers of less than 40 m thickness which so frequently occur during the early evening. Nevertheless regular dirty operations such as sootblowing of boilers should be carried out in day-time and not at night. Moreover, when a surface inversion persists all day or an inversion layer exists at about 100 m above the ground, any substantial discharge from a low-level chimney is to be avoided if at all possible: power to stop chimney emissions from selected factories during smogs of a specified ('No. 2') intensity is in fact possessed by Los Angeles County, U.S.A.[9].

18.7 Drift of Smoke Across Towns

Until recently it was thought that the concentration of smoke in a town increased downwind in proportion to the mass of emission along the line of the wind. It was, therefore, argued that a smokeless zone was likely to be badly contaminated by smoke from those parts of a town upwind which had not been declared smokeless zones. Recent measurements have shown, however, that this form of contamination of smokeless zones of at least 800 m diameter is not as great as might be expected and it has been concluded that, for normal conditions, an important factor is the upward dispersal of smoke by atmospheric turbulence[9].

18.8 Production of Fogs by Chemical Reactions in the Atmosphere

Appreciable haze is produced when effluent gases containing even small quantities of ammonia are discharged into an atmosphere containing sulphur oxides or other acid gases. Due consideration should, therefore, be given to the relative position of chimneys discharging acid and alkaline gases such as ammonia. An investigation of Teesside mist is described in Reference 10.

The smog of Los Angeles, which is slight in density by comparison with British smogs, is caused by chemical reaction between unsaturated hydrocarbons discharged from oil refineries and petrol engines with ozone and oxides of nitrogen formed in the atmosphere by intense ultraviolet light radiation. This smog only develops under inversion conditions and usually occurs between August and November. It is lachrymatory, injures vegetation and attacks rubber. A concise summary of Los Angeles problems and successes is given in Reference 12.

Johnstone has shown[11] that SO_2 in foggy air is catalytically oxidized to SO_3 (a toxic constituent of industrial town smog) by traces of manganese sulphate, formed by reaction of fine manganese-bearing ash with SO_2 and oxygen in flue gas.

19

Heights of Chimneys

G. NONHEBEL

19.1 Principles

Symbols		Units
b	Proportion of time that wind blows towards an octant of 45°	—
C_o	Ground-level of pollution at place of interest	$\mu g/m^3$
D	Diameter of chimney mouth	m
D_s	Rate of deposition of particles	mg/m^2 day
f	Free-falling speed of particles in still air	m/s
g	Acceleration due to gravity	m/s^2
h	Vertical diffusion (Pasquill)	m
h_b	Height of building to ridge	m
h_c	Height of chimney above base level	m
h_e	Height of place above chimney base	m
h_f	Final height of chimney, corrected for downdraught	m
h_w	Maximum width of building	m
Δh	Plume rise	m
H	Effective height of emission	m
L	Height of inversion lid above ground	m
Q	Rate of emission of gaseous pollutant	g/s
Q_d	Rate of emission of fine particles smaller than 20 μm	g/s
Q_H	Heat content of chimney effluent above ambient air	MW
s	Restoring acceleration per unit vertical displacement for adiabatic motion in the atmosphere (stability parameter), Reference 49	s^{-2}
T	Ambient temperature at plume height	K
u	Wind velocity (usually at average of plume height)	m/s
v	Emission velocity from chimney	m/s
w	Rate of emission of dust of a stated size range	g/s
x, y, z	Distance alongwind, crosswind and vertical from base of chimney or source of pollution	m
x_L	Distance at which $\sigma_z = 0.47L$	m
α	Parameter in plume rise equation (19.4)	—
θ	Angular spread of plume (Pasquill)	degrees
$\partial\theta/\partial z$	Vertical potential temperature gradient in atmosphere (reference 49)	°C/m
σ_y	Standard deviation in the crosswind direction of the plume concentration distribution	m
σ_z	Standard deviation in the vertical of the plume concentration distribution	m
ϕ	Function related to deposition of particles of stated size, equation (19.20)	
Γ	Adiabatic lapse rate of temperature	°C/km
χ	Concentration of pollutant at H	g/m^3

A chemical engineer concerned with the specification for the design of a plant for the purification of waste gases which are to be discharged to atmosphere cannot properly fulfil his function if he does not know to what extent the gas must be purified.

A small proportion of the effluent from a chimney will reach the ground by the process of eddy diffusion whatever the height of discharge. Until a few years ago the height of a new chimney was chosen more or less by guesswork except when a minimum natural draught was required. *The Report of the (Government) Committee on Air Pollution*[1] (the Beaver Committee) drew attention to the knowledge that is being accumulated on chimney design to secure adequate dispersal of flue gases and, as a result, plans for new chimneys are examined either by the Alkali Inspectorate or by Local Authorities (Chapter 2).

The general rules which should be followed when deciding the height for a new chimney were first comprehensively discussed by Nonhebel[2]. Much more has since been learnt on plume dispersion.

The principle adopted is that the concentration of pollutants reaching the ground from a new plant should be sufficiently low to avoid damage to amenity and the health of people, animals and vegetation taking into account existing pollution from other sources. In the case of SO_2 this background pollution may be derived from local combustion sources such as houses and factories or even from large conurbations many miles away[3].

Empirical methods based on measurements around isolated power stations are now available for estimation of the maximum time-mean ground-level concentration (glc). These are only valid, however, when the plume of flue gases flows smoothly away from the chimney mouth; that is when the plume is not affected by downwash or downdraught nor by those thermal or surface-induced turbulent currents of air rising and falling to the ground which cause serious looping of the plume. By virtue of its (thermal) buoyancy the plume then follows an upward path downwind of the chimney to a calculable effective height. The maximum time-mean glc of the pollutant is then calculated by means of the well-established equation for eddy diffusion from this effective plume height. Even with a wind constant in direction this maximum calculated glc, which is for a sampling period of 3–10 min varies by an inverse power law. Hence it is essential to state the sampling time to which any measured or calculated glc refers; this is usually one hour or one day when considering medical effects.

When arranging the layout of a new factory or extensions it is becoming common practice to conduct as many hot effluents as possible to a single tall insulated chimney thereby increasing the thermal rise of the total volume of flue gases which increases with their total heat content above the ambient air. When processes are intermittent or the flue gas quantities vary throughout the day individual flues should be provided in the chimney; this is now standard practice with large power stations and with small boiler plants supplying a seasonal heating load.

19.2 Downdraught

19.2.1 General Rules

Figure 19.1(a) indicates the pattern of air flow when wind blows over buildings or hills[4]. The effects rise to about $2\frac{1}{2}$ times the height of the building and extend downwind for a distance of about nine times the height unless the width of the building is less than the height. The Electricity Commissioners' rule is that power station chimneys should be at least $2\frac{1}{2}$ times the height of

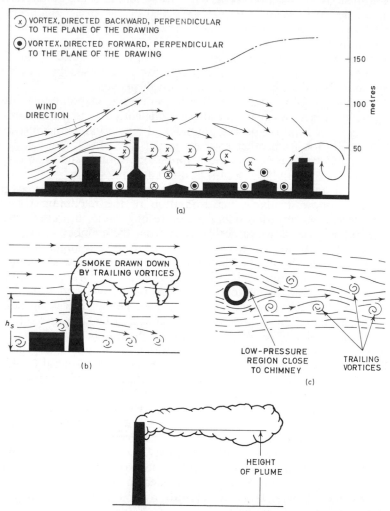

Figure 19.1 Effect of buildings and chimneys on smoke plumes. (a) Pattern of flow over factory buildings. The flow is seriously disturbed below the broken line[4]. Chimney plumes are affected by buildings upstream as shown and downstream. (b) Chimney lower than $2\frac{1}{2}$ times height of adjacent building—effect on smoke. (c) Plan of (b). (d) Downwash pulling plume axis below chimney top

adjacent buildings[5] in order to overcome this effect, known as down-draught. At high wind speeds even this height may be insufficient[6,21] to obviate downdraught completely. The term 'adjacent' for a building of the same height as that to which the chimney is attached is $< 3\frac{1}{2}$ times the cross-wind width of the latter[7]. When possible the longitudinal axis of a building should be at right-angles to the prevailing wind. For a detailed account of air flow past buildings see Reference 80.

19.2.2 Wind Tunnel Tests

In difficult cases such as when there are several large structures near a proposed chimney it is advisable to conduct wind tunnel tests to determine the chimney height[9,10]. As the National Physical Laboratory has made many such tests they should first be consulted on previous experience; they will carry out tests for a fee. The path of the plume is followed by emitting an oil smoke from the model chimney. A mixture of helium and air is used to simulate the thermal buyancy of the flue gases. The air speed in the tunnel and the smoke effluent velocity are adjusted to give the same ratio of momentum per second per square metre area as would apply on the full scale. Photographs are taken with stroboscopic illumination, e.g. 20 flashes in 2 seconds in order to show an integrated pattern of the smoke flow, see Figure 19.10.

19.2.3 Effective Height when Downdraught Occurs

The formula used for calculation of chimney height for a given ground-level concentration of gas (Section 19.9) is subject to correction when the discharge is affected by downdraught.

A relationship derived by Lucas[16] for industrial plants may be expressed in the form given in equation (19.1); it should not be applied to massive emissions from power stations.

If h_f = final height of chimney corrected for downdraught

h_s = effective height of chimney (as used in diffusion calculations, Section 19.7.6)

h_b = height of building to ridge

h_w = either maximum width of building or h_b, whichever is the smaller.

$$h_f = \underset{\substack{\text{effective} \\ \text{height}}}{h_s} + \underset{\substack{\text{additional height} \\ \text{to allow for downdraught}}}{[0{\cdot}6h_w + 0{\cdot}4(h_b - h_s)]} \tag{19.1}$$

Equation (19.1) is only applicable when h_s has values between $(h_b - h_w)$ and $(h_b + 1{\cdot}5h_w)$. When $h_s > (h_b + 1{\cdot}5h_w)$, then $h_f = h_s$; or when $h_s < (h_b - h_w)$, then $h_f = h_b$. h_f must always be 3 m above the ridge of the building.

19.3 Velocity of Discharge (Downwash)

Chimneys should be as slender as possible, free from large overhangs, and should not be surrounded by architectural disguises such as ornamental towers. Observations of existing factories indicate that many chimneys are far too wide.

Sherlock and Stalker[9] found that the principal feature of the wake formed by a chimney is the tall, vertical eddies which form downwind as shown in plan in Figure 19.1(c). Effluent can be drawn down by these eddies into any region of downdraught from adjacent buildings and so to the ground, as illustrated in Figure 19.1(b). A low-pressure region, into which gases may be drawn, also forms immediately downwind from the chimney and is the cause of blackening and corrosion of the sides of the chimneys; the general effect is to lower the effective height of a chimney (Figure 19.1(d)). This phenomenon is known as downwash and can be seen in Figure 19.10.

Wind tunnel tests have shown that downwash is substantially avoided when the effluent velocity is greater than 1·5 times the wind velocity (except in gales). The wind velocity giving the highest glc from large plants is 10 m/s[3]. Hence the effluent velocity should be at least 15 m/s under full load conditions for chimneys having an external diameter at the top up to about 4 m. Multi-flue power station chimneys of diameters about 20 m require effluent velocities of over 25 m/s. A velocity of 30 m/s has been found necessary for short 3 m stacks protruding above the roofs of large office buildings[11]. As with downdraught the National Physical Laboratory has accumulated considerable information on wind-tunnel tests on downwash.

Full scale experimental evidence on the adverse effects of downwash has been obtained from a 100 m high chimney. It was found that when the effluent velocity was less than half the wind speed at 6 m/s the buoyancy rise of the plume was halved and the pollution reaching the ground level was substantially increased (Reference 18, pages 385 and 410).

Since some compromise is necessary with small installations, the Ministry of Environment advice[12] to Local Authorities concerned with approval of chimneys for new boiler plant is that the effluent velocity should be on a sliding scale ranging from 7·5 m/s for boilers rated up to 13 500 kg/h steam output to 15 m/s for boilers rated at 200 000 kg/h.

One method to eliminate downwash from small chimneys discharging dust-free gas is to install around the chimney mouth a horizontal disc with a total diameter equal to about three chimney diameters, see photograph in Reference 29. A conical skirt suspended around the stack top would also reduce downwash. Neither device would increase the back pressure on the discharge, but there are obvious mechanical objections.

Another objection to low effluent velocities is that wind can then eddy down inside a chimney to a depth of several diameters, thereby cooling the walls of even an insulated chimney below the dew point of the flue gases. Particles adhere to the dew and later strip off after they have built up to a thickness of a few mm. They then fall near the chimney in the form of 'blobs' from dusty flue gases and smuts from oil-fired furnaces. For small diameter chimneys a minimum effluent velocity of 2 m/s is required to prevent this ingress of air into a chimney[13] (sometimes described as flow inversion). Higher velocities are required for larger diameter chimneys.

The problem of downwash and air ingress has been overcome by the addition of a nozzle to the chimney mouth. On small oil-fired plants these nozzles have been found to cure the problem of smut emission. Nozzles have also been fitted to chimneys built to serve large plants which will use a single chimney capable of taking the gases from future extensions, e.g. oil refineries. The nozzle is removed when the plant is extended—sometimes by helicopter.

The design of the nozzle should be for minimum pressure drop, e.g. a half-venturi. It is essential that the flue gas should not leave the internal surface of the nozzle at any point.

When there is a high emission velocity from a chimney, irrespective of whether a nozzle is fitted, a back pressure of about one mb is produced by the velocity head at exit. There may also be a positive pressure within the base of the chimney when there is fan-assisted draught. Since most chimneys are lined with insulating brick, the condition can arise that corrosive gases will penetrate this lining and cause structural damage to the structural outer shell. In the case of combustion gases this is caused by the action of sulphuric acid (containing also traces of hydrochloric and nitric acids) formed when the gases are cooled below the dew-point by contact with the cold exterior wall of the chimney. The trouble is also frequent with unlined brick chimneys. This difficulty must be met by use of an impervious acid-resisting metal or a suitable heat-resisting plastic lining between the insulating lining and the structural shell. The practice with large multi-flued power station chimneys is to use a metal flue: these flues project above the chimney shell by about one-third of the external chimney diameter in order to obviate downwash.

In the case of acid gases from chemical plants, for example, oxides of nitrogen from nitric acid absorption towers, it is economic to use a high emission velocity in order to minimize expenditure on the austenitic steel flue. There is then a risk of noise generation with emission velocities greater than 45 m/s and advice should be taken from acoustic specialists when designing for this condition.

If there is a risk of chokage of a nozzle by dust in the flue gases, air inflow on to the interior surface of wide chimneys producing blob emission can probably be prevented by hanging a metal sleeve inside the top of the chimney. This sleeve should leave an annular gap of about 0·3 m and contain within it a smooth restriction sufficient to raise the velocity of gas up through the annular gap to more than 3 m/s. Wind eddying down the centre of the chimney will then only strike the sleeve which is heated by flow of gas on both sides and will not therefore be cooled to the dew point. This arrangement would not, of course, prevent downwash.

For information on corrosion damage to chimneys by combustion flue gases, see Reference 30.

19.4 Looping of Plumes

Looping of a plume occurs when there is an unstable temperature gradient in the lower atmosphere such as when the heat from the sun rapidly warms the ground. Vertical spreading of the plume is at a maximum and the pollutant may be rapidly brought to the ground near the chimney in the form of intermittent puffs of a few minutes duration, Figure 19.2. The cause is the rise of 'bubbles' of warm air from the ground; these thermals are used by birds and glider pilots. The bubbles of warm air are replaced by downward currents of cooler air. Hence looping can be expected to be pronounced over the centre of large built-up areas and over a large industrial heat island (such as a power station of several thousand megawatt capacity where the heat losses by radiation could exceed 5 per cent of the heat input).

In the U.K. looping is seldom observed with chimneys higher than 100 m[18]. In the U.S.A. unexpectedly high concentrations have been measured

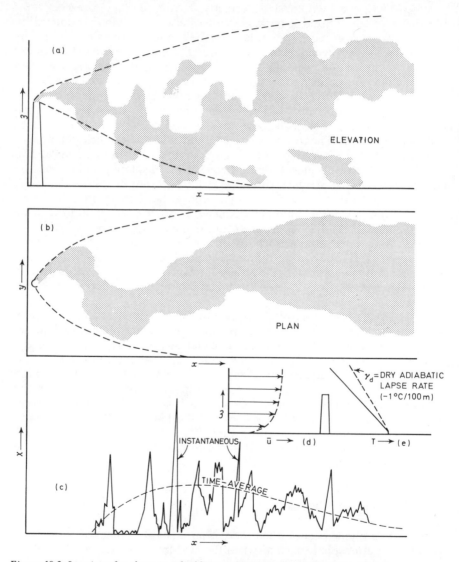

Figure 19.2 Looping of a plume in a highly unstable atmosphere. These five diagrams represent all the major factors concerned with dispersion of a plume. (a) and (b) show elevation and plan view of a looping plume; the shaded areas represent an instantaneous view and the dashed lines the hourly mean plume outlines. (c) shows plots of ground-level concentration χ downwind at distance χ. (d) and (e) are plots of profiles of wind and temperature. Similar charts for other weather conditions will be found in Reference 21. (Reproduced by permission of American Institute of Mechanical Engineers, New York)

chimney. It is hoped to reduce the looping by planting many thousand trees

In the U.K. this would be difficult to arrange because of the difficulty of predicting the thermal activity at a site to allow for flight arrangements.

19.5 Behaviour of Wet Plumes

Plumes of effluent warm air from chemical plant dryers and absorption towers may cool to their dewpoint during their passage through flues and chimneys. They then contain a mist of fine water. When this evaporates as it mixes with the ambient air, the whole plume is cooled and tends to droop down below the chimney. Thus the plumes from the two London power stations at which the SO_2 is removed in absorption towers can be seen at times to dip by 50 m below chimneys 100 m high. When the plume from a relatively low chimney serving a dryer is odorous the smell at ground level can be a cause of vigorous complaint.

The remedy in most cases it to lag the flues and chimney and to maintain the effluent gases at a temperature well above the dew point, and preferably above 110°C in order to evaporate adventitious water drops.

A plume containing water vapour but no mist may still form a mist downwind of the chimney but the latent heat of condensation is retained within the plume and is mostly reabsorbed when the water mist evaporates. Consequently the plume does not fall, but it may only have a thermal plume rise (Section 19.8.4) half that of a non-condensing plume.

19.6 Chimneys for Industrial Fuel-burning Plants

The Ministry of Environment has issued a 'Memorandum on Chimney Heights' for the use of Local Authorities and factory designers[12]. This contains alignment charts for determination of height of chimney for SO_2 emissions from fuel-burning plant emitting SO_2 quantities within the range 1·5 to 81·5 kg/h (3–1800 lb/h). The heights in the charts are related to five types of District which range from open country with no background pollution to a large city or an urban area of mixed heavy industrial and dense residential property. One alignment chart corrects for downdraught by equation (19.1). The suggestions on minimum effluent velocities have been given in Section 19.3.

Small-scale examples of these charts are given in Figures 19.3 and 19.4. For design purposes use should be made of the full Memorandum. The technical background involved in the preparation of this document is described by Ireland[14] and Nonhebel[15]. The Memorandum has been used by some cities in the U.S.A. It does not apply to chemical plant and power stations, etc., registered under the Alkali Act (Chapter 2).

The Beaver Report[1] recommended that the minimum height of chimney for industrial plant should be 37 m. It is of interest to record that following

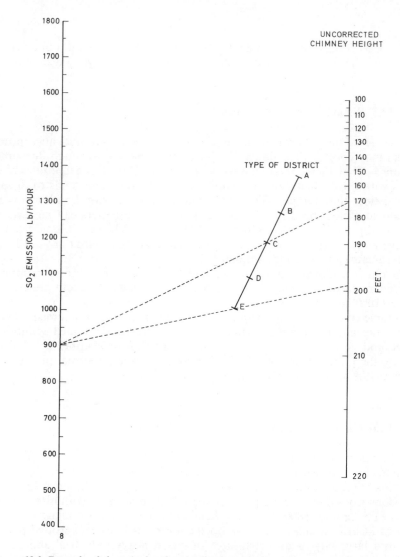

Figure 19.3 Example of chart (reduced scale) for determination of 'uncorrected' chimney height for boilers and furnaces

Conversion factors: 1000 lb/h = 126 g/s: 100 ft = 30·48 m.

(From Chimney Heights, issued by Ministry of Housing and Local Government, 2nd edn., 1967. Reproduced by permission of The Controller of Her Majesty's Stationery Office; Crown Copyright reserved)

this suggestion complaints on some small chemical plants with lower chimneys, particularly granulated fertilizer plants, were eliminated when the chimneys were raised to 37 m at the request of the Alkali Inspector[18]. This height can be regarded as the minimum requirement for works with noxious or odorous effluents.

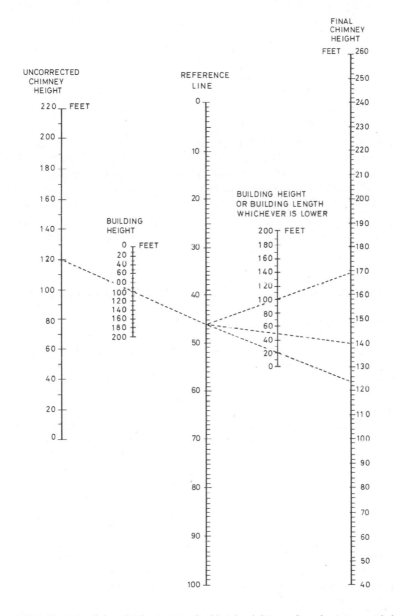

Figure 19.4 Example of chart for determining final height of chimney from the uncorrected chimney found from Figure 19.3 and the height of an adjacent building. (Reproduced by permission of The Controller of Her Majesty's Stationery Office; Crown Copyright reserved)

19.7 Heights of Chimneys for New Plant

From the previous sections it will be seen that a design engineer considering chimneys for a new plant should:

   (i) Combine as many effluents as possible into a single chimney—with multiple flues if desirable.

  (ii) Use a minimum height of 37 m or $2\frac{1}{2}$ times the height of adjacent buildings.

 (iii) Ensure that the velocity of discharge is more than 15 m/s.

 (iv) Endeavour to obtain information on the possibility of serious looping of the plume from the height of chimney considered suitable from (vi).

  (v) Check that dust and fume removal will be sufficient to give an invisible plume (Section 19.21).

 (vi) Choose a height of chimney, from experience with similar plants elsewhere if available, and then calculate the maximum one-hour maximum ground level concentration for Pasquill weather categories A, B, C and D and corresponding wind velocities as will be described in Section 19.8, taking into account the effect of local landscape.

(vii) Check that the worst glc will be acceptable to government pollution authorities (such as U.K. Alkali Inspectorate), see also Section 19.16.

19.8 Calculation of Ground-level Concentrations of Pollutants

19.8.1 Situations and Conditions

Calculations are necessary for normal full load conditions of maximum emission of the pollutant to be considered and for those upset conditions when release of the pollutant is greater because of failure of equipment, e.g. of sulphur removal plant in an oil refinery. The duration of these upset conditions should be noted.

The essential calculations necessary are that for the maximum one-hour glc on the circle at chimney base level around the chimney at which the highest glc occurs, and that at any more distant sensitive places such as hospitals and schools. If there is more than one chimney, calculation should be made of the addition by the smaller emitters to that from the principal emitter at the sensitive places of interest and at selected points on the circle of maximum glc, such as when the chimneys are in line with frequent winds.

When the effluent is SO_2, calculation should be made of the 24-hour glc addition at nearby places to regular daily measurements of SO_2 made by Local Authorities (the U.K. measurements are published by Warren Spring Laboratory, Stevenage).

A map to the scale 1:25000 is desirable for the determination of the height above chimney base level of the places of interest.

Calculations by the methods given later in this Section show that the conditions giving the highest glc are generally those in daytime with Category A weather, wind 2–3 m/s and Category C, wind 8–12 m/s.

19.8.2 Steps in the Calculation

The calculation of glc for a constant wind direction is in three parts:
 (i) Calculation of the plume rise from the velocity-momentum and heat emission in the chimney discharges for normal full load and significant upset conditions.
 (ii) Calculation of the 3-minute glc from the plume rise and the rate of emission of pollutant. A separate calculation is necessary for each weather category.
 (iii) Calculation of the time-average glc required, e.g. hour or day. If longer periods are to be considered, the frequency of wind velocities in each direction and the frequency of weather categories must be taken into account.

The steps in the calculation are illustrated by worked examples given at the end of this section.

19.8.3 Plume Rise due to Velocity

The plume rise for a gas emitted at near-atmospheric temperature with an effluent velocity greater than 10 m/s is given by the equation for a momentum jet in a cross wind and is[21]

$$\Delta h = D(v/u)^{1\cdot4} \tag{19.2}$$

For a gas having a density substantially different from that of the ambient air, v is multiplied by the ratio of the densities.

This equation does not apply when the gas temperature is considerably above that of the ambient air ($> 50°C$) and the emission greater than $50 \ m^3/s$. The plume rise is then estimated by the equations given in the next section; these empirical equations include the uplift given by the discharge velocity provided there is no downwash.

19.8.4 The Rise of a Hot Gas Plume

Numerous theoretical and empirical formulae have been deduced for the rise of hot gas plumes from combustion sources and there is still controversy on the most reliable equation to use for this most important estimation. Measurements of plume rise from power station chimneys and some of the derived equations were discussed by specialist research workers in 1968[19].

Provided the chimney is of sufficient height to avoid downdraught and serious looping of the plume, and the emission velocity is sufficient to prevent downwash, most of the theoretical equations reduce to

$$\Delta h = \alpha Q_H^b u^c \tag{19.3}$$

where Q_H is the heat content of the effluent above ambient air temperature, usually taken as $10°C$, u the wind speed and b and c are constants. α is related to the height of emission above the ground and therefore takes some account of the turbulence of the air above the chimney.

Theoretical deductions for the values of the coefficients α, b and c are not substantiated by observations of plume rise. Empirical equations have therefore been deduced from a limited number of observations—limited because of the great expense. The most reliable data have been obtained by the British Central Electricity Laboratory (C.E.R.L.) by the use of no-lift balloons liberated in the chimney, by searchlights and by use of back-scatter of laser beams—a method called LIDAR (light detection and ranging); and by the Tennessee Valley Authority (T.V.A.) using infra-red photography and SO_2 meters suspended from helicopters. A LIDAR trace is shown in Figure 19.5.

Visual and white light photographs tend to give misleading data partly because the plume often disappears at distances of less than 1000 m and partly because the upper edge of the plume tends to behave differently from the lower edge both aerodynamically and in respect of photographic contrast. There can also be unexpected geometric errors; these do not apply to the LIDAR method[50].

The C.E.R.L. measurements (Lucas[18]) fit the equation

$$h = \alpha Q_H^{\frac{1}{4}} u^{-1} \qquad (19.4)$$

where $\alpha = 475 + 2/3(h_c - 100)$ for the range $60 < h_c < 130$ m, $3 < MW < 67$, $2 < u < 18$, chimney diameters 3·5–7 m. Lucas suggests that α will be larger than that given above when h_c is greater than 130 m because turbulence diminishes with height and has indicated that the 2/3 factor might be 2. Equation (19.4) is consistent with the theoretical study by Priestley[38] and for this reason it should be permissible to extrapolate beyond the conditions of observations[32].

For chimneys of heights between 47 and 100 m the A.S.M.E. Standard APS-2 uses a substantially lower value for α to allow for the increased turbulence above these lower chimneys[22,23], namely

$$\alpha = 470(0·67 + 5·7 \times 10^{-3})(h_c - 47) \qquad (19.5)$$

This equation is supported qualitatively by observations reported on page 257 of Reference 19. Equation (19.4) is used for chimneys taller than 100 m.

Turbulence produced by the ground and by buildings prevents assessments of plume rise from chimneys lower than 47 m except when the chimney is completely isolated from other chimneys and is on level ground.

A later independent survey of all published measurements in Germany, U.K., and U.S.A. by Briggs[19,49] fits the equation

$$\Delta h = 3·3 Q_H^{\frac{1}{4}} x_f^{\frac{2}{3}} u^{-1} \qquad (19.6)$$

where x_f is the distance downwind at which the plume begins to level out, which is also about the distance above the point of highest ground-level concentration of pollutant. For large heat emissions Briggs suggests $x_f = 10h_c$ although Figure 19.5 shows that plumes may continue to rise for double this distance. For heat emissions from 'selected reliable observations' and for neutral and unstable atmospheric stabilities Briggs claims that equation (19.6) has an error of ± 7 per cent for Q_H $6 < MW < 91$. Further investigation is required to define the value of x_f to be used for smaller and larger heat emissions.

For stable conditions (Categories D/E–F, Table 19.2) at the heights at which the plume travels, the average final height of the plume centre line is given by Briggs as

$$\Delta h = 5 \cdot 9 \, Q^{\frac{1}{4}} (us)^{-\frac{3}{8}} \tag{19.7}$$

where $s = (g/T \partial\theta/\partial z)$ and $\partial\theta/\partial z$ is the mean potential temperature gradient in °C/m from the top of the chimney to the top of the plume, namely

$$\partial\theta/\partial z = \partial T/\partial z + \Gamma$$

Γ is the adiabatic lapse rate of temperature in the air, 9·8°C/km. The value suggested for $\partial\theta/\partial z$ for the stable condition E is 9°C, but it is better to obtain meteorological advice for each site. The number of measurements used for derivation of equation (19.7) is limited and further work is required.

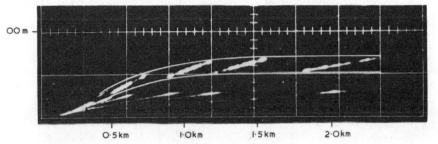

Figure 19.5 *Lidar Scan of the two plumes from Tilbury power station chimneys. The continuous white lines enclose the outline of the B plume.*
For additional photos see Hamilton, P. H., Reference 18, page 160.
(*Central Electricity Generating Research Laboratories*)

Table 19.1 shows a comparison of calculations of plume rise by the above methods. The agreement is sufficiently good for estimation of ground-level concentration of pollutants.

From a study of the information available in 1970 the author considers that the Briggs equation (19.6) with $x_f = 10 h_c$ and $u = 10$ m/s should be used for the estimation of plume height in the diffusion equations which follow as it covers the whole range, from the relatively small heat emissions from chemical plants to those from 1000 MW_E power stations.

Table 19.1 PLUME RISE (CENTRE LINE) CALCULATED BY THE A.S.M.E.-APS-2, BRIGGS AND LUCAS EMPIRICAL EQUATIONS FOR RANGE OF HEAT EMISSIONS AND CHIMNEY HEIGHTS

u, m/s Stability Equation	10 m/s Mildly unstable to neutral, C/D, D						4 m/s Stable, E
	APS-2 19/5	Briggs 19/6	Lucas 19/4	Briggs 19/6	Lucas 19/4*	Briggs 19/6	Briggs 19/7
h_c, metres	50	50	100	100	200	200	50–200
Q_H, MW	*Plume rise. Δh*						
2	40	25	60	40	80	65	70
30	75	65	110	100	160	160	170
120	110	100	160	165	225	255	270
250	130	130	190	205	270	330	350

* For this height of chimney, $\alpha = 475 + 2(h_c - 100)$.

19.8.5 Other Plume Rise Formulae

A comprehensive review of several theoretical and empirical formulae has been made by Briggs[8,19,49]. Empirical formulae are also discussed in References 23–25.

Briggs showed that nearly all measurements fit the relationship $\Delta h \propto u^{-1}$. This rules out several well known formulae used in the 1960s. Thus the theoretical formula of Bosanquet[37] used in the first edition of this book reduces to $h \propto u^{-2}$ (Blokker[25]) and the practical formula given in the A.S.M.E. Guide[21] gives $h \propto u^{-3}$. The frequently quoted CONCAWE formula[24,25] proposed by some European oil companies, $\Delta h \propto u^{-\frac{3}{4}}$, relies mainly on visual observations of plumes from Duisberg and Darmstadt power stations with only a small range of wind speed; these observations also fit the Briggs equation (19.6).

19.8.6 Plume Flow above Landscape

Observations in wind-tunnel and site smoke tests have shown that a plume is lifted by a height equal to that of a long ridge[43]. The effect was noticed qualitatively by measurements of glc downwind of Llynfi power station situated in an enclosed steep valley[44]. It is now accepted that a plume is given an uplift nearly equal to that of the height of a long ridge over which it is passing at right angles even when the plume height is several hundred metres above the ridge and the ridge is within 5 km of the chimney. In these circumstances it is not necessary to substract the height of the ridge from the plume height above chimney base.

This cannot be true when the plume flows at a smaller angle to the ridge since the wind tends to be diverted along the valley. In the absence of wind-tunnel observations it is suggested for initial calculations that half the height of a ridge of rising longer than 1000 m is subtracted from the plume height when the angle of incidence of the wind is 45–90° and that the full height of the ridge is subtracted when the incidence is less than 45°.

It is, however, always essential that the plume centre line should not intersect the turbulent boundary layer which is likely to extend to 30 m above a ridge[43]. Even then the full height of an isolated hill below the plume must be substracted from the plume height because the wind flow divides round the hill and does not lift appreciably. (Equation (19.10) below is to be used.)

When there is a ridge at a distance of less than 2000 m *upwind* of the chimney, the full height of the ridge above the chimney base must be subtracted from the plume height[18,19]. This correction is frequently overlooked.

The height H above a place of interest used in the diffusion calculations (Section 19.7.8) is therefore the sum of the heights of the chimney, h_c, and the plume rise, Δh, less adjustment for the height h_e of the place above the base of the chimney less the height of inhabited buildings h_b. This last may vary from 5 m for a simple dwelling house to over 100 m with tall blocks. Hence

$$H = h_c + \Delta h - h_e - h_b \qquad (19.8)$$

19.9 Estimation of Ground-level Concentrations

Given the height to which the centre line of the plume rises, the ground-level concentration (glc) at any distance downwind is calculated with the aid of equations for the dispersion of gaseous release from an elevated source proposed by Pasquill[27].

Two previously much used equations for this dispersion are that by Bosanquet and Pearson, 1936[37] and that by Sir Graham Sutton, 1947[26] of the U.K. Meteorological Office. These and other equations have been reviewed by the U.S. Atomic Energy Commission[8]. Pasquill (also of the U.K. Meteorological Office) states that the Sutton equations are only reliable for specifying the average distribution over a few hundred metres downwind of a source operating for a few minutes on level unobstructed terrain with a steady wind direction and neutral conditions of atmospheric stability[27]. The parameters in his equations make allowance for the effect of wide variations in atmospheric turbulence with the variations in atmospheric stability which occur in reality and data for which was not available to Sutton. Pasquill's stability coefficients have been verified up to distances of 5 km by Kawabata[33], see also Reference 8, page 102. In his original paper Pasquill expressed vertical diffusion in the form of a height h and lateral diffusion as an angular spread θ. These parameters were converted by Gifford[31] to the standard deviations σ_y and σ_z used in equations (19.9) to (19.15). Values for the variations of these standard deviations with distance are given in Figures 19.6 and 19.7. Definitions of stability categories are given in Table 19.2.

(When studying the literature care must be taken to check the definitions and dimensions of the symbols in diffusion equations, especially those having the same general meaning: several versions of Pasquill's graph for vertical diffusions and for σ_y and σ_z (see Figures 19.6 and 19.7) have been published with different numerical values through changes of definition.)

The fundamental equation for the diffusion and dilution of a plume from an elevated source assumes Gaussian distributions of material both laterally and vertically with standard deviations σ_y and σ_z for the case in which the concentration at the edge of the plume is 10 per cent of that on its axis. With the usual co-ordinate system (x along wind, y crosswind, z vertical) the expression for the distribution of concentration $\chi(x. y, z)$ from a continuous source of strength Q at position (O, O, H) for a wind constant in velocity with height, and assuming that the effect of the ground can be represented by an image source (pages 139 and 292 of Reference 26b), i.e. assuming that total reflection of the plume takes place at the earth's surface and that there is no deposition, is:

$$\chi(x, y, z; H) = \frac{Q}{2\pi\sigma_y\sigma_z u} \times \exp\left[-\frac{1}{2}\left(\frac{y}{\sigma_y}\right)^2\right]\left\{\exp\left[-\frac{1}{2}\left(\frac{z-H}{\sigma_z}\right)^2\right]+\right.$$

$$\left.+\exp\left[-\frac{1}{2}\left(\frac{z+H}{\sigma_z}\right)^2\right]\right\} \tag{19.9}$$

This is essentially one of Sutton's equations[26]. χ is a mean over the same time interval as the time interval for which the σ's and u are representative

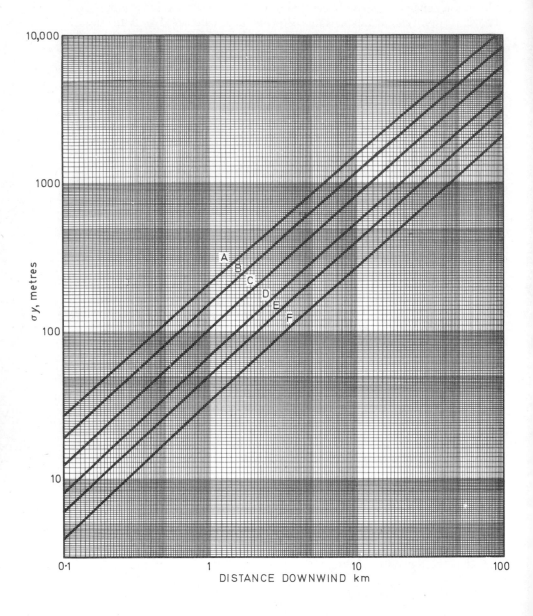

Figure 19.6 Horizontal dispersion coefficient σ_y as a function of downwind distance from the source. Derived from Pasquill[27]; this version reproduced from U.S. Bureau of Health Workbook[20]

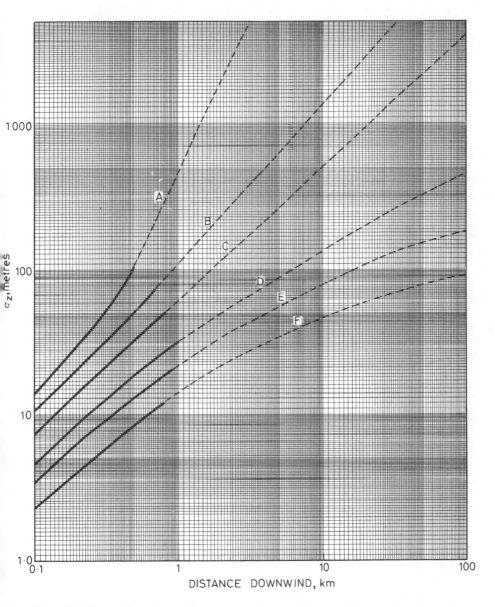

Figure 19.7 Vertical dispersion coefficient σ_z as a function of downwind distance from the source. Derived as for Figure 19.6

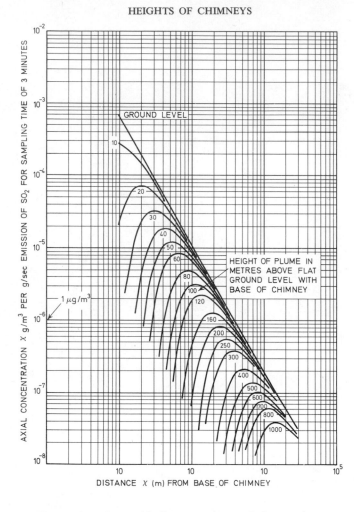

Figure 19.8 Change of axial ground-level concentration with distance from source for various plume heights (m). Pasquill stability category C; wind speed 5 m/s. Ordinate gives g/c in g/m^3 for 1 g/s emission of pollutant from chimney

and, following Sutton, is conventionally taken as a 3-minute mean (though the Workbook issued by the U.S.A. National Air Pollution Control Administration states that the (same) values of σ are representative for a sampling time of 10 minutes[20]).

Although any consistent system of units may be used, the literature was mostly standardized by 1968 as follows:

χ in g/m^3, or for radioactive emissions in curies/m^3. For pollution of the atmosphere by chemical species it is more convenient to use $10^6\chi = C_0$ in $\mu g/m^3$, Q in g/s, u in m/s and σ_y, σ_z, H, x, y, and z in m. Values σ_y and σ_z are discussed later.

When θ is in m^3/s, χ is in parts per million by volume.

For concentrations calculated for chimney base level, i.e. z = 0, equation (19.9) simplifies to:

$$\chi(x, y, 0; H) = \frac{Q}{\pi \sigma_y \sigma_z u} \exp\left[-\frac{1}{2}\left(\frac{y}{\sigma_y}\right)^2\right] \exp\left[-\frac{1}{2}\left(\frac{H}{\sigma_z}\right)^2\right] \quad (19.10)$$

The most important concentration for air pollution calculations is that at ground level under the centre line of the plume, i.e. for $y = 0$, $z = 0$. Then

$$\chi(x, 0, 0; H) = \frac{Q}{\pi \sigma_y \sigma_z u} \exp\left[-\frac{1}{2}\left(\frac{H}{\sigma_z}\right)^2\right] \quad (19.11)$$

An example of curves relating χ with distance from the source of various heights of plume above the place of interest is shown in Figure 19.8.

The highest concentration occurs when

$$\sigma_z = H/\sqrt{2} = H/1\!\cdot\!414 \quad (19.12)$$

This equation follows by differentiation of equation (19.11) with respect to σ_z and making the simplifying assumption that the ratio σ_y/σ_z is a constant independent of distance. Then

$$C_o = \frac{0\!\cdot\!117 \times 10^6 \, Q}{\sigma_y \sigma_z u} \text{ in } \mu g/m^3 \quad (19.13)$$

This simple equation for the highest ground level concentration is all that is needed for most problems once the height of the plume above the place of interest has been calculated for appropriate wind speeds. ($0\!\cdot\!117$ is the reciprocal of $e\pi$.)

If the integral of the *crosswind* distribution

$$\int_{-\infty}^{+\infty} \chi(x, y, 0)dy$$

is considered, the condition for this quantity to be a maximum occurs when

$$\sigma_z = H \quad (19.14)$$

For a ground level source with no effective plume rise ($H = 0$), such as when a leak of an acid gas or odorous substance occurs:

$$\chi(x, 0, 0; H) = \frac{Q}{\pi \sigma_y \sigma_z u} \quad (19.15)$$

provided the duration of the release of pollutant is longer than the travel time x/u from the source to the place of interest.

To avoid confusion it is preferable to refer to the highest maximum 3-minute concentration along the x axis rather than to the maximum of the maximum 3-minute concentrations (or other time average).

These equations give the maximum ground-level concentrations at any distance down wind under the plume axis, but the duration of the sampling period must be stated, see Section 19.19.

Dilution Factor. The ratio (initial concentration/ground concentration) in g/m^3 gives the dilution of the pollutant at point x, y, z. The concept of dilution factor is necessary when dealing with the emission of odours of unknown chemical concentration and composition since it is possible to determine the approximate concentration to which the original effluent must be diluted to be below the limit of perception by skilled assessors[78]. The concept is also better understood by laymen.

Table 19.2 KEY TO PASQUILL STABILITY CATEGORIES[8,27]

A. Extremely unstable conditions; B. Moderately unstable conditions; C. Slightly unstable conditions; D. Neutral conditions and for all overcast conditions during day or night, irrespective of wind speed and for any sky condition during the hour preceding or following night; E. Slightly stable conditions; F. Moderately stable conditions.

Surface wind speed (at 10 m) m/s	Insolation			Night-time conditions (including one hour before sunset and after dawn)	
	Strong	Moderate	Slight	Thin overcast or $\geq \frac{4}{8}$ low cloud	$\leq \frac{3}{8}$ cloud
2	A	A–B	B	—	—
2–3	A–B	B	C	E	F
3–5	B	B–C	C	D	E
5–6	C	C–D	D	D	D
6	C	D	D	D	D

For A–B take averages of σ for A and B, etc.

Strong incoming solar radiation corresponds to a sun altitude greater than 60° with clear skies: slight insolation to a sun altitude from 15° to 35° with clear skies. Incoming radiation that would be strong with clear skies can be expected to be reduced to moderate with $\frac{5}{8}$ to $\frac{7}{8}$ cloud cover of middle height and to slight with broken low clouds.

In order to avoid use of unrealistic values of σ_y and σ_z derived from insufficient observations at a proposed site, Pasquill preferred in his original paper[27] to express σ_z in terms of a vertical spread h where $\sigma_z = h/2 \cdot 15$; and σ_y in terms of an angular spread θ; $\sigma_y = x \tan \theta/4 \cdot 3$. His tables for values of θ reduce to the following, where the subscript refers to the stability category

$$\theta_A = \tfrac{1}{3}(260 - 40 \log x) \qquad \theta_D = \tfrac{1}{3}(80 - 10 \log x)$$
$$\theta_B = \tfrac{1}{3}(185 - 25 \log x) \qquad \theta_E = \tfrac{1}{3}(65 - 10 \log x)$$
$$\theta_C = \tfrac{1}{3}(130 - 20 \log x) \qquad \theta_F = \tfrac{1}{3}(40 - 5 \log x)$$

The numerical coefficient 2·15 is the 10 per cent ordinate of the normal Gaussian distribution curve (4·3 = 2 × 2·15).

When Pasquill's values for θ and h are used, equation (19.8) for the 3-minute glc under the centre line of the plume reduces to

$$C_o = \frac{168 \times 10^6 \, Q \exp\left[-2 \cdot 303(H/h)^2\right]}{\theta h \times u} \qquad (19.16)$$

For calculation of cross wind glc it is necessary to revert to equation (19.9).

Pasquill Stability Categories

The values of the standard deviations σ_y and σ_z in equations (19.9) to (19.11) vary with the turbulent structure of the atmosphere, the surface roughness, the effective height of the plume, the wind speed, the distance from the source (chimney) and the sampling time over which the concentration is to be estimatimated—which in these equations is 3–10 minutes. Sutton chose working values for σ_y and σ_z in equation (19.9) for neutral conditions of stability. When experimental data for other stabilities became available Pasquill made provisional estimates for σ_y and σ_z over relatively open country for six categories of stability which he specified qualitatively in terms of insolation, state of the sky and wind speed. The key to Pasquill's categories is given in Table 19.2.

Ideally the values of σ_y and σ_z during the occurrence of each stability category should be measured during all seasons at any proposed site for a new factory, together with wind direction and velocity at expected average plume height. In practice this is seldom practicable, nor are measurements available from a local Meteorological Station and consequently values of σ_y and σ_z are read for the required distance from the general curves of values estimated by Pasquill. Small-scale charts of these values are given in Figures 19.6 and 19.7. Readers who are unable to make photographic enlargements of these charts for more precise readings will find large-scale charts for σ_y and σ_z in Reference 20, Figures 3.2 and 3.3. Charts for Pasquill's vertical spread $h = 2 \cdot 15 \, \sigma_z$ on a suitable scale are also to be found in Reference[39], Figure (i), which may be more readily obtainable by British readers. References 20 and 39 both give charts for rapid estimation of glc for plume heights up to 250 m.

The frequency of occurrence of Pasquill's stability categories at a few places in Britain is given in Table 19.3. Values for the main synoptic hours,

Table 19.3 ANNUAL (10-YEAR) AVERAGE FREQUENCY OF OCCURRENCE OF PASQUILL'S STABILITY CATEGORIES FOR SELECTED PLACES IN BRITAIN, EXPRESSED AS ROUNDED PERCENTAGES[39]

Location	Stability category					
	A	B	C	D	E	F
Calshot (coast)	1	8	15	45	12	19
Cranwell aerodrome	2	7	16	45	12	18
Croydon airport	2	9	17	38	12	22
Glasgow, Renfrew airport	2	5	13	36	14	30
Holyhead (coast)	2	8	13	56	9	12
Hurn airport	1	9	16	37	11	26
Manchester, Ringway airport	2	7	15	44	10	22
Tynemouth (coast)	1	10	24	30	16	19

00.01; 06.00; 12.00; 18.00 h, in January, April, July, October and for a few other places may be obtained from the Meteorological Office H.Q., Bracknell[41]. The frequency of occurrence of Categories A and B at midday is up to 9 per cent for Category A and up to 30 per cent for Category B during the summer months. It is therefore desirable to estimate the glc during the occurrence of the categories and their duration at places of interest to check that they are not likely to be excessive.

19.10 Time—Average Concentrations

Equation (19.9) gives the maximum concentration of pollutant at a point downwind of a chimney during any time sample of 3 minutes. Since the wind varies in direction and speed and the variations have a complicated pattern in frequency and amplitude, particularly close to the ground, the glc varies greatly from moment to moment. Lucas states that the concentration pattern only becomes fairly steady when averaged over an hour[18]. It is in fact becoming common practice for pollution specialists to use the one-hour average glc of SO_2 as the significant parameter in considering the magnitude of air pollution from a source (e.g. by ASME[21]). Health Authorities mostly use measured 24-hour average concentrations of SO_2 because this is the measurement made continuously by many Local Authorities, particularly in the U.K. These records, of course, measure the 'background' pollution derived from all points of the compass. It is these extensive records, in combination with similar records for smoke, which are used by physicians considering the effects of SO_2 on the population. Effects of SO_2 on vegetation have been expressed in terms of exposure to concentrations over 4, 8 and 24 hours.

It follows from the above discussion that the ratios one hour/3 min and 24 hours/3 min are the most important when considering the significance of the glc from a new or existing chimney. What applies to SO_2, on which most information is available, will apply to other pollutants. Obviously 'sniffs' of highly toxic gases would be significant but these would be controlled by normal safety regulations.

The above 3-min ratios are dependent on variations with time of the ratio σ_z/σ_y and the wind speed. It is implicit that the wind direction remains constant within the usual 30° sector commonly employed in meteorological records.

There are insufficient records of the variations of σ_z/σ_y with time for generalizations to be applied and it is therefore necessary to use available records for measurements of the 3-min maximum glc of SO_2 over prolonged surveys. Analysis of the highly complicated records taken during the Tilbury survey[18] indicate that the one-hour/3-min ratios can be simplified to the following[50]:

Steady wind conditions	$\frac{3}{4}$
Average conditions	$\frac{1}{2}$
Certain unstable conditions	$\frac{1}{4}$

For the highly unstable conditions, Category A, Maynard Smith[75] suggests that the ratio may be 1/15. This would only apply for a 1–2 m/s wind. For most cases, the highest glc are found when the stability is Category C and the wind 8–12 m/s (a flat peak). For this condition, the ratio suggested and used in the worked examples is $\frac{3}{8}$ (average of $\frac{1}{2}$ and $\frac{1}{4}$).

For the ratio daily mean/3 min maximum, the factors 1/10 and 1/12 were found at High Marnham[3] and Tilbury[18]. As there were more measurements at High Marnham, the factor suggested is 1/10.

Note 1. The ratio of max. 3 min/max. hour and day under the centre line of the plume were lower at High Marnham—namely 1·5 and 6 respectively (Reference 18, page 429). It does not seem appropriate to use these factors in design calculations, taking into account that the maximum rate of discharge of pollutant is used for Q, and that the wind is continuously swinging by a few degrees.

Note 2. In the first edition of this book the factors quoted were those supplied by Meade to the author of Reference 2. These were obtained from a few measurements at chimney height taken downwind of the UKAEA Harwell reactor over a period of only 30 minutes. Meade's ratios follow a 1/5 power law.

Note 3. Measurements of smoke by Hino[40] from three power stations in flat and slightly hilly situations together with those by other workers including those at High Marnham show that the ratio follows a 1/2 power law for sampling durations from 10 minutes to 5 hours, i.e. $C_{o\,max} \propto \tau^{-1/2}$. This power law is supported by the theoretical studies reviewed by Hino. He remarks that the 1/5 power law seems to be valid for sampling times up to 10 minutes. The 1/2 power law gives a ratio 3 mm/one hour of 2·5.

19.11 Worked Examples on Chimney Height

1. Estimate the highest value of the one-hour glc on the circle around a chimney of 110 m height emitting 400 g/s of a polluting gas in a flue gas stream having a heat content of 15 MW. The meteorological conditions to be taken are Pasquill stability Category C and wind speed at 10 m/s. State the approximate radius of the circle.

2. What will be the highest 3-min glc from this plant when the stability category is A and the wind speed 2 m/s?

3. Estimate the highest one-hour glc at 5 km downwind where there is a hospital whose patients are likely to be affected by the pollutant.

The ground on which the hospital stands is a ridge 32 m higher than the base of the chimney and the wind flow from the chimney is roughly at an angle of 30° to the line of the ridge. The windows of the hospital wards are 8 m above ground level.

4. Estimate the addition to the one-hour glc of example 3 from an upwind extension of the factory comprising a second 50 m chimney emitting 200 g/s pollutant with a heat content of 10 MW. Assume that this second chimney is at a distance 500 m crosswind from the direct line between the first chimney and the hospital.

Note. Q is calculated from the quantity, specific heat and temperature of the flue gases leaving the mouth of the chimney. For U.K. conditions the average temperature of the ambient air may be taken as 10°C. The chimney designer is usually only given the temperature of the gas entering the base of the chimney. For continuously operating plant with gas rates in excess of 10^5 m³/h and a well insulated chimney, the temperature drop up the chimney has been measured as less than 10°C. For smaller plants the temperature loss should be calculated assuming an external air flow past the chimney of 15 m/s.

Solutions

1. Plume rise, $\Delta h = \dfrac{[475 + 2/3(110 - 100)]15^{\ddagger}}{10} = 97$ m (equation (19.4)).

Plume height above base of chimney, $H = 100 + 97 = 207$ m (equation (19.8)).

For the highest 3 min glc at stability Category C, $\sigma_z = H/\sqrt{2} = 146$ m (equation (19.12)).

For Category C stability, $x = 2550$ m.

From Figure 19.6, $\sigma_y = 250$ m.

From equation (19.13), $C_o = \dfrac{0 \cdot 117 \times 400}{250 \times 146 \times 10} = 128 \times 10^{-6}$ g/m³

$$= 128 \ \mu g/m^3.$$

An approximate check can be read from Figure 3 of Reference 39. This gives the distance for the highest glc as 2550 m and a concentration of 75 g/m³ for a wind speed of 5 m/s and an emission of one g/s. Hence for an emission of 400 g/s and wind of 10 m/s, $C_o = 150 \ \mu g/s$.

The one-hour glc will be 3/8 of the 3 min glc for the slightly unstable conditions of Category C = 56 $\mu g/m^3$.

2. For a wind speed of 2 m/s, the plume rise $\Delta h = 485$ m and $H = 595$ m. For Category A stability, $\sigma_z = H/\sqrt{2} = 420$ m.

The distance of the highest glc for this value of σ_z is $x = 980$ m.
At 980 m, σ_y (Category A) = 210 m.
By equation (19.13), the highest 3-min glc =

$$= \frac{0.117 \times 400}{210 \times 420 \times 2} = 2.66 \times 10^{-4} \text{ g/m}^3$$

$$= 226 \ \mu\text{g/m}^3.$$

Measurements around High Marnham power station indicated that this type of peak seldom persists for more than 15 min[3]. M. Smith[75] suggests that the ratio of 3-minute to one-hour glc for very unstable atmospheric stability (Category A) is 15.

3. The net plume height above the hospital windows $H = 207 - 32 - 8 = 167$ m.
A 5 km downwind and for Category C stability, $\sigma_y = 450$, $\sigma_z = 265$.
From equation (19.11),

$$C_o = \frac{400}{3.14 \times 450 \times 265 \times 10} \exp\left[-\frac{1}{2}\left(\frac{167}{265}\right)^2\right] = 88 \ \mu\text{g/m}^3, \text{ 3 min glc.}$$

One-hour glc = 33 μg/m³.

4. From equations (19.4) and (19.6),
Plume rise $\Delta h = [470\{0.67 + 5.7 \times 10^{-3}(50 - 47)\}]10^{\frac{1}{4}}/10$
$= 58.$
Plume height above chimney base = $50 + 58 - 40 = 68 = H$.
At 5 km distance and Category C stability, $\sigma_y = 450$, $\sigma_z = 265$.
From equation (19.10) and with a 10 m/s wind,

$$C_o = \frac{400}{3.14 \times 450 \times 465 \times 10} \exp\left[-\frac{1}{2}\left(\frac{500}{450}\right)^2\right] \exp\left[-\frac{1}{2}\left(\frac{68}{265}\right)^2\right] \text{g/m}^3$$

$$= 61 \times 10^{-6} \times 0.546 \times 0.968 \text{ g/m}^3$$

$$= 32 \ \mu\text{g/m}^3.$$

If the additional chimney were exactly upwind of the hospital, the addition to the glc would have been 59 μg/m³. As it would be 500 m crosswind, the glc addition is reduced by the factor 0.546.

19.12 Accuracy of Estimate

In their review of the accuracy of estimates, the ASME guide concluded that carefully designed power station chimneys have achieved their purpose in ameliorating air pollution, and they state 'the weight of evidence indicates that calculations have turned out very well indeed even though formal proof is lacking. This may possibly represent over-design rather than accurate design.' Only during the Tilbury survey[18,19] have measurements been made both of plume height and ground level concentration of pollutant. Scriven (Reference 19, page 220) concluded from these measurements that, in the absence of stable layers (inversions) the simple diffusion formula for highest one-hour glc can never be exceeded by a factor of 20–50 per cent (which is about the same as the inherent experimental errors). He adds that the effects of stable layers can at most increase the above limits by a further 80 per cent.

19.13 Inversion Conditions

The effect of an atmospheric temperature inversion above a chimney discharge is that of a lid which restricts the vertical diffusion and prevents the plume from rising. All the gases in the discharge then diffuse to ground and at some distance beyond the point of normal highest glc they become uniformly mixed. Consequently the previous dispersion equations have to be modified. By definition in equation (19.8), the concentration at the edge of the plume is one-tenth of that at the plume centre line and the height of the upper edge above this centre line is $H = 2 \cdot 15 \, \sigma_z$. When the top edge of the plume reaches the lid of stable air bounding the inversion at height L above the ground, mixing downwards occurs. Hence up to the distance x_L from the chimney, equation (19.12) holds, and $\sigma_z = L/2 \cdot 15 = 0 \cdot 37 \, L$. Thereafter downward mixing begins to occur and is complete at a distance $2x_L$—that is by then the plume in uniformly mixed with the air between the height L and the ground. (See Reference 27, page 43; Reference 20, page 7.) For places beyond the distance $2x_L = L$, the concentration of pollutant at any height below L and crosswind distance y is given by

$$\chi(x, y, z; H) = \frac{Q}{\sqrt{2\pi}\,\sigma_y \, L \, u} \exp\left[-\frac{1}{2}\left(\frac{y}{\sigma_y}\right)^2\right] \qquad (19.17)$$

Along the centre line of the plume, $y = 0$ and

$$C_o = \frac{Q}{u} \cdot \frac{1}{2 \cdot 51 \, L \, \sigma_y} \qquad (19.18)$$

Increase in the glc by an inversion may be ignored when the plume height H is smaller than $0 \cdot 75 \, L$. On very rare occasions, the plume centre line is reflected down to the ground to the same point as the highest maximum glc, and the latter is doubled. This occurs when the plume height H lies within the limits L and $0 \cdot 75 \, L$.
    Then

$$C_o = \frac{2Q}{e\pi u H^2} \times 2 = \frac{0 \cdot 47 \, Q}{u L^2} \qquad (19.19)$$

Experience indicates that this condition seldom occurs (page 409 of Reference 18 and page 486 of Reference 75).

19.13.1 Radiation Inversions

Radiation inversions extending upwards from the ground occur frequently on clear nights in the United Kingdom; if the plume height is higher, it does not diffuse below the inversion boundary and the glc is reduced virtually to zero. These inversions seldom extend above 50 m, though they reached a height of over 100 m during the 5-day London smog of 1952.

The temperature gradient in a radiation inversion, that is the increase in temperature with height, falls off quite rapidly with increase in height from the ground. The analysis of 4000 balloon ascents during 5 years at Cardington in the absence of strong winds gave the average frequency of temperature increase between layers of height 30 and 75 m during inversion conditions as follows.

°C temperature increase between layers of heights 30 and 75 m from ground.

Average per cent frequency	6	5	4	3	2	1	0	−1 neutral.
over 5 years	0·025	0·025	0·18	0·3	˙1·9	11	78	8·1

Figures are available for heights up to 300 m[47].

A warm plume would rise through an inversion with a temperature difference of only 1°C. Only during 0·4 per cent of the year was the temperature difference greater than this.

That plumes with a high heat content will rise through an inversion has been shown in aerial photographs taken above several London power stations beside the Thames estuary during a smog in 1962. Specially coloured smoke from a plume with a heat emission of 15 MW from a 92 m high chimney penetrated an inversion at a height of 240 m[29,46]. Hence equations (19.17) and (19.18) apply mainly to small heat emissions.

19.13.2 Elevated Inversion

Warm southerly winds travelling from the ocean are cooled by contact with the sea, thus generating upper air inversion. Strong inversions were found at 800 m during the Northfleet Lido studies of plume rise[19]. Inland the inversion was higher. Above the lower boundary of this type of inversion there may be a wind of 10 m/s. No measurements are available on the temperature gradient at the lower boundary of such inversions. This type of inversion could be of importance above factories situated on high ground close to the sea; also above large coastal power stations.

Another type of elevated inversion is the subsidence inversion. These are in high latitudes in high pressure systems associated with polar air masses, and with oceanic high pressure systems found at latitudes 30 N and 30 S. They are the meteorological cause of the smogs which occur in Los Angeles. (For further information, see Reference 8.) For a discussion of the conditions when plumes are released into air subsiding during hot weather on to large bodies of water such as rivers or lakes, see Reference 18, page 429. A plume released into subsiding air will reach a maximum height and then return to the ground at a distance of a few hundred metres, even if the lapse rate in the environment is adiabatic. This mechanism could explain the high concentrations of pollutant found occasionally even with tall stacks at high rates of emission. The phenomenon is less likely to occur on the coast because of the rapid development of sea breezes during itense solar radiation.

19.13.3 Fumigation

The term fumigation is used to describe the rapid mixing downwards to the ground of pollutant that has accumulated above a radiation inversion in a gentle wind. It occurs on a clear morning soon after the sun begins to dissipate the inversion, and newly developed convective eddies stir the pollutant downwards for up to two hours. Sea breeze circulations have the same effect.

The concentration of pollutant in a broad band under the plume can be estimated by equation (19.17).

19.14 Wind-tunnel Studies of Landscapes

Studies of the path of a plume over hilly terrain are of considerable assistance as a means of checking conclusions on the height required for a chimney based on previous experience and check calculations, but they cannot give the complete answer to the problem of height of plume required to ensure that the centre line of the plume passes well clear of the high ground. Unfortunately they are expensive, partly because of the cost and time to make a model of the terrain extending up to 10 km from the chimney. The scale used is 1/1000 to 1/2000.

The buoyancy of hot gases is simulated by using a stream of a mixture of helium and air from the model chimney. For observation of the plume travel smoke is produced by dropping a fine stream of 'cosmetic oil' on to a small hotplate in the gas stream to the model chimney.

Dynamic similarity with the full-scale cannot be achieved in a wind tunnel because the simultaneous reproduction of Froude and Reynolds numbers is not possible. It has been concluded that scaling parameters are best based on equality of the densimetric Froude number, but ensuring that the Reynolds number is maintained sufficiently high in the wind tunnel to keep the flow turbulent. It is then just possible to operate the tunnel at air speeds equivalent to 10 m/s real wind speed (about 1 m/s in tunnel). In practice, interest is primarily with real wind speeds of 10–15 m/s (see Section 19.8).

The inlet air to a tunnel has first to be smoothed completely by grids. Turbulence corresponding with that of the open air wind near the ground is then produced by special vanes on the floor of the tunnel upwind of the model. It is not possible to reproduce the 'swing of the wind' direction found in the open air.

Conditions in the tunnel are checked over flat ground roughened in the model with corrugated packing cardboard before introducing the model of the landscape.

It follows from this brief description that specialist meteorological physicists are required for setting up this type of study. A thorough examination of the actual landscape under several weather conditions is highly desirable since critical points may be missed by study of maps alone. Organizations which have suitable wind tunnels for these studies on behalf of clients are the National Physical Laboratory Aero Division and the Aerodynamics Department of Bristol University. (The Central Electricity Generating Board has also its own tunnel at Marchwood Engineering Laboratories, Southampton. This is larger than the Bristol tunnel.)

N.P.L. Tunnel. This is an open-sided tunnel containing a turntable of 2·5 m diameter on which the model is mounted with the chimney just outside the circumference, Figures 19.9 and 19.10. The model is rotated to show the effect of different wind directions. Upwind disturbances cannot be studied with the turntable arrangement. Photographic records of smoke flow are taken as described in Section 19.2.2.

Figure 19.9 Landscape model (scale 1/1760) on turntable in open-sided wind tunnel, National Physical Laboratory. The left side of the tunnel is open for observation. The air flow is smoothed and drawn across the model by the induced draught fan. The model is of a proposed coastal power station at New Plymouth, New Zealand. The height of the conical hill near the chimney is 150 m. (Courtesy of New Zealand Electricity Department, and Preece Cardew and Rider, Brighton. Crown Copyright reserved)

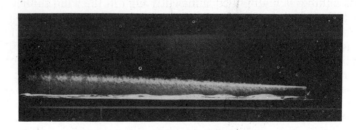

Figure 19.10 View of model in Figure 19.9 showing plume integrated over 2 seconds. Chimney height 183 m; diameter 15·3 m; efflux velocity 23 m/s; wind speed 15 m/s, both at site. Downwash is occurring because the effluent velocity is too low for such a wide chimney. (Courtesy of New Zealand Electricity Department, and Preece Cardew and Rider, Brighton. Crown Copyright reserved)

The author's confidence in tests in this tunnel was increased when it was found that a dip in the travel of the model plume as it passed over an estuary was also noticed with smoke test on the actual site. The model tests (scale 1/1760) indicated that the chimney height should be increased from 175 to 185 m.

Bristol Tunnel. This is a closed tunnel 10 m long, 5·5 m wide and 2·3 m high. It is large enough for observers to watch the smoke travel from all sides of the model, see Figure 19.11. Terrain upwind of the chimney can be included. As there is no turntable, it is necessary to rebuild the model for each wind direction to be studied. Smoke travel is recorded on colour cine-film. Samples of tunnel air are withdrawn continuously from points on the model to a mass spectrometer and analysed for helium, thus giving records of ground-level concentrations averaged over a few minutes.

Figure 19.11 Wind tunnel model (scale 1/1000) at Bristol University of projected 2640 MW power station beside the Firth of Clyde (right). Chimney height 240 m, emission velocity 15 m/s, wind 10 m/s at site. Top right shows village at 7 km distance and 150 m height above sea level. Hills to the right of photo (West) rise to 175 m and to 440 m to the South-West. (Courtesy South of Scotland Electricity Board)

This tunnel was used to check a proposed height of 240 m for a multi-flue chimney for a power station which at full load might emit 800 t/day of SO_2. The most sensitive place at the distance, 7 km, of the highest calculated glc was a village at a height of 150 m. Between the chimney and the village were two ridges running approximately at right angles to the line under the plume. Both ridges were lower than the top of the chimney. The second higher ridge, height 150 m, was observed to give some uplift to the plume and a credit of 90 m was given. The tests indicated that a chimney lower than 240 m should not be used. The helium glc near the chimney were higher than those calculated and were at variance with measured values of SO_2 downwind of Clifty Creek power station with a similar landscape[43].

19.15 Site Smoke Tests

Kelly[45] describes successful use of inexpensive smoke rockets to assist in choice of height for a chimney in Ireland beside a 700 m wide river with hills beyond rising to 85 m. The rockets were fired at an angle to give the estimated height of plume. The tests showed the downward currents of air caused by the hills and indicated the minimum height of chimney to prevent impingement of smoke on the hills.

Better information would be obtained, but at much greater expense, with smoke trails from large generators laid from helicopters or crop spraying type slow speed aeroplanes during weather conditions likely to give the highest glc. The method should be valuable in countries having predictable weather conditions, but is not regarded as practicable for the British Isles and W. Europe.

19.16 Acceptable Ground-level Concentrations

The international standard method of expressing concentrations of air pollutants is in micrograms SO_2 per cubic metre of air at ambient temperature. Many workers still express concentrations in volumes of SO_2 per million or hundred million of air which has the advantage that it is independent of temperature and pressure.

$$\text{One p.p.h.m. } SO_2 = 27 \cdot 5 \ \mu g/m^3 \text{ at } 10°C \text{ and } 1 \text{ atm.}$$

The concentration of pollutants reaching inhabited areas from a chimney must be sufficiently low to avoid damage to the health of people, livestock and vegetation. There is still little reliance to be obtained from physicians on the effect of pollutants on all classes of the population, ranging from the very young to the very old and including those with respiratory diseases such as bronchitis.

The recommended maximum values for healthy working adults exposed to pollutants in factory atmospheres during an 8-hour working day are issued annually by the American Conference of Governmental Industrial Hygienists[51]. They are republished at intervals by the British Ministry of Social Security for use by British industry under the Factory Acts[52]. The Alkali Inspector's standard, for general pollution of the open atmosphere, is that the minimum height of a new chimney should be such that the calculated 3-min maximum glc does not exceed one-thirtieth of that allowable in factory atmospheres[53]. Thus the limit for chlorine would be 3000/30 = 100 $\mu g/m^3$.

Chimney heights may then be estimated with sufficient accuracy by using the charts in the Ministry Memo described in Section 19.6. For pollutants other than SO_2, divide the emission rate of SO_2 on the charts by the ratio of the recommended threshold limits given in Reference 52 for the particular pollutant to that for SO_2—see also Section 19.16.

The chimney height so given may be adjusted in light of local topographical and meteorological conditions as well as population density, including local background concentration.

The concentration of SO_2 in towns receives special consideration. It is considered as indicating the concentration of gaseous pollutants from all sources of combustion. Thus there is evidence that 3:4 benzpyrene is present in coal smoke and that this substance is carcinogenic. There is no doubt that presence of smoke and possibly other particulates, and of other products of combustion such as oxides of nitrogen and partly burnt hydrocarbons, increases the susceptibility of people to SO_2[61]. The literature is voluminous. Much of it is summarized in Reference 55, and in the Proceedings and reports of discussions of the Annual Conferences held by the National Society for Clean Air, London; these give some references to supporting medical literature.

Most of the measurements in towns are for 24-hour samples. Thus Local Authorities in the U.K. operate over 1100 smoke and SO_2 daily recorders throughout the year, the readings of which are published[54]. The numerous measurements made in the principal cities in Europe and the U.S.A. are not published in similar convenient form. The British method for daily measurements which uses inexpensive apparatus with manual titration of absorbed acid is described in Reference 58. The SO_2 recorders for 3-minute measurements around High Marnham and Tilbury power stations are described in Reference 59, but see also Reference 18 for improvements. Methods used in the U.S.A., including automatic apparatus, are described in Reference 55.

Most medical investigation relates the effects of SO_2 on people with the daily 24-hour records for the towns where the atmosphere is seriously contaminated by smoke. Evidence was accumulated during the 1960s that SO_2 is less harmful to people in absence of domestic coal smoke than was previously thought. It is also known[55] that industrial workers exposed to more than 1000 p.p.h.m. pure SO_2 (27000 $\mu g/m^3$) are unaffected; reports are, however, for places free from 'smoke' and particulates.

Whilst no physicians will at present give a threshold limit value, which must not be exceeded, for SO_2 concentrations in towns, it appears that London patients with chronic lung disease suffer from an accentuation of symptoms when the daily average SO_2 exceeds 500 $\mu g/m^3$ in presence of 250 $\mu g/m^3$ of smoke.

In London and other towns the 24-hour figure contains morning and evening hourly peaks more than 30 per cent higher than the daily average[54]. On the other hand the SO_2 inside houses has been found to be 30–50 per cent of that in the open air[56]; hence people with lung complaints are advised to stay indoors during 'smogs'[61].

Medical evidence given at Public Enquiries in Great Britain in 1968–69 on proposed large new sources of combustion flue gas emission from tall chimneys indicated that adverse effects on the population of towns would not occur with calculated one-hour concentrations below 400 $\mu g/m^3$, including background concentration derived mainly from houses. (This last is taken from the Local Authority records mentioned above. Peak concentrations are excluded when the chimney is sufficiently high to discharge pollutants above ordinary radiation inversions.)

19.17 Effect of Pollutants on Vegetation

The effects of air pollution on plants and soil is summarized in a report by the Agricultural Research Council[76]. All plants are more sensitive during the growing season. Conifers are the species of forest tree most sensitive to sulphur dioxide. Zahn[57] states that the threshold concentration for their continuous exposure to SO_2 is 540 $\mu g/m^3$, and that 2100 $\mu g/m^3$ can be tolerated for one hour.

Grass absorbs fluorides readily. The consequence is that cattle and sheep to a lesser extent grazing on contaminated pastures develop fluorosis, rotting of teeth and bones. It has been found by the Central Veterinary Laboratory that pastures should not contain more than 30 p.p.m. fluorides (dry weight). This concentration has been avoided around aluminium smelters in the U.S.A. by designing scrubbers which in combination with tall chimneys will maintain the concentrations of fluorides in the air below 1 $\mu g/m^3$ (Reference 77).

19.18 Reduction of Emissions of Sulphur Dioxide

The emission of large tonnages of SO_2 into the atmosphere has been the subject of concern since 1930. A 2600 MW power station burning oil of 3 per cent S content will discharge 800 tonnes/day of SO_2 at full load, and a chimney of about 240 m height is necessary for adequate dispersion to obtain acceptable ground level concentrations of SO_2 in the vicinity. The SO_2 is however carried along by the wind and finally brought down by rain as dilute sulphuric acid. Some is also absorbed by moist vegetation. It has been found that part of the acid is neutralized by ammonia liberated by decaying vegetation[63]. The long-term effects are not known, but are causing considerable disquiet among ecologists.

Battersea power station, London, has used a wet washing process since 1932. This, and a 1950 plant at Bankside, London, use the alkalinity of the river water and some chalk to neutralize the acidity of the absorbed SO_2. It is necessary to oxidize the sulphite to sulphate before discharge to river. The process has very limited application. Trials have also been made of processes in which neutralized wash water is recirculated and calcium sulphate removed as wet sludge[66]. The process is difficult to control because calcium sulphate forms supersaturated solutions which readily form scale on the absorption grids. There are also processes which produce ammonium sulphate which can be sold as fertilizer.

All wet washing processes have the disadvantage that condensation and re-evaporation of water droplets formed when the wet gases issue from the chimney top cause the plume to droop, sometimes almost to house level from a 100 m high chimney. The visibility of the plume is also a disadvantage.

Pilot plant results of some promise obtained by Esso have shown that the sulphur in fuel oil can be removed as calcium sulphate or sulphide by partial combustion of the oil in a 'pre-combustion chamber' containing continuously replenished fluidized limestone particles[64]. Calcium sulphate from small plants would be discarded. Both sulphide and sulphate can be regenerated to lime by fuel oil with production of 6–10 per cent SO_2 mixture from which pure SO_2 can be extracted and sold as liquid SO_2. Alternately the SO_2 could be reduced to elementary sulphur. The process has the advantage that vanadium compounds in the oil are also removed, thus reducing boiler deposits.

The most promising of the processes for the extraction of SO_2 (about 0·1 per cent volume concentration) from the flue gases leaving a large oil-fired boiler is known as the aluminized soda process. The absorbent is regenerated by 'synthesis gas' produced from naphtha with the production of the H_2S which is converted to elementary sulphur in a Claus kiln. There are also processes which produce sulphuric acid by oxidation of the SO_2 in the flue gases to SO_3 and collection of 70 per cent H_2SO_4 in electrostatic precipitators. This concentration of acid has a strictly limited market. These and other processes have been expertly reviewed in Reference 19, page 309.

All absorbent processes are subject to the necessity for discarding absorbent through gradual accumulation of dust, chlorides and nitrates, a difficulty which is not sufficiently appreciated by their proponents. Only the largest power stations could hope to have a plant of viable size to produce sulphur or SO_2 because of the high capital and running costs which would increase greatly with decrease in output. No process yet developed would fully cover its costs by sales, largely because the price of sulphur is likely to remain low through increasing production by oil refineries. Processes which produce elementary sulphur are to be preferred because it is easy to handle and store without risk. Finally no power station staff would like to have a large chemical manufacturing unit within its flue-gas stream, particularly when on full load which is the time when the SO_2 removal plant is most required.

Because of all the objections to removal of SO_2 from flue gases it is more likely that this air pollution problem will be reduced by more use of fuel oil from which the sulphur has been partially removed as H_2S and converted into elementary sulphur. Use of low sulphur oil and coal is being increasingly required in parts of a few British and U.S. towns[67]. It was not practicable or economic in 1970 to reduce the S content of the heavy residual oils used in power stations from 3–5 per cent to 2 per cent. Nevertheless Fuller[65] has stated that the operating cost in 1969 of reducing to 1·3 per cent the overall average S content of 2·7 per cent in the 30 mm tonnes/yr of fuel oil used in the U.K. would be £45 million. With a capital cost of £50m, and capital charges of 20 per cent, the total cost would be less than £2 per tonne of oil fired. This is almost competitive with the non-effluent wet-washing process.

19.19 Deposition of Grit and Dust

The rate of deposition of particulate matter on the ground is expressed as mg/m^2 day[58].

The concentration of grit, dust and fumes in flue gases is now strictly controlled as described in Chapters 2 and 13 and References 51, 53, 67, 68.

Fume and dust smaller than 20 μm are carried to ground level by eddy diffusion with the flue gas. Hence the highest concentration reaching the ground can be estimated from the concentration in the chimney effluent and equation (19.13). Thereafter the concentration can be estimated with less certainty by the general equation (19.10). This equation assumes total reflection of the gas stream when the plume reaches the ground, which will be true of gases but not of fine dust since some of it adheres to the ground. The highest rate of deposition per second of fine dust and fume is therefore proportional to the product of the concentration, and free falling speed of particles, f.

Hence the maximum rate of deposition of particles smaller than 20 μm is given by

$$D_s = 86\,C_o f Q_d \text{ mg/m}^2 \text{ day} \qquad (19.20)$$

where Q_d is the rate of emission of fine dust in g/s, C_o is the 24-hour glc of the dust in $\mu g/m^3$ and f is the free-falling speed in m/s in still air of the predominant size of particle.

D_s is so small in weight that it can usually be ignored. It becomes important, however, in times of visible covering power (Section 19.20).

Grit and dust larger than 20 μm fall out of the plume at a finite rate according to size and the calculation of the rate of deposition is complicated. Since deposits of dust falling on the ground from a chimney are blown around by turbulent eddies, it is more realistic to consider the amount of dust which falls within an octant (a section of 45°) around the base of a chimney during a period of one month.

Bosanquet et al.[69] have shown that when dust of free-falling speed f is emitted horizontally at height H into a horizontal wind of velocity u the average monthly rate of dust deposition at some distance x from the chimney is given by

$$D_s = 0.33 \times 10^6\, \frac{wb\phi}{H^2} \text{ mg/m}^2 \text{ day} \qquad (19.21)$$

where ϕ is a function of $[(f/u).(x/H)]$ and is given by Figure 19.12 and b is the proportion of time that the wind blows into the octant.

The deposition rate under the axis of the plume is given by

$$\text{Axial } D_s = 1.5 \times 10^6\, \frac{w\phi}{H^2} \text{ mg/m}^2 \text{ day} \qquad (19.22)$$

The method of calculation is as follows:

(i) Arrange the size analysis of the dust (example in Table 13.11) into convenient groups, using the geometric mean size as in Table 14.8. The free falling speed of the particles can be interpolated from Table 14.11.

(ii) Obtain the value of ϕ for each size group from the corresponding velocity ratio f/u and a chosen distance ratio represented by x/H where H is the height of the plume. For most dust emissions the highest value of D_s is obtained at about $x/H = 6$.

(iii) For design purposes it is best to assume that the proportion b of the month during which the wind blows constantly within an octant does not exceed 0.5 as it is most unusual for the wind to blow in any (octant) direction for more than 40 per cent of one month. Naturally, if a sensitive place is to be considered which is not downwind of the most frequent wind direction the value of b to be used is taken from 10-year wind records for the place.

(iv) Calculate the rates of deposition D_s for each size group. Summate the results to give the total deposition rate.

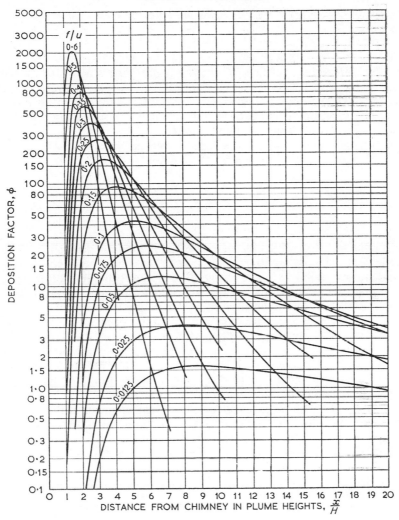

Figure 19.12 Factor for estimation of rate of deposition of particles, see equation (19.20)

From a study of records of standard deposit gauges, Nonhebel suggested[2] that the estimated dust deposit over a month from a new chimney should not exceed a rate D_s of 130 mg/m² day.

Fume. When the particulate material is a fine fume of particle size 0·1–0·5 μm the mechanism of deposition will no longer be gravity but molecular type diffusion and wash-out by rain. This case becomes important with the possible release of radioactive material such as Sr and Cs through failures of protective filters. A method of calculation for this case with convenient tables and graphs is given in Reference 73. The method would possibly be applicable to fine chemical fume emissions which are so dilute that no coagulation occurs in flues.

19.20 Obscuring Power of Deposited Dust

19.20.1 General

The rate of deposition of dust by weight is not always a reliable measure of the degree with which it becomes noticeable. Thus a small grit fall may cause only the slightest inconvenience provided it does not get in the eyes and cause irritation: it is believed that particles below 75 μm would not cause this trouble. The same weight of deposit in the form of 1 μm particles would, on the other hand, have a large covering power and would give a noticeable film on the surface on to which it fell.

19.20.2 Acceptable Limit for Rate of Coverage of Surfaces by Deposited Dust

The human eye has difficulty in resolving individual dots such as dust particles less than 100 μm diameter. Carey[70] has shown that coverage of a neutral surface by 0·4 per cent of fine dust is about the limit of perception by the unaided eye at a distance of a few feet. He has therefore proposed the hypothesis that a dust deposit outdoors giving a coverage of below 0·04 per cent per day should not give rise to complaints because, on average, there is sufficient rain within every 10-day period to wash away the deposited dust.

If these conditions are to be met, the daily coverage should not exceed 0·04 per cent at any point. When comparing this proposed maximum coverage with calculated results, due consideration should be given to the directional frequency of the wind over 10 day periods.

This hypothesis of coverage gives the design engineer concerned with emissions of fine dust a further criterion of the suitability of the combination of dust arrestor and chimney height under consideration.

Coverage can be calculated from the following relation: per cent coverage per day

$$= 100 \times \frac{\text{Rate of deposition by volume per unit area covered per day}}{\text{Diameter of deposited particles}} \qquad (19.23)$$

The covering power can be readily calculated from the table of size grade proportions and emissions set up for the preceding calculation of weight rate of deposition D_s, equation (19.21). As fine dust gives the greatest covering power, the calculation should be made at the distance giving the greatest deposition of dust smaller than 20 μm and distances immediately before it.

The British Standard deposit gauge[58] has been strongly criticized on the grounds that fine dust in particular can be entrained out of the collecting bowl in dry weather. A more reliable type of gauge which measures the covering power of deposited dust has been developed by the Central Electricity Research Laboratories[72]. There are, however, insufficient systematic records of measurements taken with this gauge on which to base a judgment of an acceptable figure for measurements in towns.

The C.E.R.L. gauge is undoubtedly superior to the B.S. standard gauge for monitoring existing plants to check that they have not been a cause of complaint by the public, e.g. in respect of soiling of washing. As they are directional, they are also a defence against unjustified complaints made when the wind was not blowing from the chimney to the place of complaint.

19.21 Assessment of Effective Dissipation of Visible Dusty Plumes

The elimination of dark smoke from factory chimneys during the decade 1960–70 has resulted in more attention being paid to the appearance of chimney plumes. Occasionally plumes are visible for several kilometres; these have been termed persistent plumes and are the cause of public complaint. A large emission of visible material would cause persistence in a variety of atmospheric conditions, but modern methods of flue gas cleaning ensure that at worst it only occurs when atmospheric dilution is limited by a stable layer of air or an inversion. In these atmospheric conditions there are often clouds above a plume.

From a study of plumes from several coal- and oil-fired power stations, Jarman et al.[71] suggest that the design rule for avoidance of persistent plumes is to arrange that the dusty gas is diluted to invisibility before the turbulence produced by the effluent has been completely dissipated. Mathematically this means that the 'contrast' against clouds should be reduced below 0·005 before the plume has travelled one kilometre. The definition of 'contrast' and a worked example of its calculation from the quantity and size of the fine dust particles is given in the original paper.

As regards existing plant, it is suggested that if the visible length of a plume exceeds 1 km under cloudy skies during normal lapse conditions, it is very likely that in stable conditions the plant will produce a persistent plume.

References to Chapters

The first numbers in the following list refer to chapter numbers. With regard to the Reports published by the Ministry of Housing and Local Government this is now the Ministry of the Environment. Where British Standards are referred to it is important to check from the British Standards Yearbook that the latest edition and all amendments are consulted.

1 1.1. NONHEBEL, G. A commercial plant for the removal of smoke or oxides of sulphur from flue gases, *Trans. Faraday Soc.* **32**, 1291 (1936).

1.2. Legislation for England and Wales on effluents can be divided into categories as follows:
  (i) Discharge of trade effluents into non-tidal waters
    (*a*) *The River Boards Act*, 1948
    (*b*) *The Rivers (Prevention of Pollution) Act*, 1951
    (*c*) *The Thames Conservancy Act*, 1932 and
        The Lee Conservancy Acts, 1868 and 1938
    (*d*) *The Rivers (Presention of Pollution) Act*, 1961
    (*e*) *Water Resources Act*, 1963 and 1968 (Discharge to Underground Strata)
  (ii) Discharge of trade effluent into estuaries, tidal waters and the sea
    (*a*) *The Rivers (Prevention of Pollution) Acts*, 1951 and 1961
    (*b*) *The Clean Rivers (Estuaries and Tidal Waters) Act*, 1960
    (*c*) *The Sea Fisheries Regulation Act*, 1888
    (*d*) *The Harbours Acts*, 1814 and 1847, and Local Acts
    (*e*) *The Oil in Navigable Waters Act*, 1955
    (*f*) *The Coast Protection Act*, 1949
    (*g*) *The Crown Estate Act*, 1961
    (*h*) *Salmon and Freshwater Fisheries Act*, 1965
  (iii) Discharge of trade effluent into public sewers
    (*a*) *The Public Health Act*, 1936
    (*b*) *The Public Health (Drainage of Trade Premises) Act*, 1937
    (*c*) *The Public Health Act*, 1961
    (*d*) *The London County Council (General Powers) Act*, 1953
    (*e*) *The Radioactive Substances Act*, 1960

  Similar but separate legislation applies to Scotland.
  The Federation of British Industries have published a technical review of this legislation: *The Disposal of Trade Effluent in England and Wales*, London (1962).

1.3. *Annual Reports on Alkali &c., Works by the Chief Inspectors* for 1957–1960 inclusive (95th–97th Reports) H.M.S.O.

1.4. CARTER, J. S. *The Alkali &c., Works Regulation Act*, 1906 and *Alkali &c., Works Orders*, 1928 onwards. *Chemical Engineering Practice*, Vol XI, Chapter 7, ed. by Cremer, H. W. and Watkins. Butterworths, London. *Report of the Ministry of Housing and Local Government for* 1959. H.M.S.O. (1960).

1.5. KING, R. A. 'Economic utilization of sulphur dioxide from metallurgical gases', *Industr. Engng. Chem.* **42**, 2241–8 (Nov. 1950).

1.6. FORREST, J. S. and LOWE, H. J. 'Performance and scope for improvement in power station electrostatic precipitators.' *Proc. of Conference on The Mechanical Engineer's Contribution to Clean Air*, p. 45, 1957 (London, Institution of Mechanical Engineers).

1.7. CURRIE, R. M. *Work Study*. Sir Isaac Pitman and Sons Ltd. London. Published by British Institute of Management (1960).

1.8. BINSTED, D. S. 'Work study in project planning of a chemical process. Part II, Description of techniques.' *Chem. & Ind. (Rev.)* No. 3, 59 (1961).

1.9. OLIVE, T. R. 'Modern chemical engineering revamps conventional contact process.' *Chem. Engng* **57**, 103 (Oct. 1950).

1.10. MARSDEN, L. 'The use of models in plant design,' *Chart. Mech. Eng.* **8**, 618 (1961).

1.11. FARROW, D. J. 'The use of layout models in chemical plant design,' *Industr. Chem.* **38**, 279 (1962).

1.12. POPE, A. *Wind-tunnel Testing*. Chapman and Hall, London (1954).

1.13. PATTERSON, R. C. and ABRAHAMSEN, R. F. 'Floor modeling of furnaces and ducts,' *J. of Engineering for Power. Trans. ASME Series A*, **84**, 345 (1962).

1.14. HAWKSLEY, P. G. W., BADZIOCH, S. and BLACKETT, J. H. *Measurement of Solids in Flue Gases*, British Coal Utilization Research Association, Leatherhead (1961).

1.15. ARCHBOLD, M. J. 'Observations and experiences resulting from a precipitator improvement program,' *Combustion, N.Y.* **32**, 22 (May 1961).

1.16. COLLINS, K. E. and STEELE, D. J. 'A recording vane air flowmeter,' *Trans. Soc. Inst. Tech.* **13**, 255 (1961).

1.17. LOWE, H. J. and LUCAS, D. H. 'The physics of electrostatic precipitation,' *Brit. J. Appl. Phys.* Supplement No. 2, S.40 (1953).

1.18. Ministry of Housing and Local Government. Taken for granted. *Report of the Working Party on Sewage Disposal*. H.M.S.O. (1970).

1.19. WISDOM, A. S. The law on the Pollution of Waters. Shaw and Sons Ltd, London 1956.

2 2.1. CARTER, J. S. *The Alkali &c., Works Regulation Act*. 1906 and *Alkali &c., Works Orders*, 1928 to 1958, *Chemical Engineering Practice*, 1959, Vol. II, Chapter 7, ed. by Cremer, H. W. and Watkins, S. B. Butterworths, London. Report of the Ministry of Housing and Local Government for 1959. H.M.S.O. (1960).

2.2. *One hundred and third Annual Report on Alkali &c. Works*, H.M.S.O. (1960).

2.3. Ministry of Housing and Local Government. *Grit and Dust*. H.M.S.O. (1967). This memorandum advises on methods of measurement and gives recommended maximum levels of emission from coal- and oil-fired boilers, and furnaces where the gases are not in direct contact with material being heated.

2.4. PEMBERTON, J. 'The effects of air pollution on health and vegetation,' Chapter 4, *Air Pollution*, ed. by M. W. Thring, Butterworths, London (1967).

2.5. Report of Government committee on Air Pollution (Chairman: Sir Hugh Beaver). Cmd. 9322 H.M.S.O. (1954). Interim Report Cmd. 9011 H.M.S.O. (1953).

2.6. DAVIES, C. N. *Dust is Dangerous*. Faber and Faber, London (1954).

2.7. DRINKER, P. and HATCH, T. *Industrial Dust*, McGraw-Hill, London (1954).

2.8. FIFE, I. and MACHIN, E. A. *Redgrave's Factories Acts*. Twenty-first Edition. Butterworths, London.

2.9. Ministry of Housing and Local Government. *Grit and Dusts: the measurement of emissions from boiler and furnace chimneys. Standard levels of emission*. H.M.S.O. (1967).

2.10. Ministry of Housing and Local Government. *Chimney Heights*, 2nd Edition. H.M.S.O. (1967). A separate set of the charts on 'permatrace' is obtainable.

A general introduction to the use of instruments for gas purification plants will be found in a booklet *Chemical Plant Instrumentation—Some Notes on the Use of Measuring Instruments*, published by the Association of British Chemical Manufacturers, London (1960).

3 3.1. JONES, E. B. *Instrument Technology, Vol. 1*, 1st ed. *(Measurement of Pressure, Level, Flow and Temperature)*.1953; 2, 1st ed. *(Analysis)*, 1956; 3, 1st ed. *(Telemetering and Control)*. Butterworths, London (1957).

3.2. MILLER, J. T. (Ed.). *Instrument Manual*, 3rd ed. U.T.P., London (1960).

3.3. CONSIDINE, D. M. (Ed.). *Process Instruments and Controls*, 1st ed. McGraw-Hill, New York (1957).

3.4. B.S. 1041 *Code for Temperature Measurement*.

3.5. AIKMAN, A. R., MCMILLAN, J. and MORRISON, A. W. 'Static and dynamic performance of sheathed industrial thermometers,' *Trans. Soc. Instrum. Tech.* **5**, 138 (1953).

3.6. GODRIDGE, A. M., JACKSON, R. and THURLOW, G. C. 'The industrial measurement of gas temperature,' *Trans. Soc. Instrum. Tech.* **5**, 103 (1956).

3.7. D.S.I.R. Notes on Applied Science No. 12. *Calibration of Temperature Measuring Instruments*. H.M.S.O.

3.8. B.S. 1780 *Bourdon tube pressure and vacuum gauges.*

3.9. BUDENBERG, C. F. 'The Bourdon pressure gauge,' *Trans. Soc. Instrum. Tech.* **8**, 751 (1956).

3.10. B.S. 1042 *Methods for the measurement of fluid flow in pipes.*

3.11. CLARKE, W. J. 'Fluid flow through square edged orifice plates,' *Trans. Soc. Instrum. Tech.* **4**, 139 (1952).

3.12. CLARKE, W. J. 'Flow Measurements: some problems and devices of special interest,' *Trans. Soc. Instrum. Tech.* **11**, 234 (1959).

3.13. Symposium on Flow Measurement. *Trans. Soc. Instrum. Tech.* **11**, 114 (1959).

3.14. BALLS, V. W. 'Liquid flow control,' *Trans. Soc. Instrum. Tech.* **8**, 43 (1956).

3.15. *I.S.A. Annual Symposium on Analysis Instrumentation.* Plenum, N.Y.

3.16. Analytical reviews. *Analyt. Chem.* **41** (1969).

3.17. NOGARE, S. D. and JUVET, R. S. *Gas–liquid chromatography theory and practice,* Interscience, N.Y. (1962).

3.18. SCHUPH, O. E. *Gas Chromatography*, Interscience, N.Y. (1968).

3.19. GLASSER, L. G. 'Optical method of process stream analysis,' *Proc. National Conference on Instrumental Methods of Analysis, Chicago,* Paper No. A157-2-1-1 (1957).

3.20. RUSKIN, R. E. (Ed.). *Humidity and moisture measurements and Control in Science and Industry. Vol. I: Principles and methods of Measurement of Humidity in Gases.* Reinhold, N.Y. (1965).

3.21. MATTOCK, G. 'Electrode problems in plant pH measurement,' *Trans. Soc. Instrum. Tech.* **11**, 114 (1959).

3.22. YOUNG, A. J. *An Introduction to Process Control System Design,* 1st ed. Longmans, London (1965).

3.23. ECKMAN, D. P. *Automatic Process Control,* 1st ed. John Wiley, New York (1958).

3.24. B.S. 1523: Pt. 1. 1967. *Glossary of Terms used in Automatic Controlling and Regulating Systems.*

3.25. 'Minimum safety requirements for instruments using electricity,' *E.E.U.A.* (1970).

3.26. AGAR, J. 'On-line Liquid and Gas Density Measurement,' *Measurement and Control,* **I**, 14 (1968).

3.27. HILL, D. W. and POWEL, T. *Non-dispersive Infra-red Gas Analysis in Science, Medicine and Industry.* Hilgar, London (1968).

3.28. SCOTT, J. A. 'Automatic control of Distillation Columns by continuous Gas Chromatography,' *Measurement and Control,* **I**, 55 (1968).

3.29. HARRIOTT, P. *Process Control.* McGraw-Hill, New York.

3.30. WILLIAMS, T. J. 'Computers in Process Control—Annual Review,' *Ind. Eng. Chem.* **61**, 76 (1969).

4 4.1. SPIERS, H. M. *Technical Data on Fuel,* 5th ed. Table 251, 'Average properties of gaseous fuels,' pp. 317-8. British National Committee, World Power Conference, London (1950).

4.2. LOWRY, H. H. Correlation of the Bureau of Mines–American Gas Association Carbonization Assay Tests with Coal Analysis. Contribution 92, Carnegie Institute of Technology, Coal Research Laboratory, May 1941. (Published as *Amer. Inst. Min. Metall. Engrs Tech. Publication No.* 1332, 1941.)

4.3. SHVARTS, S. A. and SHINKAREVA, S. O. 'Balance sheet of the coking process,' (Coke & Chem.), *Kharkov,* No. 8, 6–11 (1959).

4.4. WOOD, L. J. and WILMAN, W. G. *Science in the Use of Coal.* Paper No. 18, Chemical nature of coal tar pitch. Proceedings of Conference, Sheffield. Published by Institute of Fuel (1958).

4.5. RICHARDS, R. O. and TAYLOR, A. 'The cooling of coke oven gas,' *Yearbook of the Coke Oven Managers' Association,* 447 (1961).

4.6. B.S. 3156:1968. *Methods for the Analysis of Fuel Gases. Pt. 2. Special Determinations.*

4.7. SILVER, L. 'Gas cooling with aqueous condensation,' *Trans. I. Chem. E., Lond.* **25**, 30–42 (1947).

4.8. HOLLINGS, H. and HUTCHINSON, W. K. 'Gas purification,' *J. Inst. Fuel* **8**, 360–71 (1935).

4.9. COLBURN, A. P. and HOUGEN, O. A. 'Design of cooler condensers for mixture of vapours with non-condensing gases,' *Industr. Engng Chem.* **26**, 1178–82 (1934).

4.10. COOPER, C. and PRIESTLEY, J. J. (Eds.) *King's Manual of Gas Manufacture.* Section 7a. 1956 edition. Walter King, London (1956).

4.11. POLLARD, R. 'Ancillary plant for the gas industry,' *Yearbook of the Coke Oven Managers' Association* 240–58 (1955).

4.12. BADGER, E. H. M. *J. Soc. Chem. Ind., Lond.* **65**, 166 (1946).

4.13. FRANCOMBE, K. W. *Trans. I. Gas E., Lond.* **99**, 132 (1949–50).

4.14. Chief Inspectors of Alkali &c. Works, *Ninety-sixth Annual Report*, H.M.S.O., London, 42 (1960).

4.15. SILVER, L. and HOPTON, G. U. *J. Soc. Chem. Ind., Lond.* **61**, 37 (1942).

4.16. MORRIS, G. A. and JACKSON, J. *Absorption Towers.* Butterworths, London (1953).

4.17. PRIESTLEY, J. J. *King's Manual of Gas Manufacture.* Section 7B. Walter King, London (1960).

4.18. BRADLEY, G. W. J. 'Some points on crude benzole recovery,' *Yearbook of the Coke Oven Managers' Association*, 202 (1937).

4.19. BUCKLEY, W. E. 'Some points on crude benzole recovery,' *Yearbook of the Coke Oven Managers' Association*, 205 (1937).

4.20. RUDDY, R. H. 'Some points on crude benzole recovery,' *Yearbook of the Coke Oven Managers' Association*, 207 (1937).

5 5.1. HIRSCHFELDER, J. O. *et al. Molecular Theory of Gases and Liquids,* Wiley, N.Y. (1954).

5.2. REID, R. C. and SHERWOOD, T. K. *Properties of gases and liquids,* McGraw-Hill, N.Y. (1966).

5.3. HECHT, G. *et al. Berechnung thermodynamischer Stoffwerte von Gasen und Flüssigkeiten,* VEB, Leipzig (1966).

5.4. LANDOLT-BÖRNSTEIN, 'Zahlenwerte und Funktionen,' Bd II-5-a 513, Springer Verlag (1969).

5.5. *International Critical Tables,* McGraw-Hill.

5.6. PERRY, J. H. *Chemical Engineers Handbook*, McGraw-Hill, Fourth edition (1963). Equilibrium data: section **14**, pp. 2–11. Diffusion: section **14**, pp. 19–24. Plate efficiencies: section **18**, p. 23.

5.7. GILLILAND, E. R. in SHERWOOD, T. K. *Absorption and Extraction*, N.Y. p. 11 (1937).

5.8. KEYES, J. J., PIGFORD, R. L. 'Diffusion in a ternary gas system with application to gas separation,' *Chem. Eng. Sci.* **6**, 215 (1957).

5.9. WILKE, C. R. 'Diffusional properties of multicomponent gases,' *Chem. Eng. Progr.* **46**–2, 95 (1950).

5.10. BIRD, R. B. *et al. Transport Phenomena*, 1st ed., Wiley, N.Y. (1960), 554–572.

5.11. MÜLLER, R. 'The exponential temperature dependence of gas side mass transfer coefficients' (in German), *Chem. Ing. Tech.* **40**–7, 344 (1968).

5.12. HIMMELBLAU, D. M., BISSCHOFF, K. B. 'Mass Transfer,' *Ind. Eng Chem. Fund.* **58**–12, 33 (1966), **60**–1, 67 (1968).

5.13. LEWIS, W. K., WHITMAN, W. G. 'Principles of gas absorption,' *Ind. Eng. Chem.* **16**, 1215 (1924).

5.14. JUDSON KING, C. 'The additivity of individual phase resistances in mass transfer operations,' *AIChEJ*, **10**–5, 671 (1964).

5.15. SEMMELBAUER, R. 'Calculation of the height of packing in packed towers' (in German), *Chem. Eng. Sci.* **22**, 1237 (1967).

5.16. RAIMONDI, P., TOOR, H. L. 'Interfacial resistance in gas absorption,' *AIChEJ*, **5**, 86 (1959).

5.17. MATSUYAMA, T. 'The rate of absorption of CO_2 in water,' *Mem. Fac. Engng. Kyoto Univ.* **15** (1953), abstract in German in *Chem. Ing. Tech.* **26**, 347 (1954).

5.18. DANCKWERTS, P. V., KENNEDY, A. M. 'Kinetics of liquid film processes in gas absorption,' *Trans. Inst. Chem. Eng.* 32-s, 54 (1954).

5.19. HIGBIE, R. W. 'The rate of absorption of a pure gas into a still liquid during short periods of exposure,' *Trans. Amer. Inst. Chem. Eng.* **31**, 365 (1935).

5.20. FÜRST, H., NITSCH, W. 'Interfacial resistance in physical gas absorption' (in German), *Chem. Ing. Tech.* **42**–3, 108 (1970).

5.21. TUNG, L. N., DRICKAMER, H. G. 'Diffusion through an interface,' *J. Chem. Phys.* **20**, 6 (1952).

5.22. EMMERT, R. E., PIGFORD, R. L. 'A study of gas absorption in falling liquid films,' *Chem. Eng. Progr.* **50**, 87 (1954).

5.23. SCHRAGE, R. W. *A Theoretical study of Interphase Mass Transfer*, Columbia Univ. Press, N.Y., 75 (1953).

5.24. WHITMAN, W. G. *Chem. Met. Eng.* **29**, 146 (1923).

5.25. VON WROBLEWSKI, S. 'On the laws after which gases are being transferred in liquid, solid–liquid and solid bodies' (in German), *Ann. Phys.* Leipzig, Neue Folge, Bd 11, 481 (1877).

5.26. DANCKWERTS, P. V. 'Significance of liquid film coefficients in gas absorption,' *Ind. Eng. Chem.* **43**, 1460 (1951).

5.27. KISHINEVSKY, M. 'Two approaches to the theoretical analysis of absorption processes,' *J. Appl. Chem.* USSR, **28**, 811, 927 (1955).

5.28. TOOR, H. L., MARCHELLO, J. 'Film-penetration model for mass and heat transfer,' *AIChEJ*, **4**, 97 (1958).

5.29. HATTA, S. *Technol. Repts Tohoku.* Imp. Univ. **10**, 119 (1932), excerpt in Sherwood, T. K., Pigford, R. L. *Absorption and Extraction*, McGraw-Hill, 2nd ed., p. 324 (1952).

5.30. DANCKWERTS, P. V. 'Absorption by simultaneous diffusion and chemical reaction,' *Trans. Faraday Soc.* **46**, 300 (1950).

5.31. VAN KREVELEN, D. W., HOFTYZER, P. J. 'Kinetics of gas–liquid reactions,' *Rec. Trav. Chim.* Pays-Bas, **67**, 563 (1948).

5.32. PIGFORD, R. L. 'Simultaneous absorption and chemical reaction,' *Ind. Eng. Chem.* **45**, 1247 (1953).

5.33. BRIAN, P. L. T. *et al.* 'Penetration theory for gas absorption accompanied by a second order chemical reaction,' *AIChEJ*, **7**, 226 (1961).

5.34. BRIAN, P. L. T. 'Gas absorption accompanied by an irreversible reaction of general order,' *AIChEJ*, **10**, 5 (1964).

5.35. ASTARITA, G. *Mass Transfer with Chemical Reaction*, Elsevier, Amsterdam (1967).

5.36. PEACEMAN, D. W. *Liquid side resistance in gas absorption with and without chemical reaction*, thesis M.I.T., Cambridge, Mass. (1951).

5.37. ONDA, K. *et al.* 'Gas absorption accompanied by complex chemical reactions, reversible reactions,' *Chem. Eng. Sci.* **25**, 753 (1970). See also 'Consecutive reactions,' *Chem. Eng. Sci.* **25**, 761 (1970) and 'Parallel reactions,' *Chem. Eng. Sci.* **25**, 1023 (1970).

5.38. SECOR, R. M., BEUTLER, J. A. 'Penetration theory for diffusion accompanied by a reversible chemical reaction with generalized kinetics,' *AIChEJ*, **13**–2, 365 (1967).

5.39. HUANG, C. J., KUO, C. H. 'Mathematical models for mass transfer accompanied by reversible chemical reaction,' *AIChEJ*, **11**–5, 901 (1965).

5.40. DIRKEN, M. N. J., MOOK, H. 'Rates of absorption of carbon dioxide in liquids' (in German), *Biochem. Z.* **219**, 452 (1930).

5.41. VIELSTICH, W. 'Kinetics of mass transfer between gases and liquids' (in German), *Chem. Ing. Tech.* **28**, 543 (1956).

5.42. KRAMERS, H. *et al.* 'Absorption of nitrogen tetroxide by water jets,' *Chem. Eng. Sci.* **14**, 115 (1961).

5.43. KWANTEN, F. J. G. 'Investigation of gas absorption with laminar liquid jets' (in Dutch), *Polytech. Tijdschr.* Ed. Procestechniek **24**–7, 232 (1969), **24**–8, 266 (1969), **24**–9, 304 (1969).

5.44. CULLEN, E. J., DAVIDSON, J. F. 'Absorption of gases in liquid jets,' *Trans. Faraday Soc.* **52**, 113 (1956).

5.45. ONDA, K. *et al.* 'Measurement of the gas side mass transfer coefficient by liquid jet,' *Kagaku Kogaku*, **4**–2, 247 (1966).

5.46. LYNN, S. *et al.* 'Absorption studies in the light of the penetration theory with long and short wetted wall columns,' *Chem. Eng. Sci.* **4**–2, 49–67 (1955).

5.47. WHITMAN, W. G., DAVIS, D. S. 'Comparative absorption rates for various gases,' *Ind. Eng. Chem.* **16**, 1233 (1924).

5.48. DANCKWERTS, P. V., GILHAM, A. J. 'The design of gas absorbers; Methods for predicting rates of absorption with chemical reaction,' *Trans. Inst. Chem. Eng.* **44**, T42 (1966).

5.49. STEPHENS, E. J., MORRIS, G. A. 'Determination of liquid film absorption coefficients: a new type of column and its application to problems of absorption in the presence of chemical reaction,' *Chem. Eng. Progr.* **47**, 232 (1951).

5.50. ANDREW, S. P. S. 'Scale up in absorption and distillation,' *Symposium Univ. of Manchester Institute of Science and Technology* (March 1969).

5.51. HOBLER, T. *Mass Transfer and Absorbers*, Pergamon, London (1966).

5.52. RANZ, W. E., DICKSON, PH. F. 'Mass and heat transfer rates for large gradients of concentration and temperature,' *Ind. Eng. Chem. Fund,* **4**–3, 345 (1965).

5.53. KIRK-OTHMER. *Encyclopedia of Chemical Technology*, 2nd ed. **1**, 44. Wiley, N.Y. (1963).

5.54. KOHL, A., RIESENFELD, F. *Gas Purification*, McGraw-Hill, N.Y. (1960).

5.55. NORMAN, W. S. *Absorption, Distillation and Cooling Towers*, 2nd ed. Longmans (1962).

5.56. MORRIS, G. A., JACKSON, J. *Absorption Towers*, Butterworths, London (1953).

5.57. SPRINGE, W., SCHMIDT, E. O. *Fortschritte der Verfahrenstechnik* (1952–1967), Verlag Chemie, Weinheim, W. Germany.

5.58. FOUST, A. L. *et al. Principles of Unit Operations*, Wiley, N.Y. (1960).

5.59. SHARMA, M. M., DANCKWERTS, P. V. 'Chemical methods of measuring interfacial area and mass transfer coefficients in two fluid systems,' *Brit. Chem. Eng.* **15**–4, 522 (1970).

5.60. VAN KREVELEN, D. W., HOFTYZER, P. J. 'Kinetics of simultaneous absorption and chemical reaction,' *Chem. Eng. Progr.* **44**–7, 529 (1948).

5.61. VAN KREVELEN, D. W., HOFTYZER, P. J. 'Studies of gas absorption,' *Rec. Trav. Chim. Pays-Bas*, **66**, 49 (1947).

5.62. MIKA, V. 'Model of packed absorption column,' *Collect. Czech. Chem. Commun.* **32**–8, 2933 (1967).

5.63. DE WAAL, K. J. A., BEEK, W. J. 'A comparison between chemical absorption with rapid first order reaction and physical absorption in one packed column,' *Chem. Eng. Sci.* **22**, 585 (1967).

5.64. KOLEV, N. N. 'Calculation of the effective surface in Raschig ring packings' (in German), *Verfahrenstechnik* **4**–1, 29 (1970).

5.65. TEUTSCH, TH. 'Absorption in packed towers' (in German), *Chem. Ing. Tech.* **37**–12, 1224 (1965).

5.66. ANDREW, S. P. S. 'Aspects of gas–liquid mass transfer,' *Alta Technologica Chimica, Accademia Nazionale Dei Lincei, Roma* (1961).

5.67. American Institute of Chemical Engineers, *Bubble Tray Design Manual*, N.Y. (1958).

5.68. ASANO, K. *et al.* 'Vapour phase mass transfer coefficients in tray towers,' *Kagaku Kogaku*, **4**–2, 369 (1966).

5.69. ASANO, K., FUJITA, S. 'Liquid phase mass transfer coefficients in tray towers,' *Kagaku Kogaku*, **4**–2, 330 (1966).

5.70. DYTNERSKII, Y. I. 'The theory and calculation of heat and mass transfer in tray towers,' *Int. Chem. Eng.* **6**–2, 204 (1966).

5.71. DILLON, G. B., HARRIS, I. J. 'The determination of mass transfer coefficients and interfacial areas in gas–liquid contacting systems,' *Can. J. Chem. Eng.* 307 (Dec. 1966).

5.72. EBEN, C. D., PIGFORD, R. L. 'Gas absorption with chemical reaction on a sieve tray,' *Chem. Eng. Sci.* **20**, 803 (1965).

5.73. SMITH, R. K., WILLS, G. B. 'Application of penetration theory to gas absorption on a sieve tray,' *Ind. Chem. Eng. Process Des. Develop.* **5**–1, 39 (1966).

5.74. SHARMA, M. M., GUPTA, R. K. 'Mass transfer characteristics of plate columns without downcomers,' *Trans. Inst. Chem. Eng.* **45**, T169 (1967).

5.75. ANDREW, S. P. S., HANSON, D. 'The dynamics of nitrous gas absorption,' *Chem. Eng. Sci.* **14**, 105 (1961).

5.76. PORTER, K. E. *et al.* 'Interfacial areas and liquid film mass transfer coefficients for a 3 ft diameter bubble cap plate derived from absorption rates of carbon dioxide into water and caustic soda solutions,' *Trans. Inst. Chem. Eng.* **44**, T274 (1966).

5.77. ZIEMINSKI, S. A. 'Behaviour of air bubbles in dilute aqueous solutions,' *Ind. Chem. Eng. Fund*, **6**–2, 233 (1967).

5.78. CALDERBANK, P. H. 'Mass transfer coefficients in gas–liquid contacting with and without mechanical agitation,' *Trans. Inst. Chem. Eng.* **37**, T173 (1959).

5.79. HUGHMARK, G. A. 'Holdup and mass transfer in bubble columns,' *Ind. Eng Chem. Process Des. Develop.* **6**–2, 218 (1967).

5.80. SMITH, R. B., DRESSER, T., OHLSWAGER, S. 'Tower capacity rating ignores trays, *Hydrocarbon Process,' Petrol. Refiner*, **40**–5, 183 (1963).

5.81. SIDEMAN, S. *et al.* 'Mass transfer in gas–liquid contacting systems,' *Ind. Eng. Chem.* **58**–7, 47 (1966).

5.82. ATROSHCHENKO, V. I. *et al.* 'Absorption of nitrogen oxides in sieve tray columns (diameter 1 ft),' *J. Appl. Chem. USSR*, **33**–2, 288 (1960), **38**–12, 2619 (1965).

5.83. KOCHERGIN, N. A. *et al.* 'Columns with perforated trays for absorption of CO_2 from gases by monoethanol solution' (in Russian), *Khim. Prom. Moscow*, **11**, 866 (1963).

5.84. KOHL, A. L. 'Plate efficiency with chemical reaction. Absorption of carbon dioxide in monoethanolamine solutions,' *AIChEJ*, **2**, 264 (1956).

5.85. DANCKWERTS, P. V. 'Temperature effects accompanying the absorption of gases in liquids,' *Appl. Sci. Res.* **A–3**, 385 (1952).

5.86. DANCKWERTS, P. V. 'Gas absorption accompanied by first order reaction: concentration of product, temperature rise and depletion of reactant,' *Chem. Eng. Sci.* **22**, 472 (1967).

5.87. CHILTON, T. H., COLBURN, A. P. 'Distillation and Absorption in packed columns,' *Ind. Eng. Chem.* **27**, 255 (1935).

5.88. SHERWOOD, T. K., PIGFORD, R. L. *Absorption and Extraction*, 2nd ed. McGraw-Hill, N.Y. (1952).

5.89. LEVA, M. *Tower packings and packed tower design*, The United States Stoneware Co. (1951).

5.90. VAN KREVELEN, D. W., HOFTYZER, P. J. 'Graphical design of gas–liquid reactors,' *Chem. Eng. Sci.* **2**, 145 (1953).

5.91. KIRSCHBAUM, E. *Distillation and Rectification*, Chem. Publishing Co., Brooklyn (1948).

5.92. GAUTREAUX, M. F., O'CONNELL, H. E. 'Effect of length of liquid path on plate efficiency,' *Chem. Eng. Progr.* **51**–5, 232 (1955).

5.93. VERHOEYE, L., MUSSCHE, M. 'Estimation of the efficiency of sieve trays,' *Ind. Chim. Belge*, T**35**–5, 391 (1970), T**35**–6, 493 (1970).

5.94. POLL, A., SMITH, W. 'Froth contact heat exchanger,' *Chem. Eng. (New York)*, **71**, 111 (Oct. 26, 1964).

5.95. COGGAN, C. G., BOURNE, J. R. 'The design of gas absorbers with heat effects,' *Trans. Inst. Chem. Eng.* **47**, T96, T160 (1969).

5.96. DRICKAMER, H. G., BRADFORD, J. R. 'Overall plate efficiency of commercial hydrocarbon fractionating columns as a function of viscosity,' *Trans. Amer. Inst. Chem. Eng.* **39**, 319 (1943).

5.97. O'CONNELL, H. E. 'Plate efficiency of fractionating columns and absorbers,' *Trans. Amer. Inst. Chem. Eng.* **42**, 741 (1946).

5.98. LOCKHART, F. J., LEGGET, C. W. 'New fractionating-tray designs,' *Advan. Petrol. Chem. Refining*, Vol. I, Chapter 6, Interscience Publishers Inc., New York (1958).

5.99. BILLET, R. 'Optimization and comparison of mass transfer columns,' *Paper presented at the International Symposium on Distillation, Brighton* (Sept. 1969).

5.100. BILLET, R. 'Recent investigation of column internals and their optimization,' *J. Chem. Eng. Jap.* **2**–1, 107 (1969).

5.101. HOFTYZER, P. J. 'Liquid distribution in a column with dumped packing,' *Trans. Inst. Chem. Eng.* **42**, T109 (1964).

5.102. PORTER, K. E. *et al.* 'Liquid flow in packed columns, Part II,' *Trans. Inst. Chem. Eng.* **46**, T74 (1968).

5.103. PONTER, A. B. *et al.* 'The influence of mass transfer on liquid film breakdown,' *Int. J. Heat Mass Transfer*, **10**, 349 (1967).

5.104. KRELL, E. 'The solid–liquid boundary in chemical engineering,' *Brit. Chem. Eng.* **12**, 562 (1967).

5.105. ZUIDERWEG, F. J., HARMENS, A. 'The influence of surface phenomena on the performance of distillation columns,' *Chem. Eng. Sci.* **9**, 89 (1958).

5.106. BOND, J., DONALD, M. B. 'The effect of absorption on the wetted area of absorption towers,' *Chem. Eng. Sci.* **6**, 237 (1957).

5.107. ECKERT, J. S. 'Design techniques for sizing packed towers,' *Chem. Eng. Progr.* **57**–9, 54 (1961).

5.108. PRAHL, W. H. 'Pressure drop in packed columns,' *Chem. Eng. (New York)*, **76**–17, 89 (1969); 'Liquid density distorts packed column correlation,' *Chem. Eng. (New York)*, **77**–24, 109 (1970).

5.109. SHERWOOD, T. K. *et al.* 'Flooding velocities in packed columns,' *Ind. Eng. Chem.* **30**, 765 (1938).

5.110. LOBO, W. E. *et al.* 'Limiting capacity of dumped tower packings,' *Trans. Amer. Inst. Chem. Eng.* **41**, 693 (1945).

5.111. ECKERT, J. S. 'Selecting the proper distillation column packing,' *Chem. Eng. Progr.* **66**–3, 39 (1970).

5.112. JAMESON, G. J. 'Prediction from a model for liquid distribution in packed columns,' *Trans. Inst. Chem. Eng.* **45**, T74 (1967).

5.113. DUTKAI, E., RÜCKENSTEIN, E. 'New experiments concerning the distribution of a liquid in a packed column,' *Chem. Eng. Sci.* **25**, 483 (1970).

5.114. PORTER, K. E., TEMPLEMAN, J. J. 'Liquid flow in packed columns, Part III,' *Trans. Inst. Chem. Eng.* **46**, T86 (1968).

5.115. WELLER, O. C. 'Evaluation of fractionating devices,' *Trans. Inst. Chem. Eng.* **45**, CE275 (1967).

5.116. FAIR, J. R., MATTHEWS, R. L. 'Better estimate of entrainment from bubble-cap trays,' *Petrol. Refiner,* **37**–4, 153 (1958).

5.117. FAIR, J. R. 'How to predict sieve tray entrainment and flooding,' *Petro/Chem. Eng.* **33**–10 (1961).

5.118. HOPPE, K., MITTELSTRASS, M. 'Principles of calculation and working range of standardized sieve trays' (in German), *Chem. Tech. (Leipzig),* **18**, 533 (1966).

5.119. Fritz W. Glitsch & Sons Inc., *Ballast tray design Manual,* Bulletin No. 4900 (Revised).

5.120. BOLLES, W. L., in Smith, B.D. *Design of equilibrium stage processes,* McGraw-Hill Book Company, Inc. (1963).

5.121. DAVIES, J. A. 'Bubble-trays—design and layout,' *Petrol. Refiner,* **29**, 8–93, 9–121 (1950).

5.122. BOLLES, W. L. 'Optimum bubble-cap tray design,' *Petrol. Process,* **11**, 2–64, 3–82, 4–72, 5–109 (1956).

5.123. MITTELSTRASS, M., HOPPE, K. 'Process-technical principles of the characterization of column trays' (in German), *Chem. Ing. Tech.* **39**, 801 (1967).

5.124. Arbeitsgemeinschaft Chemische Verfahrenstechnik, Brochure 'In behalf of the chemical industry' (in German), Cologne.

5.125. KIRSCHBAUM, E. *Destillier- und Rektifiziertechnik,* 4th, new, enlarged edition, Springer Verlag (1969).

5.126. American Institute of Chemical Engineers, *Tray efficiencies in distillation columns,* Final report from the University of Delaware (1958).

5.127. ROGERS, M. C., THIELE, E. W. 'Pressure drop in bubble-cap columns,' *Ind. Eng. Chem.* **26**, 524 (1934).

5.128. DAVIES, J. A. 'Bubble tray hydraulics,' *Ind. Eng. Chem.* **39**, 774 (1947).

5.129. HOPPE, K., MITTELSTRASS, M. *Grundlagen der Dimensionierung von Kolonnenböden,* Verlag Theodor Steinkopf, Dresden (1967).

5.130. COLBURN, A. P. 'Effect of entrainment on plate efficiency in distillation,' *Ind. Eng. Chem.* **28**, 526 (1936).

5.131. SÜNDERMANN, U. 'Hydraulics of sieve trays provided with large diameter holes' (in German), *Chem. Tech. (Leipzig),* **19**, 267 (1967).

5.132. HUGHMARK, G. A., O'CONNELL, H. E. 'Design of perforated plate fractionating towers,' *Chem. Eng. Progr.* **53**–3, 127 (1957).

5.133. FAIR, J. R., in Smith, B. D. 'Design of equilibrium stage processes,' McGraw-Hill Book Company, Inc. (1963).

5.134. CHASE, J. D. 'Sieve-tray design, Part I,' *Chem. Eng. (New York),* **74**–16, 105 (1967).

5.135. ZENZ, F. A. *et al.* 'Find sieve tray weepage rates,' *Hydrocarbon Process.* **46**–12, 139 (1967).

5.136. SCHULZ, H. 'Standardization of towers and the influence of this on design, construction, fabrication and optimal operation' (in German), *Chem. Tech. (Leipzig),* **19**–11, 661 (1967).

5.137. JESSER, B. W., ELGIN, J. C. 'Studies of liquid holdup in packed towers,' *Trans. Amer. Inst. Chem. Eng.* **39**, 277 (1943).

5.138. FINCH, R. N., VAN WINKLE, M. 'A statistical correlation of the efficiency of perforated trays,' *Ind. Eng. Chem. Process Des. Develop.* **3**, 106 (1964).

5.139. NARSIMHAN, G. 'Determination of economic gas velocity for plate absorbers,' *Chem. Eng. Progr.* 620 (Dec. 1962).

5.140. SCHMID, H. (ed. by Schwab, G. M.) *Handbuch der Katalyse, Bd II, Katalyse in Lösungen* (in German), J. Springer, Vienna (1940). Refers to original papers by Abel, E. and Schmid in *Z. Physik. Chem.* (1928–30).

5.141. FORSYTHE, W. R. and GIAUQUE, W. F. 'The entropies of nitric acid and its mono- and tri-hydrates. Their heat capacities from 15 to 300 K. The heats of dilution of 298·1 K. The internal rotation and free energy of nitric gas. The partial pressures over its aqueous solution,' *J. Amer. Chem. Soc.* **64**, 48 (1942); **65**, 2479 (1943).

5.142. GIAUQUE, W. F. and KEMP, J. D. 'The entropies of nitrogen tetroxide and nitrogen dioxide. The heat capacity from 15 K to the boiling point. The heat of vaporization and the vapour pressure. The equilibria $N_2O_4 = 2NO_2 = 2NO + O_2$,' *J. Chem. Phys.* **6**, 40 (1938).

5.143. ABEL, E., SCHMID, H. and STEIN, M. 'Spectroscopic determination of equilibrium between nitric acid, nitrogen monoxide and nitrogen dioxide' (in German), *Z. Elektrochem.* **36**, 692 (1930).

5.144. BURDICK, C. L. and FREED, E. S. 'The equilibrium between nitric oxide, nitrogen peroxide and aqueous solution of nitric acid,' *J. Amer. Chem. Soc.* **43**, 518 (1921).

5.145. CHAMBERS, F. S. JR. and SHERWOOD, T. K. 'Absorption of nitrogen dioxide by aqueous solutions,' *Ind. Eng. Chem.* **29**, 1415 (1937).

5.146. EPSHTEIN, D. A. 'The Equilibrium of $NO—NO_2—HNO_3—H_2O$ at $0°$' (in Russian), *J. Gen. Chem. Moscow,* **9**, 792 (1939).

5.147. TAYLOR, G. B. 'Vapour pressure of aqueous solutions of nitric acid,' *Ind. Eng. Chem.* **17**, 633 (1925).

5.148. AUNIS, G. II. 'Verification of the Margules–Duhem equation for nitric acid–water systems at $20°$' (in French), *J. Chim. Phys.* **49**, 103 (1952).

5.149. VANDONI, R. and LAUDY, M. 'Measurement of the partial vapour pressures of nitric acid–water systems and verification of the Margules–Duhem equation. 1. Measurement of the partial vapour pressures of nitric acid–water systems at $20°$' (in French), *J. Chim. Phys.* **49**, 99 (1952).

5.150. BODENSTEIN, M. and BOËS, F. 'Formation and decomposition of the higher oxides of nitrogen' (in German), *Z. phys. Chem.* **100**, 68 (1922).

5.151. VERHOEK, F. H. and DANIELS, F. 'The dissociation constants of nitrogen tetroxide and of nitrogen trioxide,' *J. Amer. Chem. Soc.* **52**, 1250 (1931).

5.152. WAYNE, L. G. and YOST, D. M. 'Kinetics of the rapid gas-phase reaction between NO, NO_2 and H_2O,' *J. Chem. Phys.* **19**, 41 (1951).

5.153. CARBERRY, J. J. 'Some remarks on chemical equilibrium and kinetics in the nitrogen oxides–water system,' *Chem. Eng. Sci.* **9**, 189 (1959).

5.154. CAUDLE, P. G. and DENBIGH, K. G. 'Kinetics of the absorption of nitrogen peroxide into water and aqueous solutions,' *Trans. Faraday Soc.* **49**, 39 (1953).

5.155. CHAMBERS, F. S. JR. and SHERWOOD, T. K. 'The equilibrium between nitric oxide, nitrogen peroxide and aqueous solutions of nitric acid,' *J. Amer. Chem. Soc.* **59**, 316 (1937).

5.156. DEKKER, W. A., SNOECK, E. and KRAMERS, H. 'The rate of absorption of NO_2 in water,' *Chem. Eng. Sci.* **11**, 61 (1959).

5.157. DENBIGH, K. C. and PRINCE, A. J. 'Kinetics of nitrous gas absorption in aqueous nitric acid,' *J. Chem. Soc.* 790 (1947).

5.158. BODENSTEIN, M. 'Formation and Decomposition of nitrous oxides of high valency' (in German), *Phys. Chem.* **100**, 68 (1922); 'Rate of reaction between nitric oxide and oxygen,' *Zeitschrift, f. Elektrochimie,* **24**, 183 (1918).

5.159. PETERS, M. S. and HOLMAN, J. L. 'Vapour- and Liquid-phase Reactions between nitrogen dioxide and water,' *Ind. Eng. Chem.* **47**, 2536 (1955).

5.160. PETERS, M. S., ROSS, C. P. and KLEIN, J. E. 'Controlling mechanism in the aqueous absorption of nitrogen oxide,' *AIChEJ,* **1**, 105 (1955).

5.161. WENDEL, M. M. and PIGFORD, R. L. 'Kinetics of nitrogen tetroxide absorption in water,' *AIChEJ,* **4**, 249 (1958).

5.162. ANDREW, S. P. S. and HANSON, D. 'The dynamics of nitrous gas absorption,' *Chem. Eng. Sci.* **14**, 105 (1961).

5.163. BODENSTEIN, M. 'Velocity of reaction between nitric oxide and oxygen, (in German), *Z. Elektrochem.* **24**, 183 (1918).

5.164. ZELDERS, H. G. 'Symposium on Manufacture of Nitric Acid—Corrosion Problems in Nitric Acid Manufacture' (in Dutch), *Chem. Weekl.* **52**, 66 (1956).

5.165. JANAF Thermochemical Tables, The Dow Chemical Company, Midland, Michigan.

5.166. TERESHCHENKO, L. YA., PANOV, V. P., POZIN, M. E. 'Equilibrium between nitrogen oxides and nitric acid solutions,' *J. Appl. Chem. USSR,* **41**–3, 474 (1968).

5.167. BEATTIE, I. R., BELL, S. W. 'Dinitrogen Tetroxide,' *J. Chem. Soc.* 1681 (1947).

5.168. WALDORF, D. M., BABB, A. L. 'Vapour-Phase Equilibrium of NO, NO_2, H_2O and HNO_2,' *J. Chem. Phys.* **40**, 1165 (1964; **39**, 432 (1963).

5.169. ASHMORE, P. G., TYLER, B. J. 'The Formation and Thermodynamic Properties of Nitrous Acid Vapour,' *J. Chem. Soc.* 1017 (1961).

5.170. KARAVAEV, M. M. 'Equilibrium in the Gas-Phase Formation of Nitrous Acid,' *Russian Journal of Physical Chemistry,* **36**–5, 566 (1962).

5.171. USUBILLAGA, A. N. *Kinetics of nitrous acid formation and decomposition.* Thesis. Univ. Ill., U.S.A. (1962).

5.172. SCHMID, G., BAEHR, G. 'Rate of formation of nitrous acid from nitric oxide and nitric acid at higher acid concentrations' (in German), *Z. Physik. Chem.* **41**, 8 (1964).

5.173. KOVAL, E. J., PETERS, M. S. 'Reactions of aqueous nitrogen dioxide,' *Ind. Eng. Chem.* **52**, 1011 (1960).

5.174. DEKKER, W. A. *Investigations on rate of absorption of NO_2 in water* (in Dutch). Thesis, Technical University Delft. Netherlands (1958).

5.175. HOFMEISTER, H. K., KOHLHAAS, R. 'Absorption of NO—NO_2-mixtures in a laminar water jet' (in German), *Ber. d. Bunsengesellschaft* **69**-3, 232 (1965).

5.176. GERSTACKER, see discussion part in reference 5.42.

5.177. MOLL, A. J. *The Rate of Hydrolysis of Nitrogen Tetroxide.* Thesis. Univ. Washington (1966).

5.178. CHÉDIN, J. 'A quantitative description of mixtures consisting of nitric acid and water' (in French), *Journal. Chimie, Physique,* **49**, 109 (1952).

5.179. SOLC, M. 'Kinetics of the reaction between nitric oxide and oxygen,' *Collect. Czech. Chem. Commun.* **31**, 489 (1966); **30**, 257 (1965).

5.180. MORRISON, M. E., RINKER, R. C., CORCORAN, W. H. 'Rate and mechanism of gas phase oxidation of parts-per-million concentrations of nitric oxide,' *Ind. Eng. Chem. Fund.* **5**-2, 175 (1966).

5.181. ASHMORE, P. G., BURNETT, M. G., TYLER, B. J. 'Reaction of nitric oxide and oxygen,' *Trans. Faraday Soc.* **58**, 685 (1962).

5.182. GREIG, J. D., HALL, P. G. 'Thermal oxidation of nitric oxide at low concentrations,' *Trans. Faraday Soc.* **63**, 655 (1967).

5.183. KADLAS, P., VESELY, S. 'Absorption of NO_2 in a column under foaming conditions' (in Czech), *Chem. Prümsl.* **10**-35, 565 (1960).

5.184. CARRINGTON, T., DAVIDSON, N. 'Shock waves in Chemical kinetics: The rate of dissociation of N_2O_4,' *J. Phys. Chem.* **57**, 418 (1953).

5.185. BODENSTEIN, M. 'Formation and decomposition of higher nitrous oxides,' *Phys. Chem.* **100**, 68 (1922).

5.186. HELLMER, L. 'Optimization of two-phase mass transfer in technical nitric acid manufacturing' (in German), *Dechema Monographien,* **15**, 127 (1964).

5.187. HESKY, H. 'Manufacturing of nitric acid in one column at low pressure' (in German), *Chem. Ing. Tech.* **33**-1, 27 (1961).

5.188. HORTON, A. 'The effect of pressure in large nitric acid plants,' *European Chemical News, Large Plant Suppl.* p. 76 (Sept. 30, 1966).

5.189. ANON. 'Process Costs Nitric Acid,' *Chemical and Process Engineering,* p. 11 (Jan. 1966).

5.190. THEOBALD, H. *Measurements of the equilibrium nitric acid/nitrous gases* (in German), *Chem. Ing. Tech.* **40**-15, 763 (1968).

5.191. HAMER, P., JACKSON, J. and THURSTON, E. F., *Industrial Water Treatment.* Butterworths, London (1961).

6 6.1. DIXON, B. E. 'Some aspects of the absorptive mechanism in centrifugal absorbers,' *Trans. I. Chem. E.* **32**, supplement S 85 (1954).

6.2. CHAMBERS, H. H. and WALL, R. G. 'Some factors affecting the design of centrifugal gas absorbers,' *Trans. I. Chem. E.* **32**, supplement S 96 (1954).

6.3. ALCOCK, J. F. and MILLINGTON, B. W. 'A double rotor centrifugal absorber,' *Trans. I. Chem. E.* **32**, supplement S 135 (1954).

6.4. MOORE, A. S. and SHALE, C. C. 'Removing gas by agitated absorption,' *U.S. Bureau of Mines Report* 5730 (1961).

7 7.1. REED, R. M. and UPDEGRAFF, N. C. 'Removal of hydrogen sulfide from industrial gases,' *Industr. Engng Chem.* **42**, 2269 (1950).

7.2. BARBOUTEAU, L. and DE LA BRUNIÈRE. Communication to Congress of Gas, Aix-les-Bains. Published by Association Technique du Gaz, Paris 8e (1959).

7.3. MILLER, F. E. and KOHL, A. L. 'Selective absorption of hydrogen sulfide,' *Oil Gas J.* **51**, 175 (1953).

7.4. BENSON, H. E., FIELD, J. H. and JIMESON, R. M. 'CO_2 absorption employing hot potassium carbonate solutions,' *Chem. Engng Progr.* **50** (7), 356 (1954).

7.5. BENSON, H. E., FIELD, J. H. and HAYNES, W. P. 'Improved process for CO_2 absorption uses hot carbonate solutions,' *Chem. Engng Progr.* **52** (10), 433 (1956).

7.6. KOHL, A. L. and RIESENFELD, F. C. *Gas Purification.* 1960, Chapter 5, 'Alkaline salt solutions for hydrogen sulfide and carbon dioxide absorption,' McGraw-Hill, New York.

7.7. BARBOUTEAU, L. and GUILLO, R. *Communication to International Congress of Gas, Stockholm.* Published by Union Internationale de l'Industrie de Gaz, Bruxelles (1961).

7.8. KOHL, A. L. and RIESENFELD, F. C. *Gas Purification.* 1960, Chapter 6, 'Water as an absorbent for gas impurities,' McGraw-Hill, New York.

7.9. MCFADDIN, D. E. 'H$_2$S and CO$_2$ corrosion of carbon steel in natural gas processing plants,' *Oil Gas J.* **50**, 98 (1951).

7.10. MUHLBAUER, H. F. and MONOGBRAN, P. R. 'New equilibrium data for sweetening natural gas with ethanolamine solutions,' *Oil Gas J.* 140 (April 1957).

7.11. PASTERNAK, R. 'Selective removal of H$_2$S in the present of CO$_2$ by DIK liquor,' *Brennst Chemie,* **43**, 65 (1962).

8 8.1. HOPTON, G. U. and GRIFFITH, R. H. 'Removal of hydrogen sulphide from fuel gas,' *I. Gas E. Comm.* 288 (1945).

8.2. GRIFFITH, R. H. and MORCOM, A. R. 'The interconversion of iron oxides and sulphides,' *J. Chem. Soc.* 786 (1945).

8.3. HOPTON, G. U. 'Removal of hydrogen sulphide from coal by means of iron oxide,' *Gas J.* 254 (1948); 100–2, 105–6 (14 April); 158–60, 163–4, 169 (21 April); 218, 223 (28 April).

8.4. BRAMSLEV, E. *Some applications of Chemical Kinetics on Problems in the Gas Industry.* 6th International Gas Conference, New York, IGU/15–55 (1955).

8.5. HOPTON, G. U. 'Developments in oxide purification plants,' *Gas J.* **269**, 291–2, 297–300, 304–5 (30 January 1952).

8.6. PRIESTLEY, J. J. and BOUCH, W. E. 'Modern trends in gas purification,' *Gas J.* **303**, 130 (27 July 1960).

8.7. RICKETTS, T. S. 'The Westfield high-pressure coal-gasification plant,' *I. Gas E. Publ.* 567 (June 1960).

8.8. MOORE, D. B. 'Recent developments in gas purification,' *Gas World* **143**, 153 (14 January 1956).

8.9. POWDRILL, J. 'Operation of Liquid and Gastechnik Purification Plants at Cardiff,' *I. Gas E. Publ.* 551 (1959).

8.10. REEVE, L. 'Desulphurization of coke-oven gas at Appleby–Frodingham,' *J. I. Fuel* **31**, 319 (1958).

8.11. WILLIAMSON, R. H. and GARSIDE, J. E. 'An application of the fluidized solids technique to coal gas purification,' Part I. *Inst. Gas Engrs. Comm.* 345 (November 1948); Part II. *Inst. Gas Engrs. Publ.* 357 (November 1949).

8.12. JOHNSON, E. 'Theory of fluidization and its application to sulphur recovery by solvent extraction,' *Inst. Gas Engrs. Comm.* 378 (1950).

8.13. MOIGNARD, L. A. 'The performance of oxide purifiers,' *Gas Council Research Comm.* GC 7 (1952).

8.14. SPEERS, J. A. 'Influence of packing density in purifiers on resistance to gas flow,' *Gas J.* **252**, 636 (17 December 1947).

8.15. *Safety Recommendations* issued by Institution of Gas Engineers 1950, pp. 1, 2, 5, 9, and 9a.

8.16. RADFORD, D. E. *The use of low density, low iron content mixtures for gas purification.* Australian Gas Industry Convention, 1960. Paper No. 4.

8.17. PLANT, J. H. G. and NEWLING, W. B. S. 'Catalytic removal of organic sulphur compounds from coal gas,' *I. Gas E. Comm.* 344 (1948).

8.18. DICKINSON, R. G. and PAULING, L. 'The crystal structure of molybdenite,' *J. Amer. Chem. Soc.* **45**, 1466 (1923).

8.19. BORGARS, B. A. and BRIDGER, G. W. 'Catalysts used in the manufacture of ammonia,' *Chem. & Ind. (Rev.)* 1426 (19 November 1960).

8.20. J.C.S. 786 (1945).

8.21. NICKLIN, T. and BRUNNER, E. *I. Gas E. Comm.* 593 (1961).

8.22. NICKLIN, T. and HOLLAND, B. H. *The Removal of Hydrogen Sulphide from Coke-oven Gas by the Stretford Process.* European Symposium 'Cleaning of Coke Oven Gas', Saarbrücken (21 March 1965).

9 9.1. GRIFFITHS, H. 'The properties and applications of adsorptive carbons,' *J. I. Fuel* **8**, 277–95 (1935).

9.2. BRUNAUER, S. *The adsorption of gases and vapours. Vol. I, Physical Adsorption.* Oxford University Press, London (1945).

9.3. LAMB, A. B., WILSON, R. E. and CHANEY, N. K. 'Gas mask absorbents,' *Industr. Engng Chem.* 420 (May 1919).

9.4. (a) *Industrial Solvents and Flammable Liquids,* Fire Protection Society, London (1959).
  (b) COWARD, H. F. and JONES, G. W. 'Limits of inflammability of gases and vapours,' *U.S. Bureau of Mines, Bull.* No. 503 (1952).
  (c) duPont de Nemours & Co., E. I. *Solvent Properties Comparison Chart,* 1959 (Wilmington, Del.).

9.5. RADIER, H. H. 'Flame arrestors,' *J. I. Petrol.* **25**, 377–81 (1939).

9.6. EDELEANU, I. 'The recovery of gasoline from field and refinery gases with special reference to the Bayer Charcoal Process,' *J. I. Petrol. Tech.* **14**, 286–317 (1928).

9.7. HOUGEN, O. A. and MARSHALL, W. R. JR. 'Adsorption from a fluid stream flowing through a stationary granular bed,' *Chem. Engng Progr.* **43** (4), 197–208 (1947).

9.8. HOLLINGS, H., PEXTON, S. and CHAPLIN, R. 'The recovery of benzole from coal gas, with particular reference to the use of active charcoal,' *Trans. I. Chem. E. Lond.* **7**, 85–107 (1927).

9.9. HOLLINGS, H. and HAY, S. 'The recovery of benzole by active carbon,' *J. Soc. Chem. Ind., (Rev.),* **53** (7), 143–55 (1934).

9.10. ERMENC, E. D. 'Designing a fluidized bed adsorber,' *Chem. Eng.* **68**, 87 (1961).

9.11. ROWSON, H. M. 'Fluid bed adsorption of carbon disulphide,' *Brit. Chem. Engng.* **8**, 180 (1963).

10 10.1. LATHAM, A., BOWERSOCK, D. C. and BAILEY, B. M. 'Cryogenics—fertile fields ahead,' · *Chem. Engng News,* 60 (3 August 1959).

10.2. PERRY, J. H. *Chemical Engineers Handbook,* 4th edn., 20–91 (1963).

10.3. Safety roundtable, *Chem. Engng Progr.* **55**, No. 6, 54 (1959).

10.4. SHERWOOD, T. K. and PIGFORD, R. L. *Absorption and Extraction,* McGraw-Hill (1952).

10.5. TEPE, J. B. and DODGE, B. F. 'Absorption of carbon dioxide by sodium hydroxide in a packed column,' *Trans. Amer. I. Chem. E.* **39**, 255 (1943).

10.6. Summary Technical Report of Division 11, U.S. National Defence Research Committee (1946), Vol. 1. *Improved Equipment for Oxygen Production.*

10.7. KARWAT, E. 'Air separation—carbon dioxide removal by adsorption,' *Chem. Engng Progr.* **55**, No. 5, 79 (1959).

10.8. *British Patent* 671,859.
  British Patent 617,327.

10.9. *German Patent* 837,106.

10.10. FRANKL. *German Patent* 490,878.

10.11. HAUSEN, H. *Handbuch der Kältetechnik,* Springer-Verlag, Vol. 8, p. 260 (1957).

10.12. HAUSEN, H. *Warmeübertragung in Gegenstrom, Gleichstrom und Kreuzstrom.* Springer-Verlag, 434 (1950).

10.13. HAUSEN, H. Feuchtigkeitsablagerung in Regeneratoren, Z.V.D.I, *Beiheft Verfahrenstechnik,* **2**, 62 (1937).

10.14. SAUNDERS, O. A. and SMOLENIEC, S. *Heat Regenerators,* Presented to the VII International Congress of Applied Mechanics (Sept. 1948).

10.15. WARD, D. E. 'Some aspects of the design and operation of low temperature regenerators,' *Advances in Cryogenic Engng.* Plenum Press, **6**, 525 (1960).

10.16. DENTON, W. H. *et al.* 'Purification of hydrogen for distillation,' *Trans. I. Chem. E., Lond.* **36**, 179 (1958).

10.17. TRUMPLER, P. R. *British Patent* 657,748.

10.18. BARANOV, G. M. 'The main trend in the designing of large gaseous oxygen plants,' *Progress in Refrigeration Science and Technology,* Pergamon Press, Vol. 1 (1960).

10.19. DENTON, W. H. and WARD, D. E. 'Application and design of plate-fin heat exchangers,' *Brit. chem. Engng* **5**, 18 (1960).

10.20. TRUMPLER, P. R. and DODGE, B. F. 'The design of ribbon packed exchangers for low temperature air separation plants,' *Trans. Amer. I. Chem. E.* **43**, 75 (1947).

10.21. LOBO, W. E. and SKAPERDAS, G. T. 'Air purification in the reversing exchanger,' *Trans. Amer. I. Chem. E.* **43**, 69 (1947).

10.22. WARD, D. E. 'The application of regenerators and heat exchangers,' *Brit. Chem. Engng* **5**, 15 (1960).

10.23. WEBSTER, T. J. 'The influence of pressure on the equilibrium between carbon dioxide and air,' *Proc. Roy. Soc.* A**214**, 61 (1952).

10.24. CRAWFORD, D. B. 'Elliott oxygen process and impurity removal system,' *Chem. Engng Progr.* **46**, No. 2, 74 (1950).

10.25. MANTELL, C. L. *Adsorption.* McGraw-Hill (1951).

10.26. COCHRANE, G. S. 'Molecular sieves for gas drying,' *Chem. Engng* **66**, No. 17, 129 (1959).

10.27. HERSH, C. K. *Molecular Sieves.* Reinhold (1961).

10.28. LEDOUX, E. 'Avoiding destructive velocity through adsorbent beds,' *Chem. Engng* **55**, No. 3, 118 (1948).

10.29. CHILTON, T. H. and COLBURN, A. B. 'Heat transfer and pressure drop in empty, baffled and packed tubes,' *Trans. Amer. I. Chem. E.* (Swampscott Meeting), **26**, 166 (1931).

10.30. LENFESTEY, A. G. 'Secondary surface heat exchangers,' *Brit. Chem. Engng* **5**, 27 (1960).

10.31. *British Patent* 615,683.

10.32. GARDNER, J. B. 'Some factors in the safe operation of air separation units,' *Trans. I. Chem. E.* **39**, A43 (1961).

10.33. KERRY, F. G. 'Safe design and operation of low temperature air separation plants,' *Chem. Engng Progr.* **52**, No. 11, 441 (1956).

10.34. *British Patent* 835,751.

10.35. PARKS, J. C. and HINKLE, E. A. *Safety in air and ammonia plants.* American Institute of Chemical Engineers, **5**, 32 (1963).

10.36. CERMAK, J. *Brit. Chem. Eng.* **14**, No. 6, 813 (June 1969).

10.37. KOHL, H. L. and RIESENFELD, F. C. *Gas Purification.* McGraw-Hill (1960).

10.38. *U.S. Patent* 1,533,773.

10.39. *U.S. Patent* 2,242,323.

10.40. MULLOWNEY, J. F. 'Which CO_2 removal scheme is best?' *Petrol. Refin.* **36**, 149 (1957).

10.41. GUILLAUMERON, P. 'Liquefaction for separating hydrogen from coke oven gas,' *Chem. Engng* **56**, No. 7, 105 (1949).

10.42. RUHEMANN, M. *Separation of Gases.* Oxford University Press (1949).

10.43. BARDIN, J. S. and BEERY, D. W. 'Producing ammonia synthesis gas,' *Petrol. Refin.* **32**, 99 (1953).

10.44. BAKER, D. F. 'Low temperature processes purify industrial gases,' *Chem. Engng Progr.* **51**, No. 9, 399 (1955).

10.45. JESTER, M. R. 'Ammonia synthesis gas from a petroleum refinery vent-gas,' *Trans. I. Chem. E.* **36**, 133 (1958).

10.46. BOHLKEN, S. F. 'Heat exchanger explosion at a nitrogen-wash unit,' *Chem. Engng Progr.* **57**, No. 4, 49 (1961).

10.47. HIZA, J. 'Cryogenic impurity adsorption from hydrogen,' *Chem. Engng Progr.* **56**, No. 10, 68 (1960).

10.48. LEWIS, W. K. *et al.* 'Adsorption equilibria hydrocarbon gas mixtures,' *Industr. Engng Chem.* **42**, 1319 (1950).

10.49. DOKOUPIL, Z. *et al.* 'On the equilibrium between the solid phase and the gas phase of the systems H_2–N_2, H_2–CO, and H_2–N_2–CO,' *Appl. sci. Res., Hague* A, **5**, 182 (1955).

10.50. DOKOUPIL, Z. 'Phase Equilibrium of the nitrogen–hydrogen system in the critical region of hydrogen,' *Advances in Cryogenic Engng*, Plenum Press, **6**, 446 (1960).

10.51. KEELER, R. M. and TIMMERHAUS, K. H. 'Poisoning and reactivation of ortho-para hydrogen conversion catalyst,' *Advances in Cryogenic Engng*, Plenum Press, **4**, 296 (1960).

10.52. WEITZEL D. H. *et al.* 'Design data for ortho-parahydrogen converters,' *Advances in Cryogenic Engng*, Plenum Press, **3**, 73 (1960).

10.53. *U.S. Patent* 2,810,454.

10.54. MEISZENER, E. *V.D.I. Zeitschrift* **83**, No. 35, 1003 (1939).

10.55. *B.I.O.S. Final Report No.* 591. 'Large scale production of oxygen and atmospheric gases.'

10.56. KAZARNOVSKAYA, L. I. and DYKHNO, N. M. 'Catalytic combustion of small quantities of methane in oxygen,' *Kislorod*, No. 2, 28 (1959).

10.57. FASTOVSKII, V. G. and PETROVSKII, YU V. 'Rectification process for the production of pure krypton,' *Khim. Prom.* No. 3, 476–480 (1957).

10.58. DEATON, W. M. and HAYNES, R. D. *Helium Production at the Bureau of Mines Keyes, Okla., Plant.* Information Circular 8018, U.S. Dept. of the Interior, Bureau of Mines, 1961.

10.59. The Dragon Project: Progress Report, *Nucl. Engng* **6**, No. 66, 454 (1961).

10.60. *British Patent* 771,405.

10.61. COLLINS, J. J. 'Where to use molecular sieves,' *Chem. Engng Progr.* **64**, No. 8, 66 (Aug. 1968).

10.62. BURNETT, R. W. and TURNBULL, W. T. 'Industrial Applications of molecular sieves,' *Brit. Chem. Engng* 261 (April 1966).

10.63. WARRIOR, J. R. and WOOD, M. J. 'Molecular sieve drying,' *Chem. and Proc. Engng* 97 (Oct. 1969).

10.64. *British Patent* 855,378.

10.65. WRIGHT, G. T. *Chem. Chem. Engng Progr.* **57**, No. 4, 9 (April 1961).

10.66. MATTHEWS, L. G. *Chem. Engng Progr.* **57**, No. 4, 12 (April 1961).

10.67. LANG, A. 'Safety in air and ammonia plants,' **7**, 60 (1965).

10.68. BOYNES, W. J. 'Safety in air and ammonia plants,' **8**, 7 (1966).

10.69. VOOGD, J. and TIELROOY, J. *Hydrocarbon Proc.* 46, No. 9, 115 (Sept. 1967).

10.70. BRADLEY, J. R. and NIMMO, N. M. 'Safety in air and ammonia plants,' **10**, 84 (1968).

10.71. LEE, M. N. Y. and COLLINS, J. J. 'Safety in air and ammonia plants,' **11**, 69 (1969).

10.72. SCHOLZ, W. H. *Advances in Cryogenic Engng* **15**, 406 (1969).

10.73. FIRTH, I. *New Scientist*, **39**, No. 610, 332 (15 Aug. 1968).

10.74. RAMIREZ, R. *Chem. Eng.* **80** (16 Dec. 1968).

10.75. WILSON, R. M. and NEWSON, H. R. *J. Petrol. Techn.* **20**, No. 4, 341 (April 1968).

11 11.1. EMMETT, P. H. (ed.) *Catalysis.* 1954–7, Vols. 1–5. Reinhold, New York.

11.2. GRIFFITH, R. H. *The Mechanism of Contact Catalysis.* Oxford University Press, London (1946).

11.3. STEINBRECHER, A. H. 'Electrolytic production of hydrogen gas,' *Oil & Soap,* **16**, 36 (1939).

11.4. The International Electrolytic Plant Co., Brochure (1932).

11.5. *Air Pollution Abatement Manual.* Chapter 13, Odor measurement and control, manufacturing Chemists' Association, Washington D.C.

11.6. CRONAN, C. S. 'Where tail gas oxidation stands to-day,' *Chem. Engng.* **66**, 66 (12 Jan. 1959).

11.7. MCCABE, L. C. 'Catalytic combustion of odor-producing agents may be applied to all types of gases where oxygen is available,' *Industr. Engng Chem.* **45**, 109A (1953).

11.8. WAGMAN, D. D., KILPATRICK, J. F., TAYLOR, W. G., PITZER, K. S. and ROSSINI, F. D. 'Heats, free energies and equilibrium constants of some reactions involving O_2, H_2, H_2O, C, CO, CO_2 and CH_4,' *J. Res. Nat. Bur. Stand.* **34**, 143 (1945).

11.9. SEBASTIAN, J. J. S. and RIESZ, C. H. 'Sulfur-resistant catalysts for reforming propane,' *Industr. Engng Chem.* **43**, 860 (1951).

11.10. Catalysts and Chemical Inc. *Technical Bulletin No.* 072159.

11.11. ZEANDLE, W. W. and KLEIN, G. F. 'Purification of ammonia synthesis gas,' *Chem. Engng Progr.* **48**, 352 (1952).

11.12. DUNWOODY, W. B. and PHILLIPS, J. R. 'More ammonia with least investment,' *Petrol. Refin.* **35**, 169 (Dec. 1956).

11.13. WAGMAN, D. D., KILPATRICK, J. E., PITZER, K. S. and ROSSINI, F. D. *J. Res. Nat. Bur. Stand.* **35**, 467 (1945).

11.14. KILPATRICK, J. E., PROSEN, E. G., PITZER, K. S. and ROSSINI, F. D. *J. Res. Nat. Bur. Stand.* **36**, 559 (1946).

11.15. PROSEN, E. J., PITZER, K. S. and ROSSINI, F. D. *J. Res. Nat. Bur. Stand.* **34**, 403 (1945).

11.16. REITMEZER, R. E. and FLEMING, H. W. 'Acetylene removal from polyethylene grade ethylene,' *Chem. Engng Progr.* **54**, 48 (Dec. 1958).

11.17. STANTON, W. K. 'Which acetylene removal scheme is better?' *Petrol. Refin.* **38**, 177 (May 1959).

11.18. MAXTED, E. B. and PRIESTLY, J. J. 'Removal of sulphur compounds from town gas by catalytic hydrogenation,' *Gas J.* **247**, 471, 535, 556, 593 (1946).

11.19. WEDGEWOOD, E. 'Actions, reactions and side reactions of catalytic sulphur removal,' *Institute of Gas Engineers.* Publication No. 5251 (May 1958).

11.20. PLANT, J. H. G. and NEWLING, W. B. S. 'The catalytic removal of organic sulphur compounds from coal gas,' *Trans. Inst. Gas Engrs.* **98**, 308 (*Communication No.* 344) (1948–9).

11.21. ANON. 'Removal of organic sulphur from town gas,' *Coke & Gas* **15**, 462 (Dec. 1953).

11.22. FLETCHER, W. 'The treatment of nitric acid plant tail gas,' *Brit. Chem. Engr.* **5**, 789 (Nov. 1960).

11.23. DONAHUE, J. L. 'System designs for the catalytic decomposition of nitrogen oxides,' *J. Air Poll. Control Ass.* **8**, 209 (Nov. 1958).

11.24. 'Limits of flammability of gases and vapours,' *U.S. Bureau of Mines Bulletin No.* 503 (1952).

11.25. HOUDRY, J. T. and HAYES, C. T. 'Versatility of oxidation catalysts for industrial air pollution,' *J. Air Poll. Control Ass. Amer.* **7**, 183 (1957).

11.26. WARSH, A. J. and ROMEO, P. L. 'Recent Advances in Catalytic Processing as Applied to Nitrogen Fertilizer Complexes,' Paper presented before the 57th Annual Meeting AIChE, Boston, Mass. (8 Dec. 1964).

11.27. OBADITCH, C. J. 'The Catalytic Treatment of Nitric Acid Tail Gas,' Paper presented before a Symposium of The Institution of Chemical Engineers (North Western Branch), Manchester (16 Nov. 1965).

12 12.1. STAIRMAND, C. J. 'The design and performance of modern gas-cleaning equipment,' *J. I. Fuel* **29**, 58 (1956).

12.2. STAIRMAND, C. J. 'The design and performance of cyclone separators,' *Trans. I. Chem. E., Lond.* **29**, 256 (1951).

12.3. TER LINDEN, A. J. 'Investigations into cyclone dust collectors,' *Proc. I. Mech. E., Lond.* **160**, 233 (1949).

12.4. STAIRMAND, C. J. Institute of Mechanical Engineers Conference on The Mechanical Engineer's Contribution to Clean Air, 1957, Discussion p. 114.

12.5. FORREST, J. S. and LOWE, H. J. 'Present performance and scope for improvement in power station electrostatic precipitators,' Institute of Mechanical Engineers Conference on The Mechanical Engineer's Contribution to Clean Air, 42 (1957).

12.6. STAIRMAND, C. J. and KELSEY, R. M. 'The role of the cyclone in reducing atmospheric pollution,' *Chem. & Ind. (Rev.)*, 1324 (15 Oct. 1955).

12.7. JOHNSON, J. C. and GOODWIN, G. C. 'Mechanical grit and dust collectors,' Institute of Mechanical Engineers Conference on the Mechanical Engineer's Contribution to Clean Air, 60 (1957).

12.8. STAIRMAND, C. J. 'Dust collection by impingement and diffusion,' *Trans. I. Chem. E., Lond.* **28**, 130 (1950).

12.9. NUKIYAMA, S. and TANASAWA, Y. 'Experiment on atomization of liquid, III–IV,' *Trans. Soc. mech. Engrs Japan* **5**, 63 (1939).

12.10. PEARSON, J. L. *et al.* 'The removal of smoke and acid constituents from flue gases by non-effluent water process,' *J. I. Fuel* **8**, 119 (1935).

12.11. JENNINGS, R. F. 'Blast-furnace gas cleaning,' *J. Iron St. Inst.* **164**, 305 (1950).

12.12. JOHNSTONE, H. F. *et al.* 'Gas absorption and aerosol collection in a venturi atomizer,' *Industr. Engng Chem. (Anal.)* **46**, 1601 (1954).

12.13. SKREBOWSKI, J. K. and SUTTON, B. W. 'Development of a radioactive aerosol for testing filter fabrics,' *Brit. Chem. Engng* **6**, 12 (1961).

12.14. BOUCHER, R. M. G. 'Sur le fonctionnement de l'epurateur à microbrouillards,' 'Aerojet-Venturi,' *Chal. et Industr.* **33**, 363 (1952).

12.15. *Treating dusty gases by means of a washing liquid.* Pease Anthony Equipment Co. BP 655, 038 (17 Sept. 1947).

12.16. LAPPLE, C. E. and KAMAK, H. J. 'Performance of wet dust scrubbers,' *Chem. Engng Progr.* **51**, 110 (1955).

12.17. SPROULL, W. T. 'Collecting high resistivity dust and fumes,' *Industr. Engng Chem. (Anal.)* **47**, 940 (1955).

12.18. DEUTSCH, W. 'The movement and charging of the electricity carrier in the cylinder condenser,' *Ann. Phys., Lpz.* **68**, 335 (1922).

12.19. LADENBURG, R. L. *et al.* 'Studies of physical phenomena in so-called electric gas purification,' *Ann. Phys. Lpz.* **5**, 863 (1930).

12.20. LITTLE, A. 'Practical aspects of electrostatic precipitator operation—experiments on a pilot plant,' *Trans. I. Chem. E., Lond.* **34**, 259 (1956).

12.21. STAIRMAND, C. J. 'Removal of grit, dust and fume from exhaust gases from chemical engineering processes,' *The Chemical Engineer,* No. 194, CE 310 (Dec. 1965).

12.22. VACEK, A. and SCHERTLER, A. 'Waste gas cleaning systems of oxygen steel plants,' *Iron and Steel Instutute* 1957, Meeting on Air Pollution in the Iron and Steel Industry, 71 (Sept. 1957).

12.23. HERSEY, H. J. JR. 'Reverse-jet filters,' *Industr. Chem. Mfr.* **31**, 138 (1955).

12.24. HEINRICH, R. F. and ANDERSON, J. R. 'Electro-precipitation,' *Chemical Engineering Practice* (ed. by H. W. Cremer and T. Davies). Butterworths, London, **III**, 7, 484 (1957).

12.25. WHITE, H. J. *Industrial electrostatic precipitation.* Addison-Wesley Publishing Co. Inc. and Pergamon Press, London (1963).

12.26. STAIRMAND, C. J. 'Selection of gas cleaning equipment: a study of basic concepts,' *Filtration and Separation* **1**, 1 (1970).

12.27. WHITE, P. A. F. and SMITH, S. E. *High-efficiency air filtration*. Butterworths, London (1964).

Part B

13 13.1. DEUTSCH, W. 'Bewegung und Ladung der Elektricitätsträger im Zylinder Kondensator,' *Annalen der Physik,* **68**, 335 (1922).

13.2. WHITE, H. J. 'Particle Charging in Electrostatic Precipitation,' *Amer. Inst. Elect. Engrs.* **76**, 1186 (1951).

13.3. LOWE, H. J. and LUCAS, D. H. 'The Physics of Electrostatic Precipitation,' *Brit. J. Appl. Phys.* **2**, 540 (1953).

13.4. SPROULL, W. T. 'Collecting High Resistivity Dusts and Fumes,' *Industr. Engng Chem.* **47**, 940 (1955).

13.5. LOWE, H. J., DALMON, J. and HIGNETT, E. T. 'The Precipitation of Difficult Dusts. Proc. Colloquim on Electrostatic Precipitators,' *Inst. Elect. Engrs.* Paper II (1965).

13.6. TREVOR-BUSBY, H. G. and DARBY, K. 'Efficiency of Electrostatic Precipitators as Affected by the Properties and Combustion of Coal,' *J. Inst. Fuel,* **36**, 184–197 (1963).

13.7. WATSON, K. S. and BLECHER, K. J. 'Further Investigation of Electrostatic Precipitators for Large Pulverized Fuel-Fired Boilers,' *Air and Water Pollution Int. Jnl.* **10**, 573 (1966).

13.8. LOWE, H. J. 'Recent Advances in Electrostatic Precipitators for Dust Removal,' *Phil. Trans. Roy. Soc. Lond.* **265**, 301 (Nov. 1969).

13.9. HEINRICH, D. O. 'The Science and Art of Electro-precipitation,' *Engng Boiler House Rev.* **68**, 179 (1953).

13.10. The Ionising Radiations (Sealed Sources) Regulations, S.I., 1961, No. 1470, London, H.M.S.O.

13.11. WHITE, H. J. *Industrial Electrostatic Precipitation*, Chapter 8, Pergamon Press, Oxford (1963).

13.12. B.S. 2811:1969, *Smoke Density Indicators and Recorders*.

13.13. CROSS, P. A. E., LUCAS, D. H. and SNOWSHILL, W. L. 'The design of an "Everclean" window for the observation of the optical density of flue gases,' *J. Inst. Fuel,* **34**, 503 (1961).

13.14. B.S. 2742:1969. *Notes on the Use of the Ringelmann Chart*.

13.15. EASTON, J. A. 'Deposits in Centrifugal Dust Collectors of the Tubular Type,' *J. Inst. Fuel,* **28**, 50 (1955).

13.16. JARMAN, R. T. and DE TURVILLE, C. M. 'The Visibility and Length of Chimney Plumes,' *Atmospheric Environment,* **3**, No. 3, 257–280 (1969).

13.17. BROOKS, W. J. D., HOLMES, L. and LEASON, D. B. 'Power Station Oil Burner Systems for Low Excess Air Operation,' *I. Inst. Fuel,* **38**, 218–237 (1965).

13.18. NONHEBEL, G. 'Recommendations on heights for new industrial chimneys,' *J. Inst. Fuel* **33**, 479, see also chapter 19 (1960).

13.19. STAIRMAND, C. J. 'Design and performance of modern gas-cleaning equipment,' *J. Inst. Fuel,* **29**, 58 (1956).

Part E

*13.20. *Iron and steel—Progress towards clean air*. (a) *Review of progress* (P. A. Matthews); (b) *Some practical problems* (J. H. Flux). National Society for Clean Air, Clean Air Conference (Oct. 1969).

13.21. 'Practical suggestions for the reduction of the emission of smoke, dust and grit at coke ovens.' Special Publication 5, The British Coke Research Association (1969).

Part A

14 14.1. BADZIOCH, S. 'Correction for anisokinetic sampling of gas-borne dust particles,' *J. Inst. Fuel* **33**, 106 (1960).

14.2. STAIRMAND, C. J. 'The sampling of dust-laden gases,' *Trans. I. Chem. E.* **29**, 15 (1951).

14.3. B.S. 3405:1971. *Measurement of Grit and Dust Emission*.

14.4. HAWKSLEY, P. G. W., BADZIOCH, S. and BLACKETT, J. H. *Measurement of Solids in Flue Gases*, British Coal Utilization Research Association, Leatherhead (1961).

14.5. ANON. 'Sampling of gas-borne particles,' *Engineering* **152**, 141, 181 (1941).

14.6. *British Standard* 893: 1940. *Method of testing dust extraction plant and the emission of solids from chimneys of electric power stations*.

Part B

14.7. *British Standard* 2955:1958. *Glossary of Terms Relating to Powders.*

14.8. *British Standard* 3406: Part 1:1961. *Subdivision of Gross Sample down to* 0·2 *ml.*

14.9. *British Standard* 410:1969. *Test sieves.*

14.10. *British Standard* 1796:1952. *Methods for the use of British Standard Fine-mesh Test Sieves.*

14.11. GONELL, H. W. 'Ein Windsichtverfahren zur Bestimmung der Kornzusammensetzung Staubförmiger Stoffe,' *Z. Ver. dtsch Ing.* **62**, 945 (1928). Richtlinien für die Bestimmung der Zusammensetzung von Stauben nach Korngrosse und Fallgeschwindigkeit, V.D.I. Berlin (1936).

14.12. SKREBOWSKI, J. K. *Miniature Elutriator.* Private communication. (An account of the apparatus is given in B.S. 3406, see reference 16.)

14.13. ROLLER, P. S. 'Separation and size distribution of microscopic particles—air analysis for fine powders,' *U.S. Bur. Mines, Tech. Paper No.* 490 (1931).
ROLLER, P. S. 'The bulking properties of microscopic particles,' *Industr. Engng Chem.* **22**, 1206 (1930).

14.14. *British Standard* 3406:1962. *Methods for the Determination of Particle Size of Powders: Part 3. Air or Gas Elutriation Methods.*

14.15. ANDREASEN, A. H. M. 'Uber die Feinheitbestimmung und ihre Bedeutung für die Keramische Industrie,' *Ber deut. Keram. Ges.* **11**, 675 (1930).

14.16. *British Standard* 3406:1963. *Methods for the Determination of Particle Size of Powders: Part 2. Liquid Sedimentation Methods.*

14.17. STAIRMAND, C. J. *A New Sedimentation Apparatus for Particle Size Analysis in the Sub-Sieve Range.* Symposium on Particle Size Analysis, Suppl. to *Trans. I. Chem. E.* **25**, 128 (1947).

14.18. Early work has been described by BROWN, J. F. and SKREBOWSKI, J. K. in *The Physics of Particle Size Analysis, Brit. J. app. Phys.* Suppl. No. 3, S27 (1954). Stemming from this, a low sensitivity model was built in U.S.A. operating on γ-radiation. ROSS, C. P. 'Particle size analysis by gamma-ray adsorption,' *Anal. Chem.* **31**, No. 3, 337 (1959). See also Reference 33.

14.19. *British Standard* 3625:1963. *Eyepiece and Screen Graticules for Determination of Particle Size of Powders.*

14.20. *British Standard* 3406:1963. *Methods for the Determination of Particle Size of Powders: Part 4. Optical Microscope Method.*

14.21. FAIRS, G. L. 'The use of the microscope in particle size analysis,' *Chem. J. Ind. (Rev.)* **62**, 374 (1943); 'Development in the technique of Size Analysis by microscopical examination,' *J. R. micr. Soc.* **71**, 209 (1951); 'The technique of particle size analysis in the sub-sieve range,' *Symposium on Recent Advances in Mineral Dressing, Inst. Min. Met.* **59**, 59 (1953).

14.22. STAIRMAND, C. J. 'Rapid air elutriator for examination of stack dusts,' *Engineering*, **171**, 585 (1951).

14.23. EADIE, F. S. and PAYNE, R. E. 'New instrument for analysing particle size distribution,' *Iron Age,* **174**, No. 19, 99 (1954).

14.24. LUCAS, D. H. 'The grading of fly-ash—A "once-through" process giving samples for microscopic examination,' *Engineering* **177**, 272 (1954).

14.25. WALTON, W. H. 'The application of electron microscopy to particle size measurement.' Supplement to *Trans. I. Chem. E.* **25**, 64 (1947).

14.26. CARTWRIGHT, J. 'The physics of particle size. The electron microscopy of air-borne dusts,' *Brit. J. Appl. Phys.* Suppl. No. 3, 109 (1954).

14.27. SCHÖNE, E. Uber Schälmmanalyse und einer neuen Schlämmapparat, H. Müller-Verlag, Berlin (1867).

14.28. ROSE, H. E. 'Determination of the extinction coefficient-particle size relationship for spherical bodies,' *J. Appl. Chem.* **2**, 80 (1952).

14.29. CAREY, W. F. and STAIRMAND, C. J. 'Size analysis by photographic sedimentation,' *Trans. I. Chem. E.* **15**, 37 (1938).

14.30. HEYWOOD. 'Uniform and non-uniform motion of particles in fluids.' Advance copy of paper A1 to *Third Congress of European Federation of Chemical Engineering,* published by Institution of Chemical Engineers (June 1962).

14.31. CONLIN, S. G., LEVENE, W. J. and VOLUME, W. F. 'An instrument for size analysis of fine powders by X-ray absorption,' *J. Sci. Instrum.* **44**, 606 (1967).

14.32. Analytical Methods Committee. 'Classification of methods for determining particle size,' *The Analyst*, **88**, No. 1044 (March 1963).

14.33. *Society for Analytical Chemistry. Particle Size Analysis.* Proceedings of a conference at Loughborough University of Technology (Sept. 1966).

14.34. STERN, A. C. (Ed.). *Air Pollution* (Volume II, Chapter 21, by P. M. Giever), Academic Press (1968).

Part C

14.35. *British Standard* 2742:1969. *Notes on the use of the Ringelmann chart;* 2742 C:1957, *Ringelmann chart;* 2742 M:1960, *Miniature smoke chart.*

14.36. *British Standard* 2740:1969. *Simple smoke alarms and alarm metering devices; British Standard* 2811:1969. *Smoke density indicators and recorders.* •

14.37. LITTLEWOOD, A. 'Measurement of the optical density of smoke in a chimney,' *J. Sci. Instrum.* **33**, 495 (1956).

14.38. CROSSE, P. A. E., LUCAS, D. H. and SNOWSILL, W. L. 'The design of an "Everclean" window for the observation of the optical density of flue gases,' *J. I. Fuel* **34**, 503 (1961); *British Patent Appl. No.* 877, 918.

14.39. CROSSE, P. A. E., LUCAS, D. H. and SNOWSILL, W. L. 'The measurement of dust nuisance emitted by chimneys,' *Int. J. Air and Water Poll.* **4**, 212 (1961).

14.40. CROSSE, P. A. E., LUCAS, D. H. and SNOWSILL, W. L. 'Instrument for recording the dust nuisance emitted by chimneys,' *J. Sci. Instrum.* **38**, 12 (1961); *British Patent Appl. Nos.* 6121/53 *and* 31283/59.

14.41. LEES, B. and MORLEY, M. C. 'A routine sampler for detecting variations in the emission of dust and grit,' *J. I. Fuel* **33**, 90 (1960).

14.42. REED, L. E. 'The estimation of the darkness of smoke by visual methods,' *J. I. Fuel* **42**, 3 (1959) and private communication (1962).

14.43. LUCAS, D. H. and SNOWSILL, W. K. 'Some developments in dust pollution measurements,' *Atmospheric Environment* **1**, 631 (1967).

14.44. JARMAN, R. T. and DE TURVILLE, C. M. 'The visibility and length of chimney plumes,' *Atmospheric Environment* **3**, 257 (1969) and discussion, **4**, 000 (1970).

Part A

15 15.1. FAIRS, G. L. 'Calder–Fox scrubbers and the factors influencing their performance,' *Trans. I. Chem. E., Lond.* **22**, 110 (1944).

15.2. METALLGESELLSCHAFT, A. G. *Process for the Production of sulphuric acid,* B.P. 406116.

15.3. GREEN, H. L. and LANE, W. R. *Particulate Dusts, Clouds, Smokes and Mists,* p. 182. E. & F. N. Spon (1957).

15.4 FAIRS, G. L. 'Developments in the technique of particle size analysis by microscopical examination,' *J. R. Micr. Soc.* **71**, 209 (1951).

15.5. STAIRMAND, C. J. 'The sampling of dust-laden gases,' *Trans. I. Chem. E., Lond.* **29**, 15 (1951).

15.6. HARDIE, D. W. F. *The History of the Chemical Industry in Widnes,* p. 19. I.C.I. Limited, General Chemicals Division (1950).

15.7. TANNER, C. C., PALMER, W. H. and FOX, C. A. O. *Tar Fog,* p. 37 (1933). (Brochure produced by Manchester Oxide Co. Ltd.)

15.8. WHITE, H. J. *Industrial Electrostatic Precipitation,* Addison-Wesley Publishing Co. Ltd. and Pergamon Press, London (1963).

15.10. BOSANQUET, C. H. 'Impingement of particles on obstacles in a stream,' *Heat Vent. Engr.* **26**, 349 (1953).

15.11. FAIRS, G. L. 'High efficiency fibre filters for the treatment of fine mists,' *Trans. I. Chem. E., Lond.* **36**, 477 (1958).

15.12. MARKWARD, H. G. 'The removal of sulphuric acid mist,' *Industr. Chem.* **36**, 220 (1960).

15.13. *Ninety-second Annual Report on Alkali &c. Works,* p. 19, H.M.S.O. (1955).

15.14. *Ninety-third Annual Report on Alkali &c. Works,* p. 20, H.M.S.O. (1956). *Ninety-fourth Annual Report on Alkali &c. Works,* p. 16, H.M.S.O. (1957). *Ninety-fifth Annual Report on Alkali &c. Works,* p. 16, H.M.S.O. (1958).

15.15. MASSEY, O. D. *Demisters for Sulphuric Acid Stacks,* Manufacturing Chemists Association Inc. Air and Water Pollution Conference, p. 85 (1959).

15.16. ECKMANN, F. O. and JOHNSTONE, H. F. 'Collection of Aerosols in a venturi scrubber,' *Industr. Engng Chem.* **43**, 1358 (1951).

15.17. MEDNOKOV, E. P. 'Akusticheskaya Koagulyatsita i Osazhdenie Aerozolei' ['Acoustic Coagulation and Precipitation of Aerosols']. Translated from the Russian by Larrick, C. V., Consultants Bureau, U.S.A. (1965).

15.18. DANSER, H. W. and NEUMANN, G. P. 'Industrial sonic agglomeration and collection systems,' *Industr. Engng Chem.* **41**, 2439 (1949).

15.19. GREEN, H. L. and LANE, W. R. *Particulate Clouds, Dusts, Smokes and Mists.* E. & F. N. Spon, p. 299 (1957).

15.20. SODERBERG, C. R. 'The Industrial Applications of Sonic Energy,' *Iron Steel Engr.* **29**, 1, 87 (Feb. 1952).

15.21. NEUMANN, E. P., SODERBERG, C. R. and FOYLE, A. A. 'Design application, performance and limitations of sonic type flocculators and collectors,' *Air Pollution. Proc. U.S. Tech. Conf. Air Pollution,* McGraw-Hill, p. 388 (1952).

Part B

15.22. GILLESPIE, G. R. *Particle Size Distribution in Hygroscopic Aerosols.* Engineering Experimental Station University of Illinois, Technical Report No. 9, 20 (1953).

15.23. GILLESPIE, G. R. and JOHNSTONE, H. F. 'Particle size distribution in some hygroscopic aerosols,' *Chem. Engng Progr.* **51**, 74-F (1955).

15.24. FARR, T. D. *Phosphorus—Properties of the Element and Some of Its Compounds.* Tennessee Valley Authority Chemical Engineering Report No. 1 (U.S. Government Printing Office, Washington, D.C.), 1st edn., 18 (1950).

15.25. RANZ, W. E. and WONG, J. B. 'Jet impactors for determining the particle-size distributions of aerosols,' *A.M.A. Arch. industr. hyg. occup. Med.* **5**, 464 (1952).

15.26. RANZ, W. E. and WONG, J. B. 'Impaction of dust and smoke particles,' *Industr. Engng Chem.* **44**, 1371 (1952).

15.27. BRINK, J. A. JR. 'Cascade impactor for adiabatic measurements,' *Industr. Engng Chem.* **50**, 645 (1958).

15.28. FERRY, R. M., FARR, L. E. and HARTMANN, M. G. 'The preparation and measurement of the concentration of dilute bacterial aerosols,' *Chem. Rev.* 389 (1949).

15.29. GREENBURG, L. and SMITH, G. W. *A New Instrument for Sampling Aerial Dust.* U.S. Dept. of the Interior, Bureau of Mines, R.I. 2392 (1922).

15.30. HATCH, T., WARREN, H. and DRINKER, P. J. 'Modified form of the Greenburg–Smith impinger for field use, with a study of its operating characteristics,' *Industr. hyg. Toxicol.* **14**, 301 (1932).

15.31. KATZ, S. H., SMITH, G. W. and MYERS, W. M. *Determinations of Air Dustiness with the Sugar Tube, Palmer Apparatus and Impinger, Compared with Determinations with the Konimeter.* U.S. Pub. Hlth Bull. **144**, 69 (1925).

15.32. LASKIN, S. 'Section on Particle Size Measurement,' *Pharmacology and Toxicology of Uranium Compounds,* by C. Voegtlin, and H. C. Hodge. McGraw-Hill, New York (1949).

15.33. MAY, K. R. 'The cascade impactor,' *J. Sci. Instrum.* **22**, 187 (1945).

15.34. OWENS, J. S. 'Suspended impurity in the air,' *Proc. Roy. Soc.* **A101**, 18 (1922).

15.35. PILCHER, J. M., MITCHELL, R. I. and THOMAS, R. E. 'The cascade impactor for particle-size analysis of aerosols,' *Proc. Chem. Spec. Man. Assoc.* (Dec. 1955).

15.36. SONKIN, L. S. 'A modified cascade impactor: a device for sampling and sizing aerosols of particles below 1 micron in diameter,' *J. industr. Hyg. Toxicol.* **28**, 269 (1946).

15.37. WILCOX, J. D. 'Design of a new five-stage Cascade impactor,' *A.M.A. Arch. industr. Hyg. occup. Med.* **7** 376 (1953).

15.38. WILCOX, J. D. and VAN ANTWERP, W. R. 'A sampling technique for small air-borne particles,' *A.M.A. Arch. industr. Hlth* **11**, 422 (1955).

15.39. BRINK, J. A. JR. and CONTANT, C. E. 'Experiments on an industrial venturi scrubber,' *Industr. Engng Chem.* **50**, 1157 (1958).

15.40. STRIPLIN, M. M. *Development of Processes and Equipment for Production of Phosphoric Acid.* Tennessee Valley Authority Chemical Engineering Report No. 2 (U.S. Government Printing Office, Washington, D.C.), 1sr edn., 20 (1948).

15.41. BASKERVILL, W. H. 'The packed-tower collection of phosphoric acid,' *Amer. Inst. chem. Engrs.* **37**, 79 (1941).

15.42. BASKERVILL, W. H. 'Separating hydrated phosphorus pentoxide,' *U.S. Pat.* 2,303,318 (1942).

15.43. STRIPLIN, M. M. *Development of Process and Equipment for Production of Phosphoric Acid.* Tennessee Valley Authority Chemical Engineering Report No. 2 (U.S. Government Printing Office, Washington, D.C.), 1st edn., 47 (1948).

15.44. STRIPLIN, M. M. *Development of Process and Equipment for Production of Phosphoric Acid.* Tennessee Valley Authority Chemical Engineering Report No. 2 (U.S. Government Printing Office, Washington, D.C.), 1st edn., 114 (1948).

15.45. STRIPLIN, M. M. *Development of Process and Equipment for Production of Phosphoric Acid.* Tennessee Valley Authority Chemical Engineering Report No. 2 (U.S. Government Printing Office, Washington, D.C.), 1st edn., 45 (1948).

15.46. WALTHALL, J. H. and STRIPLIN, M. M. JR. 'Superphosphoric acid by absorption of P_2O_5 vapor,' *Industr. Engng Chem. (Industr.)* **33**, 995 (1941).

15.47. HARTFORD, C. E. and STRIPLIN, M. M. JR. 'Making phosphoric acid,' *U.S. Pat. No.* 2,247,373 (1941).

15.48. COLLINS, T. T. JR. 'The scrubbing of sulphate recovery furnace stack gases,' *Paper Ind.* No. 5, 680, No. 6, 830, No. 7, 984 (1947).

15.49. COLLINS, T. T. JR., SEABORNE, C. R. and ANTHONY, A. W. JR. 'Removal of salt cake fume from sulphate recovery furnace stack gases by scrubbing,' *Paper Tr. J.* **124**, No. 23, 45 (1947).

15.50. JOHNSTONE, H. F. and ANTHONY, A. W. JR. (Pease Anthony Equipment Co.) 'Method and apparatus for treating gases,' *U.S. Pat.* 2,604,185 (22 July 1952).

15.51. GLEDHILL, P. J. and CARNALL, P. J. 'Oxygen lancing of pig iron and subsequent fume treatment with a Pease-Anthony Venturi scrubber,' *J. Iron St. Inst.* **186**, 198 (1957).

15.52. JONES, W. P. 'Development of the Venturi scrubber,' *Industr. Engng Chem.* **41**, 2424 (1949).

15.53. EKMAN, F. O. and JOHNSTONE, H. F. 'Collection of acrosols in a Venturi scrubber,' *Industr. Engng Chem.* **43**, 1358 (1951).

15.54. JOHNSTONE, H. F., FIELD, R. B. and TASSLER, M. C. 'Gas absorption and aerosol collection in a Venturi atomizer,' *Industr. Engng Chem.* **46**, 1601 (1954).

15.55. JOHNSTONE, H. F. and ROBERTS, M. H. 'Deposition of aerosol particles from moving gas streams,' *Industr. Engng Chem.* **41**, 2417 (1949).

15.56. YOCOM, J. E. and CHAPMAN, S. 'The collection of silica fume with a Venturi scrubber,' *Air Report,* **4**, 155 (1954).

15.57. ROSS, W. H., CAROTHERS, J. N. and MERZ, A. R. 'Use of Cottrell precipitator in recovering H_3PO_4 evolved in volatilization method of treating phosphate rock,' *J. Industr. Engng Chem.* **9**, 26 (1917).

15.58. WAGGAMAN, W. H., EASTERWOOD, H. W. and TURLEY, T. B. *Investigations of the Manufacture of Phosphoric Acid by the Volatilization Process.* U.S. Dept. Agriculture, Dept. Bull. No. 1179, 11 (1923).

15.59. BEAVER, C. E. 'Cottrell electrical precipitation equipment, some technical and engineering features, recent developments and application in the chemical field,' *Trans. Amer. I. Chem. E.* **42**, 258 (1946).

15.60. CREE, K. H. 'Cottrell electrical precipitation as applied to the manufactured gas industry,' *Amer. Gas J.* **162**, 27 (1945).

15.61. STRIPLIN, M. M. *Development of Processes and Equipment for Production of Phosphoric Acid.* Tennessee Valley Authority Chemical Engineering Report No. 2 (U.S. Government Printing Office, Washington, D.C.), 1st edn., 18 (1948).

15.62. 'Atmospheric Emissions from Thermal-Process Phosphoric Acid Manufacture,' *National Air Pollution Control Administration Publication* 48, p. 21. Superintendent of Documents, U.S. Government Printing Office, Washington, D.C. (1968).

15.63. BRINK, J. A. JR. 'Mist Collection with Fiber Beds,' *Proc. Air and Water Pollution Abatement Conference,* Manufacturing Chemists' Association, Inc., 104 (1959).

15.64. BRINK, J. A. JR. 'New fiber mist eliminator,' *Chem. Engng* **66**, 183 (1959).

15.65. BERLY, E. M., FIRST, M. W. and SILVERMAN, L. 'Recovery of soluble gas and aerosols from air streams,' *Industr. Engng Chem.* **46**, 1769 (1954).

15.66. BLASEWITZ, A. G. and JUDSON, B. F. 'Filtration of radioactive aerosols by glass fibers,' *Chem. Engng Progr.* **51**, 6-J (1955).

15.67. DAVIES, C. N. 'Fibrous filters for dust and smoke,' *Proc. 9th Intern. Congr. Ind. Med.* **1948**, 162, London (1949).

15.68. DAVIES, C. N. 'The separation of air-borne dusts and particles,' *Proc. I. Mech. E.* **B1**, 185 (1952).

15.69. FIRST, M. W., MOSCHELLA, R., SILVERMAN, L. and BERLY, E. 'Performance of wet cell washers for aerosols,' *Industr. Engng Chem.* **43**, 1363 (1951).

15.70. FIRST, M. W., GRAHAM, J. B., BUTLER, G. M., WALWORTH, C. B. and WARREN, R. P. 'High temperature dust filtration,' *Industr. Engng Chem.* **48**, 696 (1956).

15.71. GADEN, E. L. JR. and HUMPHREY, A. E. 'Fibrous filters for air sterilization,' *Industr. Engng Chem.* **48**, 2172 (1956).

15.72. HUMPHREY, A. E. and GADEN, E. L. JR. 'Air sterilization by fibrous media,' *Industr. Engng Chem.* **47**, 924 (1955).

15.73. FAIRS, G. L. 'High efficiency fibre filters for the treatment of fine mists,' *Trans. I. Chem. E.* **36**, 476 (1958).

15.74. MANOWITZ, R., BRETTON, R. H. and HORRIGAN, R. V. 'Entrainment in evaporators,' *Chem. Engng Prog.* **51**, 313 (1955).

15.75. SADOFF, H. L. and ALMOF, J. W. 'Testing of filters for phage removal,' *Industr. Engng Chem.* **48**, 2199 (1956).

15.76. SILVERMAN, L. and FIRST, M. W. 'Edge and variable compression filters for aerosols,' *Industr. Engng Chem.* **44**, 2777 (1952).

15.77. THOMAS, D. J. 'Fibrous filters for fine particle filtration,' *J. Instr. Heating Ventilating Engrs.* **20**, 35 (1952).

15.78. WONG, J. B., PH.D. Thesis in Chemical Engineering, University of Illinois, *Collection of Aerosols by Fiber Mats.* University Microfilms (Ann. Arbor, Mich.) Publ. No. **7886** (1954).

15.79. CHEN, C. Y. 'Filtration of aerosols by fibrous media,' *Chem. Rev.* **55**, 595 (1955).

15.80. BRINK, J. A. JR. 'Air Pollution Control with Fibre Mist Eliminators,' *Can. J. Chem. Engng* **41**, 134 (1963).

15.81. BRINK, J. A. JR., BURGGRABE, W. F. and GREENWELL, L. E. 'Mist Removal from Compressed Gases,' *Chem. Engng Prog.* **62**, 60 (1966).

15.82. BRINK, J. A. JR., BURGGRABE, W. F. and RAUSCHER, J. A. 'Fiber Mist Eliminators for Higher Velocities,' *Chem. Engng Prog.* **60**, No. 11, 68 (1964).

15.83. BRINK, J. A. JR., BURGGRABE, W. F. and GREENWELL, L. E. 'Mist Eliminators for Sulfuric Acid Plants,' *Chem. Engng Prog.* **64**, No. 11, 82 (1968).

15.84. BRINK, J. A. JR. *Mist elimination for the future.* Third Annual National Pollution Control Conference, San Francisco (1970).

16   16.1. CHILTON, H. 'Elimination of carry-over from packed towers with special reference to natural draught water cooling towers,' *Trans. I. Chem. E.* **30**, 235 (1952).

16.2. NEWITT, D. M., DOMBROWSKI, N. and KNELMANN, F. 'Liquid entrainment (1) The mechanism of drop formation from gas or vapour bubbles,' *Trans. I. Chem. E.* **32**, 244 (1954).

16.3. JACKSON, R. and WAPLE, E. R. 'The elimination of dust and drizzle from quenching towers,' *Gas World*, p. 75 (May 1960).

16.4. MAY, K. R. 'The cascade impactor; an instrument for sampling coarse aerosols,' *J. Sci. Instrum.* **22**, 187 (1945).

16.5. STAIRMAND, C. J. 'Dust collection by impingement and diffusion,' *Trans. I. Chem. E.* **28**, 130 (1950).

16.6. STAIRMAND, C. J. 'The design and performance of cyclone separators,' *Trans. I. Chem. E.* **29**, 356 (1951).

Part A

17   17.1. DAVIES, C. N. *Dust is Dangerous.* Faber and Faber, London (1962).

17.2. GREEN, H. L. and LANE, W. R. *Particulate Clouds—Dusts, Smokes and Mist. Their Physics and Physical Chemistry and Industrial and Environmental Aspects.* E. and F. N. Spon, London (1957).

17.3. D.S.I.R. *The Investigation of Atmospheric Pollution—Research and Observations.* Last report of 32nd report for year ended 31 March (H.M.S.O.).

17.4. D.S.I.R. *The Use of the Daily Instrument for Measuring Smoke and Sulphur Dioxide.* Warren Spring Laboratory, Stevenage (1961).

17.5. *British Standard* 3406:1963. *Part 4. Methods for the determination of particle size of powders. Part 4. Optical microscope method.*

17.6. MAY, K. R. 'The cascade impactor: an instrument for sampling coarse aerosols,' *J. sci. Instrum.* **22**, 187–95 (Oct. 1945) (correction; 247, Dec. 1945).

17.7. FABER, O. and KELL, J. R. *Heating and Air-Conditioning of Buildings*. 3rd edn., Architectural Press, London (1957).
17.8. *British Standard* 2831:1957. *Methods of Test for Air Filters used in Air-Conditioning and General Ventilation* (including later amendments).

Part B
17.9. *Chemical Works Regulations*, 1922. Certificates of Approval of Breathing Apparatus, under the Factories Act, 1961, Section 30. Factory Form 1789 (H.M.S.O.) Form 893 (H.M.S.O. 1959).
17.10. *British Standard* 2091:1969. *Respirators for protection against harmful dusts and gases*. For highly toxic dusts, including radioactive materials, see *British Standard* 4555:1970. *High efficiency dust respirators* and *British Standard* 4558:1970. *Positive pressure powdered dust respirators*.
17.11. *British Standard* 3928:1969. *Sodium chloride particulate test for respirator filters*.
17.13. *British Standard* 2577:1955. *Methylene Blue Particulate Test for Respirator Canisters*.
17.14. HUNTER, J. On the absorption of gases by charcoal, *Phil. Mag.* **25**, 4th Series, 364 (1863); on the absorption of vapours by charcoal, *J. Chem. Soc.* **18**, 285 (1865); **20**, 160 (1867); **21**, 186 (1868); note on the absorption of mixed vapours by charcoal, *J. Chem. Soc.* **23**, 73 (1870); on the effect of pressure on the absorption of gases by charcoal, *J. Chem. Soc.* **24**, 76 (1871); on the effects of temperature on the absorption of gases by charcoal, *J. Chem. Soc.* **25**, 649 (1872).
17.15. HORMATS, S. 'Charcoal for military respirators,' *Armed Forces Chem. J.* **5**, (1), 34 (1951).
17.16. HASSLER, J. W. *Active Carbon*. Chemical Publishing Co., New York (1957).
17.17. RAY, A. B. 'Manufacture of activated carbon,' *Chem. Met. Engng* **28**, 977 (1923).
17.18. DE BOER, J. H. and VAN ORMONDT, J. 'Removing carbon monoxide from air and gas-mask canister therefor,' U.S.P. 2, 478, 166 (1949).
17.19. KATZ, M. *et al.* 'The oxidation of carbon monoxide by solid silver permanganate reagents: IV. Chemical composition in relation to activity,' *Canad. J. Chem.* **29**, 1059, 1065 (1951); 'V. Determination of low concentration of carbon monoxide by use of thermistors in a thermal cell,' *Canad. J. Technol.* **30**, 303 (1952).
17.20. KATZ, M. 'Detection of oxidation of carbon monoxide,' *Chem. Can.* **3**, (10), 47 (1951).
17.21. MILLER, R. R. and PLATT, V. R. (editors) *The Present Status of Chemical Research in Atmosphere Purification and Control on Nuclear-powered Submarines*. N.R.L. Report 5465. U.S. Naval Research Laboratory, Washington, D.C., U.S.A., 1960. Additional information will be found in an Annual Progress Report with the same general title, N.R.L. Report 5630, 1961.

18 18.1. 'Recommended Guide for the Prediction of Airborne Effluents,' *Amer. Soc. Mech.Eng.*, New York, N.Y. (Under revision in 1970.)
18.2. SLADE, D. H. 'Meteorology and Atomic Energy,' *U.S. Atomic Energy Commission* (1968). (Available as TID-24190 from Clearing House for Federal Scientific Information, Springfield, Virginia 22151, U.S.A.)
18.3. SCORER, R. S. *Air Pollution*. (Contains over 100 photos in colour of clouds and smoke plumes.) Pergamon Press, London (1968).
18.4. SCORER, R. S. *Natural Aerodynamics*. Pergamon Press (1958).
18.5. DAVENPORT, A. G. 'Relationship of Wind Structure to Wind Loading. Paper No. 2 at Symposium on Wind effects on buildings,' *National Physical Laboratory Symposium*, No. 16, H.M.S.O. (1965).
18.6. MEADE, P. J. 'Discussion of G. Nonhebel's paper; Recommendations on heights for chimneys,' *J. I. Fuel.* **33**, 501 (1960).
18.7. MEADE, P. J. 'The assessment of liability to smog in terms of weather,' *Proc. Nat. Soc. Clean Air*. 1960 Conference.
18.8. MEADE, P. J. 'Inversions and Air Pollution,' *Proc. Int. Clean Air Conf.* (1959). *National Society for Clean Air* (1960).
18.9. Air Pollution Control, District County of Los Angeles, Rules and Regulations, 1958, Chapter 2, Division 20, Health and Safety Code Rules 156 and 158.
18.10. EGGLETON, A. E. J. 'The chemical composition of atmospheric aerosols on Tees-side and its relation to visibility,' *Atm. Envir.* **3**, 355 (1969).
18.11. JOHNSTONE, H. F. and MOLL, A. J. 'Air pollution by formation of sulphuric acid from SO_2 in fog droplets containing dissolved catalysts,' *Industr. Engng Chem.* **52**, 861 (1960).

18.12. FULLER, L. J., CHASS, R. L. and LUNCHE, R. G. 'Profile of air pollution control in Los Angeles County.' Available from Air Pollution Control District, Los Angeles County (1969).

19 19.1. *Report of (Government) Committee on Air Pollution* (Chairman: Sir Hugh Beaver). Cmd. 9322, H.M.S.O. (1954). Interim Report Cmd. 9011, H.M.S.O. (1953).

19.2. NONHEBEL, G. 'Recommendations on heights for new industrial chimneys,' *J. I. Fuel* **33**, 479 (1960).

19.3. MARTIN, A. and BARBER, F. R. 'Investigations of Sulphur Dioxide pollution around a modern power station,' *J. I. Fuel.* **39**, 294 (1966), continued in *Atm. Envir.* **1**, 655 (1967).

19.4. National Aeronautical Research Institute of Amsterdam. 'Smoke nuisance and soot deposits of smoke stacks. The Way Ahead,' *Quart. Rev. Ned. Consult Engineering* **9**, 12 (1961).

19.5. The measures which have been taken in this Country and in Others to obviate the Emission of Soot, Grit and Gritty Particles from the Chimneys of Electric Power Stations; Report by a Committee appointed by the Electricity Commissioners, London, H.M.S.O. (1932).

19.6. STEWART, N. G., GALE, H. J. and CROOKS, R. N. *The Atmospheric Diffusion of Gases Discharged from the Chimney of the Harwell Reactor* (BEPO). A.E.R.E. Report HP/R 1452, 22 (Oct. 1954).

19.7. SCORER, R. S. and BARRETT, C. F. 'Gaseous pollution from chimneys,' *Int. J. Air Water Poll.* **6**, 49 (1962).

19.8. SLADE, D. H. 'Meteorology and Atomic Energy.' U.S. Atomic Energy Commission (1968). Available as TID/24190 from National Bureau of Standards, Clearing House for Technical Information, Springfield, Va. 22151, U.S.A.

19.9. SHERLOCK, R. H. and STALKER, E. A. 'Study of flow phenomena in the wake of smoke-stacks,' *Michigan University Engineering Research Bulletin* No. 29 (1941).

19.10. SHERLOCK, R. H. and LESHER, E. J. 'Design of power-station chimneys and buildings to prevent down-wash of the smoke plume to neighbouring areas,' *Trans. Amer. Soc. Mech. Engrs* **77**, 1 (1955).

19.11. JAMIESON, H. C. 'A variety of engineering experiences,' *J. Inst. Heat Vent. Engrs* **27**, 257 (1959).

19.12. *Chimney Heights.* Ministry of Housing and Local Government, 2nd edn., H.M.S.O. (1967). Permatrace copies of the charts are available.

19.13. 'Symposium on Chimneys,' *J. I. Fuel* **39**, 21 and 68, discussion, 431 (1966). See also BEAUMONT, M. 'Experience with multi-flue chimneys,' *J. I. Fuel* **44**, 92 (1971).

19.14. IRELAND, F. E. 'Compliance with the Clean Air Act: Technical background leading to the Ministry's Memorandum on Chimney Heights,' *J. I. Fuel* **36**, 272 (1964) and discussion, **37**, 156 (1964).

19.15. NONHEBEL, G. 'British Charts for Heights of Industrial Chimneys,' *Air & Wat. Poll. Int. J.* **10**, 183 (1966).

19.16. LUCAS, D. H. Contribution to discussion of paper by Scorer and Barrett, Reference 6. *Int. J. Air Water Poll.* **6**, 94 (1962), and private communication.

19.17. *Ninety-seventh Annual Report on Alkali Works, for* 1958, H.M.S.O. (1959).

19.18. 'Symposium on chimney plume rise and dispersion, arranged by The Central Electricity Research Laboratories,' *Atm. Envir.* **1**, 351–440 (1967). Includes important contributions in the discussion.

19.19. 'Discussion on recent research on air pollution,' *Phil. Trans. (Roy. Soc.)* **265**, No. 1161, 139–318 (1969).

19.20. TURNER, D. B. 'Workbook of atmospheric dispersion estimates,' *U.S. Public Health Service Publication No.* 999-AP-26, National Air Pollution Control Administration, Cincinnati, Ohio.

19.21. 'Recommended Guide for the Prediction of Airborne Effluents,' *Amer. Soc. Mech. Eng.*, New York. (Under revision in 1970.)

19.22. A.S.M.E. Standard APS-2, 'Recommended Guide for the control of emission of oxides of sulphur,' *Amer. Soc. Mech. Eng.*, New York (1970). See also Reference 23.

19.23. BODURTHA, F. T. 'Discussion on a proposed Canadian Standard for estimating dispersion of pollution from chimneys,' *Atm. Envir.* **3**, 484 (1969).

19.24. CONCAWE Working Group. 'The calculation of atmospheric dispersion from a stack,' Stichting CANCAWE, The Hague, Holland (1966). Discussion, see Reference 25.

19.25. 'Round Table on plume rise and atmospheric dispersion,' *Atm. Envir.* **2**, 193–250 (1968).

19.26. SUTTON, O. G. 'The theoretical distribution of airborne pollution from factory chimneys,' *Quart. J. Roy. Met. Soc.* **73**, 426 (1947). See also SUTTON, O. G. *Micrometeorology.* McGraw-Hill, New York and London (1953).

19.27. PASQUILL, F. 'The estimation of the dispersion of windborne material,' *Met. Mag.* **90**, No. 1063, 33 (1961).

19.28. PASQUILL, F. *Atmospheric Diffusion.* van Nostrand, London and New York (1962).

19.29. SCORER, R. S. *Air Pollution.* (Contains over 100 photos in colour of clouds and smoke plumes.) Pergamon Press, London (1968).

19.30. WEIN, W. 'Operating experience with power plant stacks and their design.' English translation in *Combustion* **41**, 29 (1969).

19.31. GIFFORD, F. A. 'Use of routine meteorological observations for estimating atmospheric dispersion,' *Nuclear Safety* **2**, No. 4, 47 (1961).

19.32. LUCAS, D. H., MOORE, D. J. and SPURR, G. 'The rise of hot plumes from chimneys,' *Air Wat. Poll. Int. J.* **7**, 473 (1963).

19.33. KAWABATA, Y. 'Observations of atmospheric diffusion at Tokai-mura,' *Geophys. Mag.* (Tokyo), **29**, 571 (1960).

19.36. BOSANQUET, C. H. and PEARSON, J. L. 'The spread of smoke and gases from chimneys,' *Trans Faraday Soc.* **32**, 1249 (1936).

19.37. BOSANQUET, C. H. 'The rise of a hot waste gas plume,' *J. I. Fuel* **30**, 322 and discussion, 333 (1957).

19.38. PRIESTLEY, C. H. B. 'A working theory of the bent-over plume of hot gas,' *Quart. J. Roy. Met. Soc.* **82**, 165 (1956).

19.39. BRYANT, P. M. *Methods of estimation of the dispersion of windborne material and data to assist in their application.* U.K.A.E.A. report AHSB(RP) R42, H.M.S.O. (1964).

19.40. HINO, M. 'Maximum ground-level concentration and sampling time,' *Atm. Envir.* **2**, 149 (1968) and private communication (1970).

19.41. BANNON, J. K., DODS, L. and MEADE, P. J. *Frequencies of various stabilities in the surface layer.* Meteorological Office Memo 88 (1962).

19.42. TURNER, B. (ed. of Reference 20), private communication.

19.43. SPORN, P. and FRANKENBERG, T. T. 'Pioneering experience with high stacks . . . on American Power Systems,' *Proc. Int. Clean Air*, London (1967).

19.44. CUMMINGS, W. G., REDFEARN, M. W. and JONES, W. R. 'The effect of land configuration on pollution by sulphur gases,' *J. I. Fuel* **38**, 391 (1965).

19.45. KELLY, A. G. 'Smoke rockets to establish chimney heights,' *Eng. and Blr. House Review*, p. 102 (April 1966).

19.46. ANON. 'Operation Chimney Plume,' *Engineering*, p. 30 (2 Jan. 1959). See also *The Engineer*, p. 970 (19 Dec. 1958).

19.47. CROSSLEY, A. F. and HARKER, J. A. *Vertical shear in the lower layers at Cardington.* Investigation Div. Memo No. 101, U.K. Met. Office (1966).

19.48. OGURA, Y. 'Diffusion from a continuous source in relation to finite observation interval,' *Adv. Geophy.* **6**, 149 (1959).

19.49. BRIGGS, G. A. *Plume Rise.* U.S. Atomic Energy Commission (1969). (Available as TID-25075 from Clearing House for Federal Scientific Information, National Bureau of Standards, U.S. Dept. of Commerce, Springfield, Va. 22151, U.S.A.

19.50. LUCAS, D. H. Private Communication from Central Electricity Generating Board (1970).

19.51. *Threshold Limits for air pollutants.* Published annually by A.M.A. Arch. Environ. Hlth.

19.52. *Dust and Fumes in Factory Atmospheres.* Ministry of Social Security. H.M.S.O. (Latest edition should be consulted.)

19.53. MAHLER, E. A. J. 'Standards of emission under the Alkali Act,' *Proc. Int. Clean Air Congress,* Paper III, 12, National Society for Clean Air (1966), and republished in Alkali Inspector's Report for 1966, H.M.S.O. (1967).

19.54. *The Investigation of Air Pollution. National Survey Annual Summaries for smoke, dust, SO, by volume and by lead dioxide,* Warren Spring Laboratory, Stevenage, Hertfordshire. See in particular report for 1958–66. There is a separate publication giving the position of sites.

19.55. *Air Quality Criteria for sulphur oxides.* U.S. Dept. of Health, Education and Welfare, National Air Pollution Control Administration Publication No. A.P. 50, Washington (1969).

19.56. WEATHERLY, M. L. 'Contribution to discussion on plume behaviour,' *Int. J. Air Wat. Poll.* **10**, 404.

19.57. ZAHN, R. 'Effects of sulphur dioxide on vegetation,' *Staub* **2**, No. 21, 56 (1961).

19.58. *British Standard* 1747:1969. *Methods for the measurement of air pollution. Part 1. Deposit Gauges; Part 2. Determination of suspended matter; Part 3. Determination of Sulphur Dioxide; Part 4. The lead dioxide method for reactivity of acid sulphur compounds.*

19.59. CUMMINGS, W. G. and REDFEARN, M. W. 'Instrument for measuring small quantities of sulphur dioxide in the atmosphere,' *J. I. Fuel* **30**, 628 (1957).

19.60. Progress Reports by the Medical Research Council Air Pollution Research Unit, and numerous articles by Prof. P. J. Lawther in journals dealing with air pollution.

19.61. ROYAL COLLEGE OF PHYSICIANS. *Air Pollution and Health*, Pitmans, London (1970).

19.62. *Proc. First European Congress on the influences of air pollution on plants and animals.* Wageningen Centre for agricultural publishing, Netherlands (1969).

19.63. EGGLETON, A. E. J. 'The chemical composition of atmospheric aerosols on Tees-side and its relation to visibility,' *Atm. Envir.* **3**, 355 (1969).

19.64. MOSS, G. *The desulphurizing combustion of fuel oil in fluidizing beds of lime particles.* First International Conference on Fluid Bed Combustion, Hueston Woods, Ohio.

19.65. FULLER, H. I. 'Sulphur Oxides and fuel oils,' *Proc. Clean Air Conference* (1969), National Society for Clean Air, London.

19.66. NONHEBEL, G. 'A commercial plant for removal of smoke and oxides of sulphur from flue gases,' *Trans. Faraday Soc.* **32**, 1291 (1936).

19.67. U.S. Dept. of Health, Education and Welfare, Publication 999, AP-63, *A compilation of selected air pollution control regulations.* Washington, D.C. (1968).

19.68. Ministry of Housing and Local Government. *Grit and Dust. Measurement of emission from boiler and furnace chimneys. Standards of emission.* H.M.S.O. (1967).

19.69. BOSANQUET, C. H., CAREY, W. F. and HALTON, E. M. 'Dust deposition from chimney stacks,' *Proc. I. Mech. E.* **162**, 355 (1950). Appendices of derivations in the archives of the Institution.

19.70. CAREY, W. F. 'Atmospheric Pollution in Britain: A study of dinginess,' *Int. J. Air Poll.* **2**, 1 (1959).

19.71. JARMAN, R. T. and DE TURVILLE, C. M. 'The visibility and length of chimney plumes,' *Atm. Envir.* **3**, 257 (1969). See also report of discussion of this and other papers, *Atm. Envir.* **4**,   (1970).

19.72. LUCAS, D. H. and MOORE, D. J. 'The measurement in the field of pollution by dust,' *Int. J. Air and Wat. Poll.* **8**, 441 (1964).

19.73. BRYANT, P. M. 'Derivation of working limits for continuous release rates of Sr and Cs to atmosphere in a milk producing area,' *Health Physics* **12**, 1393 (1966). See also 'Computed deposition rates per unit release rate of windborne material.' U.K. Atomic Energy Authority Report AHSB (RP) M 40 (1965). Obtainable from H.M.S.O.

19.74. NONHEBEL, G. 'Problems with Air Pollution from large Power Stations,' *Paper to Inst. Mech. Eng.* (London) Convention on Some Aspcets of Modern Thermal Power Plant, The Hague (1971).

19.75. SMITH, MAYNARD, E. 'Contribution to discussion,' *Atm. Envir.* **3**, 487 (1969).

19.76. Agricultural Research Council. *The Effects of Air Pollution on Plants and Soil.* H.M.S.O. (1967).

19.77. BIRSE, E. A. B. 'Problems in Aluminum Refineries,' *Smokeless Air*, No. **151**, 19 (1969).

19.87. *Odour Measurement and Control.* Chapter 13 of 'Air Pollution Manual'. Manufacturing Chemists' Association, Inc., Washington, D.C.

Index